AUTOMOTIVE ENGINEERING
Suspension & Steering Systems
(Classroom Manual)

Don Knowles

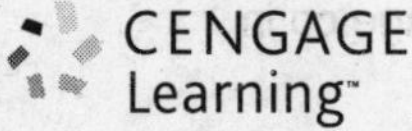

Australia • Brazil • Japan • Korea • Mexico • Singapore • Spain • United Kingdom • United States

Automotive Engineering: Suspension & Steering Systems (Classroom Manual)
Don Knowles

ISBN-13: 978-81-315-1289-0

Cengage Learning India Private Limited
418, F.I.E. Patparganj
New Delhi-110092

Tel: 91-11-43641111
Fax: 91-11-43641100

Cengage Learning products are represented in Canada by Nelson Education, Ltd.

For product information, visit www.cengage.co.in

Printed in India
First Indian Reprint 2010

CONTENTS

Preface to the India Edition

Unlike yesterday's mechanic, the technician of today and for the future must know the underlying theory of all automotive systems and be able to service and maintain those systems. Dividing the material into two volumes provides the reader with the information needed to begin a successful career as an automotive technician without interrupting the learning process by mixing cognitive and performance learning objectives into one volume.

Each Classroom Manual contains the principles of operation for each system and subsystem. The Classroom Manual also contains discussions on design variations of key components used by the different vehicle manufacturers. This volume is organized to build on basic facts and theories. The primary objective of this volume is to allow the reader to gain an understanding of how each system and subsystem operates. This understanding is necessary to diagnose the complex automobiles of today and tomorrow. Although the basics contained in the Classroom Manual provide the knowledge needed for diagnostics, diagnostic procedures appear only in the Shop Manual. An understanding of the basics is also a requirement for competence in the skill areas covered in the Shop Manual.

The Shop Manual covers the "how-to's." This volume includes step-by-step instructions for diagnostic and repair procedures. Photo Sequences are used to illustrate some of the common service procedures. Other common procedures are listed and are accompanied with line drawings and photos that allow the reader to visualize and conceptualize the finest details of the procedure. This volume also contains the reasons for performing the procedures as well as when that particular service is appropriate. The two volumes are designed to be used together and are arranged in corresponding chapters. Not only are the chapters in the volumes linked together, but also the contents of the chapters are linked.

REVIEWERS

The author and publisher would like to extend a special thanks to the following instructors who reviewed this text and offered their invaluable feedback.

Jim Addington
Lincoln Land Community College
Springfield, IL

Steve Bilger
Valdosta Technical College
Valdosta, GA

Dana Brewer
Wyoming Technical Institute
Laramie, WY

Roger Donovan
Illinois Central College
East Peoria, IL

C. Neel Flannagan
Aiken Technical College
Graniteville, SC

Eddie Shumate
Forsyth Technical Community College
Winston-Salem, NC

Randy Smith
Northeast Wisconsin Technical College
Green Bay, WI

John Wood
Ranken Technical College
St. Louis, MO

SUSPENSION AND STEERING SYSTEMS

1

Upon completion and review of this chapter, you should be able to:

- Explain how strength and rigidity are designed into a unitized body.
- Describe the design of a short-and-long arm (SLA) front suspension system.
- Explain how limited independent rear wheel movement is provided in a semi-independent rear suspension system.
- Explain the advantage of an independent rear suspension system.
- Describe the purposes of vehicle tires.
- Explain the terms positive and negative offset as they relate to vehicle wheel rims.
- Describe three different loads that are applied to wheel bearings.
- Explain the purposes of shock absorbers.
- Describe the difference between a shock absorber and a strut.
- Describe two different types of computer-controlled shock absorbers.
- Explain the advantages of computer-controlled suspension systems.
- List two types of steering linkages.
- Explain how the rack is moved in a rack and pinion steering gear.

- Describe how a power steering pump develops hydraulic pressure.
- Explain the advantages of four-wheel steering.
- Describe the result of incorrect rear wheel toe.
- Define front wheel caster.
- Explain the results of excessive negative camber.

INTRODUCTION

The suspension system must provide proper steering control and ride quality. Performing these functions is extremely important to maintain vehicle safety and customer satisfaction. For example, if the suspension system allows excessive vertical wheel oscillations, the driver may lose control of the steering when driving on an irregular road surface. This loss of steering control can result in a vehicle collision and personal injury. Excessive vertical wheel oscillations transfer undesirable vibrations from the wheel(s) to the passenger compartment, which causes customer dissatisfaction with the ride quality.

The suspension system and frame must also position the wheels and tires properly to provide normal tire life and proper steering control. If the suspension system does not position each wheel and tire properly, wheel alignment angles are incorrect and usually cause excessive tire tread wear. Improper wheel and tire position can also cause the steering to pull to one side. When the suspension system positions the wheels and tires properly, the steering should remain in the straight-ahead position if the car is driven straight ahead on a reasonably straight, smooth road surface. However, if the wheels and tires are not properly positioned, the steering can be erratic, and excessive steering effort is required to maintain the steering in the straight-ahead position.

The steering system is also extremely important to maintain vehicle safety and reduce driver fatigue. For example, if a steering system component is suddenly disconnected, the driver may experience a complete loss of steering control, resulting in a vehicle collision and personal injury. Loose steering system components can cause erratic steering, which causes the driver to continually turn the steering wheel in either direction to try and keep the vehicle moving straight ahead. This condition results in premature driver fatigue.

FRAMES AND UNITIZED BODIES

Some vehicles, such as rear-wheel-drive cars, sport utility vehicles (SUVs), and trucks, have a frame that is separate from the body (Figure 1-1). Other vehicles have a unitized body that combines the frame and body in one unit, eliminating the external frame (Figure 1-2). In a unitized body, the body design rather than a heavy steel frame provides strength and rigidity. All parts of a unitized body are load-carrying members, and these body parts are welded together to form a strong assembly.

The frame or unitized body serves the following purposes:

1. Allows the vehicle to support its total weight, including the weight of the vehicle and cargo.
2. Allows the vehicle to absorb stress when driving on rough road surfaces.
3. Enables the vehicle to absorb torque from the engine and drive train.
4. Provides attachment points for suspension and other components.

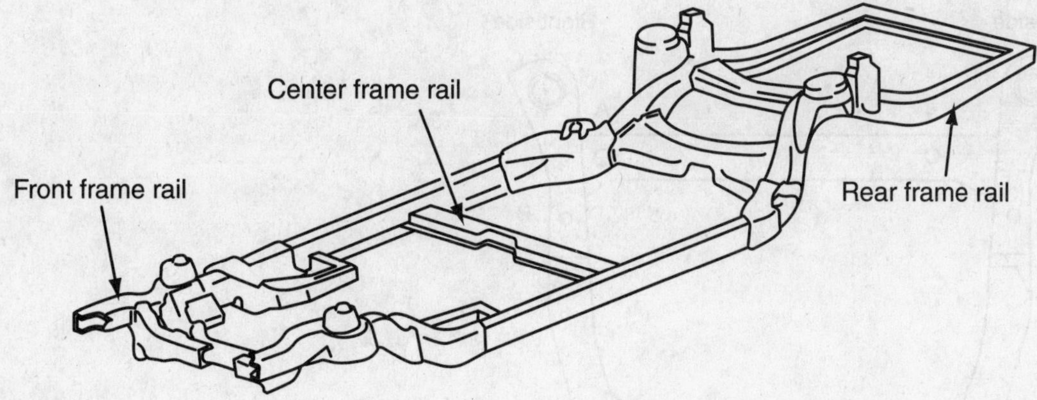

FIGURE 1-1 *Vehicle frame.*

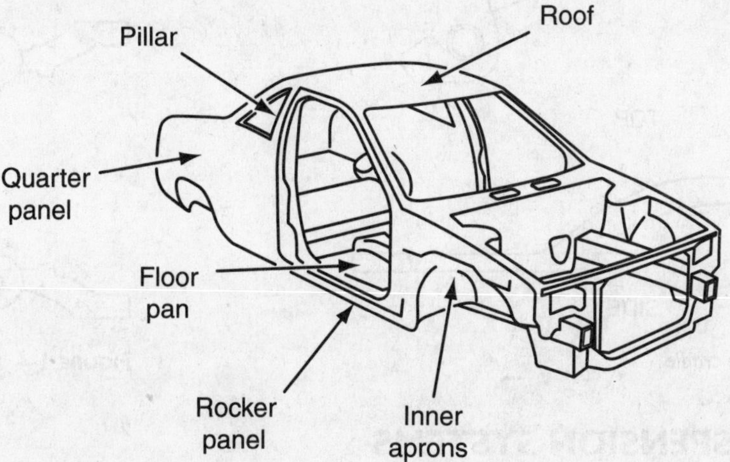

FIGURE 1-2 *Unitized body design.*

The unitized body provides a steel box around the passenger compartment to provide passenger protection in a collision. Modern automotive bodies use a wide variety of materials, such as hydroformed aluminum rails, magnesium roof frames, and carbon fiber-balsa wood composite floor panels. In most unitized bodies, special steel panels are inserted in the doors to protect the vehicle occupants in a side collision. Some unitized body components are manufactured from high-strength or ultra high-strength steels. The unitized body design is typically used in small- and mid-sized front-wheel-drive cars. A steel cradle is mounted under the front of the unitized body to support the engine and transaxle (Figure 1-3). Rubber and steel mounts support the engine and transaxle on the cradle. Large rubber bushings are mounted between the cradle and the unitized body to help prevent engine vibration from reaching the passenger compartment. Some unitized bodies have a partial frame mounted under the rear of the vehicle to provide additional strength and facilitate the attachment of rear suspension components (Figure 1-4).

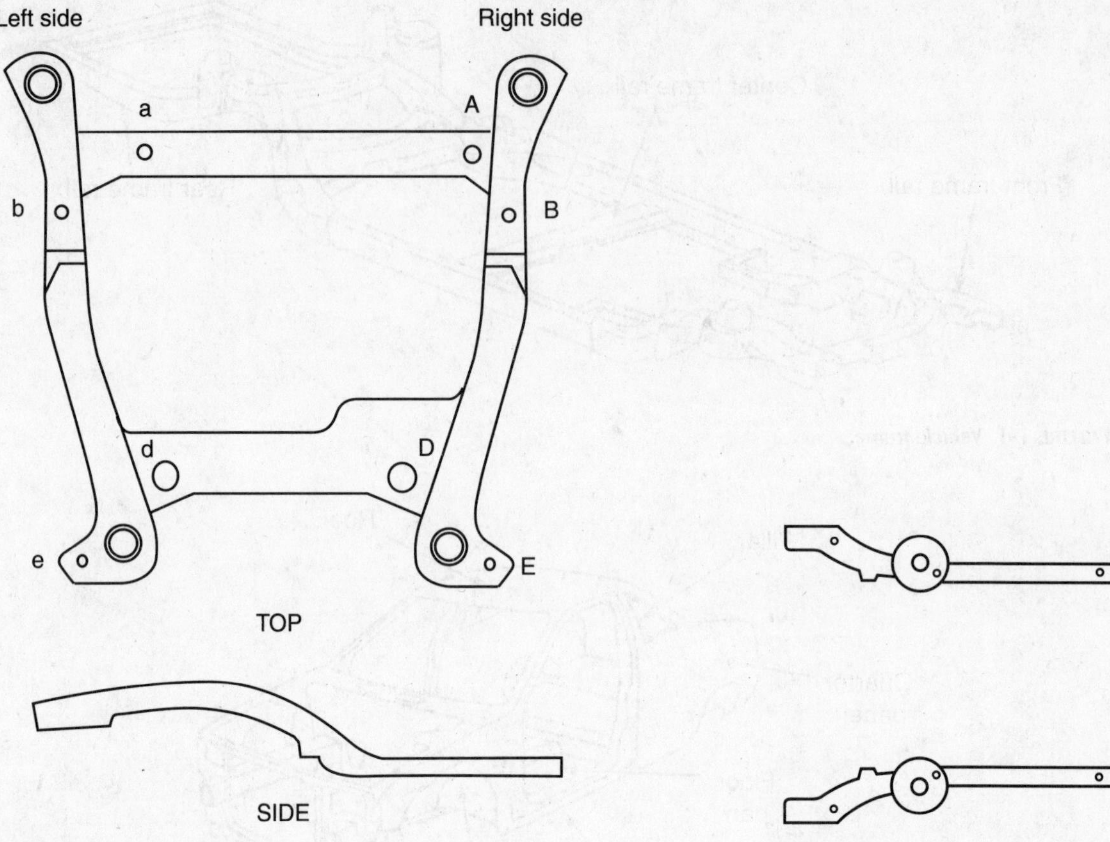

FIGURE 1-3 *Engine cradle.*

FIGURE 1-4 *Rear partial frame.*

FRONT SUSPENSION SYSTEMS

The front and rear suspension systems are extremely important to provide proper wheel position, steering control, ride quality, and tire life. The impact of the tires striking road irregularities must be absorbed by the suspension systems. The suspension systems must supply proper ride quality to maintain customer satisfaction and reduce driver fatigue, as well as provide proper wheel and tire position to maintain directional stability when driving. Proper wheel position also ensures normal tire tread life.

Typical components in a short-and-long arm (SLA) front suspension system are illustrated in Figure 1-5. This type of front suspension system has a long, lower control arm and a shorter upper control arm. The main front suspension components serve the following purposes:

1. Upper and lower control arms–control lateral (side-to-side) wheel movement.
2. Upper and lower control arm bushings–allow upward and downward control arm movement and absorb wheel impacts and vibrations.
3. Coil springs–allow proper suspension ride height and control suspension travel during driving maneuvers.
4. Ball joints–allow the knuckle and wheels to turn to the right or left.
5. Steering knuckles–provide mounting surfaces for the wheel bearings and hubs.
6. Shock absorbers–control spring action when driving on irregular road surfaces.

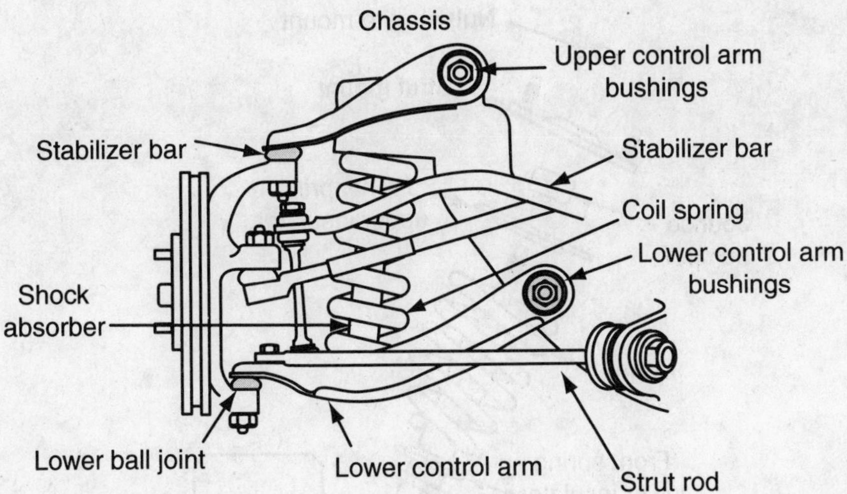

FIGURE 1-5 *Typical short-and-long arm (SLA) front suspension system.*

7. Strut rod–controls fore-and-aft wheel movement.
8. Stabilizer bar–reduces body sway when a front wheel strikes a road irregularity.

A MacPherson strut front suspension system has no upper control arm and ball joint; instead, a strut is connected from the top of the knuckle to an upper strut mount bolted to the reinforced strut tower in the unitized body (Figure 1-6). The strut supports the top of the knuckle and also performs the same function as the shock absorber in a SLA suspension system. The coil spring is mounted between a lower support on the strut and the upper strut mount. Insulators are mounted between the ends of the coil spring and the mounting locations. A bearing in the upper strut mount allows the strut and coil spring to rotate with the spindle when the front wheels are turned.

REAR SUSPENSION SYSTEMS

A typical live-axle rear suspension system has a one-piece rear axle housing. Trailing arms are connected from the rear axle housing to the chassis through rubber bushings. The coil springs are mounted between the trailing arms and the chassis (Figure 1-7). Because the rear axle housing is a one-piece assembly, vertical movement of one rear wheel causes the opposite rear wheel to be tipped outward at the top. This action increases tire tread wear and reduces ride quality and traction between the tire tread and road surface.

Many front-wheel drive cars have a semi-independent rear suspension system with an inverted steel U-section connected between the rear spindles (Figure 1-8). The inverted U-section usually contains a tubular stabilizer bar. When one rear wheel strikes a road irregularity, the inverted U-section and stabilizer bar twist, allowing some independent rear wheel movement before the wheel movement affects the opposite rear wheel. Some semi-independent rear suspension systems have a track bar and brace connected from the inverted U-section to the chassis to reduce lateral rear axle movement (Figure 1-9).

Many vehicles have an independent rear suspension system, wherein each rear wheel can move independently without affecting the position of the opposite rear wheel. This type of suspension system reduces rear tire wear and provides improved steering control. Independent rear suspension systems have a number of different configurations. A MacPherson strut independent rear suspension

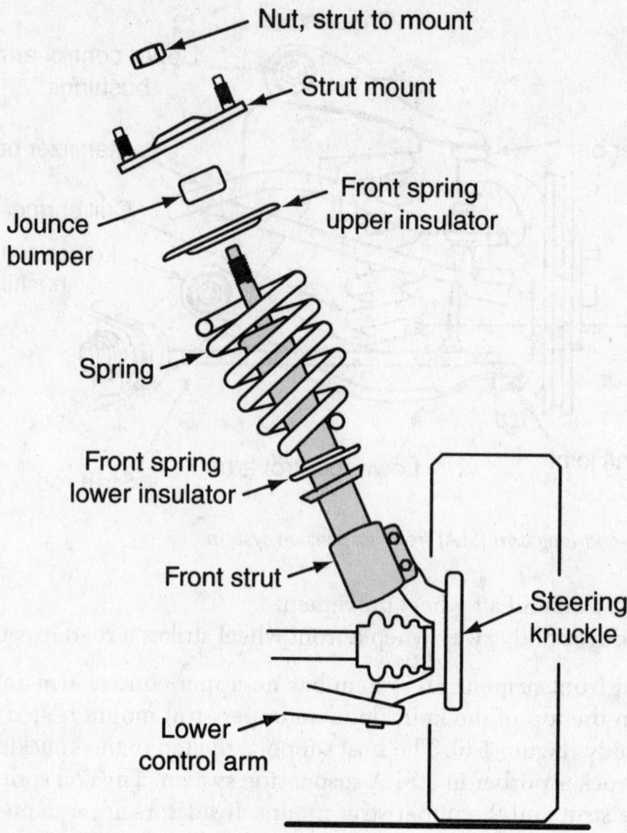

FIGURE 1-6 *Typical MacPherson strut front suspension system.*

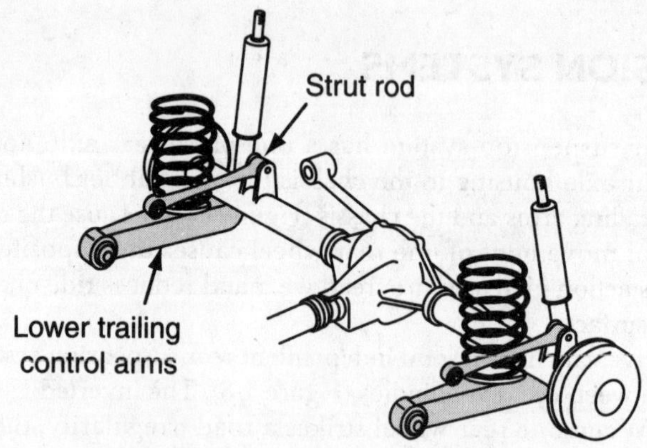

FIGURE 1-7 *Live-axle rear suspension system with coil springs.*

system has a strut and coil spring assembly connected from the top of the spindle through a upper strut mount to the chassis (Figure 1-10). No provision for strut rotation is required, because the rear wheels are not steered. Some independent rear suspension systems have a multilink design, wherein an adjustment link connected from the rear spindle to the chassis allows rear wheel position adjustment (Figure 1-11).

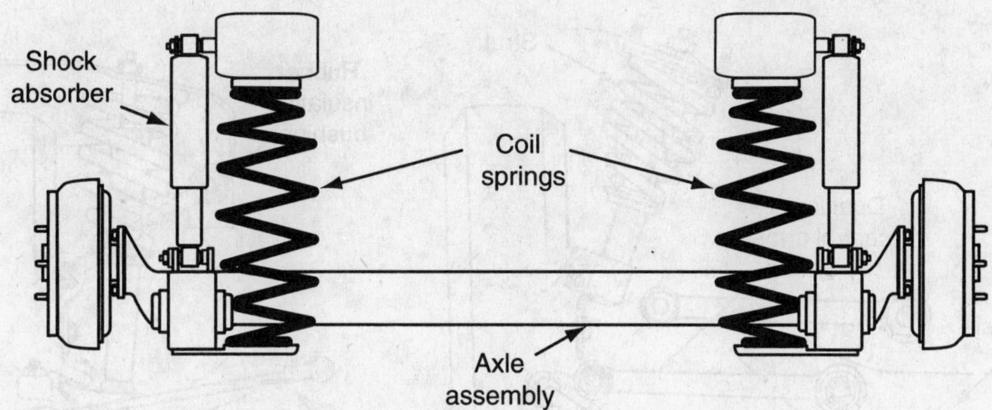

FIGURE 1-8 *Semi-independent rear suspension system.*

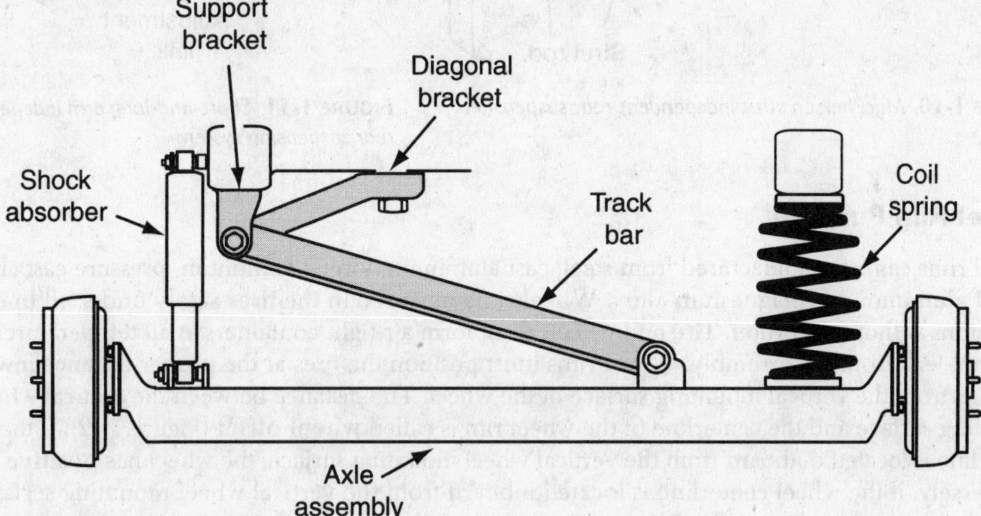

FIGURE 1-9 *Semi-independent rear suspension system with track bar and brace.*

TIRES, WHEELS, AND HUBS

Tire Purpose

Tires are extremely important because they play a large part in providing vehicle safety and ride quality! Tires are the only point of contact between the vehicle and the road surface. Vehicle tires provide these functions:

1. Tires must support the vehicle weight safely and firmly.
2. Tires must provide a comfortable ride.
3. Tires must supply adequate traction on various road surfaces to drive and steer the vehicle.
4. Tires must contribute to proper steering control and directional stability of the vehicle.
5. Tires must absorb high stresses when cornering, accelerating, and braking.
6. Tire treads must be designed to propel water off the tread and away from the tire when driving on wet highways. This action prevents water from lifting the tires off the road surface, which decreases tire traction.

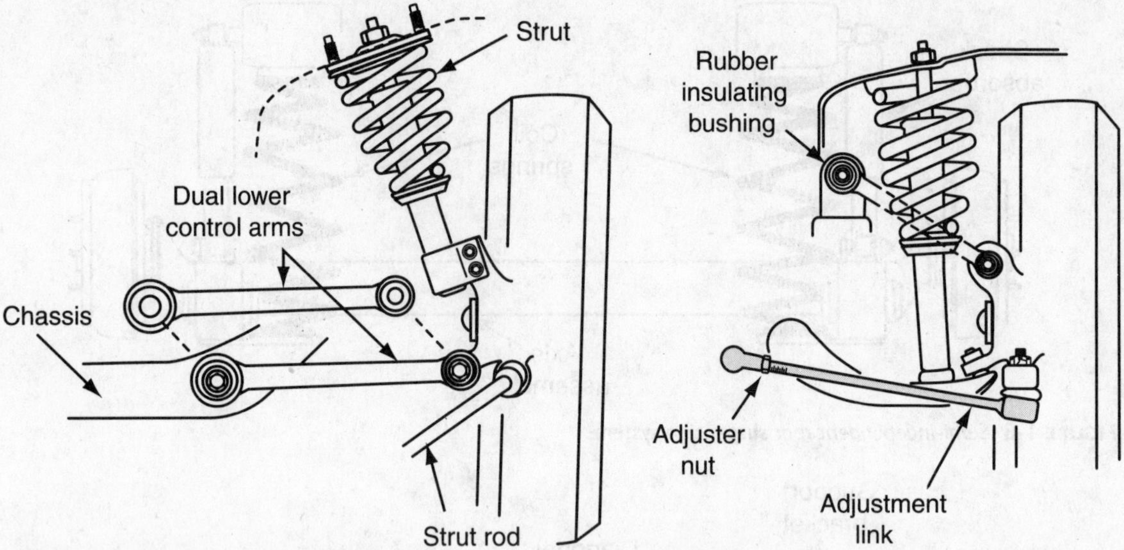

FIGURE 1-10 *MacPherson strut independent rear suspension system.*

FIGURE 1-11 *Short-and-long arm independent rear suspension system.*

Wheel Rim Purpose

Wheel rims can be manufactured from steel, cast aluminum, forged aluminum, pressure-cast chrome-plated aluminum, or magnesium alloy. Wheel rims must retain the tires safely under all operating conditions without distortion. Tire and wheels must form air-tight containers at all temperatures so air does not leak from the assembly. Wheel rims must position the tires at the proper distance inward or outward from the vertical mounting surface of the wheel. The distance between the vertical wheel rim mounting surface and the centerline of the wheel rim is called **wheel offset** (Figure 1-12). If the wheel centerline is located outboard from the vertical wheel mounting surface, the wheel has **positive offset**. Conversely, if the wheel centerline is located inboard from the vertical wheel mounting surface, the wheel has **negative offset**. Wheel rims typically have four to six mounting openings that fit over studs in the wheel hub. When a wheel rim is installed on the hub studs, tapered nuts are then tightened to the specified torque to retain the wheel and tire assembly on the hub. On many wheel rims, the openings in the wheel rim are tapered to match the tapers on the retaining nuts. These tapered openings and matching tapered nuts center the wheel rim on the hub.

WARNING: Wheel nuts must be tightened in the proper sequence to the specified torque. Failure to follow the proper wheel nut tightening procedure and torque may cause a wheel to come off a car while driving. This action usually results in serious personal injury and extensive vehicle and/or property damage.

Wheel Hubs

Wheel hubs must provide a secure mounting surface for the wheel rim and tire assembly. Wheel hubs also contain the wheel bearings that provide smooth wheel rotation with reduced friction. Wheel bearings must have a minimum amount of end play to greatly reduce wheel lateral movement. The wheel hub and bearing assemblies must carry the load supplied by the vehicle weight, and these assemblies must also guide the wheel and tire assembly (Figure 1-13). The vehicle weight is supplied to

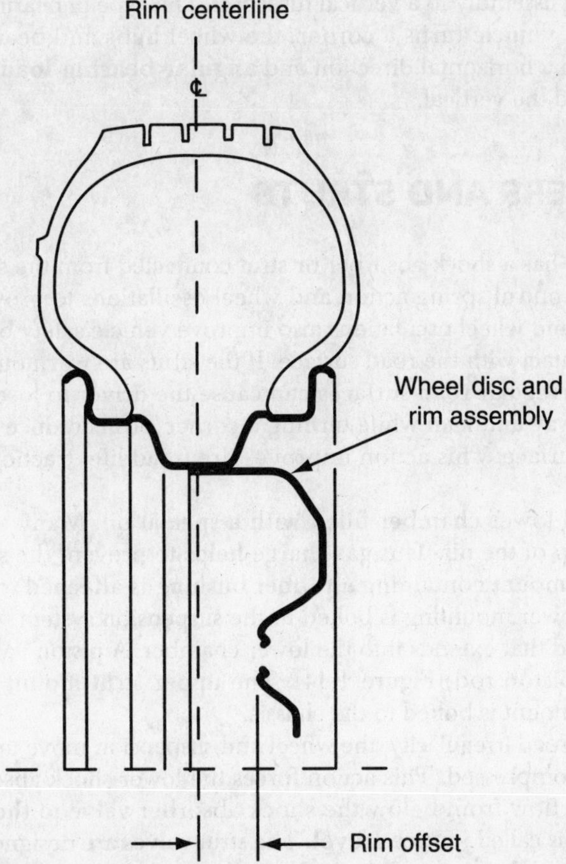

FIGURE 1-12 *Wheel rim design.*

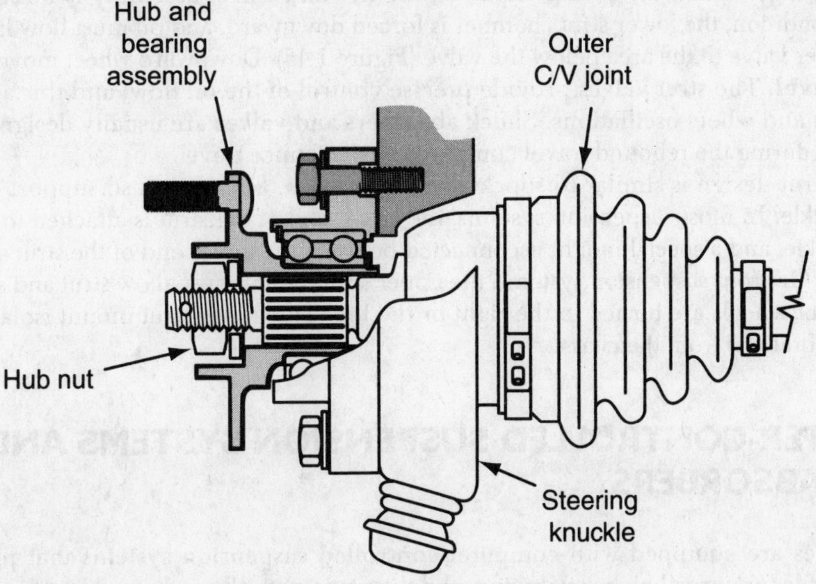

FIGURE 1-13 *Wheel bearing and hub assembly.*

the wheel hub and bearing assembly in a vertical direction. This type of bearing load is called a **radial bearing load**. When the vehicle turns a corner, the wheel hubs and bearings must carry **thrust bearing loads** supplied in a horizontal direction and **angular bearing loads** supplied in a direction between the horizontal and the vertical.

SHOCK ABSORBERS AND STRUTS

Each corner of the vehicle has a shock absorber or strut connected from the suspension system to the chassis. Shock absorbers control spring action and wheel oscillations to provide a comfortable ride. Controlling spring action and wheel oscillations also improve vehicle safety because the struts help to keep each tire tread in contact with the road surface. If the struts are worn out, excessive wheel oscillations when driving on irregular road surfaces can cause the driver to lose control of the vehicle. Struts also reduce body sway and lean while turning a corner. Struts reduce the tendency of the tire tread to lift off the road surface. This action improves tire tread life, traction, steering control, and directional stability.

Struts contain a sealed lower chamber filled with a special oil. Many shock absorbers have a nitrogen gas charge on top of the oil. This gas charge helps to prevent the shock absorber oil from foaming. A circular steel mount containing a rubber bushing is attached to the bottom end of the lower chamber, and this lower mounting is bolted to the suspension system. The upper strut housing is connected to a piston rod that extends into the lower chamber. A piston valve assembly is attached to the lower end of the piston rod (Figure 1-14). The upper strut mount is similar to the lower mounting, and the upper mount is bolted to the chassis.

When a wheel strikes a road irregularity, the wheel and suspension move upward, and the spring in the suspension system is compressed. This action forces the lower shock absorber chamber to move upward, and the oil must flow from below the shock absorber valve to the area above the valve. Upward wheel movement is called **jounce travel**. The strut valves are designed to provide precise oil flow control, and thus control the speed of upward wheel movement.

When a spring is compressed, it stores energy and then immediately expands with an equal amount of energy. When the spring expands, the tire and wheel assembly is forced downward. Under this condition, the lower strut chamber is forced downward, and oil must flow from above the shock absorber valve to the area below the valve (Figure 1-15). Downward wheel movement is called **rebound travel**. The strut valves provide precise control of the oil flow, and this action controls spring action and wheel oscillations. Shock absorbers and valves are usually designed to provide more control during the rebound travel compared to the jounce travel.

Internal strut design is similar to shock absorber design, but struts also support the top of the steering knuckle. In most suspension systems, the lower end of the strut is attached to the top of the steering knuckle, and a special mount is connected between the upper end of the strut and the chassis (Figure 1-16). On front suspension systems, the upper strut mount must allow strut and spring rotation when the front wheels are turned to the right or the left. The upper strut mount isolates wheel and suspension vibrations from the chassis.

COMPUTER-CONTROLLED SUSPENSION SYSTEMS AND SHOCK ABSORBERS

Many vehicles are equipped with computer-controlled suspension systems that provide a soft, comfortable ride for normal highway driving, and then automatically and very quickly switch to a firm

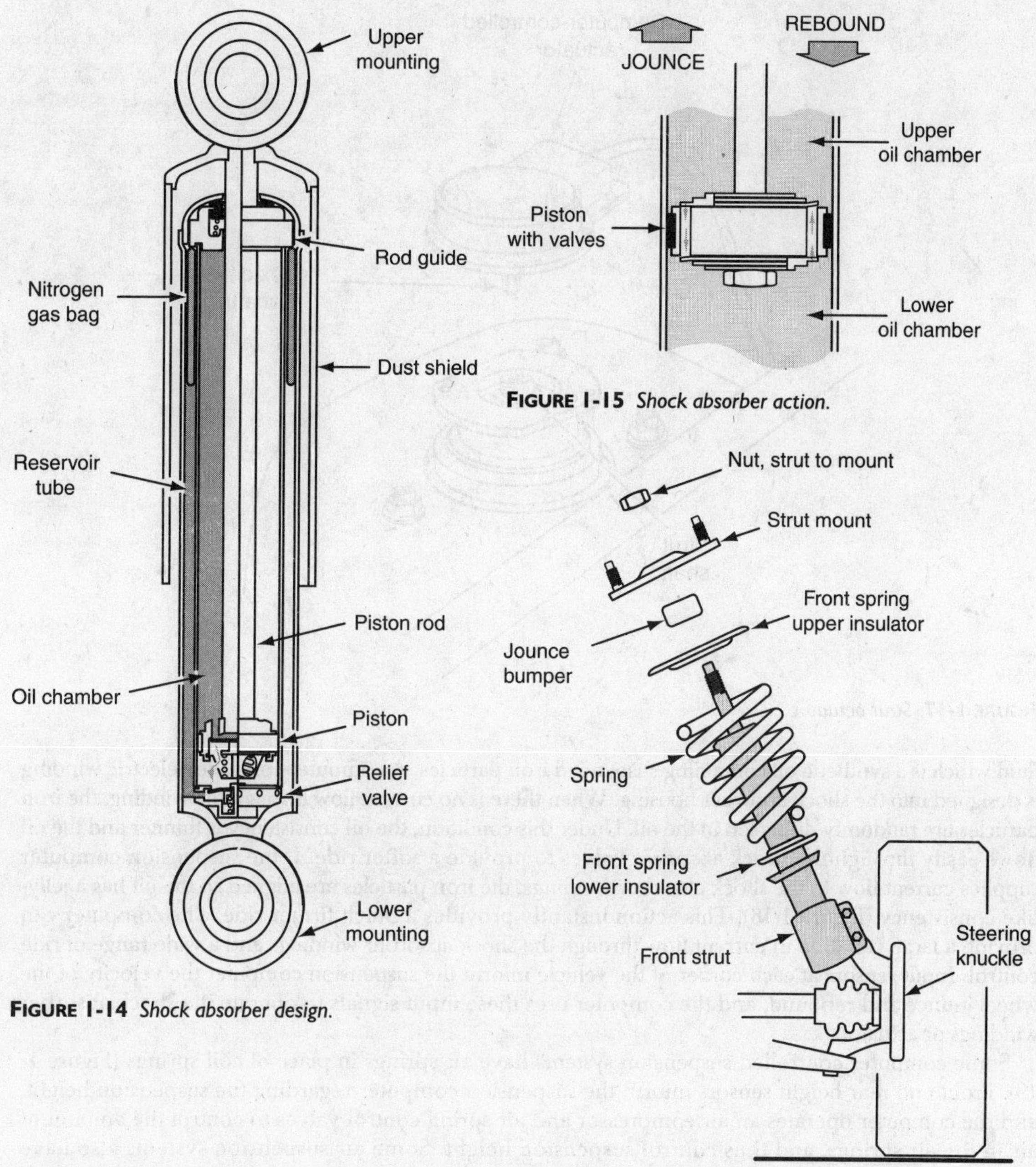

FIGURE 1-14 *Shock absorber design.*

FIGURE 1-15 *Shock absorber action.*

FIGURE 1-16 *Front strut and spring assembly.*

ride for hard cornering, braking, or fast acceleration. Computer-controlled suspension systems reduce body sway during hard cornering, and thus contribute to improved ride quality and vehicle safety. Some computer-controlled suspension systems are driver-adjustable with up to four suspension modes to allow the driver to tailor the ride quality to the driving style.

Some computer-controlled suspensions systems have electronically actuated solenoids in each shock absorber or strut. These solenoids rotate the shock absorber or strut valves to adjust the valve openings and shock absorber control (Figure 1-17). Other shock absorbers or struts contain a magneto-rheological

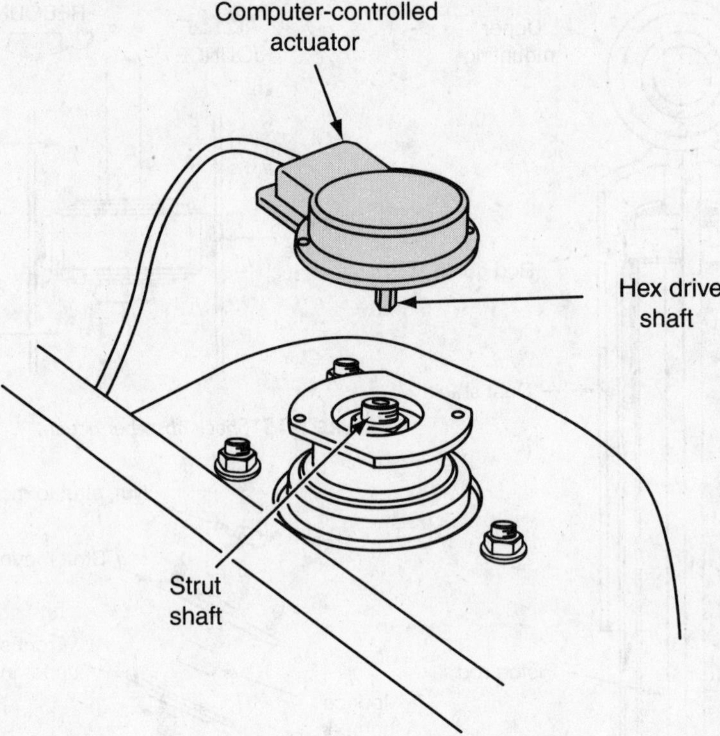

FIGURE 1-17 *Strut actuator.*

fluid which is a synthetic oil containing suspended iron particles. A computer-controlled electric winding is designed into the shock absorber housing. When there is no current flow through the winding, the iron particles are randomly dispersed in the oil. Under this condition, the oil consistency is thinner and the oil flows easily through the shock absorber valves to provide a softer ride. If the suspension computer supplies current flow to the shock absorber windings, the iron particles are aligned so the oil has a jelly-like consistency (Figure 1-18). This action instantly provides a much firmer ride. The computer can provide a large variation in current flow through the shock absorber windings and a wide range of ride control. Input sensors at each corner of the vehicle inform the suspension computer the velocity of the wheel jounce and rebound, and the computer uses these input signals to operate the shock absorber windings or actuators.

Some computer-controlled suspension systems have air springs in place of coil springs (Figure 1-19). Front and rear height sensors inform the suspension computer regarding the suspension height, and the computer operates an air compressor and air spring control valves to control the amount of air in the air springs, and thus control suspension height. Some air suspension systems also have computer-controlled shock absorbers or struts.

STEERING SYSTEMS

Steering systems are essential to provide vehicle safety, steering quality, and steering control! Steering system problems can cause the steering to pull to one side when driving straight ahead, excessive steering effort, **wheel shimmy**, or excessive steering wheel free-play. These problems all reduce vehicle safety and increase driver fatigue. Therefore, steering systems must be properly maintained.

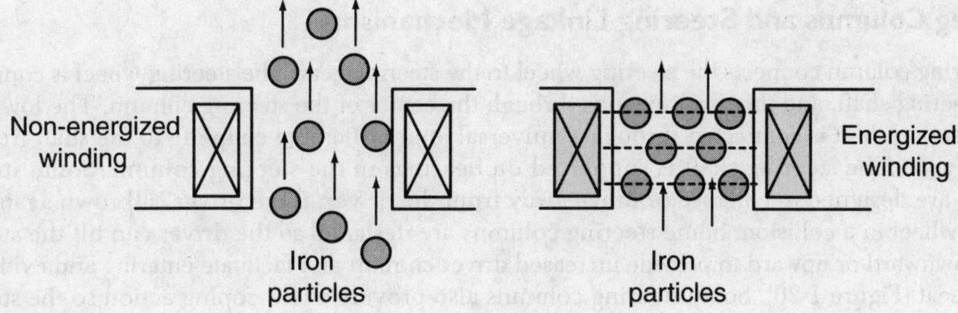

FIGURE 1-18 *Magneto-rheological fluid action in a strut or shock absorber.*

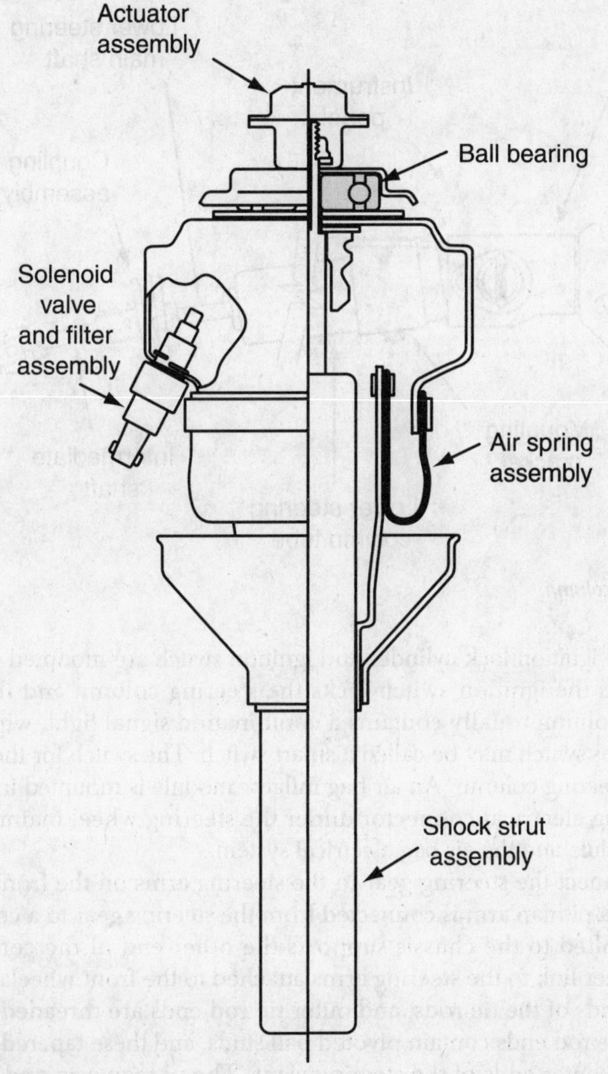

FIGURE 1-19 *Air spring and strut assembly.*

Steering Columns and Steering Linkage Mechanisms

The steering column connects the steering wheel to the steering gear. The steering wheel is connected to the steering shaft, and this shaft extends through the center of the steering column. The lower end of the steering shaft is connected through a universal joint or flexible coupling to the shaft from the steering gear. The steering shaft is supported on bearings in the steering column. Some steering columns are designed to collapse or move away from the driver, if the driver is thrown against the steering wheel in a collision. Some steering columns are designed so the driver can tilt the steering wheel downward or upward to provide increased driver comfort and facilitate entering and exiting the driver's seat (Figure 1-20). Some steering columns also provide a telescoping action so the steering wheel can be moved closer to, or farther away from, the driver. Other steering columns do not have any tilt or telescoping action. A mounting bracket retains the steering column to the instrument panel.

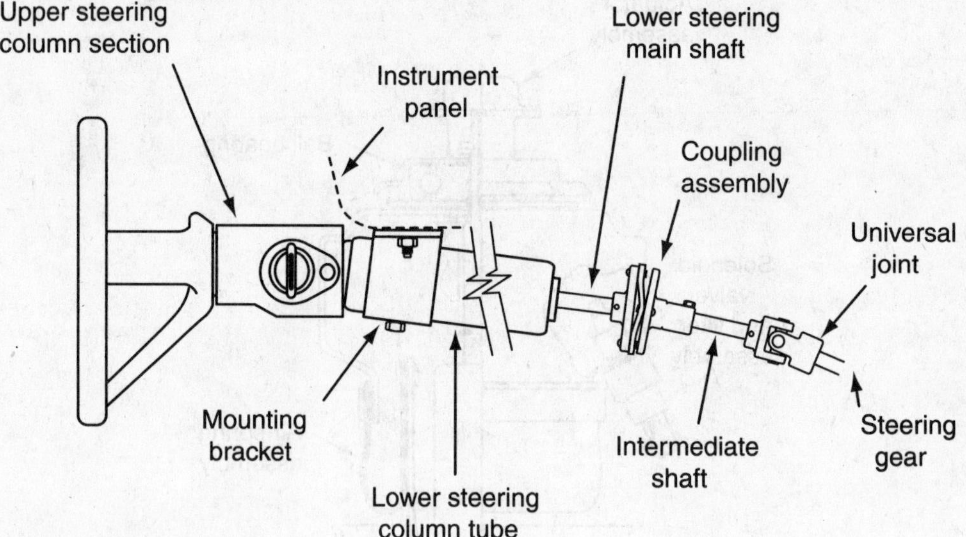

FIGURE 1-20 *Tilt steering column.*

On most vehicles, the ignition lock cylinder and ignition switch are mounted in the steering column. Removing the key from the ignition switch locks the steering column and the gear shift on many vehicles. The steering column usually contains a combination signal light, wipe/wash, dimmer, and cruise control switch. This switch may be called a smart switch. The switch for the hazard warning lights is also mounted in the steering column. An air bag inflator module is mounted in the top of the steering wheel, and a clockspring electrical connector under the steering wheel maintains electrical contact between the inflator module and the air bag electrical system.

Steering linkages connect the steering gear to the steering arms on the front wheels. In a parallelogram steering linkage, a pitman arm is connected from the steering gear to a center link (Figure 1-21). A pivoted idler arm bolted to the chassis supports the other end of the center link. Tie rods are connected from the center link to the steering arms attached to the front wheels. Pivoted ball studs are mounted in the inner ends of the tie rods, and outer tie rod ends are threaded into the outer ends of the tie rods. The outer tie rod ends contain pivoted ball studs, and these tapered studs fit into matching tapered openings in the outer ends of the steering arms. The pitman arm and idler arm position the center link so the tie rods are parallel to the lower control arms. This tie rod position is very important to maintain proper steering operation.

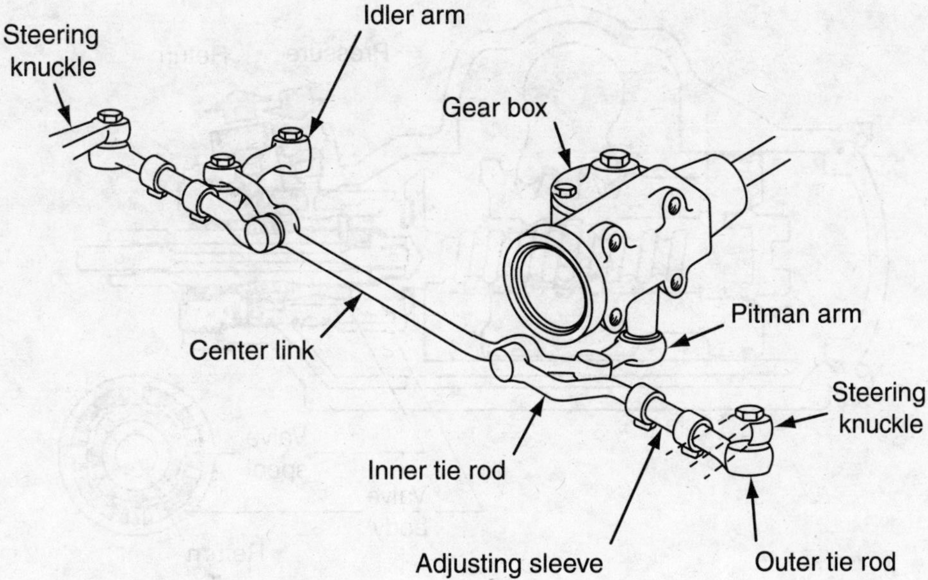

FIGURE 1-21 *Parallelogram steering linkage.*

Many vehicles have a rack and pinion steering linkage. In these linkages, the tie rods are connected through inner tie rod ends to the rack in the rack and pinion steering gear. Outer tie rod ends are connected from the tie rods to the steering arms (Figure 1-22). In this type of steering linkage, the steering gear mounting must position the tie rods so they are parallel to the lower control arms. The rack and pinion steering gear can be mounted on the cowl or the front cross member.

CAUTION: Regular inspection and maintenance of steering linkage components is very important to provide normal component life and maintain vehicle safety.

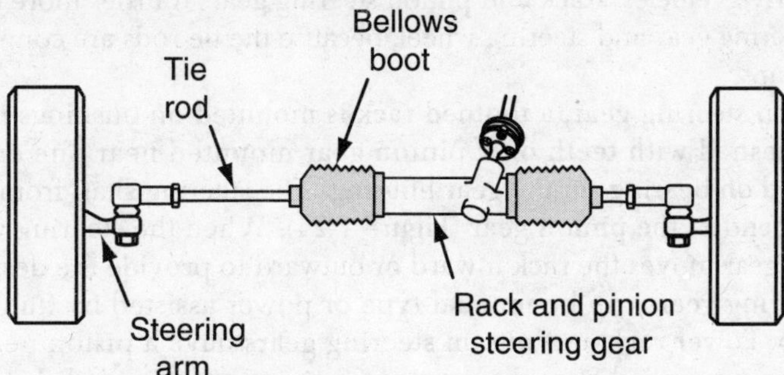

FIGURE 1-22 *Rack and pinion steering gear and linkage.*

Recirculating Ball Steering Gears

Some vehicles are equipped with a recirculating ball steering gear, wherein the steering shaft is attached to a worm gear in the steering gear. A ball nut with internal grooves is mounted over the worm gear. Ball bearings are mounted between the worm gear and ball nut grooves to reduce friction and provide reduced steering effort. Outer grooves on the ball nut are meshed with matching teeth on the sector shaft (Figure 1-23). The lower end of the sector shaft is splined to the pitman arm. When the

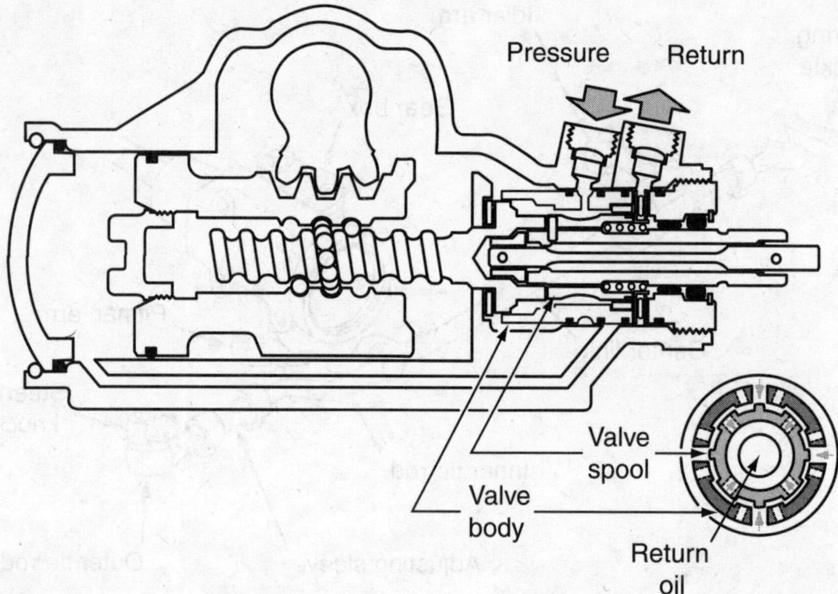

FIGURE 1-23 *Power recirculating ball steering gear.*

steering wheel is turned, the ball nut moves upward or downward on the worm gear, which rotates the sector shaft to provide the desired steering action. Recirculating ball steering gears can be manual-type with no hydraulic assist, or power-type with hydraulic assist from the power steering pump.

Rack and Pinion Steering Gears

Rack and pinion steering gears and linkages are more compact than recirculating ball steering gears and parallelogram steering linkages. Therefore, rack and pinion steering gears are usually installed on smaller, front-wheel drive vehicles. Rack and pinion steering gears transfer more road shock from the front wheels to the steering gear and steering wheel, because the tie rods are connected directly to the rack in the steering gear.

In a rack and pinion steering gear, a toothed rack is mounted on bushings in the rack housing. The rack teeth are meshed with teeth on a pinion gear mounted near one end of the gear. The pinion gear is mounted on bearings in the gear housing. The steering shaft from the steering gear is attached to the upper end of the pinion gear (Figure 1-24). When the steering wheel is turned, the rotation of the pinion gear moves the rack inward or outward to provide the desired steering action. Rack and pinion steering gears can be manual-type or power assisted by fluid pressure from the power steering pump. Power rack and pinion steering gears have a piston near the center of the rack, and fluid pressure is supplied from the power steering pump to sealed chambers on either side of the rack piston to provide steering assistance (Figure 1-25).

Power Steering Pumps

A belt surrounding the crankshaft pulley and the power steering pump pulley drives the power steering pump. The power steering pump drive belt can be a V-type (Figure 1-26) or a ribbed V-type (Figure 1-27). The ribbed V-belt contains a number of small, ribbed grooves on the underside and a flat upper side. The ribbed V-belt surrounds the pulleys on all the belt-driven components, allowing these components to be on the same vertical plane. This arrangement saves a considerable amount of underhood

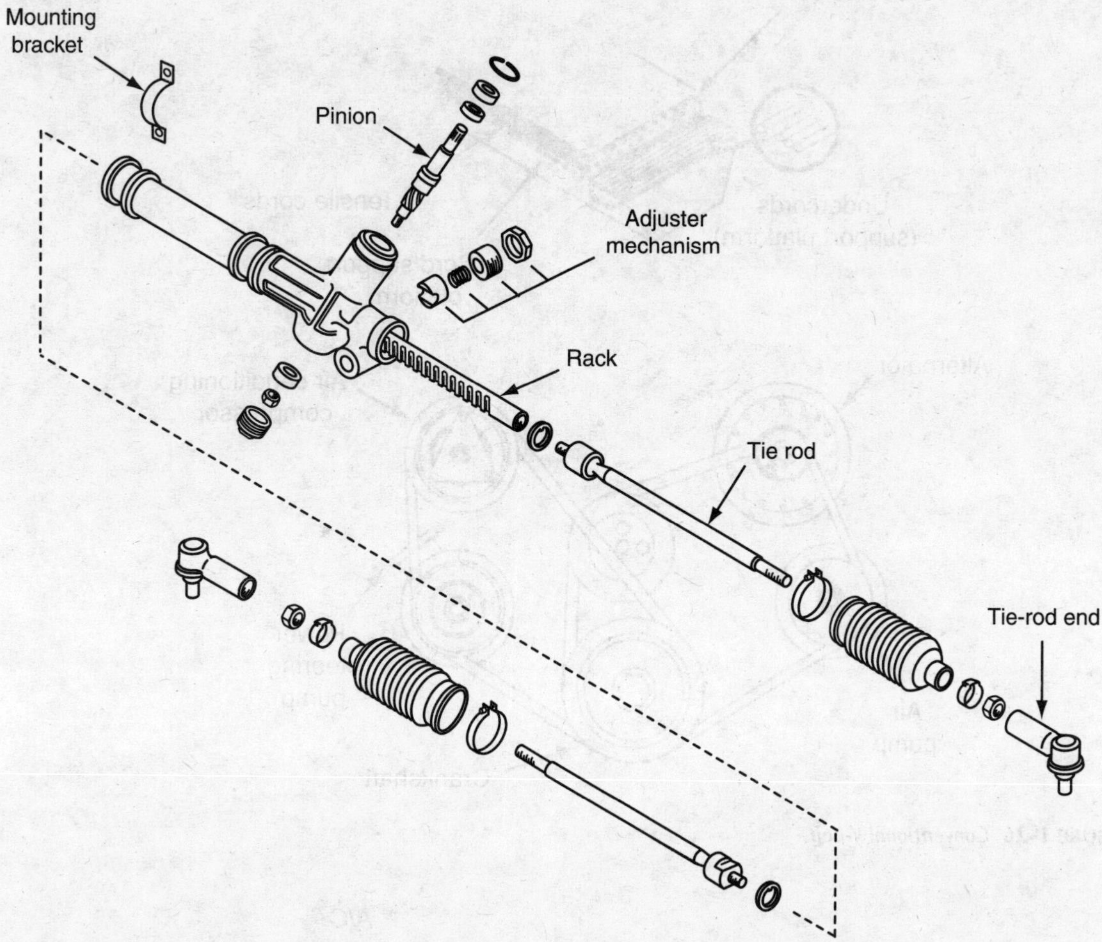

Mounting
bracket
Pinion
Adjuster
mechanism
Rack
Tie rod
Tie-rod end

FIGURE 1-24 *Manual rack and pinion steering gear.*

Fluid pumped into
the left chamber
Fluid pumped into
the right chamber

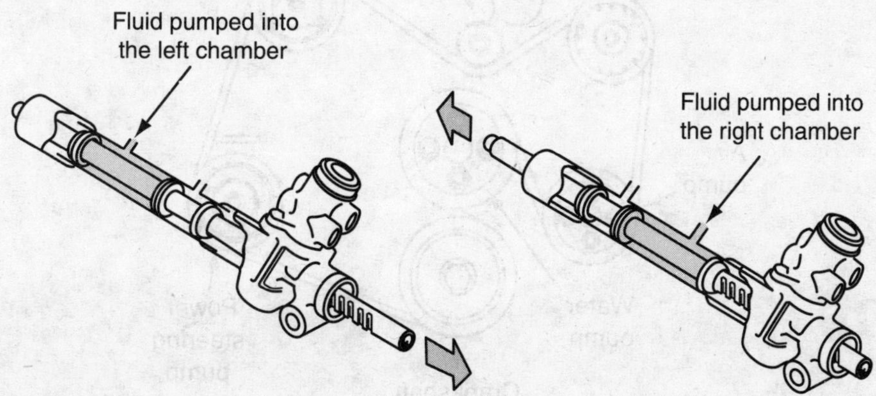

FIGURE 1-25 *Power rack and pinion steering gear with sealed rack piston chambers.*

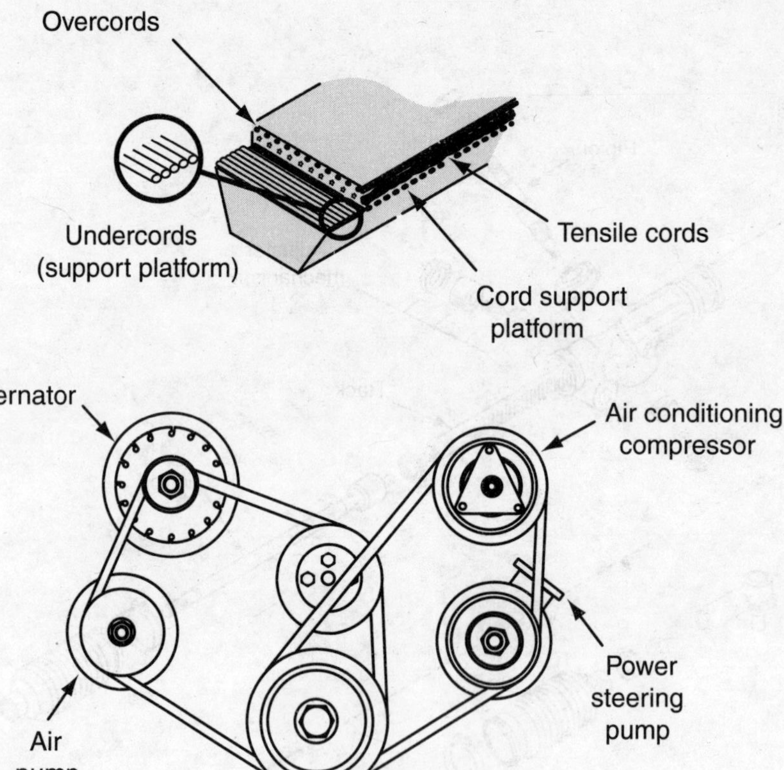

FIGURE 1-26 *Conventional V-belt.*

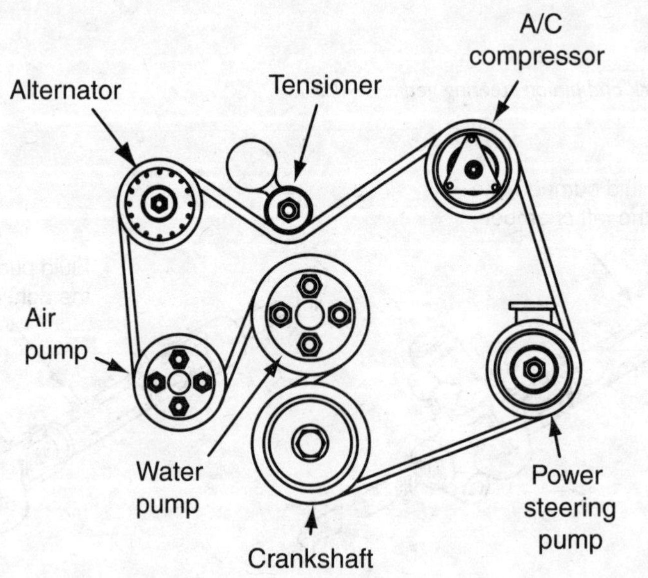

FIGURE 1-27 *Ribbed V-belt.*

space. The smooth side of the ribbed V-belt can be used to drive some components. Some power steering pumps have an integral fluid reservoir; other power steering systems have a remote fluid reservoir. The pump supplies fluid through a high-pressure hose to the steering gear, and the fluid is returned from the steering gear through a low-pressure hose to the pump (Figure 1-28). In some power steering pumps, the pump shaft is connected from the pulley to the rotor, and a number of vanes are mounted in rotor slots. The rotor and vane assembly rotates in the center of an elliptical cam ring. As the vanes rotate inside the cam ring, the spaces between the vanes change in volume. When the spaces between the vanes become smaller, pressure is applied to the fluid because the fluid cannot be compressed (Figure 1-29). This pressurized fluid is forced through the pump outlet fitting and high-pressure hose to the steering gear. A flow control valve with an integral pressure relief valve controls pump pressure.

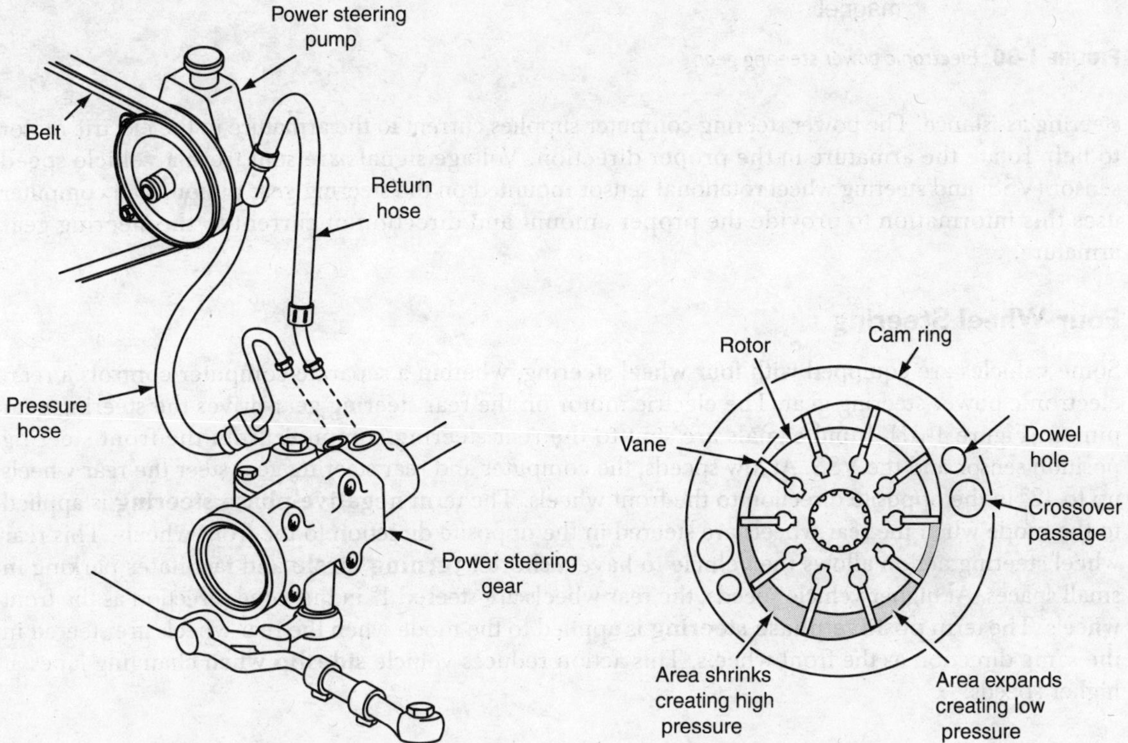

FIGURE 1-28 *Power steering system.*

FIGURE 1-29 *Power steering pump rotor and vanes.*

Electronic Power Steering Gears

Some vehicles have an electronic power steering gear in place of the hydraulic power steering gear and pump. An electronic power steering gear contains a computer-driven reversible electric motor. The electronic power steering gear is similar to a rack and pinion steering gear, but contains an electric motor in place of hydraulic controls. The armature in the electric motor is connected through a set of gears to a worm shaft, and a ball nut is mounted over the worm shaft. The armature is hollow, and the rack extends through the armature. The ball nut and worm shaft are similar to the ones in a recirculating ball steering gear. The ball nut is coupled to the rack, and fields in the motor surround the armature (Figure 1-30).

When the computer supplies current to the armature, the armature rotates and turns the worm shaft. Worm shaft rotation moves the ball nut and helps to move the rack to the right or left to provide

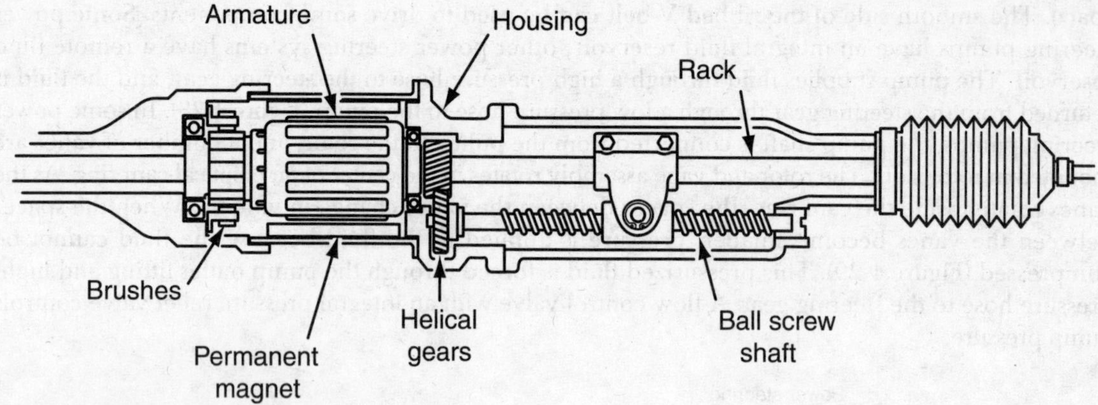

FIGURE 1-30 *Electronic power steering gear.*

steering assistance. The power steering computer supplies current to the armature in the electric motor to help rotate the armature in the proper direction. Voltage signals are sent from a vehicle speed sensor (VSS) and steering wheel rotational sensor mounted on the steering gear pinion. The computer uses this information to provide the proper amount and direction of current to the steering gear armature.

Four-Wheel Steering

Some vehicles are equipped with four-wheel steering, wherein a separate computer controls a rear, electronic power steering gear. The electric motor on the rear steering gear drives the steering gear pinion (Figure 1-31). Input signals are sent to the rear steering computer from the front steering position sensor and the VSS. At low speeds, the computer and rear steering gear steer the rear wheels up to 12° in the opposite direction to the front wheels. The term **negative-phase steering** is applied to the mode when the rear wheels are steered in the opposite direction to the front wheels. This rear wheel steering action allows the vehicle to have a shorter **turning circle** and facilitates parking in small spaces. At higher vehicle speeds, the rear wheels are steered 1° in the same direction as the front wheels. The term **positive-phase steering** is applied to the mode when the rear wheels are steered in the same direction as the front wheels. This action reduces vehicle **sideslip** when changing lanes at higher speeds.

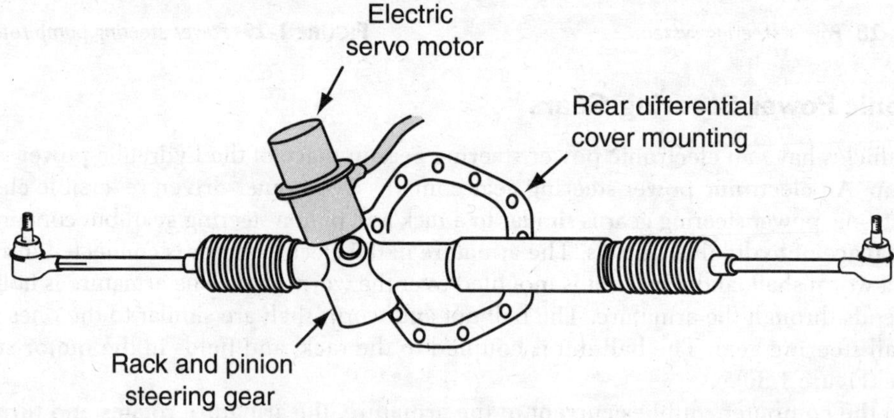

FIGURE 1-31 *Rear electronic power steering gear, four-wheel steering.*

WHEEL ALIGNMENT

Proper **wheel alignment** is extremely important to provide steering control, ride quality, and normal tire tread life. Improper wheel alignment may cause steering wander, steering pull to the right or left, or improper steering wheel return after turning a corner. Incorrect wheel alignment may contribute to harsh ride quality. Wheel alignment angles that are not within specifications may cause rapid tire tread wear.

Rear Wheel Tracking

The rear wheels must track directly behind the front wheels to provide proper steering control. The front and rear wheels must be parallel to the vehicle centerline to provide proper rear wheel tracking. If the rear wheels are tracking directly behind the front wheels, the **thrust line** is positioned at the geometric centerline of the vehicle (Figure 1-32). If the left rear wheel has excessive **toe-out**, the thrust line is moved to the left of the geometric centerline (Figure 1-33). This improperly positioned thrust line causes the steering to pull to the right and also results in rapid tread wear on the left rear tire.

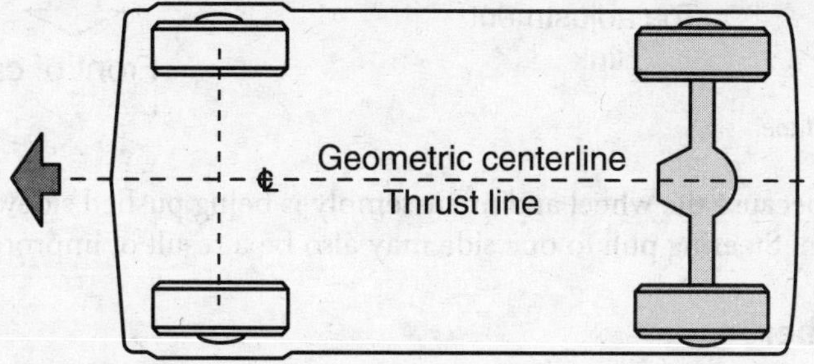

FIGURE 1-32 *Front and rear wheels are parallel to the vehicle centerline.*

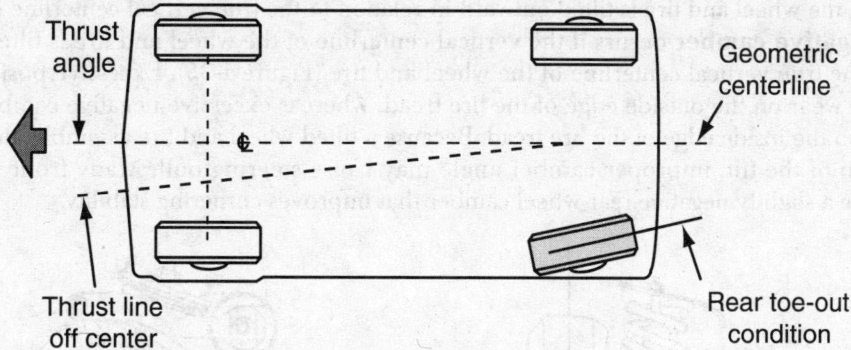

FIGURE 1-33 *Excessive toe-out on the left rear wheel moves the thrust line to the left of the geometric centerline.*

Rear Wheel Toe

A toe-out condition occurs when the distance between the front edges of the rear tires is greater than the distance between the rear edges of the rear tires. Toe-in occurs if the distance between the rear edges of the rear tires is greater than the distance between the front edges of the rear tires (Figure 1-34). On front-wheel-drive vehicles, driving forces tend to push the rear spindles backward. Therefore, these vehicles are usually designed with a zero toe-in or a slight toe-in. Improper rear wheel toe causes

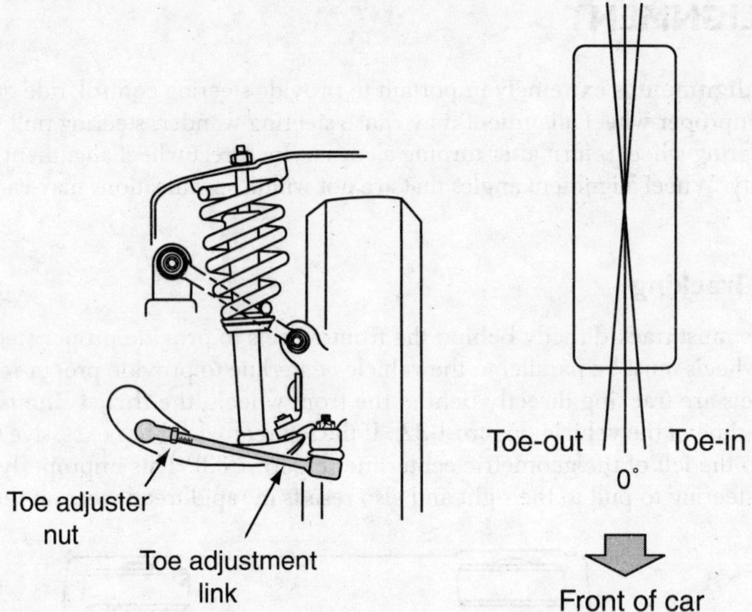

FIGURE 1-34 *Rear wheel toe.*

rapid tire tread wear because the wheel and tire assembly is being pushed sideways to a certain extent as the vehicle is driven. Steering pull to one side may also be a result of improper rear wheel toe.

Rear Wheel Camber

Camber is the angle between the centerline of the wheel and tire in relation to the true vertical centerline of the wheel and tire viewed from the front. **Positive camber** occurs when the vertical centerline of the wheel and tire is tilted outward in relation to the true vertical centerline of the wheel and tire. **Negative camber** occurs if the vertical centerline of the wheel and tire is tilted inward in relation to the true vertical centerline of the wheel and tire (Figure 1-35). Excessive positive camber causes rapid wear on the outside edge of the tire tread, whereas excessive negative camber results in rapid wear on the inside edge of the tire tread. Because a tilted wheel and tire assembly always rolls in the direction of the tilt, improper camber angle may cause steering pull. Many front-wheel-drive vehicles have a slightly negative rear wheel camber that improves cornering stability.

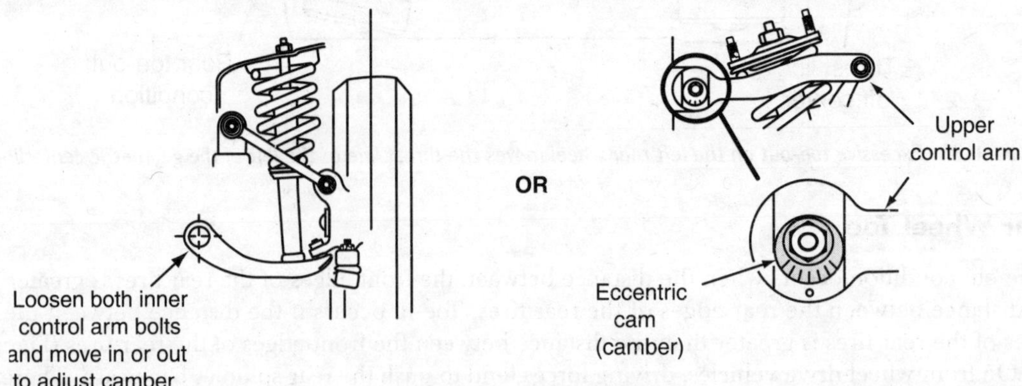

FIGURE 1-35 *Rear wheel camber.*

Front Wheel Camber

Front wheel camber is the same as rear wheel camber except for the camber setting. Many front suspension systems are designed with a slightly positive camber.

Front Wheel Caster

Caster is the tilt of a line through the tire centerline in relation to the true vertical tire centerline viewed from the side. **Positive caster** occurs when the centerline of the tire is tilted rearward in relation to the true vertical centerline of the tire. **Negative caster** occurs when the centerline of the tire is tilted forward in relation to the centerline of the tire viewed from the side (Figure 1-36). Excessive negative caster causes the steering to wander when the vehicle is driven straight ahead. Excessive positive caster causes increased steering effort and rapid steering wheel return after turning a corner. Harsh ride quality is also a result of excessive positive caster because this condition causes the caster line to be aimed at road irregularities.

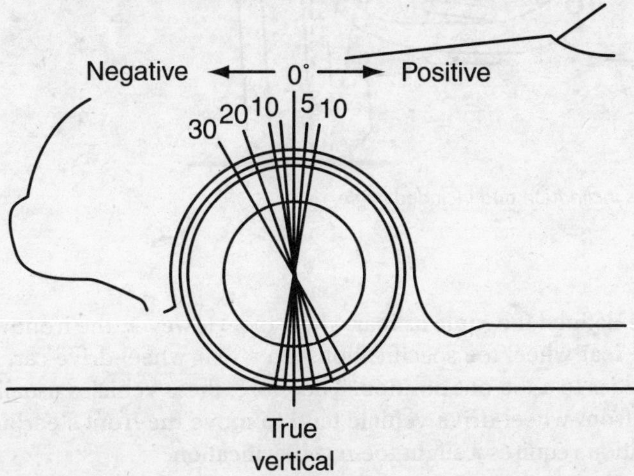

FIGURE 1-36 *Positive and negative caster.*

STEERING AXIS INCLINATION

Steering axis inclination (SAI) is the angle of a line through the centerline of the upper strut mount and the lower ball joint in relation to the true vertical centerline of the tire viewed from the front of the vehicle (Figure 1-37). The **included angle** is the sum of the SAI and camber angle. If the camber angle is negative, this angle must be subtracted from the SAI to calculate the included angle. When the SAI angle is tilted toward the center of the vehicle and the wheels are straight ahead, the height of the front spindles are raised closer to the chassis. This action allows gravity to lower the height of the vehicle. When the front wheels are turned, each knuckle moves through an arc that tends to force the tire into the ground. Because this reaction cannot occur, the chassis lifts when the front wheels are turned. When the steering wheel is released after a turn, the vehicle weight has a tendency to settle to its lowest point. Therefore, SAI helps return the wheels to the straight-ahead position after a turn, and also tends to maintain the front wheels in the straight-ahead position. However, SAI does increase steering effort, because the chassis has to lift slightly when cornering.

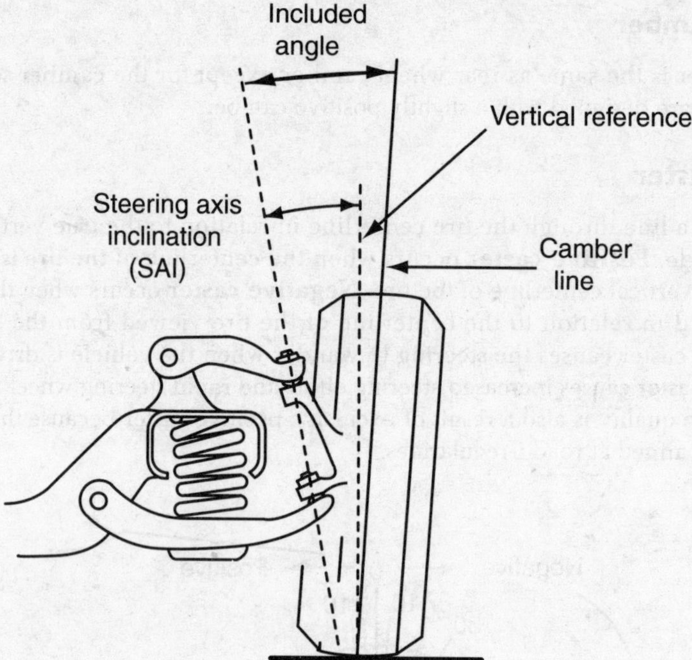

FIGURE 1-37 *Steering axis inclination and included angle.*

Front Wheel Toe

Front wheel toe may be defined the same as rear wheel toe. However, the front wheel toe specification usually differs from the rear wheel toe specification. On a rear-wheel-drive car, driving forces tend to move the steering knuckles to a toe-out position. Therefore, these vehicles usually have a slight toe-in. Drive axle forces on a front-wheel-drive vehicle tend to move the front steering knuckles to a toe-in position, and this condition requires a slight toe-out specification.

Scrub Radius

Scrub radius is the distance between the SAI line and the true vertical centerline of the tire at the road surface (Figure 1-38). Scrub radius is determined by the suspension system design, and is not adjustable. Scrub radius does affect steering quality.

Wheel Setback

Wheel **setback** occurs when one wheel is driven rearward in relation to the opposite front wheel (Figure 1-39). Setback may occur on rear wheels, but is most likely to be present on front wheels. Setback is usually caused by collision damage.

Turning Radius

Turning radius is the turning angles of the front wheels around a common center point. Because the wheel in the inside of the turn is closer to the center point, the inside wheel must turn at a sharper angle than the outside wheel (Figure 1-40). The turning angles of the front wheels are determined by the steering arm design, and these angles are not adjustable. If the steering angles during a turn are not correct, the steering arms may be bent.

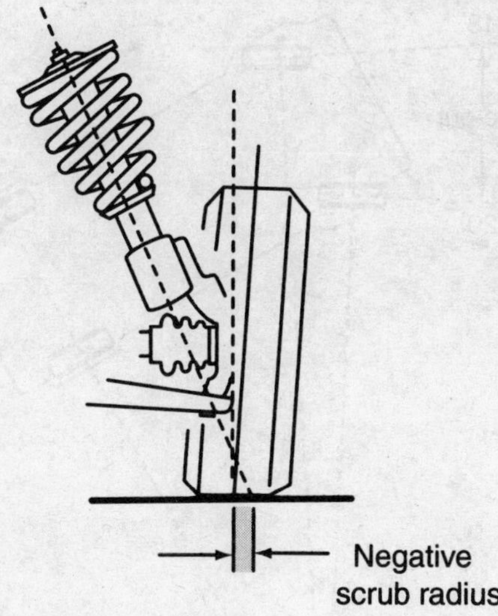

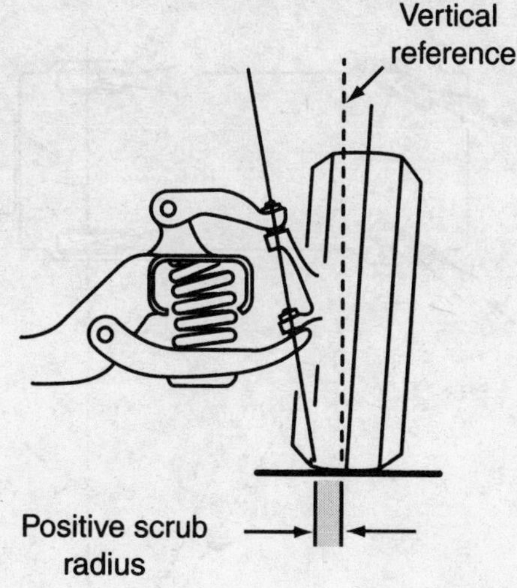

FIGURE 1-38 *Scrub radius.*

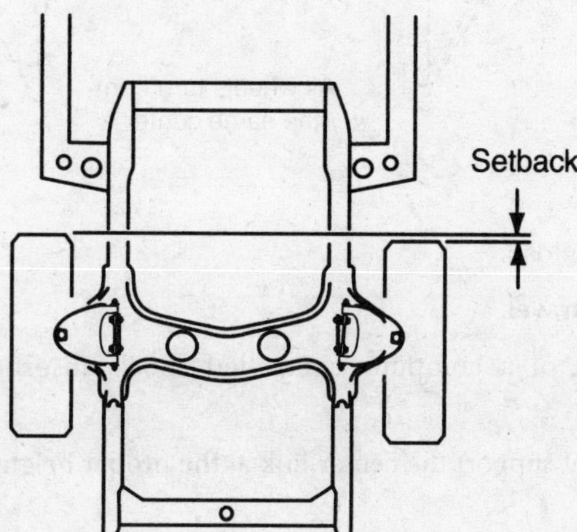

FIGURE 1-39 *Setback.*

REVIEW QUESTIONS

Short Answer Essays

1. Explain how the engine and transaxle are supported in a front-wheel-drive vehicle with a unitized body.
2. Explain the purpose of coil springs in a short-and-long arm front suspension system.
3. Describe how the top of the steering knuckle is supported in a MacPherson strut front suspension system.
4. Explain the disadvantages of a live axle rear suspension system.
5. List the various materials that can be used in the manufacture of wheel rims.
6. Describe the design of a wheel rim with positive offset.

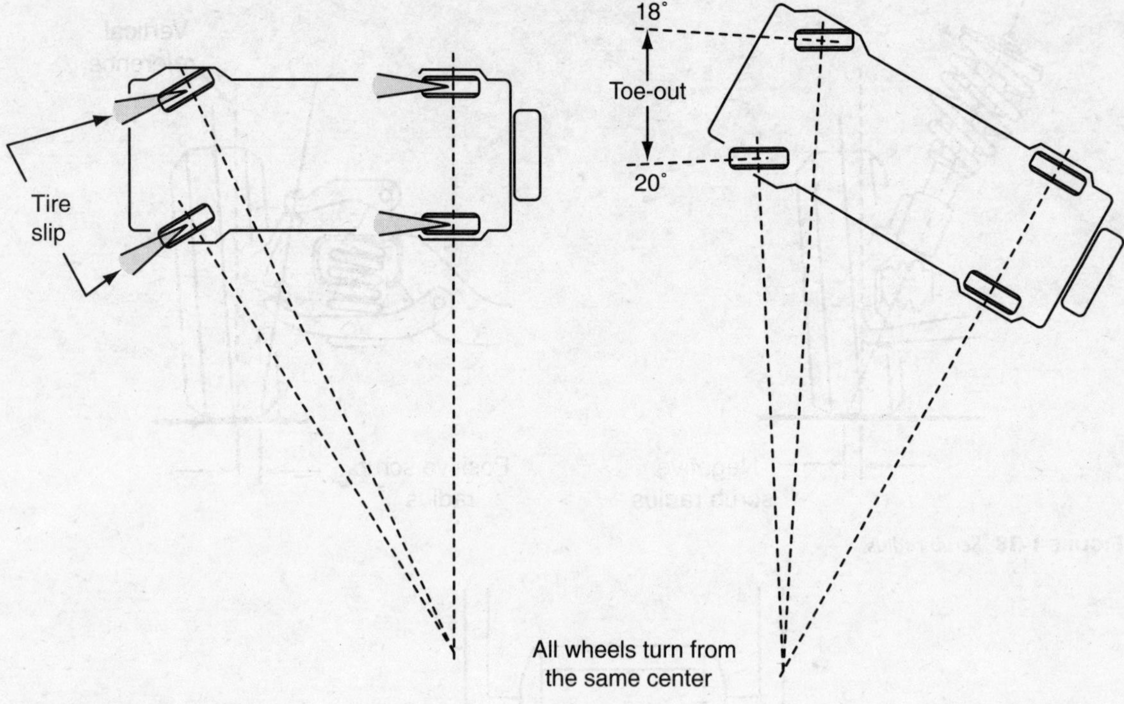

FIGURE 1-40 *Turning radius.*

7. Explain a radial bearing load.
8. Describe jounce wheel travel.
9. Explain the operation of a computer-controlled shock absorber that contains magneto-rheological fluid.
10. List the components that support the center link at the proper height in a parallelogram steering linkage.

Fill-in-the-Blanks

1. In a rack and pinion steering gear, the inner ends of the tie rods are attached to the ends of the _______________ _______________.
2. Fluid is forced from the power steering pump through a _______________ _______________ to the steering gear.
3. In an electronic power steering system, the steering computer receives input signals from the _______________ _______________ sensor and the _______________ _______________ _______________ sensor.
4. When turning the vehicle at low speeds, a four-wheel steering system provides a shorter _______________ _______________.
5. Excessive toe-out on a rear wheel may cause _______________ _______________ and rapid _______________ _______________ _______________.

6. The vehicle thrust line should be positioned at the ______________ ______________ of the vehicle.

7. If a wheel has negative camber, the tire centerline is tilted ______________ in relation to the true vertical tire centerline.

8. After completing a turn, the steering axis inclination (SAI) angle helps to return the front wheels to the ______________ ______________ position.

9. If the outside front wheel is turned at a 20° angle, the inside front wheel turning angle should be ______________°.

10. If the steering angle is not correct, the ______________ ______________ may be bent.

Multiple Choice

1. Unitized vehicle bodies have these special features and applications:
A. Unitized bodies are typically used in large rear-wheel drive vehicles.
B. Unitized bodies have special steel panels in the hood and trunk lid to protect the vehicle occupants in a collision.
C. Some members of a unitized body are load-carrying members.
D. Unitized bodies have a steel box around the passenger compartment.

2. The purpose of the upper and lower control arms in a short-and-long arm front suspension system is to:
A. Allow the steering knuckle to turn to the right or left.
B. Control spring action on irregular road surfaces.
C. Reduce body sway.
D. Control lateral (side-to-side) wheel movement.

3. A semi-independent rear suspension system has:
A. A rear axle with an inverted steel U-section containing a tubular stabilizer bar.
B. Upper and lower control arms.
C. A one-piece rear axle housing.
D. A lower ball joint.

4. All of these statements about wheel rims are true EXCEPT:
A. Wheel rims must position the tires at the proper distance inward or outward from the vertical wheel mounting surface.
B. A wheel rim with a positive offset has the center of the tire positioned outboard from the vertical wheel mounting surface.
C. A wheel rim with a neutral offset has the center of the tire positioned at the vertical center of the brake rotor.
D. A wheel rim with a negative offset has the center of the tire positioned inboard from the vertical wheel mounting surface.

5. A thrust-type bearing load is applied in a:
A. Horizontal direction.
B. Vertical direction.
C. Angular direction.
D. Radial direction.

6. Shock absorbers control spring action and help to prevent:
A. Improper wheel and tire position.
B. Wheel oscillations.
C. Excessive steering effort.
D. Slow steering wheel return after a turn.

7. In a parallelogram steering linkage, the tie rods are parallel to the:
A. Steering arms.
B. Center link.
C. Upper control arms.
D. Lower control arms.

8. All of these statements about recirculating ball steering gears are true EXCEPT:
A. Ball bearings are mounted between the worm gear and the ball nut.
B. The lower end of the sector shaft is splined to the idler arm.
C. As the steering wheel is turned, the ball nut moves upward or downward on the worm gear.
D. The steering shaft is attached to the worm gear.

9. Excessive rear wheel toe-out on the left rear wheel causes:
A. Steering pull to the right.
B. Harsh ride quality.
C. Reduced steering effort.
D. Excessive wheel oscillations.

10. When the steering axis inclination (SAI) angle is increased:
A. The steering wheel return speed is decreased.
B. The front wheels tend to remain in the straight-ahead position.
C. The included angle is decreased.
D. The front wheel toe-in is increased.

BASIC THEORIES 2

Upon completion and review of this chapter, you should be able to:

- Explain Newton's Laws of Motion.
- Define work and force.
- Define power.
- List the most common types of energy and energy conversions.
- Define inertia and momentum.
- Explain friction.
- Define mass, weight, and volume.
- Explain static unbalance.
- Define dynamic unbalance.
- Explain the compressibility of gases and the noncompressibility of liquids.
- Describe atmospheric pressure and vacuum.
- Explain venturi operation.

INTRODUCTION

An understanding of the basics is essential before you attempt a study of complex systems and components. Basic theories such as static balance, dynamic balance, and compressibility must be understood prior to a study of the components and systems in this book. If you have studied basic theories previously, the information in this chapter may be used as a review. A thorough study of this chapter will provide all the necessary background information you need before you study the suspension and steering systems in this book.

NEWTON'S LAWS OF MOTION

First Law

A body in motion remains in motion, and a body at rest remains at rest, unless some outside force acts on it. When a car is parked on a level street, it remains stationary unless it is driven or pushed. If the gas pedal is depressed with the engine running and the transmission in drive, the engine delivers power to the drive wheels and this force moves the car.

Second Law

A body's acceleration is directly proportional to the force applied to it, and the body moves in a straight line away from the force. For example, if the engine power supplied to the drive wheels increases, the vehicle accelerates faster.

Third Law

For every action, there is an equal and opposite reaction. A practical application of this law occurs when the wheel on a vehicle strikes a bump in the road surface. This action drives the wheel and suspension upward with a certain force, and a specific amount of energy is stored in the spring. After this action occurs, the spring forces the wheel and suspension downward with a force equal to the initial upward force.

WORK AND FORCE

When a **force** moves a certain mass a specific distance, **work** is produced. When work is accomplished, the mass may be lifted or slid on a surface (Figure 2-1). Since force is measured in pounds and distance is measured in feet, the measurement for work is foot-pounds (ft-lb). In the metric system, work is measured in Newton meters (Nm). If a force moves a 3,000-pound vehicle for 50 feet, 150,000 foot-pounds of work are produced. Mechanical force acts on an object to start, stop, or change the direction of the object. It is possible to apply force to an object and not move the object. For example, you may push with all your strength on a car stuck in a ditch and not move the car. Under this condition, no work is done. Work is only accomplished when an object is started, stopped, or redirected by mechanical force.

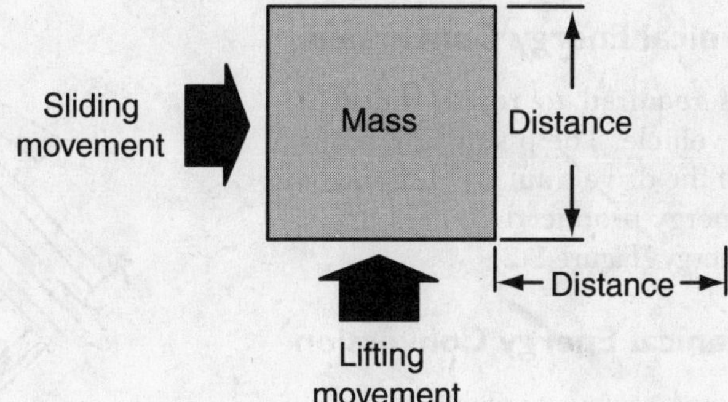

FIGURE 2-1 *Work is accomplished when a mass is lifted or slid on a surface.*

ENERGY

When **energy** is released to do work, it is called kinetic energy. This type of energy may also be referred to as energy in motion. Stored energy may be called potential energy. Energy is available in one of six forms:

1. *Chemical energy* is contained in the molecules of different atoms. In the automobile, chemical energy is contained in the molecules of gasoline and also in the molecules of electrolyte in the battery.
2. *Electrical energy* is required to move electrons through an electric circuit. In the automobile, the battery is capable of producing electrical energy to start the vehicle, and the alternator produces electrical energy to power the electrical accessories and recharge the battery.
3. *Mechanical energy* is the ability to move objects. In the automobile, the battery supplies electrical energy to the starting motor, and this motor converts the electrical energy to mechanical energy to crank the engine. Because this energy is in motion, it may be called kinetic energy.
4. *Thermal energy* is energy produced by heat. When gasoline burns, thermal energy is released.
5. *Radiant energy* is light energy. In the automobile, radiant energy is produced by the lights.
6. *Nuclear energy* is the energy within atoms when they are split apart or combined. Nuclear power plants generate electricity with this principle. This type of energy is not used in the automobile.

ENERGY CONVERSION

Energy conversion occurs when one form of energy is changed to another form. Since energy is not always in the desired form, it must be converted to a form we can use. Some of the most common automotive energy conversions are discussed in the following sections.

Chemical to Thermal Energy Conversion

Chemical energy in gasoline or diesel fuel is converted to thermal energy when the fuel burns in the engine cylinders.

Thermal to Mechanical Energy Conversion

Mechanical energy is required to rotate the drive wheels and move the vehicle. The piston and crankshaft in the engine and the drive train are designed to convert the thermal energy produced by the burning fuel into mechanical energy (Figure 2-2).

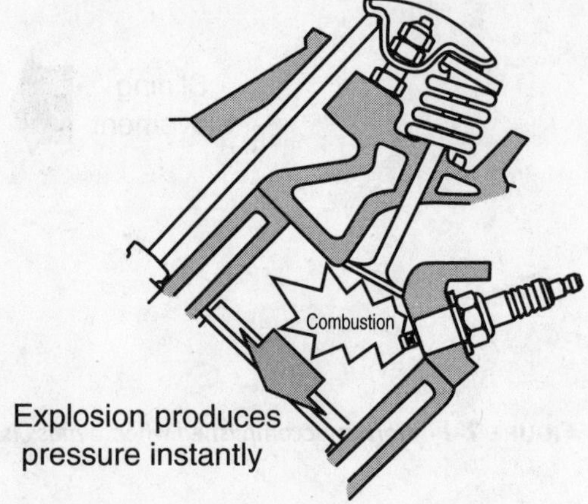

FIGURE 2-2 *Thermal energy in the fuel is converted to mechanical energy in the engine cylinders. The piston, crankshaft, and drive train deliver this mechanical energy to the drive wheels.*

Electrical to Mechanical Energy Conversion

The windshield wiper motor converts electrical energy from the battery or alternator to mechanical energy to drive the windshield wipers.

Mechanical to Electrical Energy Conversion

The alternator is driven by mechanical energy from the engine. The alternator converts this energy to electrical energy, which powers the electrical accessories on the vehicle and recharges the battery.

INERTIA

The **inertia** of an object at rest is called static inertia, whereas dynamic inertia refers to the inertia of an object in motion. Inertia exists in liquids, solids, and gases. When you push and move a parked vehicle, you overcome the static inertia of the vehicle. If you catch a ball in motion, you overcome the dynamic inertia of the ball.

MOMENTUM

Momentum is the product of an object's weight times its speed. Momentum is a type of mechanical energy. An object loses momentum if another force overcomes the dynamic inertia of the moving object.

FRICTION

Friction may occur in solids, liquids, and gases. When a car is driven down the road, friction occurs between the air and the car's surface. This friction opposes the momentum, or mechanical energy, of the moving vehicle. Since friction creates heat, some of the mechanical energy from the vehicle's momentum is changed to heat energy in the air and body components. The mechanical energy from the engine must overcome the vehicle's inertia and the friction of the air striking the vehicle. Body design has a very dramatic effect on the amount of friction developed by the air striking the vehicle. The total resistance to motion caused by friction between a moving vehicle and the air is referred to as coefficient of drag (Cd). The study of Cd is not only very complicated but also very important. At 45 miles per hour (72 kilometers per hour), half of the engine's mechanical energy is used to overcome air friction, or resistance. Therefore, reducing a vehicle's Cd can be a very effective method of improving fuel economy.

MASS, WEIGHT, AND VOLUME

A lawn mower is much easier to push than a 2,500-pound vehicle because the lawn mower has very little inertia compared to the vehicle. A space ship might weigh 100 tons here on earth where it is affected by the earth's gravitational pull. In outer space beyond the earth's gravity and atmosphere, the space ship is almost weightless. Here on earth, **mass** and **weight** are measured in pounds and ounces in the English system. In the metric system, mass and weight are measured in grams or kilograms.

Volume is a measurement of size, and it is related to mass and weight. For example, a pound of gold and a pound of feathers both have the same weight, but the pound of feathers occupies a much larger volume. In the English system, volume is measured in cubic inches, cubic feet, cubic yards, or gallons. The measurement for volume in the metric system is cubic centimeters or liters.

TORQUE

When you pull a wrench to tighten a bolt, you supply **torque** to the bolt. If you pull on a wrench to check the torque on a bolt, and the bolt torque is sufficient, torque is applied to the bolt, but no movement occurs. This torque, or twisting force, is calculated by multiplying the force and the radius. For example, if you supply a 10 lb force on the end of a 2-ft wrench to tighten a bolt, the torque is $10 \times 2 = 20$ ft-lb (Figure 2-3). If the bolt turns during torque application, work is done. When a bolt does not rotate during torque application, no work is accomplished.

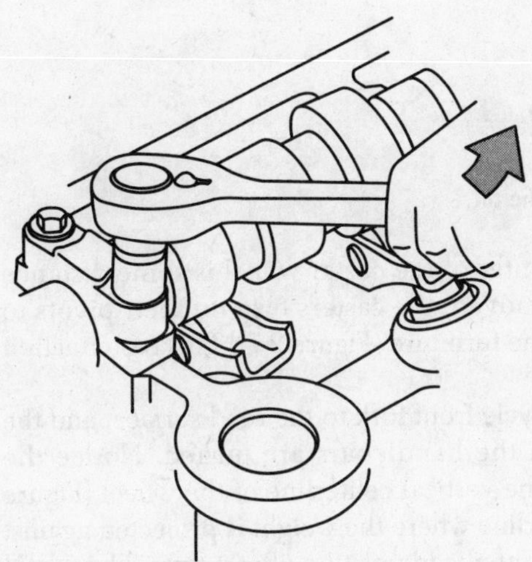

FIGURE 2-3 *Force applied to a wrench produces torque. If the bolt turns, work is accomplished.*

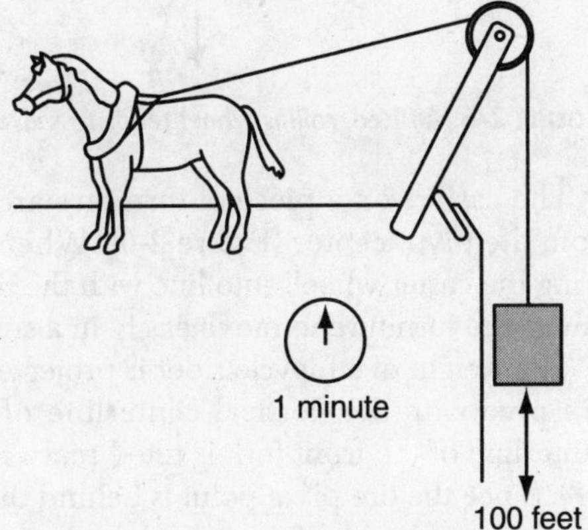

FIGURE 2-4 *One horsepower is produced when 330 pounds are moved 100 feet in one minute.*

POWER

James Watt calculated that a horse could move 330 pounds for 100 feet in one minute (Figure 2-4). If you multiply 330 pounds by 100 feet, the answer is 33,000 foot-pounds of work. Watt determined that one horse could do 33,000 foot-pounds of work in one minute. Thus, one **horsepower** is equal to 33,000 foot-pounds per minute, or 550 foot-pounds per second. Two horsepower could do this same amount of work in one-half minute, or four horsepower could complete this work in one-quarter minute. If you push a 3,000-pound (1,360-kilogram) car for 11 feet (3.3 meters) in one-quarter minute, you produce four horsepower. From this brief discussion about horsepower, we can understand that as power increases, speed also increases, or the time to do work decreases.

PRINCIPLES INVOLVING TIRES AND WHEELS IN MOTION

If you roll a cone-shaped piece of metal on a smooth surface, the cone does not move straight ahead. Instead, the cone moves toward the direction of the tilt on the cone. When you are riding a bicycle and want to make a left turn, if you tilt the bicycle to the left, it is much easier to complete the turn. The reason for this action is that a tilted, rolling wheel tends to move in the direction of the tilt. Similarly, if a tire and wheel on a vehicle are tilted, the tire and wheel tend to move in the direction of the tilt (Figure 2-5). This principle is used in front wheel alignment.

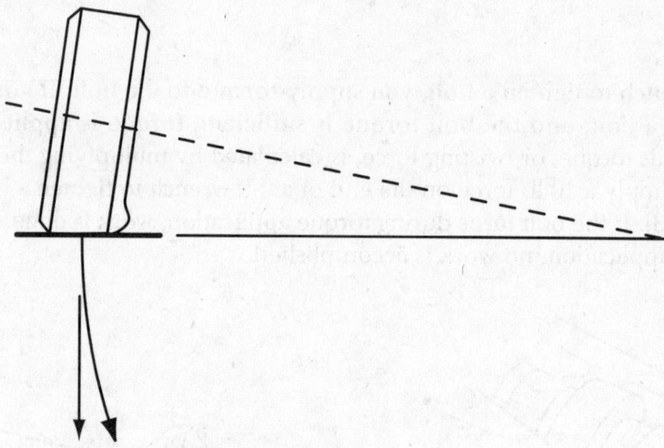

FIGURE 2-5 *A tilted, rolling wheel tends to move in the direction of the tilt.*

The casters on a piece of furniture are angled so the center of the caster wheel is some distance from the pivot center (Figure 2-6). When the furniture is moved, the casters turn on their pivots to bring the caster wheels into line with the pushing force on the furniture (Figure 2-7). This caster action causes the furniture to move easily in a straight line.

The weight of a bicycle rider is projected through the bicycle front fork to the road surface, and the tire pivots on the vertical centerline of the wheel when the handlebars are turned. Notice the centerline of the front fork is tilted rearward in relation to the vertical centerline of the wheel (Figure 2-8). Since the tire pivot point is behind the front fork centerline where the weight is projected against the road surface, the front wheel tends to return to the straight-ahead position after a turn. The wheel also tends to remain in the straight-ahead position as the bicycle is driven. This principle is applied in automotive front wheel alignment.

PRINCIPLES INVOLVING THE BALANCE OF WHEELS IN MOTION

When the weight of a tire-and-wheel assembly is distributed equally around the center of wheel rotation viewed from the side, the wheel and tire have proper **static balance.** Under this condition, the tire-and-wheel assembly has no tendency to rotate by itself, regardless of the wheel position. If the

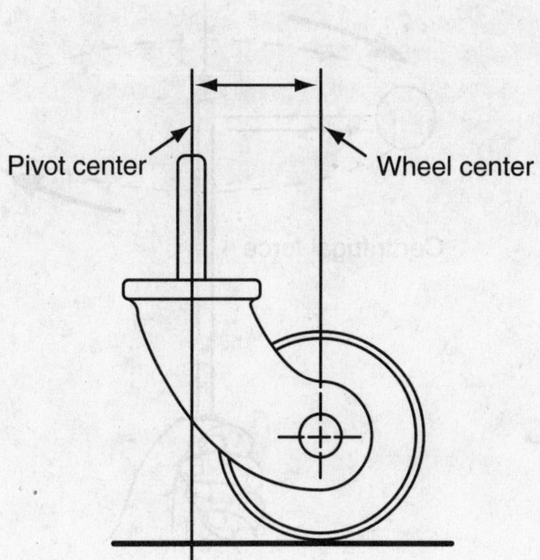

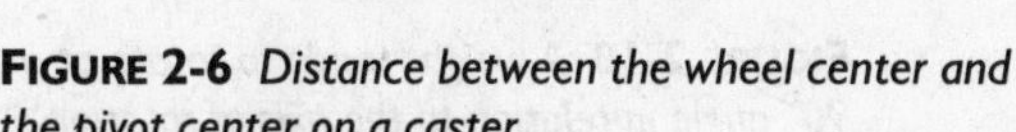

FIGURE 2-6 *Distance between the wheel center and the pivot center on a caster.*

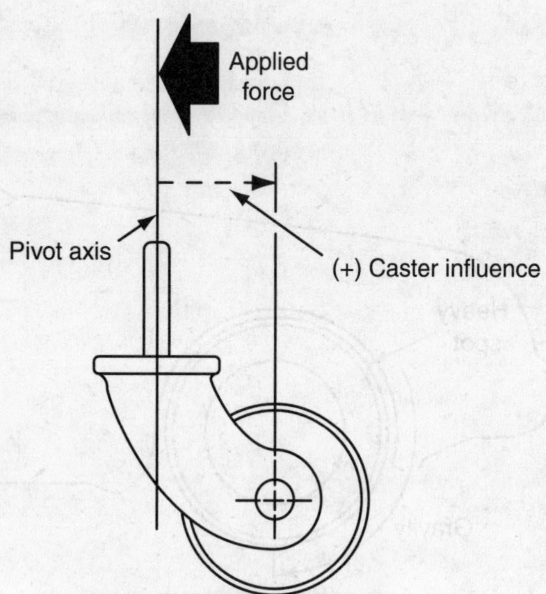

FIGURE 2-7 *Caster aligned with the pushing force provides straight-ahead movement when furniture is pushed.*

weight is not distributed equally around the center of wheel rotation, the wheel and tire are statically unbalanced (Figure 2-9). As the wheel and tire rotate, centrifugal force acts on this static unbalance and causes the wheel to "tramp" or "hop." This wheel and tire action can often be seen while looking at tires on vehicles that may pass you on a highway.

When a ball is rotated on the end of a string, the ball and string form an angle with the axis of rotation. If the rotational speed is increased, the ball and string form a 90° angle with the axis of rotation (Figure 2-10). Any weight will always tend to rotate at a 90° angle to the axis of rotation.

If two balls are positioned on a metal bar so their weight is equally distributed on the centerline of the rotational axis of rotation, the path of rotation remains at a 90° angle to the centerline of the axis when the bar is rotated. Under this condition, the metal bar and the balls are in **dynamic balance** (Figure 2-11).

If weights are placed on a metal bar so their weights are not equally distributed in relation to the centerline of the rotational axis of rotation, the weights still tend to rotate at a 90° angle in relation to the rotational axis. This action forces the pivot out of its vertical axis (Figure 2-12). When the bar is rotated 180°, the bar is forced out of its vertical axis in the opposite direction. If this condition is present, the bar has a wobbling action as it rotates. Under this condition, the bar is said to have dynamic unbalance, but static balance is maintained.

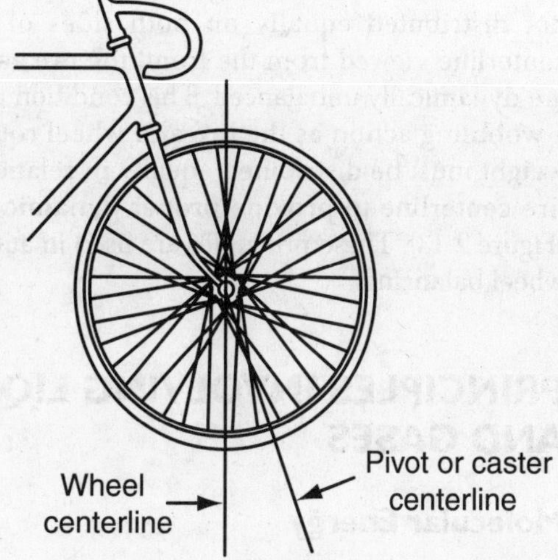

FIGURE 2-8 *If a wheel centerline and pivot point are behind the front fork centerline pivot point, the wheel tends to return to the straight-ahead position after a turn. The wheel also tends to remain in the straight-ahead position as the bicycle is driven.*

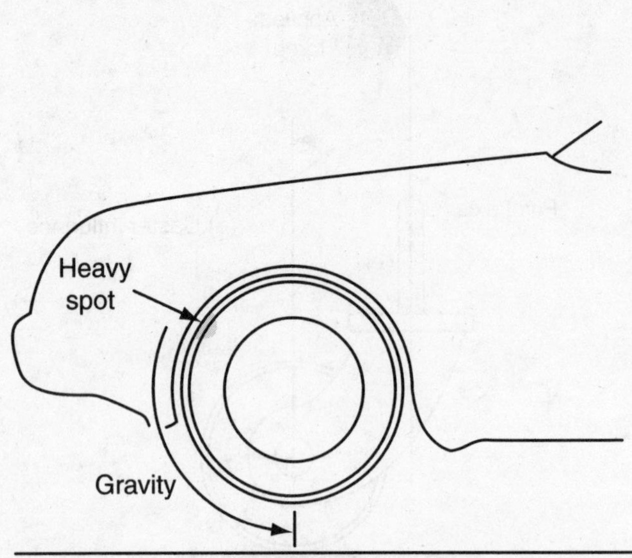

FIGURE 2-9 *Static wheel unbalance caused by unequal weight distribution around the center of the wheel rotation.*

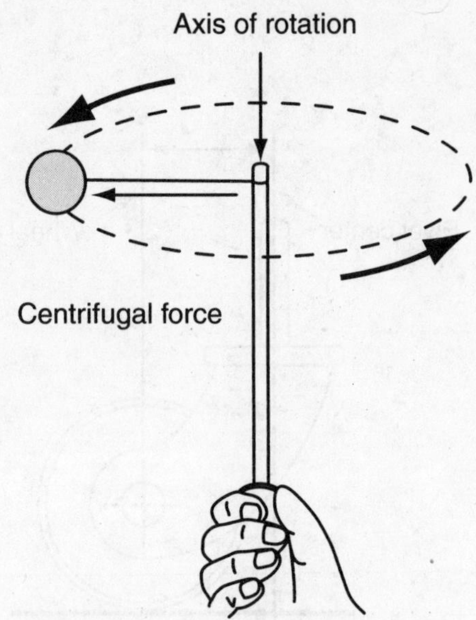

FIGURE 2-10 *A weight tends to rotate at a 90° angle in relation to the axis of rotation.*

Similarly, when the weight on a tire and wheel is not distributed equally on both sides of the tire centerline viewed from the front, the tire and wheel are dynamically unbalanced. This condition produces a wobbling action as the tire and wheel rotate. The weight must be distributed equally in relation to the tire centerline to provide proper dynamic balance (Figure 2-13). These principles are used in automotive wheel balancing.

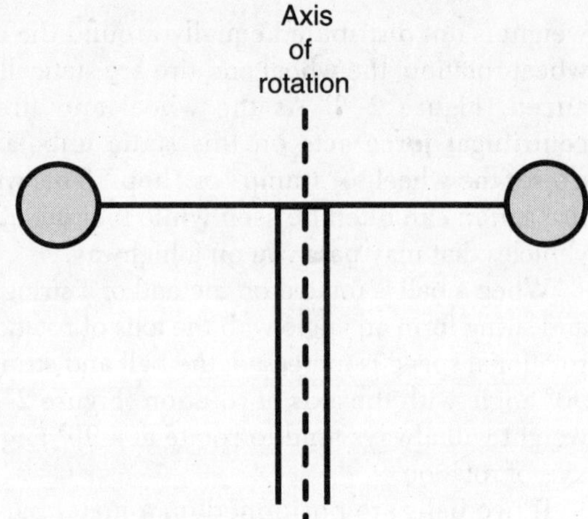

FIGURE 2-11 *When weight on a metal bar is distributed equally on the centerline of the axis of rotation, the bar and balls remain in dynamic balance during rotation.*

PRINCIPLES INVOLVING LIQUIDS AND GASES

Molecular Energy

Remember that kinetic energy refers to energy in motion. Since electrons are constantly in motion around the nucleus in atoms or molecules, kinetic energy is present in all matter. Kinetic energy in atoms and molecules increases as the temperature increases. A decrease in temperature reduces the kinetic energy. Molecules in solids move slowly compared to those in liquids or gases. Gas molecules move quickly compared to liquid molecules. Since gas molecules are in constant motion, they spread out to fill all the space available. At higher temperatures, gas molecules spread out more, whereas at lower temperatures, gas molecules move closer together.

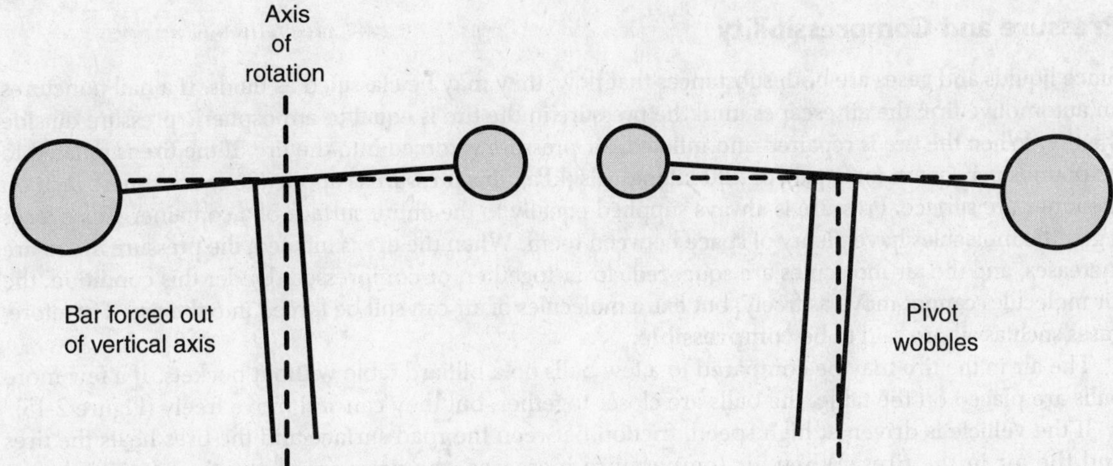

FIGURE 2-12 *When weight is not equally distributed in relation to the centerline of rotational axis, dynamic unbalance causes a wobbling action during rotation.*

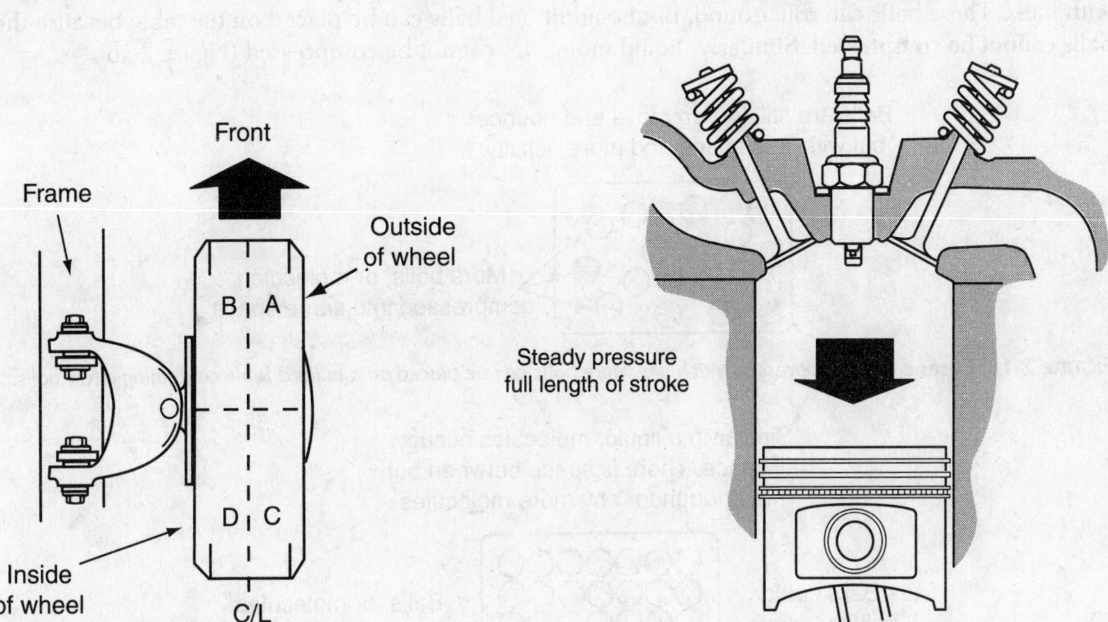

FIGURE 2-13 *Weight must be distributed equally in relation to the tire and wheel centerline.*

FIGURE 2-14 *Hot, expanding gases push the piston downward and rotate the crankshaft.*

Temperature

Temperature affects all liquids, solids, and gases. The volume of any matter increases as the temperature increases. Conversely, the volume decreases in relation to a reduction in temperature. When the gases in an engine cylinder are burned, the sudden temperature increase causes rapid gas expansion, which pushes the piston downward and causes engine rotation (Figure 2-14).

Pressure and Compressibility

Since liquids and gases are both substances that flow, they may be classified as fluids. If a nail punctures an automotive tire, the air escapes until the pressure in the tire is equal to atmospheric pressure outside the tire. When the tire is repaired and inflated, air pressure is forced into the tire. If the tire is inflated to 32 pounds per square inch (psi), or 220 kilopascals (kPa), this pressure is applied to every square inch on the inner tire surface. Pressure is always supplied equally to the entire surface of a container. Since air is a gas, the molecules have plenty of space between them. When the tire is inflated, the pressure in the tire increases, and the air molecules are squeezed closer together, or compressed. Under this condition, the air molecules cannot move as freely, but extra molecules of air can still be forced into the tire. Therefore, gases such as air are said to be **compressible**.

The air in the tire may be compared to a few balls on a billiard table without pockets. If a few more balls are placed on the table, the balls are closer together, but they can still move freely (Figure 2-15).

If the vehicle is driven at high speed, friction between the road surface and the tires heats the tires and the air in the tires. When air temperature increases, the pressure in the tire also increases. Conversely, a temperature decrease reduces pressure.

If 100 cubic feet (2.8 cubic meters) of air is forced into a large truck tire, and the same amount of air is forced into a much smaller car tire, the pressure in the car tire is much greater.

Molecules in a liquid may be compared to a billiard table without pockets that is completely filled with balls. These balls can roll around, but no additional balls can be placed on the table because the balls cannot be compressed. Similarly, liquid molecules cannot be compressed (Figure 2-16).

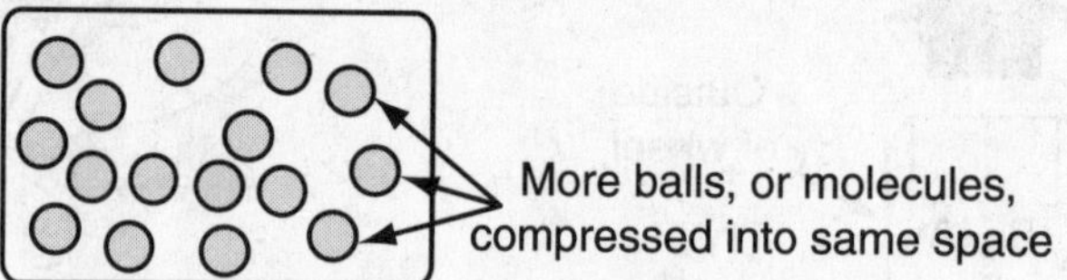

FIGURE 2-15 *Gases can be compressed much like more balls can be placed on a billiard table containing a few balls.*

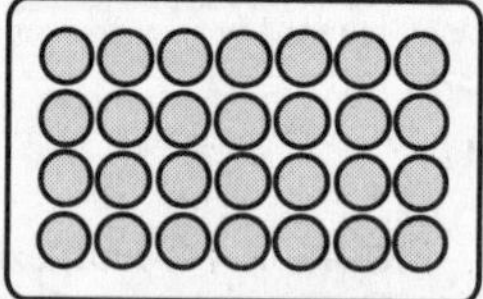

FIGURE 2-16 *Liquids are noncompressible, just as more balls cannot be added to a billiard table with no pockets that is completely filled with balls.*

Liquid Flow

If a tube is filled with billiard balls and the outlet is open, more balls may be added to the inlet. When each ball is moved into the inlet, a ball is forced from the outlet. If the outlet is closed, no more balls can be forced into the inlet (Figure 2-17).

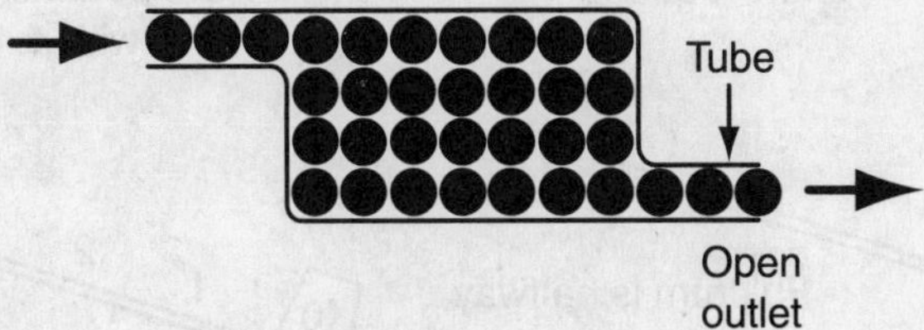

FIGURE 2-17 *Billiard ball movement in a tube filled with balls compared to liquid flow.*

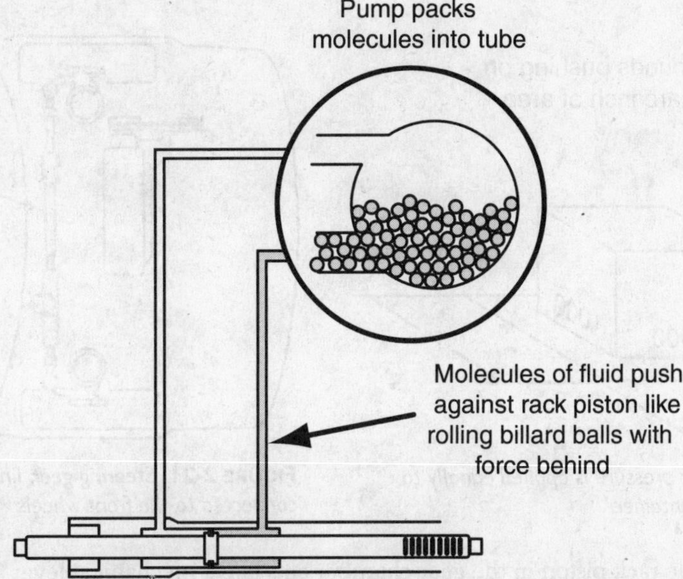

FIGURE 2-18 *Power steering pump pressure supplied to the steering gear chamber.*

The billiard balls in the tube may be compared to molecules of power steering fluid in the line between the power steering pump and steering gear. Since noncompressible fluid fills the line and gear chamber, the force developed by the pump pressure is transferred through the line to the gear chamber (Figure 2-18).

Hydraulic Fluid as a Flexible Machine

Hydraulic pressure has the same effect as a mechanical lever, because both of these items can multiply the input force to do more work. If a mechanical lever has a fulcrum at the center point and a 10-pound (lb), or 4.5-kilogram (kg), weight on one end of the lever, 10 lb (4.5 kg) of weight are required on the other end of the lever to force the lever downward and raise the weight on the opposite end. If the lever is 5 ft long and the fulcrum is placed 1 ft from the weight to be lifted, the lever has a 4 to 1 mechanical advantage. Under this condition, 2.5 lb (1.1 kg) of weight are required on the other end of the lever to lift the 10-lb (4.5 kg) weight (Figure 2-19). Therefore, a mechanical lever multiplies input force and makes it easier to do work.

When the power steering pump pressure supplied to the steering gear chamber is 1,000 psi (7,000 kPa), this pressure is applied to every square inch in the steering gear chamber (Figure 2-20). This

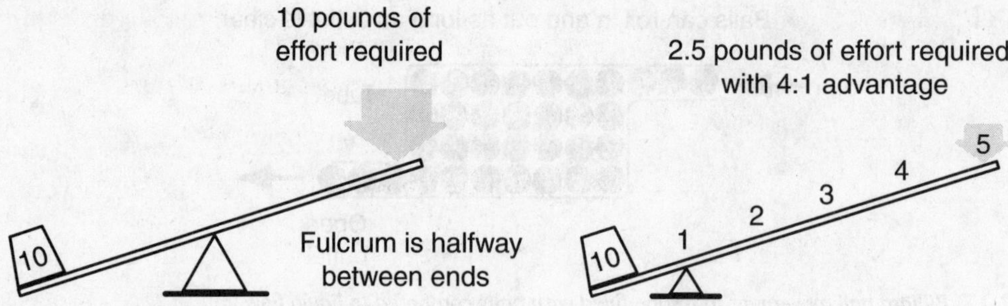

FIGURE 2-19 *A mechanical lever multiplies input force and makes it easier to do work.*

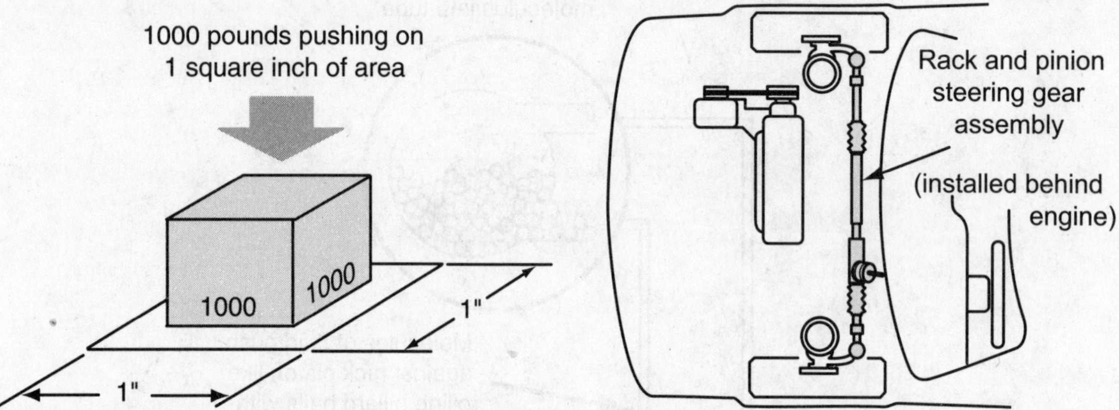

FIGURE 2-20 *Hydraulic pressure is applied equally to every square inch in a container.*

FIGURE 2-21 *Steering gear, linkages, and arms connected to the front wheels.*

pressure applied to the rack piston in the gear chamber acts like a mechanical lever and helps move the rack piston. Since the rack is connected through steering linkages and arms to the front wheels, the force on the rack piston helps the driver move the front wheels to the left or right during a turn (Figure 2-21).

CAUTION: Never completely block a pump outlet unless instructed to do so in the vehicle manufacturer's service manual. This action can result in extremely high pump pressure, damaged components, and personal injury.

ATMOSPHERIC PRESSURE

Since air is gaseous matter with mass and weight, it exerts pressure on the earth's surface. A one-square-inch column of air extending from the earth's surface to the outer edge of the atmosphere weighs 14.7 psi at sea level. Therefore, **atmospheric pressure** is 14.7 psi at sea level (Figure 2-22).

Atmospheric Pressure and Temperature

When air becomes hotter it expands, and this hotter air is lighter compared to an equal volume of cooler air. This hotter, lighter air exerts less pressure on the earth's surface compared to cooler air.

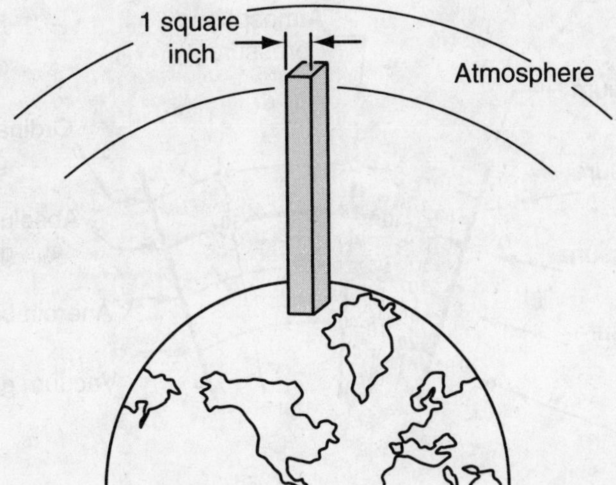

FIGURE 2-22 *A column of air one inch square extending from the earth's surface at sea level to the outer edge of the atmosphere weighs 14.7 pounds.*

If the temperature decreases, air contracts and becomes heavier. Therefore, an equal volume of cooler air exerts more pressure on the earth's surface compared to hotter air.

Atmospheric Pressure and Altitude

When you climb above sea level, atmospheric pressure decreases. The weight of a column of air is less at 5,000 feet (1,524 meters) elevation compared to sea level. As altitude continues to increase, atmospheric pressure and weight continue to decrease. At an altitude of several hundred miles above sea level, the earth's atmosphere ends, and there is only vacuum beyond that point.

VACUUM

Atmospheric pressure is generally considered to be 14.7 pounds per square inch (psi) at sea level. Presşures greater than atmospheric pressure may be measured in psi, whereas pressures below atmospheric pressure are measured in **vacuum,** or psi absolute (psia) (Figure 2-23).

A conventional pressure gauge is used to measure pressures greater than atmospheric pressure. This type of pressure gauge indicates 0 psi at atmospheric pressure, and as the pressure increases it can read up to 15 psi (Figure 2-23). A conventional vacuum gauge indicates 0 in. Hg when atmospheric pressure is applied, and as the vacuum increases this gauge reads from 0 in. Hg to 29.91 inches of mercury (in. Hg), and this may be considered a perfect vacuum. An absolute pressure gauge indicates absolute pressure in pounds per square inch gauge (psig). An absolute pressure gauge indicates 0 at a perfect vacuum, 15 psig at atmospheric pressure, and 30 psig at 15 psi on a conventional pressure gauge. An aneroid barometer reads in. Hg absolute pressure, and thus it reads 0 in. Hg absolute at a perfect vacuum and 29.92 in. Hg absolute when atmospheric pressure is present.

Pressures above atmospheric pressure measured in psi are found in these automotive systems:

1. Fuel
2. Oil

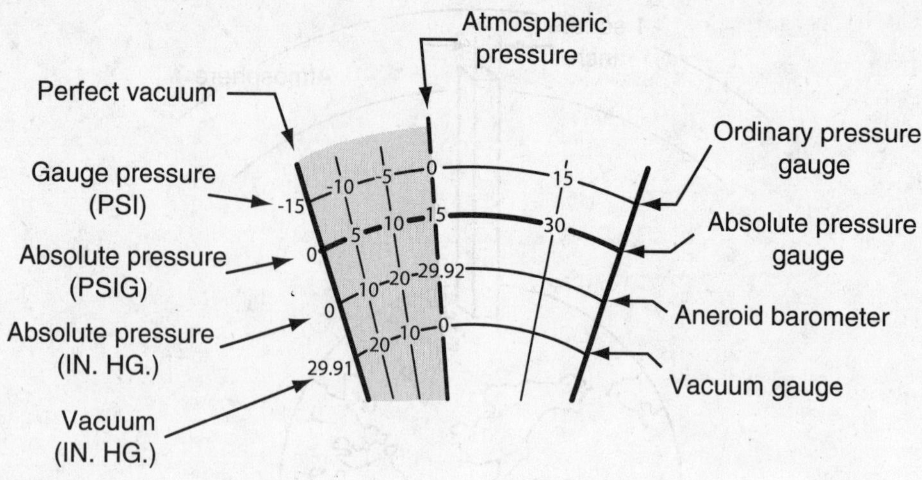

FIGURE 2-23 *Pressure and vacuum scales.*

3. Cooling
4. Power steering
5. Air conditioning
6. Turbocharger boost
7. Air springs
8. Gas-filled shock absorbers
9. Brake system during brake application

Pressures below atmospheric pressure measured in inches of vacuum are found in these automotive systems:

1. Manifold vacuum signal
2. Ported vacuum signal above the throttle
3. Carburetor venturi
4. Air-conditioning evacuation

Vacuum could be measured in psi, but inches of mercury (in. Hg) are most commonly used for this measurement. Let us assume that a manometer is partially filled with mercury, and atmospheric pressure is allowed to enter one end of the tube. If vacuum is supplied to the other end of the manometer, the mercury is forced downward by the atmospheric pressure. When this movement occurs, the mercury also moves upward on the side where the vacuum is supplied. If the mercury moves downward 10 in., or 25.4 centimeters (cm), where the atmospheric pressure is supplied, and upward 10 in. (25.4 cm) where the vacuum is supplied, 20 in. Hg is supplied to the manometer (Figure 2-24). The highest possible, or perfect, vacuum is approximately 29.9 in. Hg.

Vacuum and atmospheric pressure are used in several automotive systems. For example, atmospheric pressure is present outside the compressor inlet on an electronic air suspension system. When the compressor is running, it creates a vacuum at the inlet and in the compressor cylinder. This pressure difference causes air to move from the atmosphere surrounding the inlet into the cylinder. The compressor develops high pressure at the discharge valve, and this pressure forces air into the air springs when the pressure is lower than at the compressor outlet (Figure 2-25).

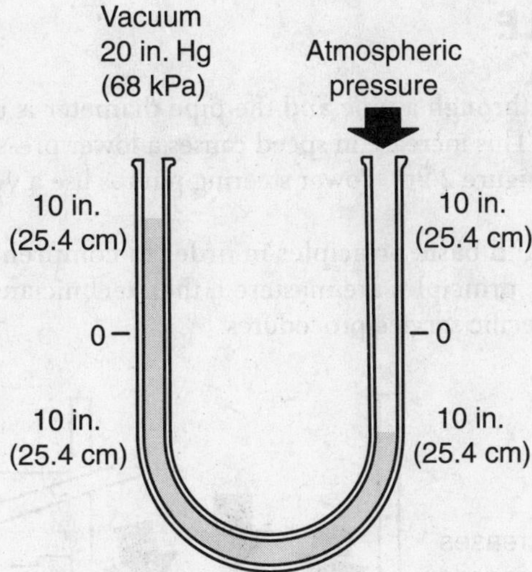

FIGURE 2-24 *A vacuum of 20 in. Hg (68 kPa) supplied to mercury in a manometer.*

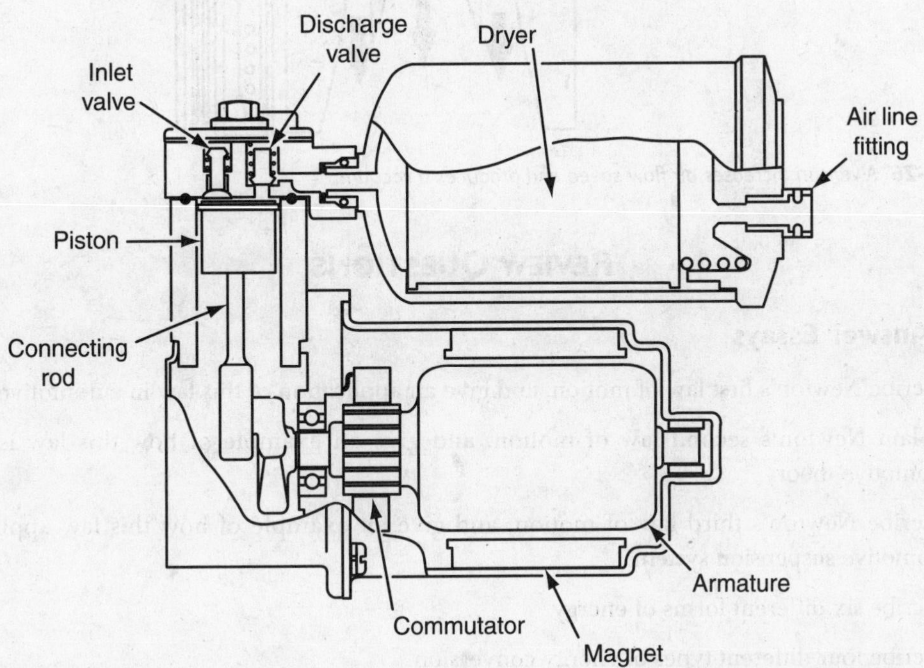

FIGURE 2-25 *An air suspension compressor creates vacuum in the cylinder, and atmospheric pressure at the inlet forces air into the cylinder. The compressor provides high pressure at the discharge valve, which moves air into the air springs.*

Pumps use high and low pressure to move liquids or gases. For example, as a power steering pump rotates, it creates a high pressure at the pump outlet by pumping against a restriction, and a low pressure at the inlet by moving fluid through a restriction. This pressure difference causes fluid to flow through the power steering system.

VENTURI PRINCIPLE

If a gas or a liquid is flowing through a pipe and the pipe diameter is narrow in one place, the flow speeds up in the narrow area. This increase in speed causes a lower pressure in the narrow area, which may be defined as a venturi (Figure 2-26). Power steering pumps use a venturi principle to assist in the control of pump pressure.

Technicians must understand basic principles in order to comprehend the complex systems on modern vehicles. When basic principles are mastered, then technicians understand both the reason for, and the result of, these specific service procedures.

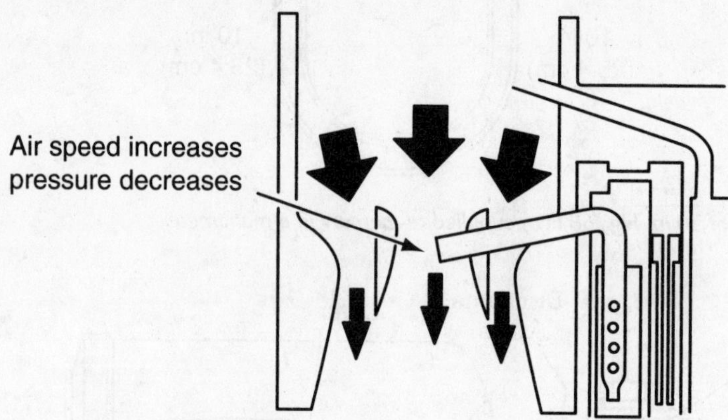

FIGURE 2-26 *A venturi increases air flow speed and produces a vacuum.*

REVIEW QUESTIONS

Short Answer Essays

1. Describe Newton's first law of motion, and give an application of this law in automotive theory.
2. Explain Newton's second law of motion, and give an example of how this law is used in automotive theory.
3. Describe Newton's third law of motion, and give an example of how this law applies to an automotive suspension system.
4. Describe six different forms of energy.
5. Describe four different types of energy conversion.
6. Explain the difference between static and dynamic inertia.
7. Explain why a rotating, tilted wheel moves in the direction of the tilt.
8. Explain why the front wheel of a bicycle tends to remain in the straight-ahead position as the bicycle is driven.
9. Define static and dynamic balance.
10. Describe the effect of temperature on the volume of a gas.

Fill-in-the-Blanks

1. Improper static wheel balance causes wheel ______________ when driving the vehicle.
2. If the tire pivot point is behind the tire and wheel centerline where the vehicle weight is projected against the road surface, the wheel tends to remain in the ______________ ______________ position when driving the vehicle.
3. Work is calculated by multiplying ______________ × ______________.
4. Energy may be defined as the ability to do ______________.
5. When one object is moved over another object, the resistance to motion is called ______________.
6. Weight is the measurement of the earth's ______________ ______________ on an object.
7. Torque is a force that does work with a ______________ action.
8. Power is a measurement for the rate at which ______________ is done.
9. To obtain proper dynamic balance, the weight must be distributed equally on both sides of a wheel and tire centerline viewed from the ______________ of the tire.
10. Vacuum is defined as the absence of ______________ ______________.

Multiple Choice

1. When an engine is running, the alternator converts:
   A. Thermal energy to mechanical energy.
   B. Electrical energy to mechanical energy.
   C. Chemical energy to electrical energy.
   D. Mechanical energy to electrical energy.

2. Work is accomplished during all of these conditions EXCEPT:
   A. When a mechanical force starts an object in motion.
   B. When a mechanical force is applied to an object, but the object does not move.
   C. When a mechanical force stops an object in motion.
   D. When a mechanical force redirects an object in motion.

3. All these statements about Newton's Laws of Motion are true EXCEPT:
   A. For every action there is an equal and opposite reaction.
   B. A body in motion remains in motion unless an outside force acts on it.
   C. A body's acceleration is directly proportional to the force applied to it.
   D. A body moves in an arc away from the force acting upon the object.

4. Torque is calculated by:
   A. Multiplying the force and the radius from the force to the object.
   B. Dividing the radius by the force.
   C. Adding the force and the distance of force movement.
   D. Subtracting the radius from the force to the object and the weight of the object.

5. When working with gases and liquids:
   A. Gases are not compressible.
   B. Liquids are not compressible.
   C. Temperature does not affect gas volume.
   D. Pressure is applied unevenly to the inside of a container surface.

6. When applying the principles of work and force:
   A. Work is accomplished when force is applied to an object that does not move.
   B. In the metric system the measurement for work is cubic centimeters.
   C. No work is accomplished when an object is stopped by mechanical force.
   D. If a 50-pound object is moved 10 feet, 500 ft-lb of work are produced.

7. All these statements about energy and energy conversion are true EXCEPT:
   A. Thermal energy may be defined as light energy.
   B. Chemical to thermal energy conversion occurs when gasoline burns.
   C. Mechanical energy is defined as the ability to do work.
   D. Mechanical to electrical energy conversion occurs when the engine drives the alternator.

WHEEL BEARINGS 3

Upon completion and review of this chapter, you should be able to:

- Explain the purposes of a bearing.
- Describe three different types of bearing loads.
- Identify the basic parts in ball bearings or roller bearings, and describe the purpose of each part.
- Describe the action between the balls and the race when a ball bearing is rotating.
- Explain the purposes of bearing snaprings, shields, and seals.
- Describe the load-carrying capabilities of ball bearings, roller bearings, tapered roller bearings, and needle roller bearings.
- Explain the advantage of tapered roller bearings compared to other types of bearings.
- Explain seal design and purpose.
- Explain the purpose of the garter spring behind a lip seal.
- Describe the purpose of flutes on seal lips.
- Describe two different types of rear axle bearings in rear-wheel-drive cars, and give the seal location for each bearing type.

INTRODUCTION

Many different types of bearings are used in the automobile. A bearing may be defined as a component that supports and guides one of these parts:

1. Pivot
2. Wheel
3. Rotating shaft
4. Oscillating shaft
5. Sliding shaft

While a bearing is supporting and guiding one of these components, the bearing is designed to reduce friction and support the load applied by the component and related assemblies. Since the bearing reduces friction, it also decreases the power required to rotate or move the component. Bearings are precision-machined assemblies, which provide smooth operation and long life. When bearings are properly installed and maintained, bearing failure is rare.

BEARING LOADS

When a bearing load is applied in a vertical direction on a horizontal shaft, it is called a **radial bearing load**. If the vehicle weight is applied straight downward on a bearing, this weight is a radial load on the bearing. A **thrust bearing load** is applied in a horizontal direction (Figure 3-1). For example, while a vehicle is turning a corner, horizontal force is applied to the front wheel bearings. When an **angular bearing load** is applied, the angle of the applied load is somewhere between the horizontal and vertical positions.

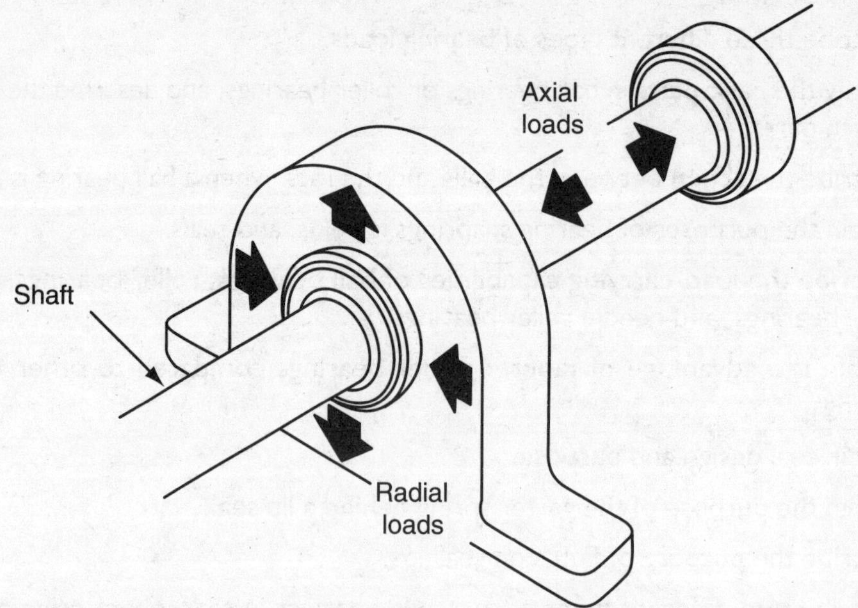

FIGURE 3-1 *Types of bearing loads.*

BALL BEARINGS

Front and rear wheel bearings may be **ball bearings** or roller bearings. Either type of bearing contains these basic parts:

1. Inner race, or cone
2. Rolling elements, balls, or rollers
3. Separator, also called a cage or retainer
4. Outer race, or cup

The **inner race** is an accurately machined component. The inner surface of the race is mounted on the shaft with a precision fit. The **rolling elements** are mounted on a very smoothly machined surface on the inner race. The surfaces on the rolling elements and the inner and outer races are case hardened to provide long bearing life. Positioned between the inner and outer races, the **separator** retains the rolling elements and keeps them evenly spaced. The rolling elements have precision-machined surfaces, and these elements are mounted between the inner and outer races. The **outer race** is the bearing's exterior ring. Both sides of this component have precision-machined surfaces. The outer surface of this race supports the bearing in the housing, and the inner surface is in contact with the rolling elements.

A **single-row ball bearing** has a crescent-shaped machined surface in the inner and outer races in which the balls are mounted (Figure 3-2). When a ball bearing is at rest, the load is distributed equally through the balls and races in the contact area. When one of the races and the balls begin to rotate, the bearing load causes the metal in the race to bulge out in front of the ball and flatten out behind the ball (Figure 3-3). This action creates a certain amount of friction within the bearing, and the same action is repeated for each ball while the bearing is rotating. If metal-to-metal contact is allowed between the balls and races, these components will experience very fast wear. Therefore, bearing lubrication is extremely important to eliminate metal-to-metal contact in the bearing and reduce wear.

A ball bearing is designed primarily to handle radial loads. However, this type of bearing can also withstand a considerable amount of thrust load in either direction, even at high speeds. A maximum capacity ball bearing has extra balls for greater radial load-carrying capacity. Ball bearings are available in many different sizes for various applications (Figure 3-4).

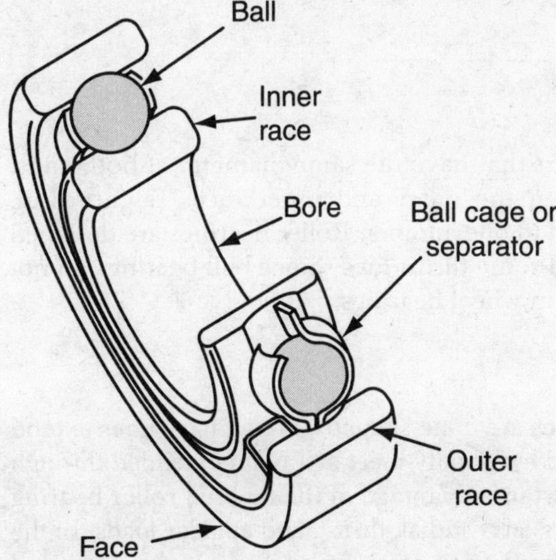

FIGURE 3-2 *Parts of a ball bearing.*

FIGURE 3-3 *When a load is applied to a ball bearing, the metal in the race bulges out in front of the ball and flattens out behind the ball.*

FIGURE 3-4 *A ball bearing.*

Double-row ball bearings contain two rows of balls side by side. As in the single-row ball bearing, the balls in the double-row bearing are mounted in crescent-shaped grooves in the inner and outer races. The double-row ball bearing can support heavy radial loads and withstand thrust loads in either direction.

Ball Bearing Seals, Shields, and Snaprings

For some applications, a ball bearing is held in place with a **snapring**. A groove is cut around the outside surface of the outer race, and the snapring is mounted in this groove. The snapring may fit against a machined housing surface, or the outer circumference of the snapring may be mounted in a groove in the housing. Ball bearings retained with a snapring are not used on wheels because they are not designed to withstand high thrust loads encountered by wheel bearings.

Bearing shields cover the space between the two bearing races on one, or both, sides of the bearing. These shields are usually attached to the outer race, but space is left between the shield and the inner race. Bearing shields prevent dirt from entering the bearing, but excess lubrication can still flow through the bearing.

A **bearing seal** is a circular metal ring with a sealing lip on the inner edge. The seals are usually attached to the outer bearing race on each side of the bearing, and the lip surface contacts the inner race. The seal lip may have single, double, or triple lips made of synthetic or nonsynthetic rubber or elastomers. Lubricant is retained in the bearing by the seal, and the seal also keeps moisture, dirt, and contaminants out of the bearing. Some rear axle bearings on rear-wheel drive cars are sealed on both sides and retained on the axle with a retainer ring (Figure 3-5).

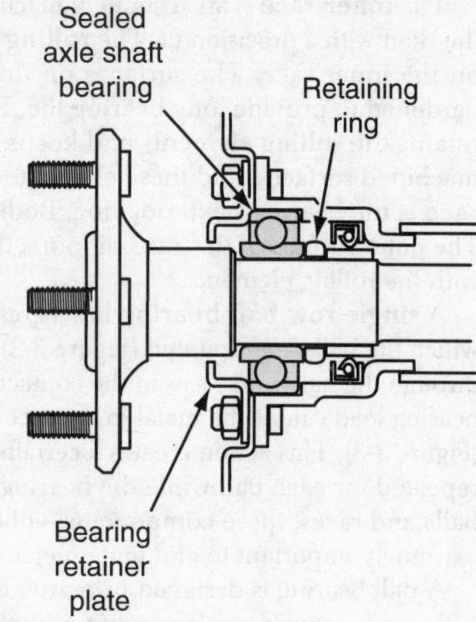

FIGURE 3-5 *Some rear axle bearings are sealed on both sides and retained on the axle with a retainer ring.*

ROLLER BEARINGS

Roller Bearing

A **roller bearing** contains precision-machined rollers that have the same diameter at both ends. These rollers are mounted in square-cut grooves in the outer and inner races (Figure 3-6). In the roller bearing, the races and rollers run parallel to one another. Roller bearings are designed primarily to carry radial loads, but they can withstand some thrust load. Since ball bearings do not withstand high thrust loads, they are usually not used in wheel bearings.

Tapered Roller Bearing

In a **tapered roller bearing**, the inner and outer races are cone shaped. If imaginary lines extend through the inner and outer races, these lines taper and eventually meet at a point extended through the center of the bearing (Figure 3-7). The most important advantage of the tapered roller bearing compared to other bearings is an excellent capability to carry radial, thrust, and angular loads. In the tapered roller bearing, the rollers are mounted on cone-shaped precision surfaces in the outer and inner races. The bearing separator has an open space over each roller (Figure 3-8). Grooves cut in the

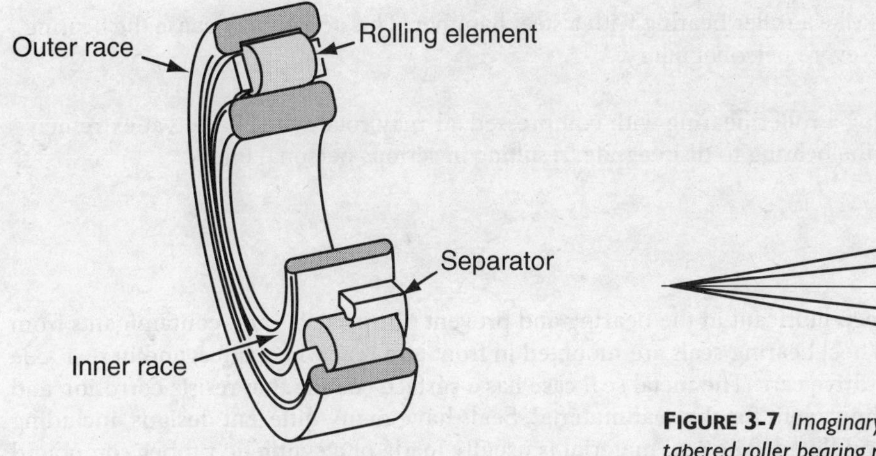

FIGURE 3-6 *Parts of a roller bearing.*

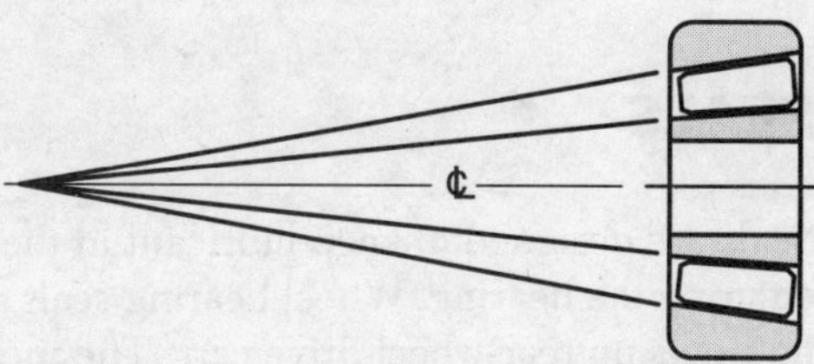

FIGURE 3-7 *Imaginary lines extending from tapered roller bearing races eventually meet at a point extending from the bearing center.*

FIGURE 3-8 *Tapered roller bearings.*

side of the separator roller openings match the curvature of the roller. This design allows the rollers to rotate evenly without interference between the rollers and the separator. Lubrication and proper endplay adjustment are critical on tapered roller bearings. A tapered roller bearing may be called a cup and cone.

Needle Roller Bearings

A **needle roller bearing** contains many small-diameter steel rollers in a thin outer race. This type of bearing is very compact, and it is used in steering gears where mounting space is limited. Most needle roller bearings do not have a separator, but the steel rollers push against each other and maintain the roller position. Rather than having an inner race, a machined surface on the mounting shaft contacts the inner surface of the rollers (Figure 3-9). The needle roller bearing is designed to carry radial loads; it does not withstand thrust loads.

FIGURE 3-9 *Needle roller bearing.*

WARNING: Never strike a roller bearing with a steel hammer. This action may cause the bearing to shatter, resulting in severe personal injury.

WARNING: Spinning a roller bearing with compressed air may rotate the bearing at extremely high speed and cause the bearing to disintegrate, resulting in serious personal injury.

SEALS

Seals are designed to keep lubricant in the bearing and prevent dirt particles and contaminants from entering the bearing. Wheel bearing seals are mounted in front and rear wheel hubs, and in rear axle housings on rear-wheel-drive cars. The metal seal case has a surface coating that resists corrosion and rust and acts as a bonding agent for the seal material. Seals have many different designs, including single lip, double lip, and fluted. The seal material is usually made of a synthetic rubber compound such as nitrile, silicon, polyacrylate, or a fluoroelastomer such as Viton. The actual seal material depends on the lubricant and contaminants that the seal encounters. All seals may be divided into two groups, springless and spring loaded. **Springless seals** are used in some front or rear wheel hubs, where they seal a heavy lubricant into the hub (Figure 3-10).

In a **spring-loaded seal**, the **garter spring** behind the seal provides additional force on the seal lip to compensate for lip wear, shaft movement, and bore eccentricity (Figure 3-11). A **fluted lip seal** may be used to direct oil back into a housing. This seal design provides a pumping action to redirect the oil back into the housing (Figure 3-12).

Some seals have a sealer painted on the outside surface of the metal seal housing. When the seal is installed, this sealer prevents leaks between the seal case and the housing (Figure 3-13).

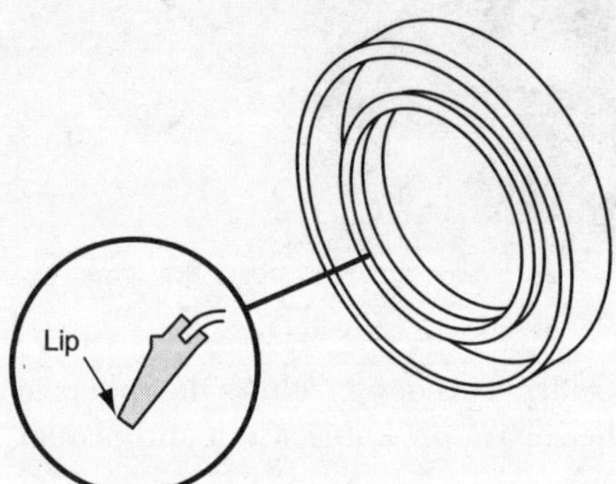

FIGURE 3-10 *Springless seal.*

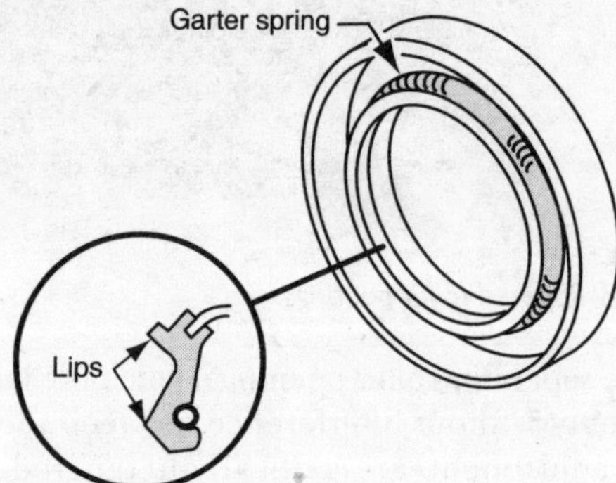

FIGURE 3-11 *Spring-loaded seal.*

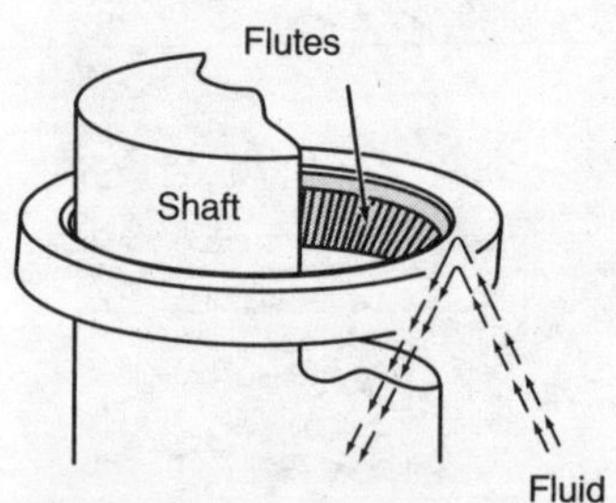

FIGURE 3-12 *Fluted lip seal redirect oil back into the housing.*

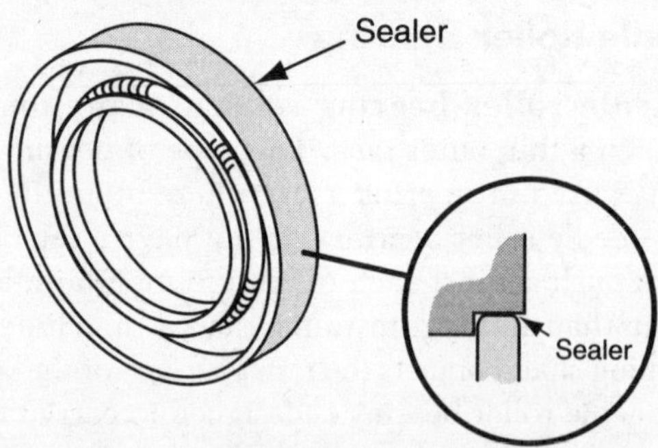

FIGURE 3-13 *Sealer painted on the seal case prevents leaks between the case and the housing.*

WHEEL BEARINGS

Some front-wheel-drive vehicles have front wheel bearing and hub assemblies that are bolted to the steering knuckles (Figure 3-14). The bearings are lubricated and sealed, and the complete bearing and hub assembly is replaced as a unit. The **bearing hub unit** is more compact than other types of wheel bearings mounted in the wheel hub. This type of bearing contains two rows of ball bearings with an angular contact angle of 32° (Figure 3-15). The inner bearing assembly bore is splined, and the inner ring extends to the outside to form a flange and spigot. The flange attached to the outer ring contains bolt holes, and bolts extend through these holes into the steering knuckle. This type of bearing attachment allows the bearing to become a structural member of the front suspension. Since the bearing outer ring is self-supporting, the main concern in knuckle design is fatigue strength rather than stiffness. The drive axle shaft transmits torque to the inner bearing race. This shaft is not designed to hold the bearing together. This type of wheel bearing is designed for mid-sized front-wheel-drive cars.

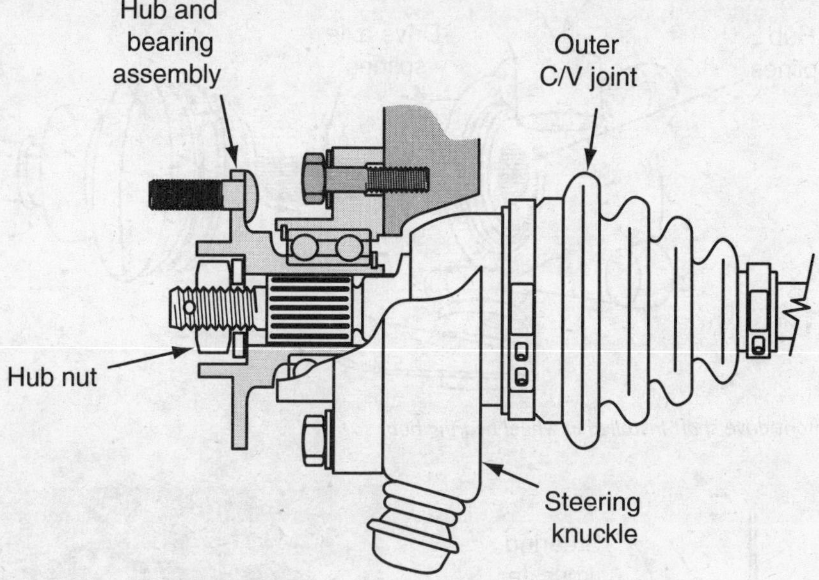

FIGURE 3-14 *Wheel bearing and hub assembly.*

FIGURE 3-15 *Double-row, sealed wheel bearing hub unit.*

Each front drive axle has splines that fit into matching splines inside the bearing hubs (Figure 3-16). A hub nut secures the drive axle into the inner bearing race. Some wheel bearing hubs contain a wheel speed sensor for the antilock brake system (ABS).

Some front-wheel-drive vehicles have a sealed bearing unit that is pressed into the steering knuckle (Figure 3-17). The wheel hub is pressed into the inner bearing race, and the drive axle is splined into the hub. This type of bearing is designed for smaller front-wheel-drive cars. These bearings may contain two rows of ball bearings, or two tapered roller bearings and a split inner race (Figure 3-18). The bearing containing two tapered roller bearings has more radial load capacity than the double-row ball bearing. However, the tapered roller bearing is more sensitive to misalignment. Both sides of the bearing are sealed, and a seal is positioned behind the bearing in the steering knuckle to keep contaminants out of the bearing area.

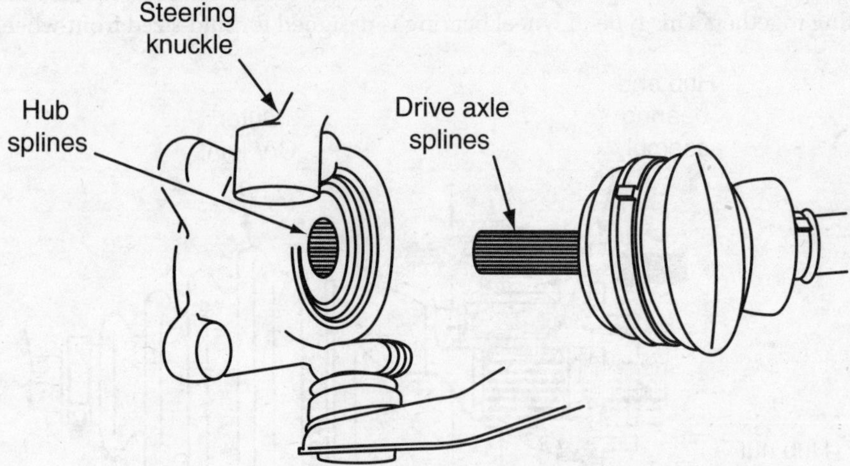

FIGURE 3-16 *Front drive shaft installed in wheel bearing hub.*

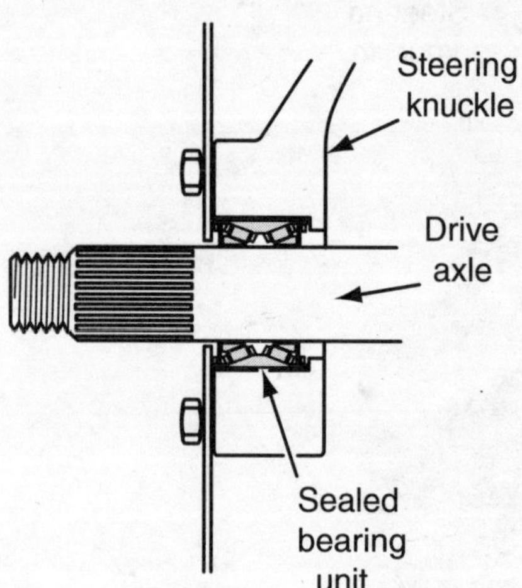

FIGURE 3-17 *Steering knuckle with pressed-in bearing.*

FIGURE 3-18 *Cutaway view of front wheel bearing that is pressed into the steering knuckle.*

Front Steering Knuckles with Two Separate Tapered Roller Bearings

Other front-wheel-drive vehicles have two separate tapered roller bearings mounted in the steering knuckles. The bearing races are pressed into the steering knuckle, and seals are located in the knuckle on the outboard side of each bearing (Figure 3-19). Correct bearing endplay adjustment is supplied by the hub nut torque. The wheel hub is pressed into the inner bearing races, and the drive axle splines are meshed with matching splines in the wheel hub.

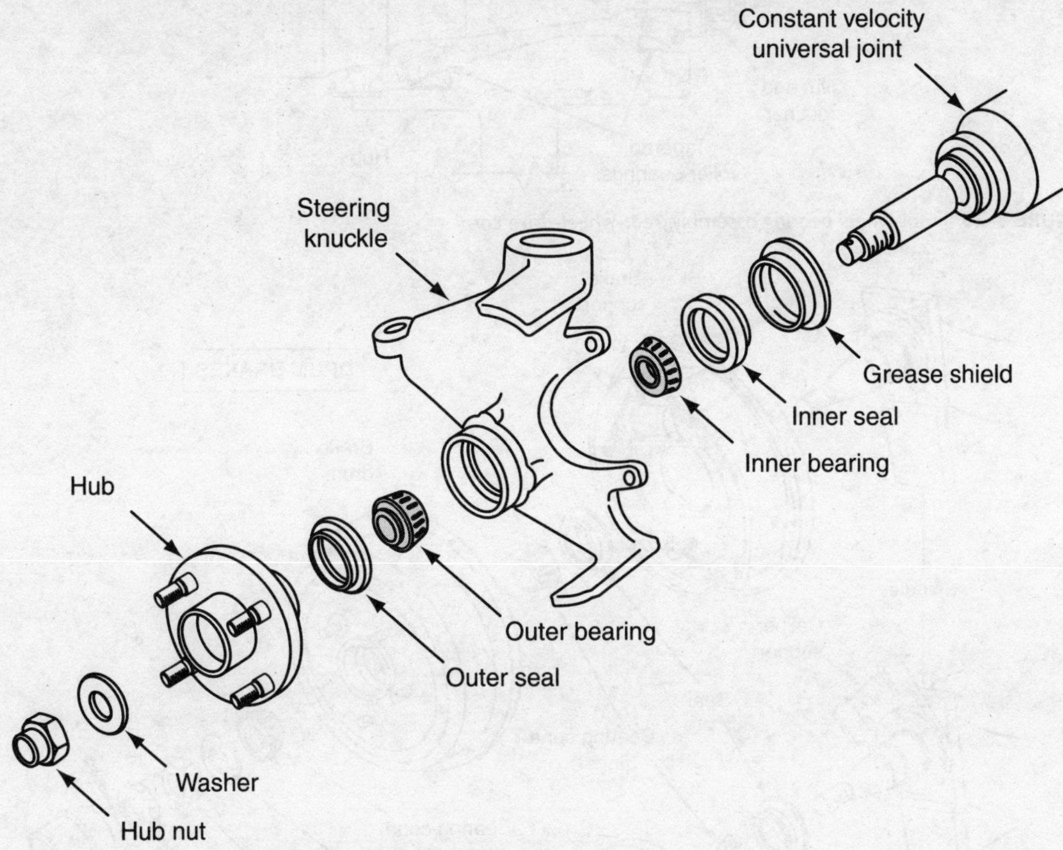

FIGURE 3-19 *Steering knuckle with two separate tapered roller bearings.*

Wheel Hubs with Two Separate Tapered Roller Bearings

Many rear-wheel-drive cars have two tapered roller bearings in the front hubs that support the hubs and wheels on the spindles. This type of front wheel bearing has the bearing races pressed into the hub. A grease seal is pressed into the inner end of the hub to prevent grease leaks and keep contaminants out of the bearings. The hub and bearing assemblies are retained on the spindle with a washer, adjusting nut, nut lock, and cotter pin. The adjusting nut must be adjusted properly to provide the correct bearing endplay. A grease cap is pressed into the outer end of the hub to prevent bearing contamination (Figure 3-20).

Some front-wheel-drive cars have two tapered roller bearings in the rear wheel hubs that are very similar to the front wheel bearings in Figure 3-20. The two tapered roller bearings in the rear wheel of a front-wheel-drive car are shown (Figure 3-21).

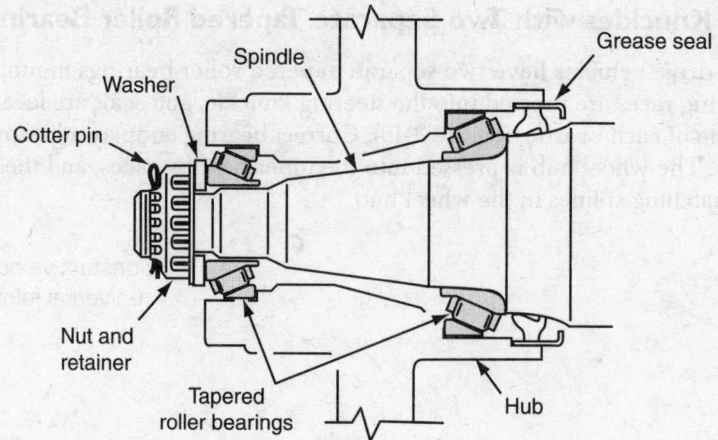

FIGURE 3-20 *Front wheel bearing assembly, rear-wheel-drive car.*

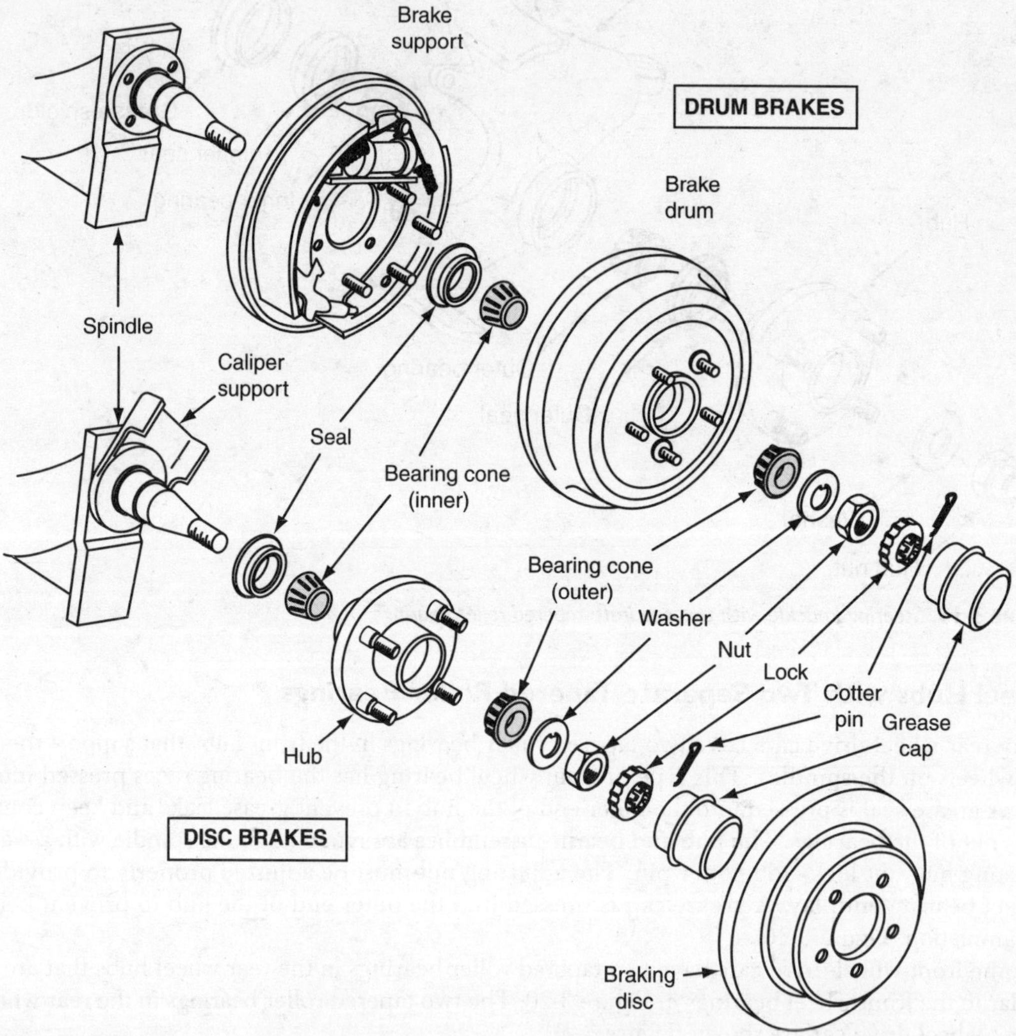

FIGURE 3-21 *Rear wheel hub with tapered roller bearings for drum or disc brakes, front-wheel-drive car.*

REAR-AXLE BEARINGS

On many rear-wheel-drive cars, the rear axles are supported by roller bearings mounted near the outer ends of the axle housing. The outer bearing race is pressed into the housing, and a machined surface on the axle contacts the inner roller surface. A seal is mounted in the axle housing on the outboard side of each bearing (Figure 3-22). This type of axle bearing is usually not sealed, and lubricant in the differential and rear axle housing provides axle bearing lubrication. The seals prevent lubricant leaks from the outer ends of the axle housing and keep dirt out of the bearings.

Other **rear-axle bearings** on rear-wheel-drive vehicles have sealed roller bearings pressed onto the rear axles. These axle bearings are sealed on both sides, and an adapter ring is pressed onto the axle on the inboard side of the bearing (Figure 3-23). The outer bearing race is mounted in the rear axle housing with a light press fit, and a seal is positioned in the housing on the inboard side of the bearing and adapter ring. A retainer plate is mounted between the bearing and the outer end of the axle. This retainer plate is bolted to the axle housing to retain the axle in the housing.

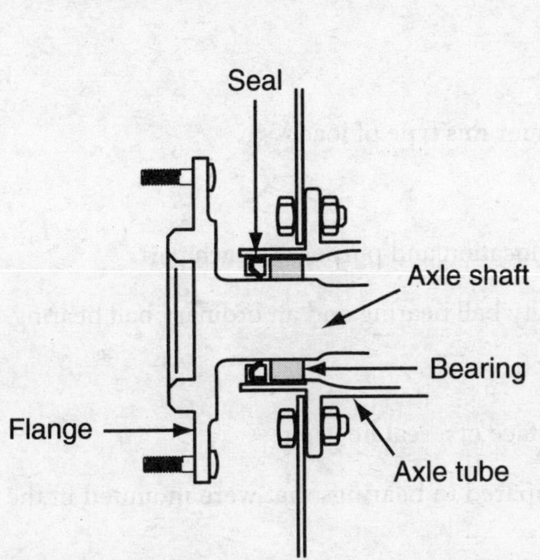

FIGURE 3-22 *Rear-axle bearing, rear-wheel-drive car.*

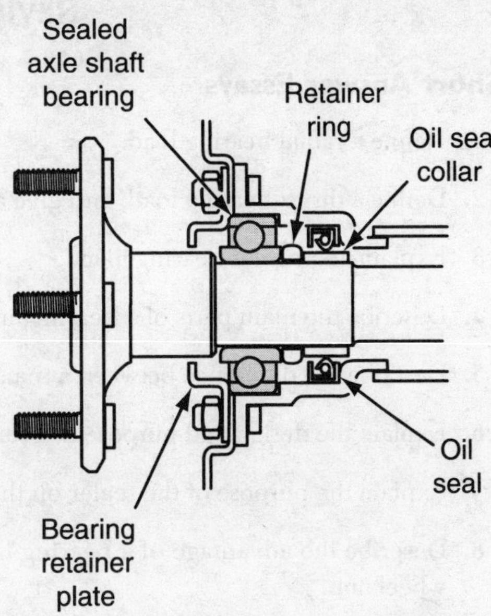

FIGURE 3-23 *Rear-axle bearing and retainer.*

BEARING LUBRICATION

Proper bearing lubrication is extremely important to maintain bearing life. Bearing lubricant reduces friction and wear, dissipates heat, and protects surfaces from dirt and corrosion. Sealed or shielded bearings are lubricated during the manufacturing process, and no attempt should be made to wash these bearings or pack them with grease.

Bearings that are not sealed or shielded require cleaning and repacking at intervals specified by the vehicle manufacturer. Always use the bearing grease specified by the vehicle manufacturer. Bearing lubricants may be classified as greases or oils. Many wheel bearings require **lithium-based** or **sodium-based grease.**

New bearings usually have a protective coating to prevent rust and corrosion. This coating should not be washed from the bearing. When rear-axle bearings are lubricated from the differential housing, the type and level of oil in the housing are important.

Vehicle manufacturers usually recommend a **Society of Automotive Engineers (SAE)** No. 90 or SAE No. 140 hypoid gear oil in the differential. In very cold climates, the manufacturer may recommend an SAE No. 80 differential gear oil. The **American Petroleum Institute (API)** classifies gear lubricants as GL-1, GL-2, GL-3, GL-4, and GL-5. The GL-4 lubricant is used for hypoid gears under normal conditions. The GL-5 lubricant is used in heavy-duty hypoid gears. Always use the vehicle manufacturer's specified differential gear oil.

CAUTION: If a bearing is operated without proper lubrication, bearing life will be very short.

The differential should be filled until the lubricant is level with the bottom of the filler plug opening in the differential housing. If the differential is overfilled, the bearings and seals may have excessive lubricant. Under this condition, the lubricant may leak past the seal. When the lubricant level is low in the differential, the lubricant may not be available in the axle housings. When this condition exists, the bearings do not receive enough lubrication and bearing life is shortened.

REVIEW QUESTIONS

Short Answer Essays

1. Define a radial bearing load.
2. Define a thrust bearing load, and give another term for this type of load.
3. Explain an angular bearing load.
4. Describe the main parts of a bearing, including the location and purpose of each part.
5. Describe the difference between a maximum-capacity ball bearing and an ordinary ball bearing.
6. Explain the design and purpose of bearing seals.
7. Explain the purpose of the sealer on the outside surface of a seal housing.
8. Describe the advantage of a bearing hub unit compared to bearings that were mounted in the wheel hub.
9. Explain how the proper bearing endplay adjustment is obtained when two tapered roller bearings are mounted in the steering knuckle.
10. Describe two different types of rear-axle bearings on rear-wheel-drive cars.

Fill-in-the-Blanks

1. A bearing can be described as a component that supports a ________________, ________________, or ________________.
2. A bearing is designed to support a load and ________________ ________________.
3. An angular bearing load is applied at an angle between the ________________ and the ________________.
4. A ball bearing is designed primarily to withstand ________________ loads.

5. A bearing shield is attached to the ________________ bearing race.

6. Lubrication and proper ________________ adjustment are important on tapered roller bearings.

7. A needle roller bearing is not designed to carry ________________ loads.

8. A springless seal may be used to seal a ________________ lubricant into a hub.

9. When a vehicle is turning a corner, the front wheel bearings must carry a ________________ load.

10. When a rear-wheel-drive vehicle has cylindrical roller bearings mounted in the rear axle housing, the inner surface on the rollers contacts a machined surface on the ________________.

Multiple Choice

1. A tapered roller bearing has:
   A. Rollers that have the same diameter at both ends.
   B. Excellent ability to carry radial, thrust, and angular loads.
   C. Horizontal inner surfaces of the inner and outer races.
   D. A separator that allows the rollers to lightly contact each other.

2. A spring-loaded seal compensates for all of these conditions EXCEPT:
   A. Seal lip wear.
   B. Shaft movement.
   C. Bore eccentricity.
   D. Wear on the seal bore.

3. When two separate tapered roller bearings are located in a front steering knuckle on a front-wheel-drive car, the wheel bearing endplay adjustment is provided by:
   A. The bearing race position.
   B. Wheel nut torque.
   C. Hub nut torque.
   D. Wheel hub position.

4. A rear-wheel hub contains two tapered roller bearings on a front-wheel-drive car. This type of wheel hub has:
   A. An adjusting nut to adjust the wheel bearing endplay.
   B. A lock washer to retain the adjusting nut.
   C. A staked-type nut lock.
   D. A seal in the outer end of the hub to prevent grease contamination.

5. On a rear-wheel-drive car, the rear axle bearings have been damaged by excessive overheating. The most likely cause of this condition is:
   A. Insufficient rear-axle bearing endplay.
   B. Excessive lubricant level in the differential.
   C. Low lubricant level in the differential.
   D. Worn rear axle seals.

6. When inspecting and servicing bearings:
   A. Some rear-wheel-drive vehicles have rear-axle bearings that are sealed on both sides.
   B. In a sealed bearing, the seal is usually attached to the inner race.
   C. Endplay adjustment is not critical on tapered roller bearings.
   D. A roller bearing can be removed by striking it with a steel hammer.

7. All of these statements about bearings are true EXCEPT:
   A. Tapered roller bearings have excellent capability to carry radial, thrust, and angular loads.
   B. Ball bearings are used in most wheel bearings.
   C. A roller bearing has rollers with the same diameter at each end.
   D. In a tapered roller bearing, the openings in the separator grooves match the curvature of the rollers.

8. While inspecting and servicing wheel hub seals:
   A. Many wheel hub seal lips are made from a plastic compound.
   B. Springless seals may be used in applications where they must seal a light fluid.
   C. A spring-loaded seal helps compensate for wheel hub bore eccentricity.
   D. The sealer on the outer surface of a seal housing improves seal and hub bore alignment.

9. When inspecting and servicing front wheel bearings on front-wheel-drive cars:
   A. Some one-piece front wheel bearing hubs are bolted to the front strut.
   B. In a one-piece front wheel bearing hub, the outer end of the drive axle is splined to the outer bearing race.
   C. When the steering knuckle contains two tapered roller bearings, the torque on the drive axle nut does not affect bearing endplay.
   D. Some front wheel bearings mounted in the steering knuckle contain two tapered roller bearings with a split inner race.

10. When inspecting and servicing rear wheel bearings on rear-wheel-drive cars:
    A. On some rear wheel bearings, a threaded adapter ring retains the bearing on the axle shaft.
    B. Roller-type rear-axle bearings may be lubricated from the oil supply in the differential.
    C. A GL-2 lubricant is recommended in hypoid-type differentials.
    D. An SAE 50 gear oil is recommended in many differentials.

Tires and Wheels

4

Upon completion and review of this chapter, you should be able to:

- Describe general tire function.
- Explain typical tire construction, and identify the purpose of each component in a tire.
- Describe three types of tire ply and belt designs.
- Give an example of a tire rating, and explain the meaning of each designation in the rating.
- Explain the purpose of the tire performance criteria (TPC) rating.
- Describe the difference between all-season tires and conventional tires.
- Explain two different types of tire load ratings.
- Describe the tire tread wear rating.
- Explain the Uniform Tire Quality Grading (UTQG) designations.
- List the precautions to be observed when selecting replacement tires.
- Define tire contact area, free tire diameter, and rolling tire diameter.
- Describe the tire motion forces while a tire-and-wheel assembly is rotating on a vehicle.

- Explain the importance of tire design quality as it relates to the tire motion forces.
- Define wheel offset.
- Define wheel tramp, and explain how static unbalance causes wheel tramp.
- Define wheel shimmy, and describe how dynamic unbalance results in wheel shimmy.
- Describe various types of tire pressure monitoring systems.

INTRODUCTION

Although tires are often taken for granted, they contribute greatly to the ride and steering quality of a vehicle. Tires also play a significant role in vehicle safety. Improper types of tires, incorrect inflation pressure, and worn-out tires create a safety hazard. When tires and wheels are out of balance, tire wear and driver fatigue are increased, which can create a driving hazard. Tires serve the following functions:

1. Tires cushion the vehicle ride to provide a comfortable ride for the occupant.
2. Tires must firmly support the vehicle weight.
3. Tires must develop traction to drive and steer the vehicle under a wide variety of road conditions.
4. Tires contribute to directional stability of the vehicle and must absorb all the stresses of accelerating, braking, and centrifugal force in turns.

TIRE DESIGN

Tire construction varies depending on the manufacturer and the type of tire. A typical modern tire contains these components (Figure 4-1, see page 73):

1. **Bead wire**
2. Bead filler
3. **Liner**
4. Steel reinforcement in the sidewall
5. Sidewall with hard side compound
6. Rayon carcass plies
7. Steel belts
8. Jointless belt cover
9. Hard undertread compound
10. Hard high-grip tread compound

The bead wire contains several turns of bronze-coated steel wire in a continuous loop. This bead wire is molded into the tire at the inner circumference and wrapped in the cord plies. The bead wire anchors the tire to the wheel. The **bead filler** above the bead reinforces the sidewall and acts as a rim extender.

Tire **sidewalls** are made from a blend of rubbers which absorbs shocks and impacts from road irregularities, prevents damage to the plies, and also contains antioxidants and other chemicals that are

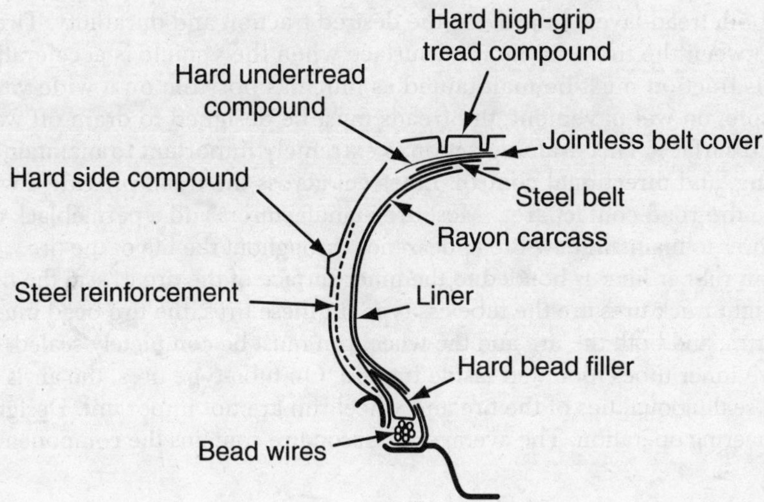

FIGURE 4-1 *Tire design.*

gradually released to the surface of the sidewall during the life of the tire. These antioxidants help keep the sidewall from cracking and protect it from ultraviolet radiation and ozone attack. Since the sidewall must be flexible to provide ride quality, minimum thickness of this component is essential. Tire manufacturers have reduced sidewall thickness by 40 percent in recent years to reduce weight and heat buildup, improve ride quality, reduce rolling resistance, and improve fuel economy. A lettering and numbering arrangement for tire identification is located on the outside of the sidewall.

The **cord plies** surround both beads and extend around the inner surface of the tire to enable the tire to carry its load. The plies are molded into the sidewalls. Each ply is a layer of rubber with parallel cords imbedded in its body. The load capacity of a tire may be increased by adding more cords in each ply or by installing additional plies. The most common materials in tire plies are polyester, rayon, and nylon. Passenger car tires usually have two-cord plies, whereas many trucks and recreation vehicles are equipped with six- or eight-ply tires to carry the heavier loads of these vehicles. In general, tires with more plies have stiffer sidewalls, which provide less cushioning and reduced ride quality.

Steel is the most common material in **tire belts**, although other belt materials such as polyester have been used to some extent. Many tires contain two steel belts. The tire belts restrict ply movement and provide tread stability and resistance to deformation. This belt action provides longer tread wear and reduces heat buildup in the tire. Steel belts expand as wheel speed and tire temperature increase. Centrifugal force and belt expansion tend to tear the tire apart at high speeds and temperatures. Therefore, high-speed tires usually have a nylon jointless **belt cover**. This nylon belt cover contracts as it is heated and helps hold the tire together, providing longer tire life, improved stability, and better handling.

Tire treads are made from a blend of rubber compounds that are very resistant to abrasion wear. Spaces between the tire treads allow tire distortion on the road without scrubbing, which accelerates wear. Modern automotive tires contain two layers of tread materials. The first tread layer is designed to provide cool operation, low rolling resistance, and durability. The outer layer, or tread, is designed for long life and maximum traction. Tread rubber is a blend of many different synthetic and natural rubbers. Tire manufacturers may use up to thirty different types of **synthetic rubber** and eight types of natural rubber in their tires. Manufacturers blend these synthetic and natural rubbers in both tread layers to provide the desired traction and durability. Tire treads must provide traction between the tire and the road surface when the vehicle is accelerating, braking, and cornering. This traction must be maintained as much as possible on a wide variety of road surfaces. For example, on wet pavement, tire treads must be designed to drain off water between the tire and the road surface. This draining action is extremely important to maintaining adequate acceleration, braking, and directional control. Lines cut across the tread provide a wiping action, which helps dry the tire-road contact area. Most tire manufacturers add a permablack compound to the rubber in their tires to maintain new-tire appearance throughout the life of the tire.

The synthetic gum rubber liner is bonded to the inner surface of the tire to seal the tire. Nearly all passenger car and light truck tires are the tubeless type. In these tires, the tire bead must provide an airtight seal on the rim, and both the tire and the wheel rim must be completely sealed. Some heavy-duty truck tires have inner tubes mounted inside the tire. On tube-type tires, the air is sealed in the inner tube, and the sealing qualities of the tire and wheel rim are not important. Designing tires is a very complex engineering operation. The average all-season tire contains the components (by weight) listed in Table 4-1.

TABLE 4-1 *Tire Components by Weight*

A typical P195/75-14 all-season tire contains:

Component	Weight
Synthetic rubber (30 types)	2.49 kg
Carbon Black (8 types)	2.27 kg
Natural Rubber (8 types)	2.04 kg
Chemicals, waxes, oils, pigments, etc. (40 types)	1.36 kg
Steel cord for belts	0.68 kg
Polyester and nylon	0.45 kg
Bead wire	0.23 kg
Total weight	9.42 kg

Tire design varies depending on the operating conditions and the load capacity of the tire. A tire designed for improved steering and handling characteristics has a nylon bead reinforcement and a hard bead filler with a slim tapered profile (Figure 4-2). This type of tire is suitable for sports car operation because the design stiffens the tire and reduces tire deflection during high-speed cornering. However, this type of tire may provide slightly firmer ride quality.

TIRE PLY AND BELT DESIGN

The most commonly used tire designs are bias, belted bias, and belted radial. In **bias-ply** or **belted bias-ply tires**, the cords crisscross each other. These cords are usually at an angle of 25° to 45° to the tire centerline. The belt-ply cord angle is usually 5° less than the cord angle in the tire casing. Two plies and two belts are most commonly used, but four plies and four belts may be used in some tires. Compared to a bias-ply tire, a belted bias-ply tire has greater tread rigidity. The belts reduce tread motion during road contact. This action provides extended tread life compared to a bias-ply tire.

In **radial-ply tires**, the ply cords are arranged radially at a right angle to the tire centerline (Figure 4-3). Steel belts are most commonly used in radial tires, but other belt materials such as fiberglass, nylon, and rayon have also been used. The steel or fiberglass cords in the belts are crisscrossed at an

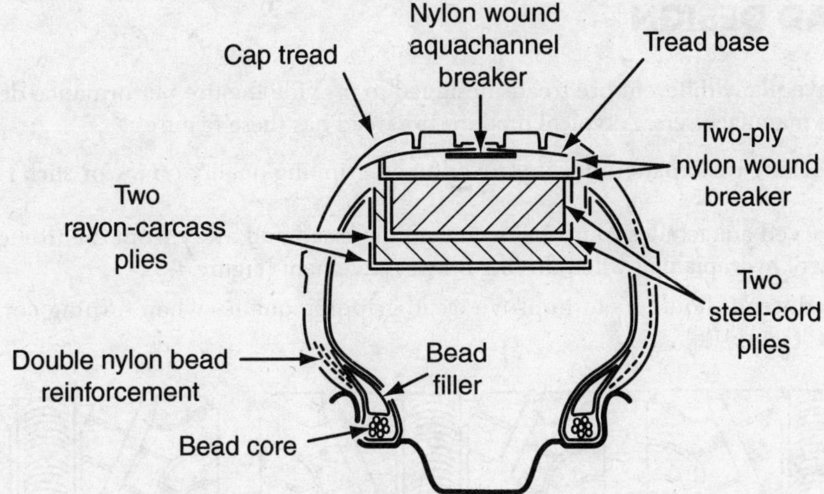

FIGURE 4-2 *Tires designed for improved steering and handling with a nylon bead reinforcement and a hard bead filler with a slim tapered profile.*

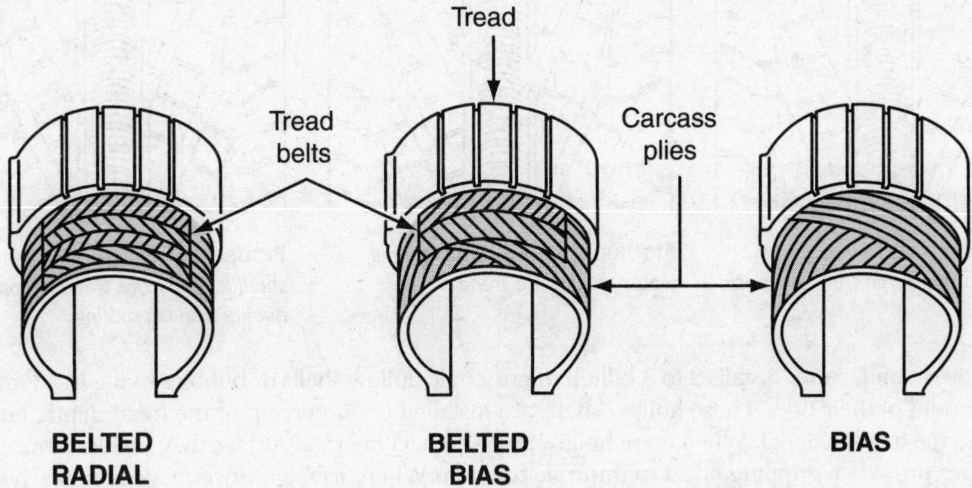

FIGURE 4-3 *Three types of tire construction: bias-ply, belted bias-ply, and belted radial-ply.*

angle of 10° to 30° in relation to the tire centerline. Many radial tires have two plies and two belts. Radial tires provide less rolling resistance, better steering characteristics, and longer tread life than bias-ply tires.

Regardless of the type of tire construction, the tire must be uniform in diameter and width. Radial runout refers to variations in tire diameter. A tire with excessive radial runout causes a tire thumping problem as the car is driven. When a tire has excessive variations in width, this condition is called lateral runout. A tire with excessive lateral runout causes the chassis to “waddle” when the car is driven.

The tire plies and belts must be level across the tread area. If the plies and/or belts are not level across the tread area, the tire is cone shaped. This condition is referred to as tire conicity. When a front tire has conicity, the steering may pull to one side as the car is driven straight ahead. A rear tire with conicity will not affect the steering as much as a front tire with conicity.

TIRE TREAD DESIGN

Vehicle tires have many different tire treads designed to provide the tire performance desired by the tire and vehicle manufacturers. A typical modern tire tread has these features:

1. An interlocking tread pattern for improved tread gripping quality on icy or slick roads (Figure 4-4).
2. Deeply carved aquachutes to propel water off the tread and away from the tire to reduce the possibility of **hydroplaning** when driving on wet pavement (Figure 4-5).
3. Reinforced tread shoulders to improve tread gripping quality when turning corners on dry pavement (Figure 4-6).

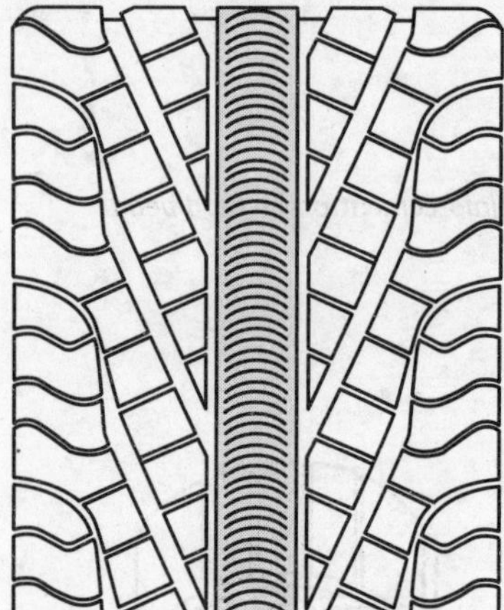

FIGURE 4-4 *Interlocking tread pattern for improved traction on icy roads.*

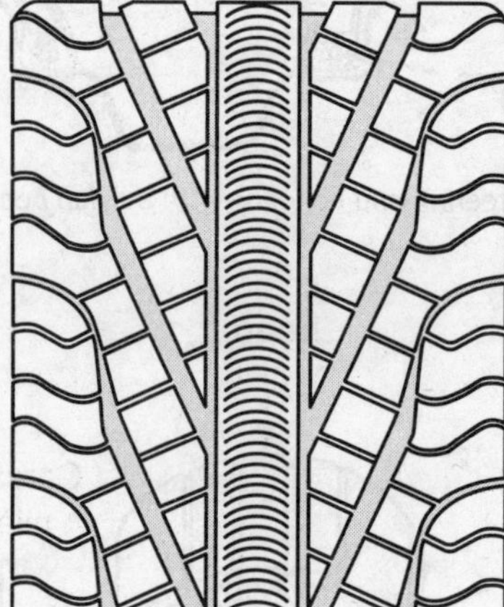

FIGURE 4-5 *Aquachutes propel water off the tire tread.*

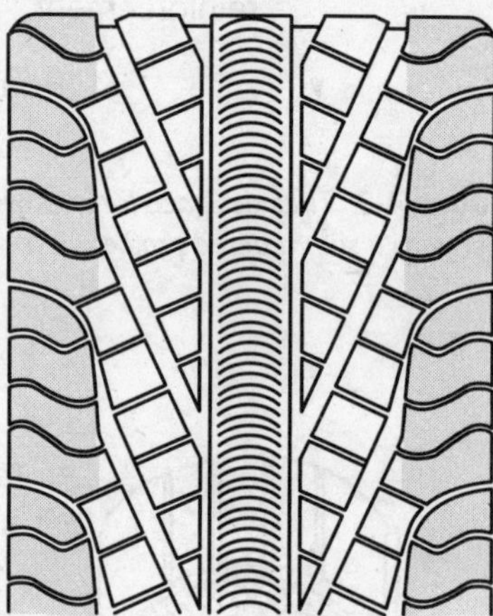

FIGURE 4-6 *Reinforced tread shoulders improve tread gripping quality while cornering.*

One tire manufacturer installs 2 to 3 billion microscopic hollow shells or bubbles in the tread material on one brand of their tires. These hollow shells are installed to 60 percent of the tread depth, and add rigidity to the tread material. When these hollow shells contact the road surface they break open, and the shell edges provide a gripping effect to improve traction. When driving on wet pavement, each time a hollow shell contacts the road surface and breaks open, a small amount of water is pulled into the hollow shell (Figure 4-7). Because this action is occurring at the millions of hollow shells in contact with the road surface, water is removed from between the tread and the road surface. This action reduces the possibility of hydroplaning. As the tire continues to rotate, water is expelled from the hollow shells when they move out of contact with the road surface.

TIRE MANUFACTURING DEFECTS

Manufacturing defects may be covered by the tire manufacturer's warranty. Possible defects include the following:

1. Separations and bulges, including tread or sidewall separation, or an open tread splice
2. Tread chunking, tearing, groove cracking, and shoulder cracking
3. Sidewall circumference fatigue, cracking, and weather cracking

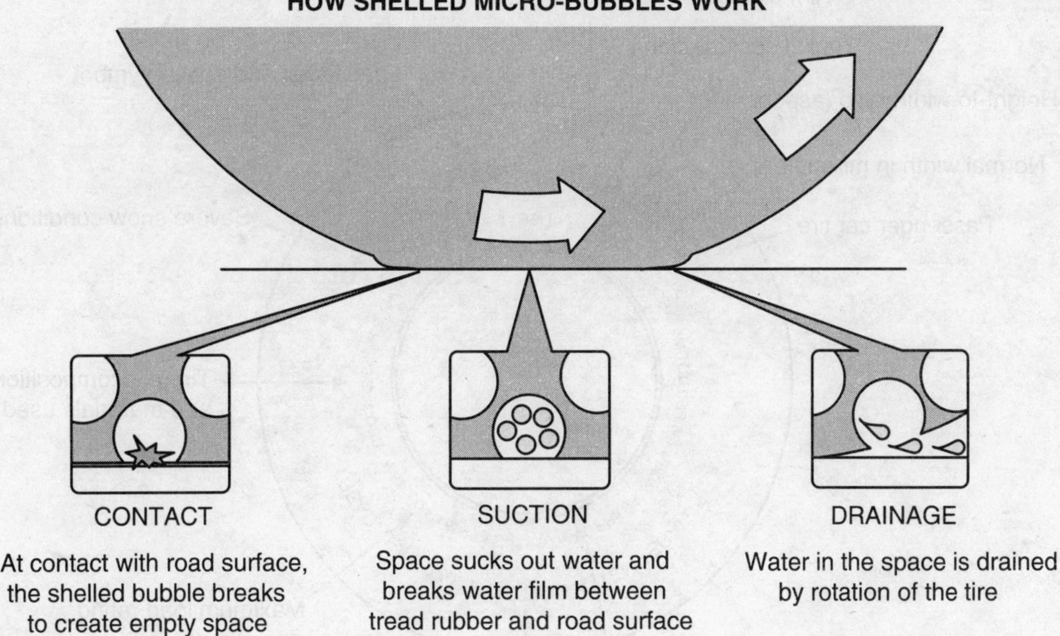

FIGURE 4-7 *Advantages of micro-bubbles in the tire tread.*

4. Bead chafing, broken wires, or a pulled bead
5. Breaks in the sidewall or tread areas
6. Excessive radial or lateral runout
7. **Conicity**

TIRE RATINGS AND SIDEWALL INFORMATION

A lot of essential information is molded into the sidewall of the average passenger car and light truck tire, including the tire rating. The tire rating is a group of letters and numbers that identify the tire type, section width, aspect ratio, construction type, rim diameter, load capacity, and speed symbol. The tire in Figure 4-8 has a P215/65R15 95H rating.

P indicates a passenger car tire. The number 215 is the size of the tire in millimeters measured from sidewall to sidewall with the tire mounted on the recommended rim width.

Aspect Ratio and Ply Design

The number 65 indicates the aspect ratio, which is the ratio of the height to the width (Figure 4-9). With a 65 aspect ratio, the tire's height is 65 percent of its width. The letter R indicates radial-ply tire construction. If the tire construction was indicated by the letters A B, the tire has a belted, bias-ply construction. The letter D represents diagonal bias-ply tire design.

Rim Diameter and Load Rating

The number 15 is the rim diameter in inches. The load index is represented by the number 95. The tire in Figure 4-8 has load rating of 1,521 pounds. Various numbers represent different maximum

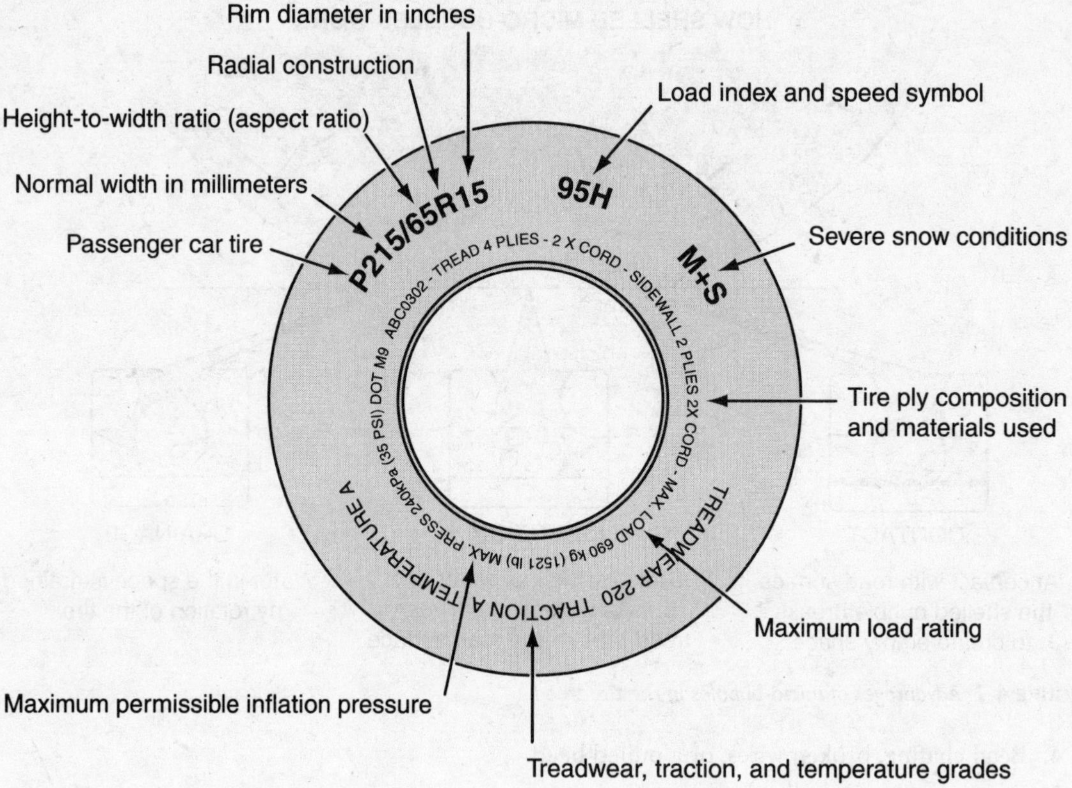

Rim diameter in inches
Radial construction
Height-to-width ratio (aspect ratio)
Normal width in millimeters
Passenger car tire
Load index and speed symbol
Severe snow conditions
Tire ply composition and materials used
Maximum load rating
Maximum permissible inflation pressure
Treadwear, traction, and temperature grades
P215/65R15
95H
M+S
ABC0302 - TREAD 4 PLIES - 2 X CORD - SIDEWALL 2 PLIES 2X CORD - MAX. LOAD 690 kg (1521 lb) MAX. PRESS 240kPa (35 PSI) DOT M9
TREADWEAR 220 TRACTION A TEMPERATURE A

FIGURE 4-8 *Tire sidewall information.*

P 215 65 R 15 89 H
TIRE TYPE
P - Passenger
T - Temporary
LT - Light truck
SECTION WIDTH
(millimeters)
205
215
etc.
ASPECT RATIO
Section Height
Section Width
60
65
70
LOAD INDEX
SPEED SYMBOL
RIM DIAMETER
(Inches)
14
15
16
CONSTRUCTION TYPE
R - Radial
B - Bias Belted
D - Diagonal (Bias)
Section width
Section height

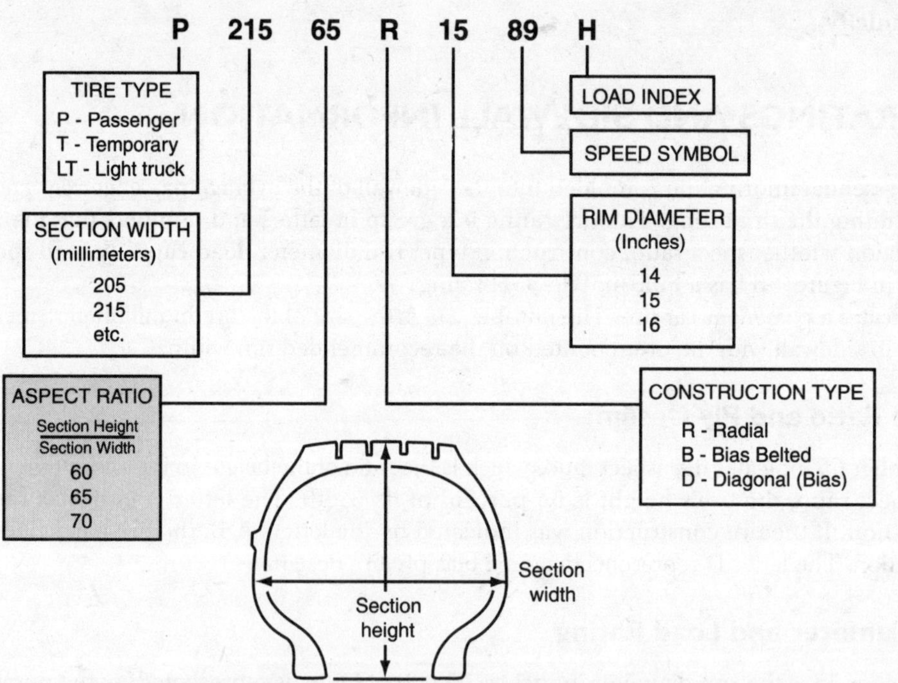

FIGURE 4-9 *Tire aspect ratio is the percentage of the tire's height in relation to its width.*

loads. The maximum load is shown on the tire in pounds (lb) and kilograms (kg) together with the maximum inflation pressure in pounds per square inch (psi) and kilograms (kg). Some tire manufacturers have used the letters B, C, or D to indicate the **load rating**. The letter B indicates the lowest load rating and the letter C represents a higher load rating. A tire with a D load rating is designed for light-duty trucks, and this tire will safely carry a load of 2,623 pounds when inflated to 65 psi.

Speed Rating

The letter H indicates the tire has a 130 miles per hour (mph) **speed rating**. Other speed ratings are:

Q – 99 mph
S – 112 mph
T – 118 mph
U – 124 mph
V – above 130 mph without service description
V – 149 mph with service description
Z – above 149 mph

Tire speed ratings do not suggest that vehicles can always be driven safely up to the maximum designated speed rating, because many different road and weather conditions may be encountered. Tire manufacturers do not endorse the operation of a vehicle in an unlawful or unsafe manner. Speed ratings are based on laboratory tests, and these ratings are not valid if tires are worn out, damaged, altered, underinflated, or overloaded. The condition of the vehicle may also affect high-speed operation.

Department of Transportation (DOT) Tire Grading

The United States Department of Transportation (DOT) regulations demand that all tire manufacturers grade all passenger car tires, except mud and snow tires, according to tread wear, traction, and temperature. This DOT tire grading may be referred to as the **Uniform Tire Quality Grading (UTQG) System**.

Tread Wear Rating

Tread wear ratings allow customers to compare tire tread life expectancies. The tread wear rating is based on the tire tread wear when tested under specific conditions on a government test track. A baseline tire has a tread wear rating of 100. A tire with a 150 tread wear rating would last 1.5 times as many miles on the test track as the baseline tire with a 100 tread wear rating. Tread wear ratings are valid only for comparison within a manufacturer's product line, and these ratings are not valid for comparisons between tire manufacturers.

Traction Rating

Traction ratings indicate the braking capabilities of a tire. To determine the traction rating, ten skid tests are completed on wet asphalt and concrete surfaces. Test conditions are carefully controlled to maintain test uniformity. The results of the ten skid tests are averaged, and the traction rating is designated as A, B, or C. An A traction rating indicates the best traction, a B rating indicates intermediate traction, and a C rating indicates acceptable traction.

Temperature Rating

The **temperature rating** indicates the tire's ability to withstand extreme heat during tire operation. To obtain the temperature rating, tires are tested on a laboratory test wheel. The temperature rating indicates how long the tire will last on the test wheel. Extremely high temperatures may cause tire materials to degenerate and thus reduce tire life or cause tire failure. The temperature ratings are A for best, B for intermediate, and C for acceptable.

DOT regulations also require tire manufacturers to place the following information on tire sidewalls:

1. Size
2. Load range
3. Maximum load
4. Maximum pressure
5. Number of plies under the tread and in the sidewalls
6. Manufacturer's name
7. Tubeless or tube-type construction
8. Type of carcass construction
9. DOT approval number, including the manufacturer's code number and date of manufacture

Some tires have a **tire performance criteria** (TPC) number molded on the sidewall (Figure 4-10). This number represents that the tire meets the car manufacturer's performance standards for traction, endurance, dimensions, noise, handling, and rolling resistance. Most car manufacturers assign a different TPC number to each tire size. Replacement tires should have the same ratings and TPC number as the original tires.

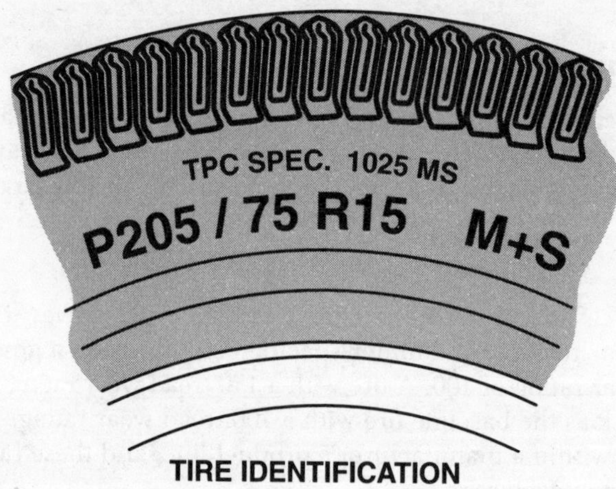

FIGURE 4-10 *Tire performance criteria (TPC) number.*

SPECIALTY TIRES

Sport Utility Vehicle (SUV) and 4 × 4 Tires

SUV tires may be classified for use on pavement or off-road. SUV tires have greater load-carrying capacity compared to passenger car tires, because of the extra loads that may be carried in an SUV. A typical pavement SUV tire has these features:

1. A silica tread compound that provides low noise levels and exceptional wet braking capability.
2. An enhanced casing system and a stable tire contact area that supplies even tread wear and responsive handling quality.

3. Larger cables in the steel belts to provide increased strength and durability.
4. Full-depth, interlocking sections in the tread that supply excellent wet and snow traction.

Compared to SUV tires for use on pavement, off-road SUV tires have stronger tread rubber to prevent cutting and chipping. Off-road SUV tires may also have thicker belt wire and more belt strands.

Tires designed for 4 × 4 vehicles may have some of the same features as SUV tires. A typical 4 × 4 tire has these additional features:

1. Two wide circumference grooves with a stepped profile to reduce hydroplaning.
2. Staggered shoulder blocks in the tread to improve lateral grip on slopes.
3. Gradual profile changes in the shoulder area of the tread to provide progressive breakaway during hard cornering.
4. Additional rubber at the base of the tread to reduce the possibility of tire damage.

Puncture sealing tires are available as an option on certain car lines, and some rubber companies sell these tires in the replacement tire market. These tires contain a special rubber sealing compound applied under the tread area during the manufacturing process. When a nail or other object up to 3/16 inch in diameter punctures the tread area, it picks up a coating of sealant. If the object is removed, the sealant sticks to the object and is pulled into the puncture. This sealant completely fills the puncture and forms a permanent seal to maintain tire inflation pressure (Figure 4-11). Puncture sealing tires usually have a special warranty. These tires can be serviced with conventional tire changing and balancing equipment.

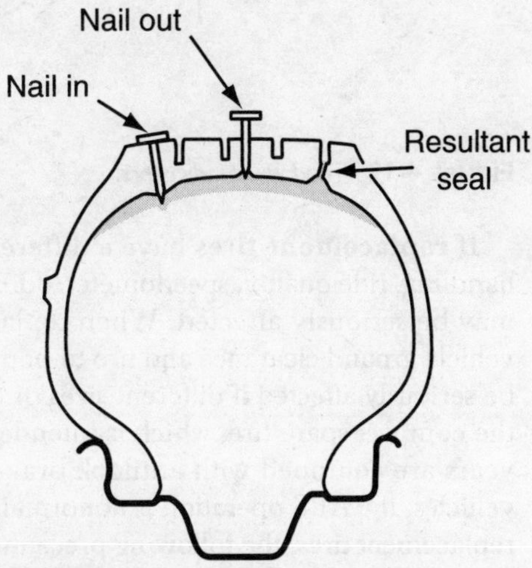

FIGURE 4-11 *Puncture sealing tire.*

Mud and snow tires are available in various ply and belt designs. These tires provide increased traction in snow or mud compared to conventional tires. Mud and snow tires are identified with an MS suffix after the tire performance criteria (TPC) number on the tire sidewall. When snow tires are installed on a vehicle, these tires should be the same size and type as the other tires on the vehicle. In areas where snow is encountered, all-season tires have replaced snow tires to a large extent. Studded tires provide improved traction on ice, but these tires are prohibited by law in many states because their use resulted in road surface damage.

Many tires sold today are classified as **all-season tires**. These tires have a 37 percent higher average snow traction compared to non-all-season tires. All-season tires may have slightly improved performance in areas such as wet traction, rolling resistance, tread life, and air retention. Improvements in tread design and tread compounds provide the superior quality in all-season tires. All-season tires are usually identified by the letters MS (for mud and snow) on the sidewall.

REPLACEMENT TIRES

Most tires have tread wear indicators built into the tread. When the tread wears a specific amount, the wear indicators appear as bands across the tread (Figure 4-12). Some car manufacturers recommend tire replacement when the wear indicators appear in two or more tread grooves at three locations around the tire.

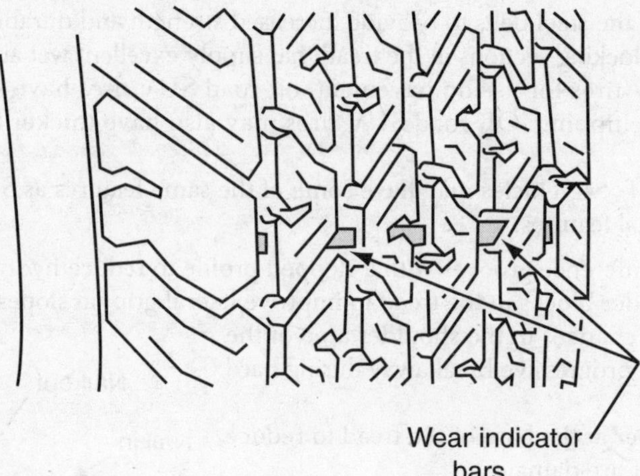

FIGURE 4-12 *Tread wear indicators.*

If **replacement tires** have a different size or construction type than the original tires, vehicle handling, ride quality, speedometer/odometer calibration, and antilock brake system (ABS) operation may be seriously affected. When replacement tires are a different size than the original tires, the vehicle ground clearance and tire-to-body clearance may be altered. Steering and braking quality may be seriously affected if different sizes or types of tires are installed on a vehicle. This does not include the compact spare tire, which is intended for temporary use. Many vehicles manufactured in recent years are equipped with antilock brakes (ABS). When different-sized tires are installed on these vehicles, the ABS operation is abnormal, which may result in serious braking defects. When selecting replacement tires, the following precautions must be observed to maintain vehicle safety:

1. Replacement tires must be installed in pairs on the same axle. Never mix tire sizes or designs on the same axle. If it is necessary to replace only one tire, it should be paired with the tire having the most tread to equalize braking traction.
2. The tire load rating must be adequate for the vehicle on which the tire is installed. Light-duty trucks, station wagons, and trailer-towing vehicles are examples of vehicles that require tires with higher load ratings than passenger car tires.
3. Snow tires should be the same type and size as the other tires on the vehicle.
4. A four-wheel-drive vehicle should have the same type and size of tires on all four wheels.
5. Do not install tires with a load rating less than the car manufacturer's recommended rating.
6. Replacement tire ratings should be equivalent to the original tire ratings in all rating designations.
7. When combining different tires front to rear on a vehicle, consult Table 4-2, and check the car manufacturer's or tire manufacturer's recommendations.

TIRE VALVES

The **tire valve** allows air to flow into the tire, and it is also used to release air from the tire. The core in the center of the valve is spring loaded and allows air to flow inward while the tire is inflated (Figure 4-13). Once the tire is inflated, the valve core seats and prevents air flow out of the tire. The small pin on the outer end of the valve core may be pushed to unseat the valve core and release air from the tire. An airtight cap on the outer end of the valve keeps dirt out of the valve, and provides an extra seal against air leakage. A deep groove is cut around the inner end of the tire valve. When the valve assembly is pulled into the wheel opening, this groove seals the valve in the opening.

TABLE 4-2 *Front to Rear Tire Combinations*

Construction		Bias on Front (Read down for rear)			Belted Bias on Front (Read down for rear)				Radial on Front (Read down for rear)		
	Series (Profile)	78 Series	70 Series	60/50 Series	78 Series	70 Series	60/50 Series	Metric	78 Series	70 Series	60/50 Series
	Conventional (83 Series)	A	No	No	A	No	No	No	No	No	No
Bias on Rear (Read across for front)	78 Series	p	A	No	A	No	No	No	No	No	No
	70 Series	A	P	No	A	A	No	No	No	No	No
	60/50 Series	A	A	P	A	A	A	No	No	No	No
Belted Bias on Rear (Read across for front)	78 Series	A	A	No	P	A	No	No	No	No	No
	70 Series	A	A	No	A	P	No	No	No	No	No
	60/50 Series	A	A	A	A	A	P	No	No	No	No
Radial on Rear (Read across for front)	Metric	A	A	No	A	A	No	P	A	A	No
	78 Series	A	A	No	A	A	No	A	P	A	No
	70 Series	A	A	No	A	A	No	A	A	P	No
	60/50 Series	A	A	A	A	A	A	A	A	A	P

P: Preferred applications. For best all-around car handling performance, tires of the same size and construction should be used on all wheel positions.

A: Acceptable but not preferred applications. Consult the car owner's manual and do not apply if vehicle manufacturer recommends against the application.

NO: Not recommended.

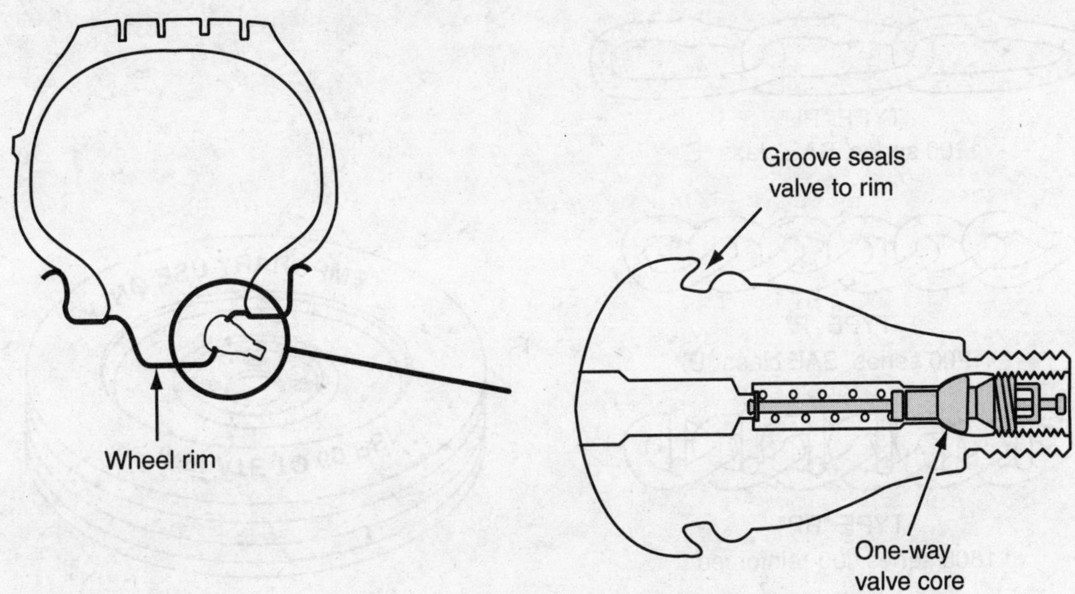

FIGURE 4-13 *Valve core.*

TIRE CHAINS

Tire chains may be used in emergency situations such as driving on snow-covered or ice-covered mountain roads. Most tire manufacturers do not recommend the use of tire chains. Use only SAE class "S" tire chains unless specified by the vehicle and tire manufacturer. Chain types include class S, type P, and type RP (Figure 4-14). These chains must be the proper size and must be installed tightly with the ends secured. Always follow the chain manufacturer's recommended installation procedure. While using chains, driving speed should be reduced. If the chains are heard striking the vehicle body, stop immediately and tighten the chains to prevent body damage.

COMPACT SPARE TIRES

Because cars have been downsized in recent years, space and weight have become major concerns for vehicle manufacturers. For this reason, many car manufacturers have marketed cars with **compact spare tires** to save weight and space. The high-pressure minispare tire is the most common type of compact spare (Figure 4-15). This compact spare rim is usually four inches wide, but is one inch larger in diameter than the other rims on the vehicle. The compact spare rim should not be used with standard tires, snow tires, wheel covers, or trim rings. Any of these uses may result in damage to these items or other parts of the vehicle. The compact spare should be used only on vehicles that offer it as original equipment. Inflation pressure in the compact spare should be maintained at 60 psi (415 kPa). The compact spare tire is designed for very temporary use until the conventional tire can be repaired or replaced. Limit driving speed to 50 mph (80 kph) when the high-pressure minispare is installed on a vehicle.

The space-saver spare tire must be inflated with a special compressor. Battery voltage is supplied to the compressor from the cigarette lighter. This type of compact spare should be inflated to 35 psi (240 kPa). After the tire is inflated, be sure there are no folds in the sidewalls.

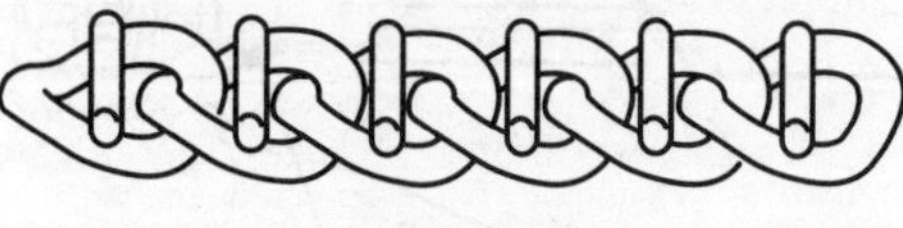

FIGURE 4-14 *Types of tire chains.*

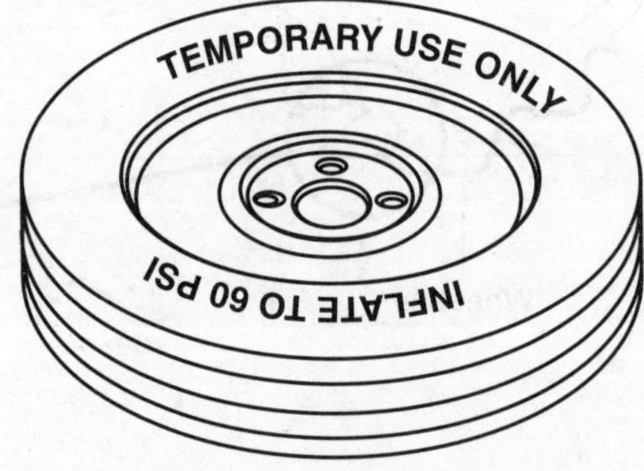

FIGURE 4-15 *Compact, high-pressure, minispare tire.*

The lightweight-skin spare tire is a bias-ply tire with a reduced tread depth to provide an estimated 2,000 miles (3,200 km) of tread life. This type of spare tire is also designed for emergency use only, and driving speed must be limited to 50 mph (80 km/h) when this tire is installed on a vehicle. Always inflate the lightweight-skin spare tire to the pressure specified on the tire placard.

RUN-FLAT TIRES

Some tire manufacturers have recently designed **run-flat tires**. Run-flat tires may be called extended mobility tires (EMT). These tires are standard equipment on the 1995 and later model Corvette and the Plymouth Prowler. Run-flat tires eliminate the need for a spare tire and a jack, saving both weight and space. Run-flat tires are designed with stiffer sidewalls that will partially support the vehicle weight without air pressure in the tire.

Run-flat tires must provide acceptable levels of inflated performance in the areas of comfort, ride, handling, and adequate deflated mobility. Run-flat tires share these same basic design objectives:

1. Minimize the difference between run-flat tires and conventional tires when the tires are inflated.
2. Enhance the handling and riding capabilities of run-flat tires when inflated.
3. Provide acceptable handling when run-flat tires have zero pressure on various vehicles.
4. Enhance low-pressure and zero-pressure bead retention on run-flat tires.
5. Provide sufficient zero-pressure durability so the vehicle can be driven a reasonable distance to a repair facility.

Run-Flat Tires with Sidewall Reinforcements

One of the most important requirements for run-flat tires is bead retention when running with low or zero pressure. Run-flat tires have improved beads to meet this requirement (Figure 4-16). Some run-flat tires have sidewall reinforcements that may be manufactured from flexible, low-hysteresis rubber, thermal resistive materials, or metallic and/or textile tissues. Run-flat tires with a high aspect ratio require increased sidewall stiffness compared to run-flat tires with a low aspect ratio.

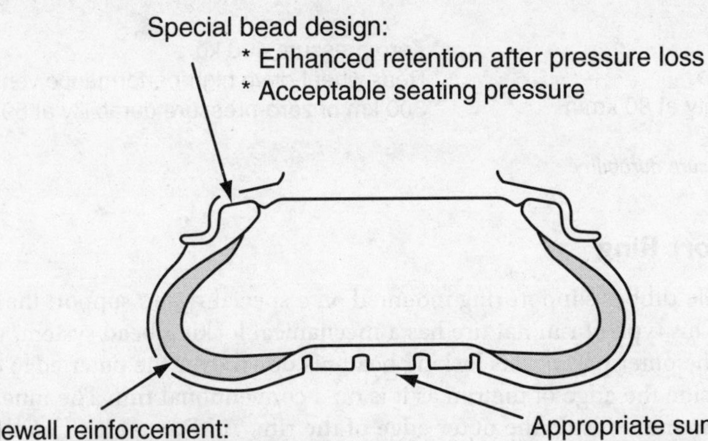

FIGURE 4-16 *Run-flat tire with sidewall reinforcement.*

Because of these sidewall reinforcements, run-flat tires are 20 to 40 percent stiffer compared to conventional tires. Therefore, run-flat tires may increase ride harshness and vertical firmness especially when the tire strikes a large road irregularity. This increase in ride harshness is not as noticeable when the tire contacts a smaller road irregularity. The increased stiffness in run-flat tires usually provides a small improvement in vehicle handling.

Run-flat tires with a low aspect ratio usually have the same or less rolling resistance compared to equivalent-size conventional tires. Because run-flat tires with a high aspect ratio have increased sidewall stiffness, these tires tend to have increased rolling resistance compared to conventional tires.

In moderate cornering and lane-change maneuvers, a run-flat tire with zero pressure provides a slight decrease in vehicle handling. The key word in the previous sentence is moderate. Run-flat tires are used with a tire pressure monitoring system, which has a warning light in the instrument panel to inform the driver when one tire has low pressure. Once the low tire pressure warning light is illuminated with the engine running, the driver should avoid high-speed driving and high-speed cornering, because run-flat tires provide reduced handling capabilities during high-speed cornering.

The zero-pressure durability of a run-flat tire varies depending on the vehicle weight, atmospheric temperature, and the tire aspect ratio. For example, a run-flat tire with a 40 aspect ratio supporting 880 lb (400 kg) provides 186 mi (300 km) of driving at 55 mph (89 km/h) (Figure 4-17). A run-flat tire with a 60 aspect ratio supporting 1,322 lb (600 kg) provides 50 mi (80 km) of driving at 55 mph (89 km/h).

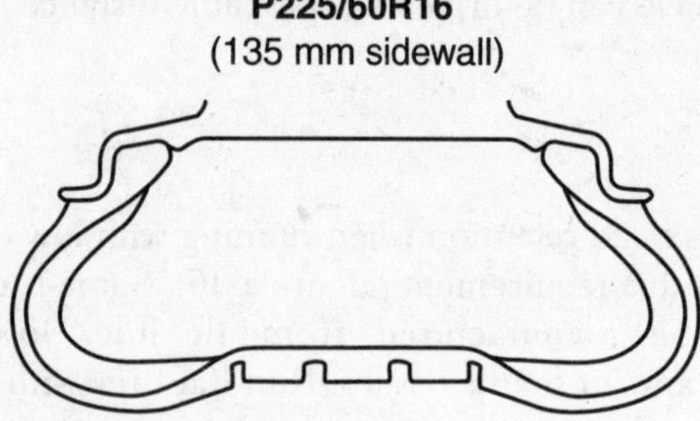

FIGURE 4-17 *Run-flat tire zero-pressure durability.*

Run-Flat Tires with Support Ring

Some run-flat tires have a flexible rubber support ring mounted on a special rim to support the tire if deflation occurs (Figure 4-18). This type of run-flat tire has a mechanical locking bead system, which "latches" the bead to the rim. The outer part of this locking bead fits down over the outer edge of the rim rather than being tucked inside the edge of the rim as it is on a conventional rim. The inner part of the locking bead system is mounted inside the outer edge of the rim. Additional load on the tire tends to tighten the latching force on the locking bead. The run-flat tire's modified shape provides improved tread grip and vehicle handling plus reduced rolling resistance. The disadvantages of this type of run-flat tire are the special rim that is required and the extra weight of the support ring. A tire pressure monitoring system is used with this type of run-flat tire.

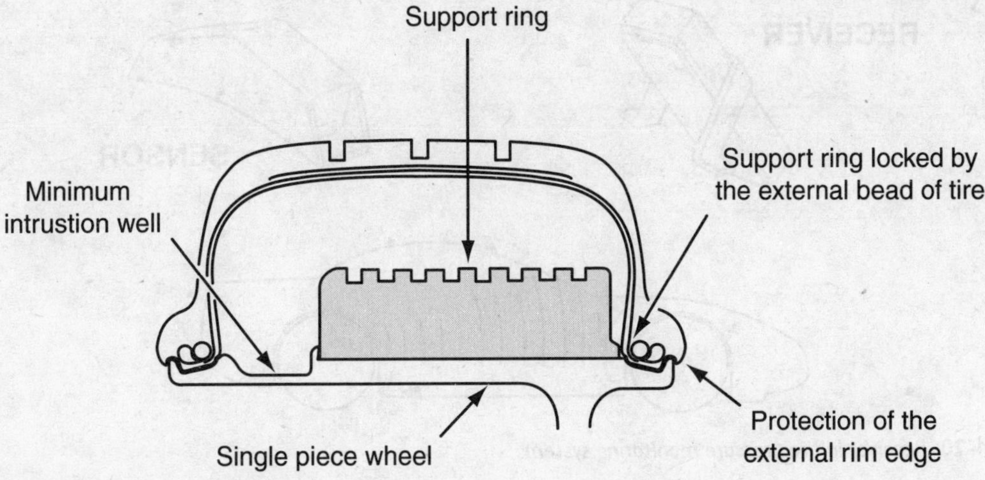

FIGURE 4-18 *Run-flat tire with support ring.*

TIRE PRESSURE MONITORING SYSTEMS

The Transportation Recall Enhancement Accountability and Documentation Act passed by the U.S. government in October 2000 requires all new vehicles to have tire pressure monitoring systems no later than the 2006 model year. A tire pressure monitoring system illuminates a warning light in the instrument panel to inform the driver if one tire has low pressure; some systems also alert the driver if tire temperature is excessive.

Some tire pressure monitoring systems have a sensor strapped in the dropwell on each rim (Figure 4-19). These sensors must be mounted on the rim directly opposite to the valve stem. Other tire pressure monitoring systems have a sensor mounted on top of each valve stem in place of the valve cap. Regardless of the sensor's mounting location, it transmits radio frequency (RF) signals. These RF signals will change if any tire is underinflated a specific amount. The RF signals are sent to a receiver that is usually mounted under the dash (Figure 4-20). On some systems the receiver illuminates the

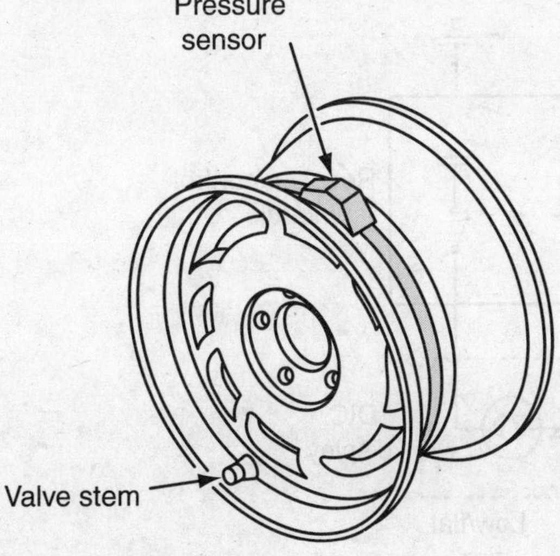

Location	Color code
Right front	Blue
Left front	Green
Right rear	Orange
Left rear	Yellow

WARNING: Pressure sensor inside tire. Avoid contacting sensor with tire changing equipment tools or tire bead.

Service note: Pressure sensor must be mounted directly across from valve stem.

FIGURE 4-19 *Tire pressure sensor.*

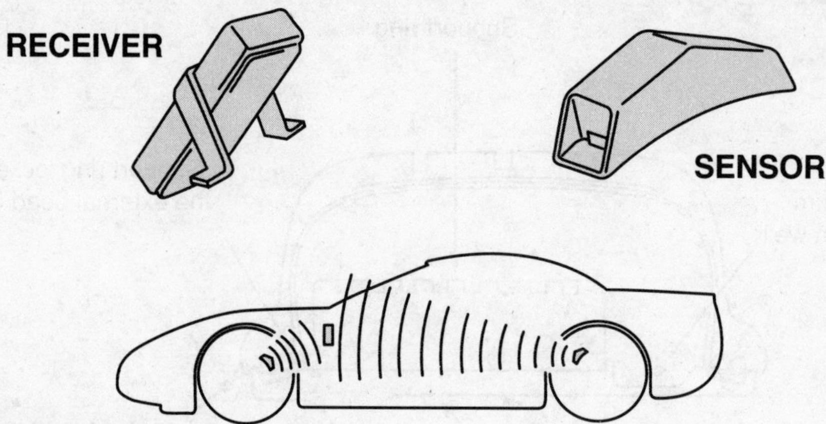

FIGURE 4-20 *Receiver in tire pressure monitoring system.*

low tire pressure warning light in the instrument panel if the pressure in any tire drops below 25 psi (172 kPa). On other systems the tire pressure warning light is illuminated with a smaller reduction in tire pressure.

Some tire pressure monitoring systems provide continuous monitoring with the vehicle stopped and the ignition switch on. Other systems will not monitor tire pressure until the vehicle is moving above a specific speed such as 25 mph (40 km/h). Some tire pressure monitoring systems have two warning lights: the low/flat tire warning light informs the driver regarding low tire pressure, and the service low tire pressure warning system (LTPWS) warning light informs the driver if there is a defect in the system (Figure 4-21). On some vehicles the low tire pressure receiver is connected to the data link connector (DLC) under the dash. A scan tool may be connected to the DLC to diagnose the tire pressure monitoring system. If a defect occurs in the system, a diagnostic trouble code (DTC) is stored in the receiver memory. A scan tool may be connected to the DLC to obtain the DTCs from the receiver.

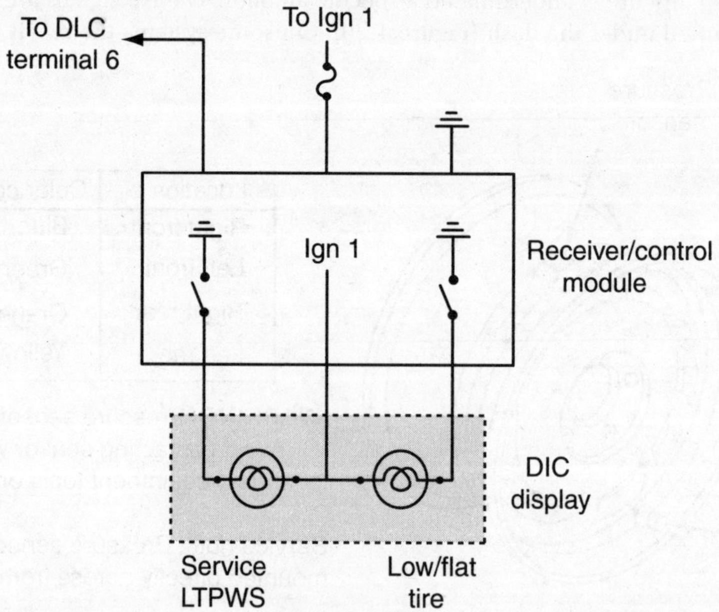

FIGURE 4-21 *Warning lights in tire pressure monitoring system.*

Other tire pressure monitoring systems use the wheel speed sensor signals on four-channel antilock brake systems (ABS) to detect low tire pressure. A tire with low air pressure has a smaller diameter, and the wheel speed sensor generates a higher frequency signal.

Some tire pressure monitoring systems have a miniature pressure sensor and computer chip about the size of a watch battery. This sensor and chip assembly is imbedded in the tire. The pressure sensor senses the actual tire pressure and sends voltage signals in relation to the tire pressure to a transceiver via a 360° circumferential antenna mounted in the tire sidewall close to the rim (Figure 4-22). A transceiver is mounted in each wheel well. The pressure sensor and computer chip do not require a battery, because they receive energy from the transceiver-generated field. Each transceiver is connected by data links to a central electronic control unit (ECU) (Figure 4-23). The transceivers relay voltage signals from the pressure sensors to the ECU. The computer chip calculates the recommended tire pressure based on data such as air temperature, tire pressure, and vehicle speed. Vehicle speed information is transmitted via data links from the powertrain control module (PCM) to the ECU. If a low tire pressure signal is received by the ECU, the instrument panel displays a warning message together with a calculated number of miles of safe travel.

FIGURE 4-22 *Antenna in a tire sidewall.*

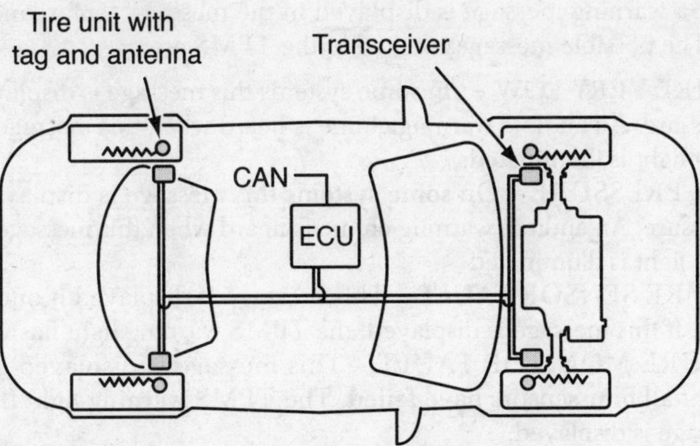

FIGURE 4-23 *Transceivers and ECU in a tire pressure monitoring system.*

Tire Pressure Monitoring Systems (TPMS) with Valve Stem Sensors

Most current TPMS have pressure sensor that are attached to the valve stem inside the tire, and these sensors require a battery (Figure 4-24). Average battery life is approximately 10 years. A retention nut is threaded onto the valve stem on the outside of the wheel rim, and a sealing grommet is positioned between this nut and the rim (Figure 4-25). The internal threads on the retention nut are positioned

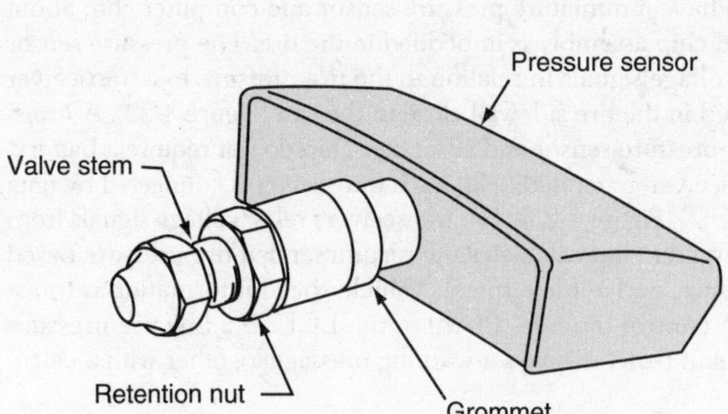

FIGURE 4-24 *Tire pressure sensor mounted on the valve stem.*

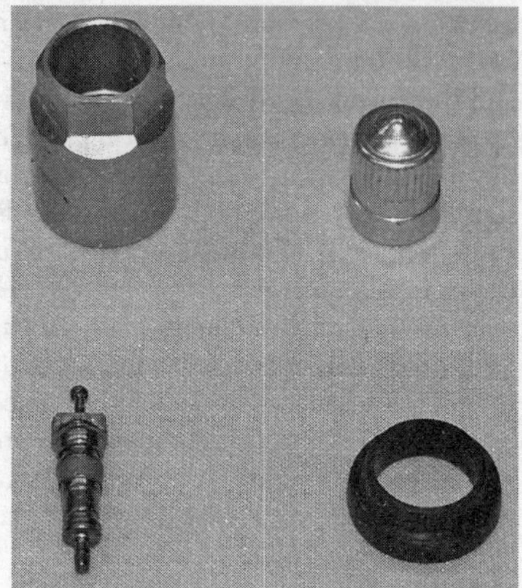

FIGURE 4-25 *Tire pressure sensor retention nut, valve cap, valve core, and grommet.*

near the bottom of the nut, and matching threads are located near the bottom end of the valve stem. A nickel-plated valve core is threaded into the internal threads in the valve stem, and a special valve cap is threaded onto the external threads at the top of the valve stem.

The valve stem acts as a radio antenna, and the TPMS module is the receiver. Each sensor transmits radio signals to the TPMS module every 60 seconds. On some SUVs the TPMS module is located behind the right-hand C pillar. The TPMS module compares the data from each tire pressure sensor to the low tire pressure limits. When the TPMS module determines that any of the four tires has a pressure below the specified pressure, this module sends voltage signals through the data links to the vehicle message center. When the message center receives voltage signals indicating low pressure in one or more tires, a warning message is displayed in the message center, and the TPMS warning light is illuminated. The possible messages related to the TPMS are:

1. WARNING TIRE VERY LOW – On some systems this message is displayed if any tire has less than 25 psi pressure. An audible warning chime is heard when this message is displayed, and the TPMS warning light is illuminated.
2. CHECK TIRE PRESSURE – On some systems this message is displayed if any tire has less than 30 psi pressure. An audible warning chime is heard when this message is displayed, and the TPMS warning light is illuminated.
3. TIRE PRESSURE SENSOR FAULT – This message is displayed if one or more sensors are malfunctioning. If this message is displayed, the TPMS warning light flashes for 20 seconds.
4. TIRE PRESSURE MONITOR FAULT – This message is displayed if the TPMS module is defective or if all four sensors have failed. The TPMS warning light flashes for 20 seconds when this message is displayed.

TPMS with Electronic Vehicle Information Center (EVIC) Display

Some TPMS provide graphic tire pressure displays and warning messages on an EVIC display in the instrument panel. These systems may have 4-tire or 5-tire monitoring capabilities. A TPMS with 5-tire monitoring capabilities also monitors the spare tire. These systems have valve stem sensors that broadcast tire pressure once per minute when the vehicle is moving at 25 mph (40 km/h) or faster. If the vehicle has a 5-tire TPMS, the sensor in the spare tire transmits a signal every hour. Each valve stem sensor transmits a unique code so the EVIC module can determine the location of the sensor. If the wheels are rotated on the vehicle, or the spare tire and wheel are installed on the vehicle, the EVIC must be reprogrammed to recognize the new wheel and tire locations.

This type of TPMS provides a warning display in the EVIC if the tire pressure drops below a specific value or increases above a certain threshold. Typically, if the tire pressure in any tire decreases below 25 psi (172 kPa), the EVIC requests a chime warning, displays a LOW PRESSURE message, and indicates the location of the tire with low pressure. If the pressure in any tire exceeds 45 psi (310 kPa), the EVIC requests a chime warning and displays HIGH PRESSURE while indicating the location of the tire with high pressure. After a few seconds the EVIC reverts to a blinking display of the tire pressure. This blinking display continues for the entire ignition cycle or until an EVIC button is pressed. When an EVIC button is pressed, the blinking display returns after 60 seconds without the chime warning. If high or low pressure is detected in the spare tire on a 5-tire system, SPARE HIGH PRESSURE or SPARE LOW PRESSURE appears on the EVIC display for 60 seconds during each ignition cycle.

TIRE CONTACT AREA

The **tire contact area** refers to the area of the tire that is in contact with the road surface when the tire is supporting the vehicle weight. The **tire free diameter** is the distance of a horizontal line through the center of the spindle and wheel to the outer edges of the tread. The **tire rolling diameter** is the distance of a perpendicular straight line through the center of the spindle to the outer edges of the tread when the tire is supporting the vehicle weight. The rolling diameter is always less than the free diameter. The difference between the free diameter and the rolling diameter is referred to as deflection. Tire tread grooves take up excess rubber and prevent scrubbing as the tire deflects in the contact area. The rolling diameter, free diameter, and contact area are shown in Figure 4-26.

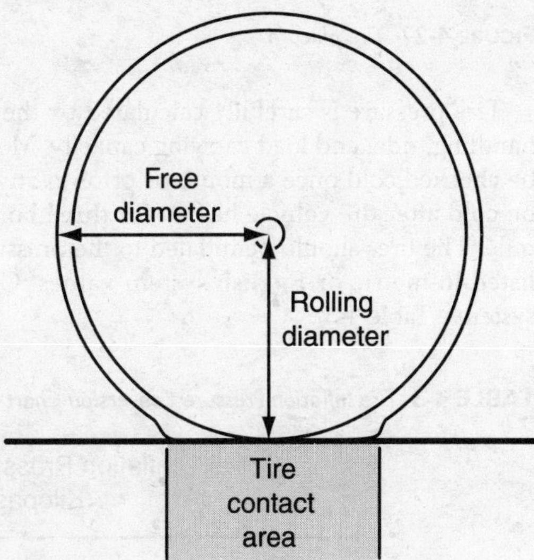

FIGURE 4-26 *Tire rolling diameter, free diameter, and contact area.*

TIRE PLACARD AND INFLATION PRESSURE

The vehicle weight is supported by the correct air pressure exerted evenly against all the interior tire surface, which produces tension in the tire carcass. Therefore, **tire pressure** is extremely important. Underinflation decreases the rolling diameter and increases the contact area, which results in excessive sidewall flexing and tread wear. Overinflation decreases the contact area, increases the rolling diameter, and stiffens the tire. This action results in excessive wear on the center of the tread. Tire pressure should be checked when the tires are cool. Since tire pressure normally increases at high tire temperatures, air pressure should not be released from hot tires. Excessive heat buildup in a tire may be caused by underinflation. This condition may lead to severe tire damage.

On many vehicles, the **tire placard** is permanently attached to the rear face of the driver's door. This placard provides tire information such as maximum vehicle load; tire size, including spare; and cold inflation pressure, including spare (Figure 4-27).

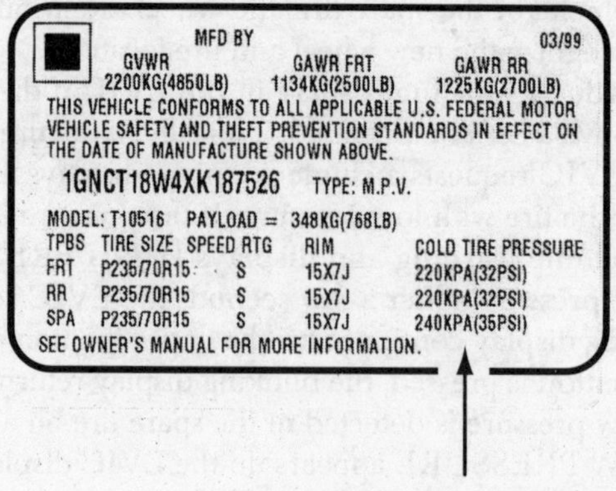

FIGURE 4-27 *Tire placard.*

Tire pressure is carefully calculated by the vehicle manufacturer to provide satisfactory tread life, handling, ride, and load-carrying capacity. Most vehicle manufacturers recommend that tire pressures be checked cold once a month or prior to any extended trip. The manufacturer considers the tires to be cold after the vehicle has sat for three hours, or when the vehicle has been driven less than one mile. The tires should be inflated to the pressure indicated on the tire placard. Tire pressures may be listed in metric or English system values. Conversion charts provide pressures in either of these systems (Table 4-3).

TABLE 4-3 *Tire Inflation Pressure Conversion Chart*

Inflation Pressure Conversion Chart
(Kilopascals to PSI)

kPa	psi	kPa	psi
140	20	215	31
145	21	220	32
155	22	230	33
160	23	235	34
165	24	240	35
170	25	250	36
180	36	275	40
185	37	310	45
190	38	345	50
200	39	380	55
205	30	415	60

Conversion: 6.9 kPa=1 psi

TIRE MOTION FORCES

When a vehicle is in motion, wheel rotation subjects the tires to centrifugal force. The tires are also subjected to accelerating and decelerating forces because of their path of travel. If a vehicle is traveling at 55 miles per hour (mph), or 88.5 kilometers per hour (km/h), the part of the tire exactly fore and aft of the spindle is also traveling at 55 mph (88.5 km/h). At the exact top of the tire, the tire speed is 110 mph (177 km/h). The tire speed actually drops to zero at the exact bottom of the tire where the arc of deceleration ends and the arc of acceleration begins. Since the tires are subjected to strong acceleration and deceleration forces, the tire construction must be uniform. A soft spot in a tire will deflect farther than the surrounding area, and this area will be subjected to rapid wear as it strikes the road surface.

Tires must have equal stiffness in the sidewalls around the tire. If a tire does not have equal stiffness in all areas around the tire sidewalls, it may cause a vibration when driving. This vibration is called **road force variation** and produces a vibration similar to the vibration caused by improper wheel and tire balance. Modern wheel balancers have a roller that is forced against the tire tread during the balance procedure, and this type of balancer detects road force variation (Figure 4-28).

Tires must be manufactured so the cords are concentric with the center of the tire. Tire conicity is a term used to describe a tire in which the cords are off-center in relation to the tire center. If the tire cords are not concentric with the tire center, the tire may cause a steering pull condition when driving. Modern wheel balancers use a roller pressed against the tire tread to detect conicity during the balance procedure (Figure 4-29).

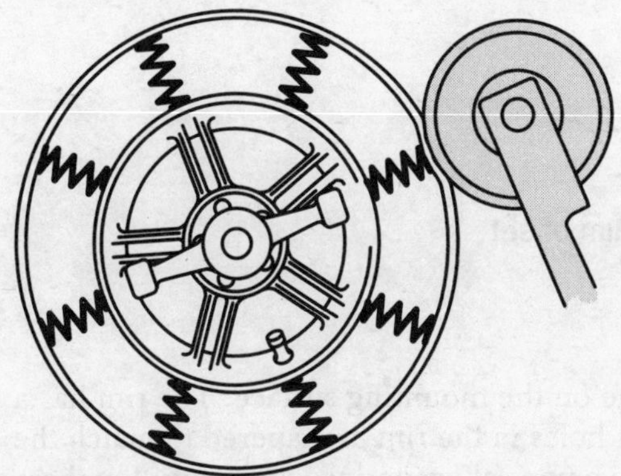

FIGURE 4-28 *The roller on some wheel balancers senses road force variation.*

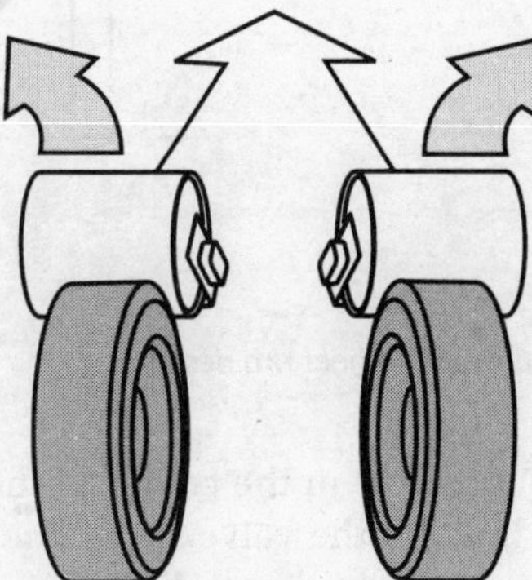

FIGURE 4-29 *The roller on some wheel balancers senses concentricity.*

WHEEL RIMS

Many **wheel rims** are manufactured from stamped or pressed steel discs that are riveted or welded together to form the circular rim. Currently, less than 50 percent of the wheel rims installed by the original equipment manufacturers (OEMs) are stamped steel type. The rim offset is the distance between the rim centerline and the mounting face of the disc (Figure 4-30). If a rim is designed with positive offset, the rim centerline is outboard of the mounting face. The rim with negative offset has the centerline inboard of the mounting face. The rim offset affects front suspension loading and operation.

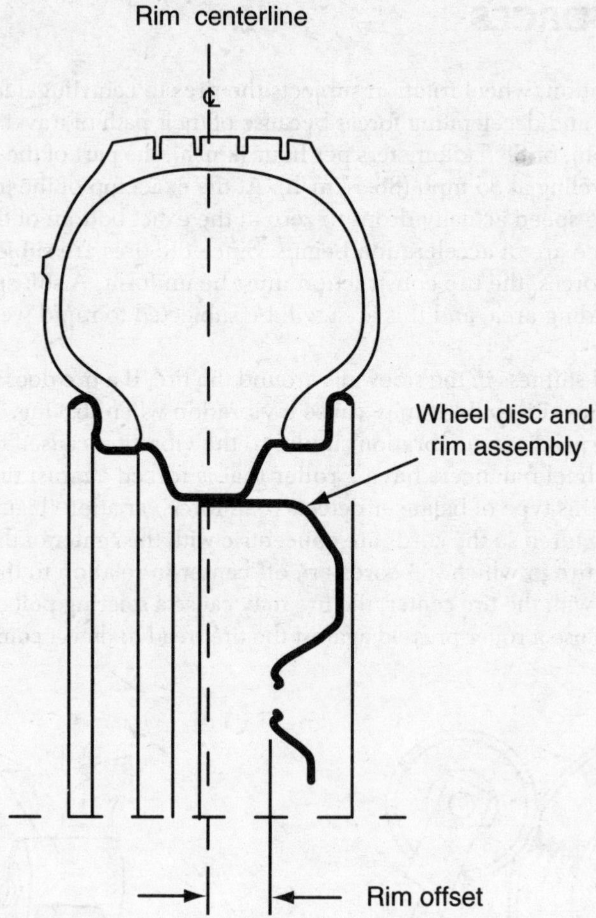

FIGURE 4-30 *Wheel rim design.*

A large hole in the center of the rim fits over a flange on the mounting surface. The rim has a small hole for the valve stem. The wheel stud mounting holes in the rim are tapered to match the taper on the wheel nuts. Some late model Ford trucks have non-self-centering wheel nuts. On these nuts, a swivel washer is attached to the inner side of each nut (Figure 4-31). When the wheel and nuts are installed, the flat side of the swivel nut fits against the wheel rim. The wheels are hub-centered, and an O-ring mounted on the hub provides improved wheel centering (Figure 4-32). If this O-ring is missing or damaged, the wheel may not be properly centered, and this condition results in wheel vibrations. The O-ring also provides a seal to prevent corrosion.

The width of the wheel is measured between the rim flanges. Rim diameter is determined by measuring across the wheel from the top to the bottom. A drop center in the rim makes tire changing easier (Figure 4-33). Rims have safety ridges behind the tire bead locations, which help prevent the beads from moving into the drop center area if the tire blows out. If the tire blows out and a bead enters the drop center area, the tire may come off the wheel.

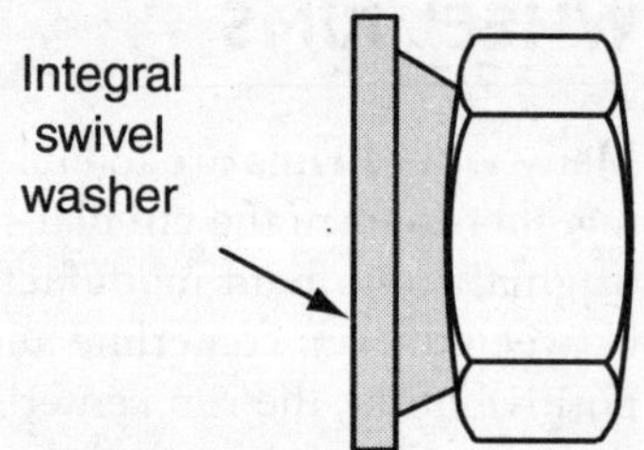

FIGURE 4-31 *Non-self-centering wheel nut design.*

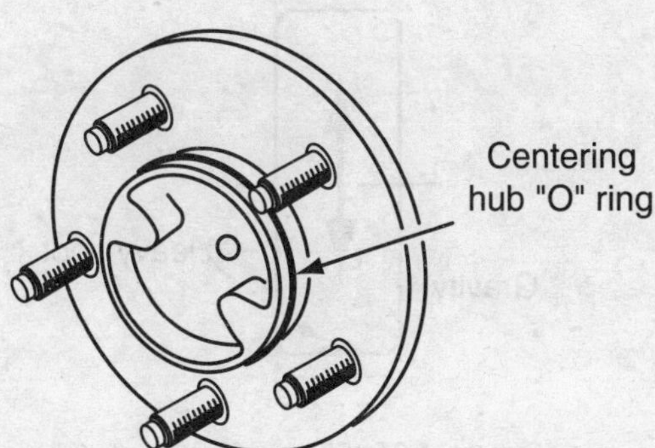

FIGURE 4-32 *Hub O-ring that provides wheel centering.*

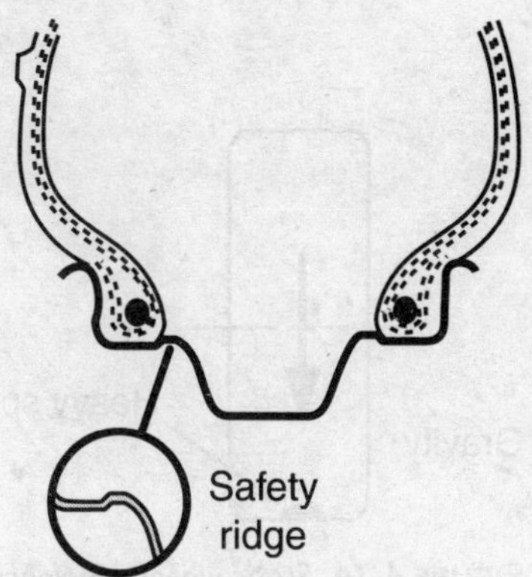

FIGURE 4-33 *Wheel rim with drop center and safety ridges.*

Cast aluminum wheels are commonly used on many vehicles by OEMs. These wheels may be polished, chromed, or painted. A cast aluminum wheel costs about twice as much as a stamped steel wheel.

Forged aluminum wheels are installed on some vehicles. They are more durable than cast aluminum wheels and have a bright finish. Forged aluminum wheels are used on heavy-load applications such as trucks. Some expensive sports cars are also equipped with forged aluminum wheels. A forged aluminum wheel is lighter than a steel wheel, but the cost of a forged aluminum wheel is considerably higher than a stamped steel or cast aluminum wheel.

Some vehicles are equipped with pressure-cast aluminum wheels that are designed to be chrome plated. Pressure-cast wheels may also be called squeeze-cast wheels. During the manufacture of a pressure-cast wheel, the molten metal is squeezed under pressure into the mold. This action squeezes all the air out of the metal and reduces the metal porosity, which provides an improved substrate for chrome plating. The chrome plating increases the cost of the pressure-cast aluminum wheel so it is considerably more expensive than other types of wheels.

Race cars may be equipped with **magnesium alloy wheels,** which are lighter than either steel or aluminum wheels.

Replacement wheel rims must be the same as the original equipment wheels in load capacity, offset, width, diameter, and mounting configuration. An incorrect wheel can affect tire life, steering quality, wheel bearing life, vehicle ground clearance, tire clearance, and speedometer/ odometer calibrations.

STATIC WHEEL BALANCE THEORY

When a tire-and-wheel assembly has proper **static balance**, it has the weight equally distributed around its axis of rotation, and gravity will not force it to rotate from its rest position. If a vehicle is raised off the floor and a wheel is rotated in 120° intervals, a statically balanced wheel will remain stationary at each interval. When a wheel and tire are statically unbalanced, the tire has a heavy portion at one location. The force of gravity acting on this heavy portion will cause the wheel to rotate until the heavy portion is located near the bottom of the tire (Figure 4-34).

Results of Static Unbalance

Centrifugal force may be defined as the force that tends to move a rotating mass away from its axis of rotation. As we have explained previously, a tire and wheel are subjected to very strong acceleration

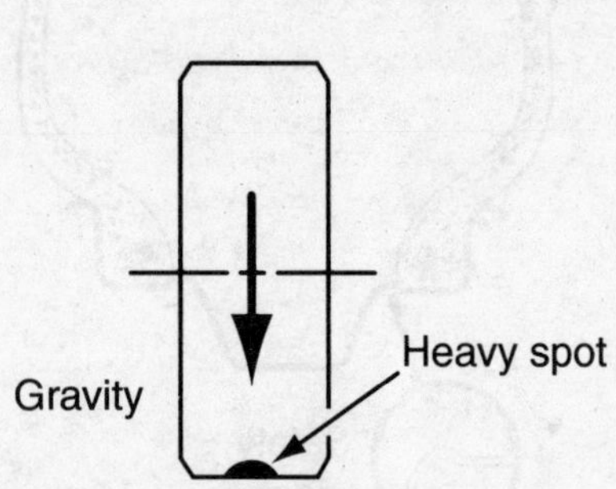

FIGURE 4-34 *Static wheel unbalance.*

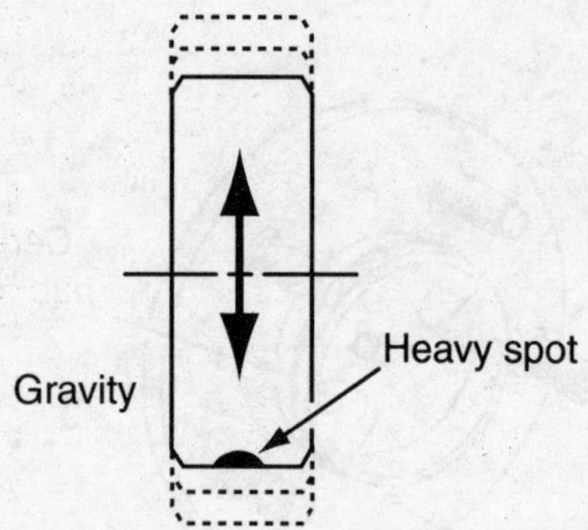

FIGURE 4-35 *Effects of static unbalance.*

and deceleration forces when a vehicle is in motion. The heavy portion of a statically unbalanced wheel is influenced by centrifugal force. This influence attempts to move the heavy spot on a tangent line away from the wheel axis. This action tends to lift the wheel assembly off the road surface (Figure 4-35).

The wheel-lifting action caused by static unbalance may be referred to as **wheel tramp** (Figure 4-36). Wheel tramp action allows the tire to slip momentarily when it is lifted vertically. When the wheel and tire move downward as the heavy spot decelerates, the tire strikes the road surface with a pounding action. This repeated slipping and pounding action causes severe tire scuffing and cupping (Figure 4-37).

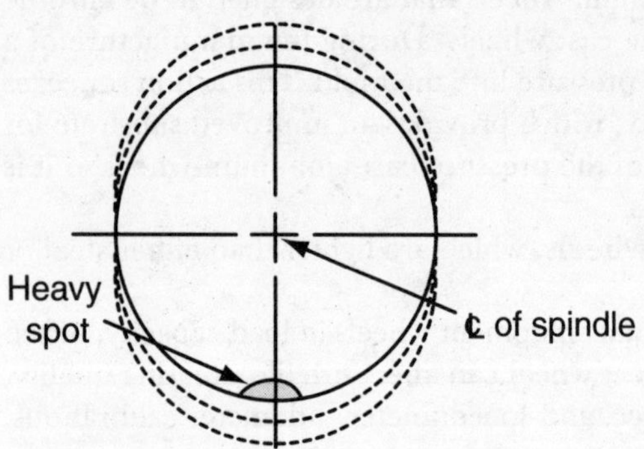

FIGURE 4-36 *Wheel tramp.*

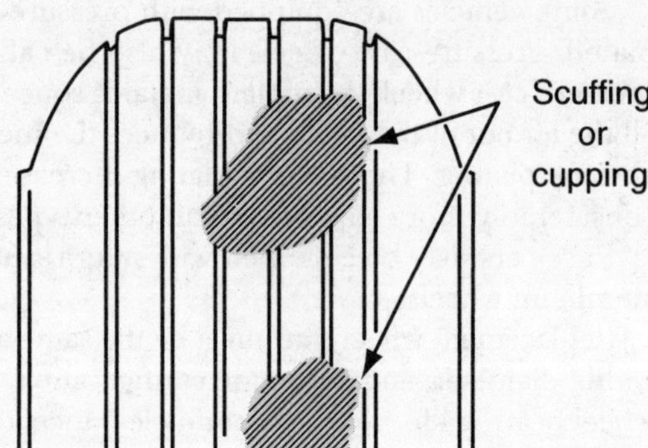

FIGURE 4-37 *Cupping tire wear caused by static unbalance.*

The vertical wheel motion from static unbalance is transferred to the suspension system and then absorbed by the chassis and body. This action causes rapid wear on suspension and steering components. The wheel tramp action resulting from static unbalance is also transmitted to the passenger compartment, which causes passenger discomfort and driver fatigue.

When a vehicle is traveling at normal highway cruising speed, the average wheel speed is 850 revolutions per minute (rpm). A statically unbalanced tire-and-wheel assembly is an uncontrolled mass of weight in motion. When a vehicle is traveling at 60 mph (97 km/h) and a tire has 2 ounces (oz), or 57 grams (g), of static unbalance, the resultant pounding force is approximately 15 pounds (lb), or 6.8 kilograms (kg), against the road surface.

DYNAMIC WHEEL BALANCE THEORY

When a tire-and-wheel assembly has correct **dynamic balance**, the weight of the assembly is distributed equally on both sides of the wheel center viewed from the front. Dynamic wheel balance may be explained by dividing the tire into four sections (Figure 4-38). In Figure 4-38, if sections A and C have the same weight and sections B and D also have the same weight, the tire has proper dynamic balance. If a tire has dynamic unbalance, section D may have a heavy spot; thus, sections B and D have different weights (Figure 4-39).

From our discussion of dynamic balance, we can understand that a tire-and-wheel assembly may be in static balance, but have dynamic unbalance. Therefore, wheels must be in balance statically and dynamically.

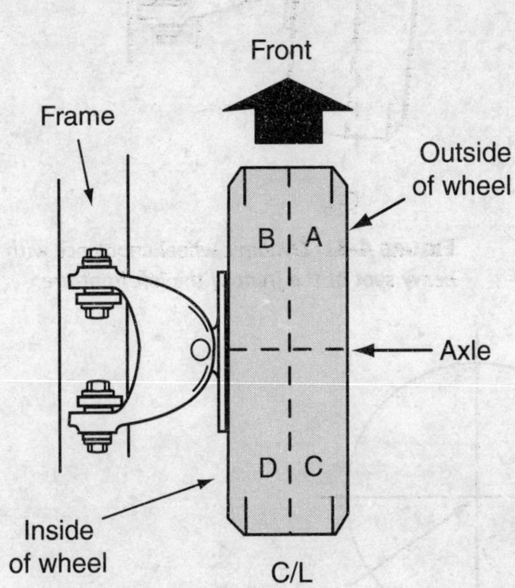

FIGURE 4-38 *Dynamic wheel balance theory.*

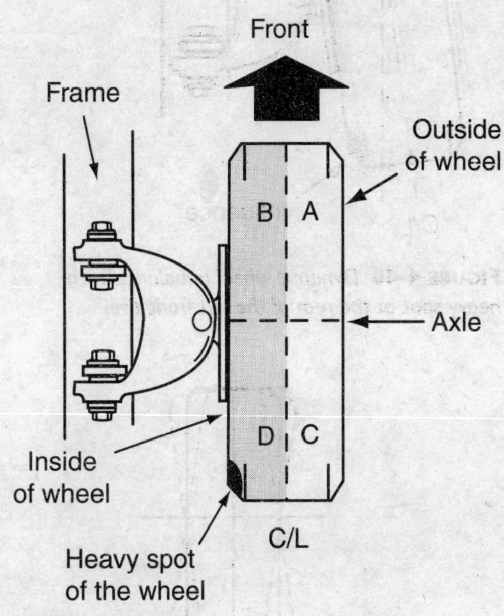

FIGURE 4-39 *Dynamic wheel unbalance.*

Results of Dynamic Wheel Unbalance

When a dynamically unbalanced wheel is rotating, centrifugal force moves the heavy spot toward the tire centerline. The centerline of the heavy spot arc is at a 90° angle to the spindle. This action turns the true centerline of the left front wheel inward when the heavy spot is at the rear of the wheel (Figure 4-40). When the wheel rotates until the heavy spot is at the front of the wheel, the heavy spot movement turns the left front wheel outward (Figure 4-41).

From these explanations, we can understand that dynamic wheel unbalance causes lateral wheel shake, or shimmy (Figure 4-42). This action causes steering wheel oscillations at medium and high speeds with resultant driver fatigue and passenger discomfort. Wheel shimmy and steering wheel oscillations also cause unstable directional control of the vehicle.

Earlier in this chapter, when discussing wheel rotation, we mentioned that a tire stops momentarily where it contacts the road surface. A wheel with dynamic unbalance is forced to pivot on the contact area, which results in excessive tire scuffing and wear. Dynamic wheel unbalance causes premature wear on steering linkage and suspension components. Therefore, dynamic wheel balance is extremely

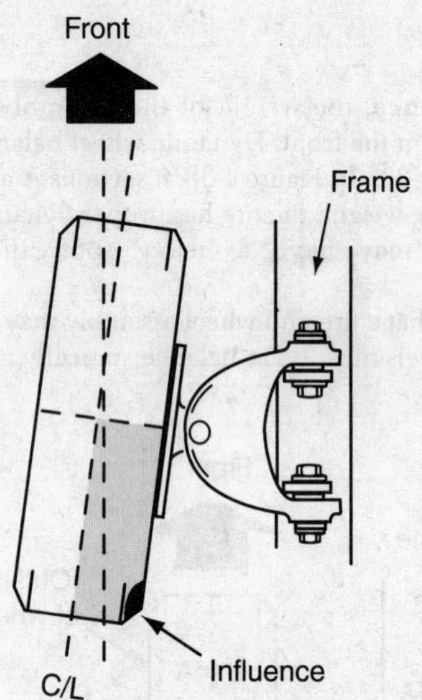

FIGURE 4-40 *Dynamic wheel unbalance with heavy spot at the rear of the left front tire.*

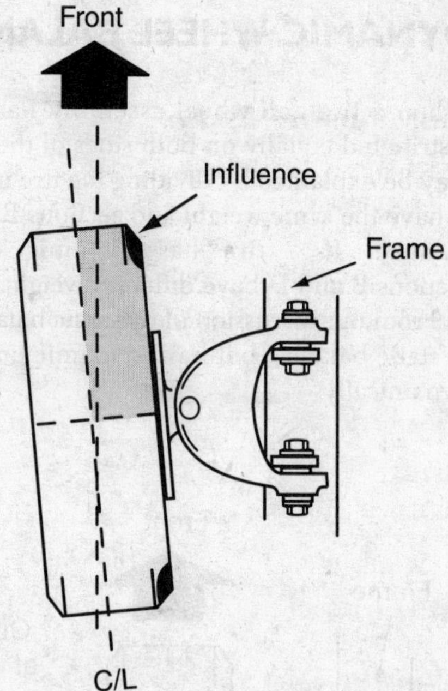

FIGURE 4-41 *Dynamic wheel unbalance with heavy spot at the front of the left front tire.*

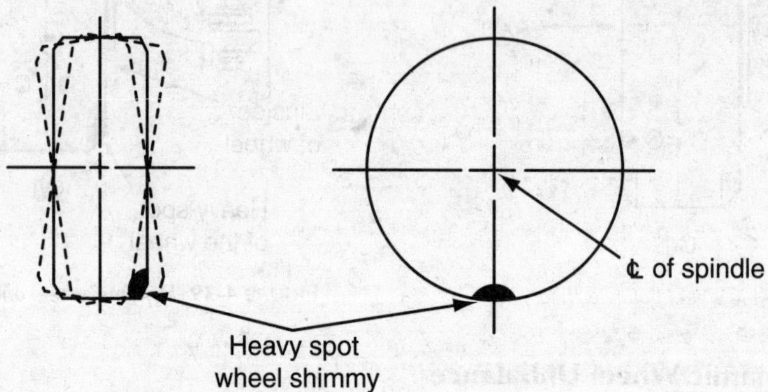

FIGURE 4-42 *Dynamic wheel unbalance causes wheel shimmy.*

important to provide normal tire life, reduce steering and suspension component wear, increase directional control, and decrease driver fatigue. The main purposes of proper wheel balance may be summarized as follows:

1. Maintains normal tire tread life.
2. Provides extended life of suspension and steering components.
3. Helps provide directional control of the vehicle.
4. Reduces driver fatigue.
5. Increases passenger comfort.
6. Helps maintain the life of body and chassis components.

REVIEW QUESTIONS

Short Answer Essays

1. State general tire functions.
2. Explain the purpose of the tire bead and bead filler.
3. Describe the purpose of antioxidants in the tire sidewall.
4. Describe the difference between a bias-ply and radial-ply tire.
5. Explain the advantages of all-season tires compared to conventional tires.
6. Describe the difference between a B and D tire load rating.
7. Explain the difference between an A and C tire temperature rating.
8. Define tire contact area and tire deflection.
9. Explain the purpose of the wheel rim drop center and safety ridges.
10. Describe the results of static unbalance.

Fill-in-the-Blanks

1. To calculate the tire aspect ratio, the tire section height is divided by the ____________.
2. All-season tires have higher average ____________ compared to non-all-season tires.
3. Studded tires cause ____________ damage.
4. Replacement tires should be installed in pairs on the same ____________.
5. When a high-pressure minispare tire is installed on a vehicle, driving speed should not exceed ____________ mph.
6. The rolling diameter of a tire is ____________ than the free tire diameter.
7. When a tire deflects in the contact area, the tread grooves take up excess rubber and prevent ____________.
8. Car manufacturers recommend that tire inflation pressures should be checked when the tires are ____________.
9. When a vehicle is traveling at 55 mph, the exact top of the tire is moving at ____________ mph.
10. The rim offset is the vertical distance between the rim centerline and the ____________ ____________ of the disc.

Multiple Choice

1. In a radial-ply tire the steel or fiberglass belt cords are crisscrossed in relation to the tire centerline at an angle of:
   A. 10° to 30°.
   B. 15° to 35°.
   C. 20° to 35°.
   D. 30° to 45°.

2. In a radial-ply tire the angle of the ply cords in relation to the tire centerline is:
   A. 60°.
   B. 72°.
   C. 85°.
   D. 90°.

3. All of these statements about radial-ply tires are true EXCEPT:
   A. A belted radial-ply tire has less rolling resistance than a belted bias-ply tire.
   B. A belted radial-ply tire provides longer tire tread life than a belted bias-ply tire.
   C. A belted radial-ply tire provides improved steering characteristics compared to a bias-ply belted tire.
   D. A belted radial-ply passenger car tire can have four plies and four belts.

4. Dynamic wheel unbalance can result in:
   A. Lateral wheel shimmy.
   B. Increased steering effort.
   C. Tire and wheel tramp.
   D. Normal tire tread life.

5. When a tire has a conicity problem:
   A. The tire has excessive lateral runout.
   B. The tire has too much radial runout.
   C. The tire is cone shaped and not level across the tread area.
   D. The tire has separation between the cord plies in the sidewall.

6. When explaining tire ratings to the customer:
   A. A P speed rating indicates the tire has a 130 mph (210 km/h) capability.
   B. Tire speed ratings are based on laboratory tests.
   C. Tire traction ratings are based on five skid tests.
   D. A tire with a C traction rating has better traction than a tire with an A traction rating.

7. Modern automotive tires usually contain:
   A. Four-ply sidewalls.
   B. An inner tread layer that provides maximum traction.
   C. Antioxidants in the sidewall rubber to help prevent cracking.
   D. One natural rubber and two synthetic rubbers.

8. All these statements about tires and wheels in motion are true EXCEPT:
   A. When a vehicle is traveling at 50 mph (80 km/h), the top of each tire is moving at 100 mph (160 km/h).
   B. Wheel rotation subjects the tires to centrifugal force.
   C. When traveling at 60 mph (96.5 km/h), the front portion of each tire is accelerating.
   D. A soft spot in a tire may cause cupped tire tread wear.

9. Dynamic wh eel unbalance causes:
   A. Cupped tire tread wear.
   B. Even wear on one edge of the tire tread.
   C. Even wear on the center of the tire tread.
   D. Feathered tire tread wear.

10. When installing replacement tires:
    A. Different tire sizes can be installed on the same axle.
    B. Snow tires can be a different type or size than the original tires on the vehicle.
    C. If the tire size is different than the original tire size, antilock brake system operation can be adversely affected.
    D. A four-wheel-drive vehicle can have different size tires on the front and rear wheels.

SHOCK ABSORBERS AND STRUTS

5

Upon completion and review of this chapter, you should be able to:

- State the three purposes of shock absorbers.
- Explain how shock absorbers contribute to vehicle safety.
- Define wheel jounce and rebound.
- Explain spring operation during wheel jounce and rebound.
- Describe shock absorber operation during wheel jounce.
- Explain shock absorber operation during wheel rebound.
- Describe the advantages of nitrogen-gas-filled shock absorbers and struts.
- Explain shock absorber ratios.
- Explain travel-sensitive shock absorber operation.
- Describe the operation of an adjustable shock absorber.
- Explain the operation of load-leveling struts and shock absorbers.

INTRODUCTION

Two front **shock absorbers** are connected from the front suspension to the chassis, and two rear shock absorbers are attached between the rear suspension and the chassis. Shock absorbers have three main purposes:

1. They control spring action and oscillations to provide the desired ride quality.
2. They help prevent body sway and lean while cornering.
3. They reduce the tendency of a tire tread to lift off the road, which improves tire life, traction, and directional stability.

Because shock absorbers control spring action, spring oscillations, and chassis oscillations, they contribute to vehicle safety and passenger comfort. If the shock absorbers are worn out, excessive chassis oscillations may occur, particularly on rough road surfaces. These excessive chassis oscillations may result in loss of steering control. Worn-out shock absorbers also cause excessive body lean and sway while cornering, which may cause the driver to lose control of the vehicle. Shock absorbers are extremely important to providing longer tire life and improving vehicle handling, steering quality, and ride quality.

Shock absorber design is matched to the deflection rate of the coil spring to control the spring action. Several different types of shock absorbers are available for special service requirements.

SHOCK ABSORBER DESIGN

The lower half of a shock absorber is a twin tube steel unit filled with hydraulic oil and nitrogen gas (Figure 5-1). In some shock absorbers, the nitrogen gas is omitted. A relief valve is located in the bottom of the unit, and a circular lower mounting is attached to the lower tube. This mounting contains a rubber isolating bushing, or grommet. A piston and rod assembly is connected to the upper half of the shock absorber. This upper portion of the shock absorber has a dust shield that surrounds the lower twin tube unit. The piston is precision fit in the inner cylinder of the lower unit. A piston rod guide and seal are located in the top of the lower unit. A circular upper mounting with a rubber bushing is attached to the top of the shock absorber.

SHOCK ABSORBER OPERATION

Shock absorbers are usually mounted between the lower control arms and the chassis. When a vehicle wheel strikes a bump, the wheel and suspension move upward in relation to the chassis. Upward wheel movement is referred to as **jounce travel.** This jounce action causes the spring to deflect or compress. Under this condition, the spring stores energy and springs back downward with all the energy absorbed when it deflected upward. This downward spring and wheel action is called **rebound travel.** If this spring action were not controlled, the wheel would strike the road with a strong downward force, and the wheel jounce would occur again. Therefore, some device must be installed to control the spring action, or the wheel would bounce up and down many times after it hit a bump, causing passenger discomfort, directional instability, and suspension component wear.

Shock absorbers are installed on suspension systems to control spring action. When a wheel strikes a bump and jounce travel occurs, the shock absorber lower tube unit is forced upward. This action forces the piston downward in the lower tube unit. Since oil cannot leak past the piston, the oil in the lower unit is forced through the piston valves to the upper oil chamber. These valves provide precise

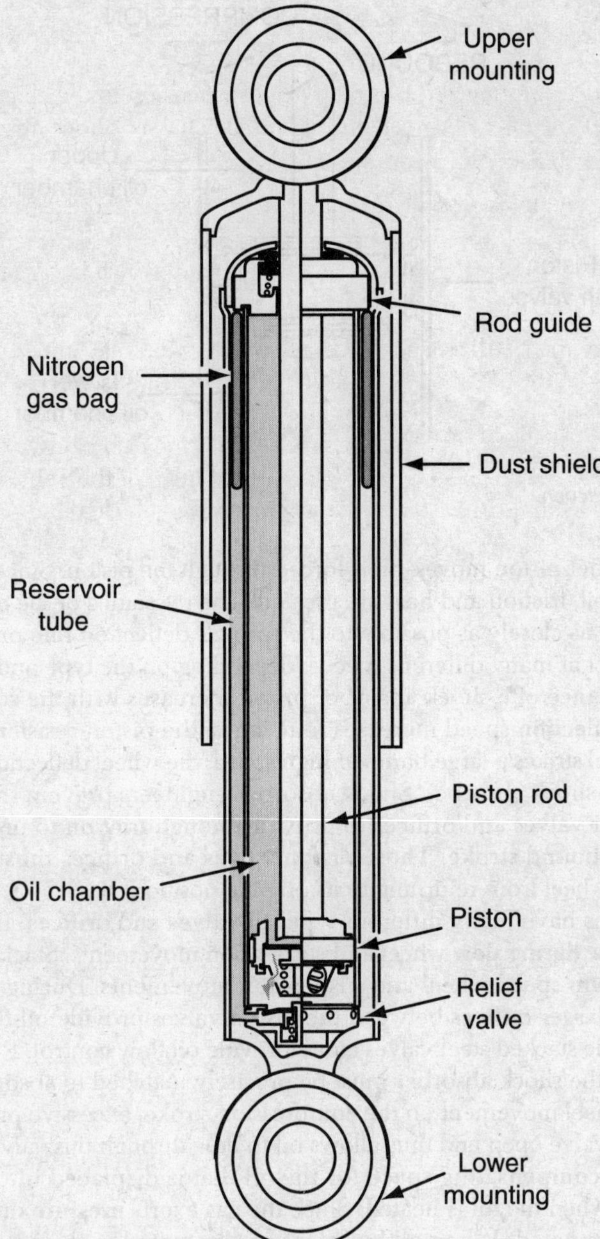

FIGURE 5-1 *Shock absorber filled with hydraulic oil and nitrogen gas.*

oil flow control and control the upward action of the wheel and suspension, which is referred to as a shock absorber compression stroke (Figure 5-2).

When the spring expands downward in rebound travel, the lower shock absorber unit is also forced downward. When this occurs, the piston moves upward in the lower tube unit, and hydraulic oil is forced through the piston valves from the upper oil chamber to the lower oil chamber. Since the valves restrict oil flow with precise control, the downward suspension and wheel movement is controlled.

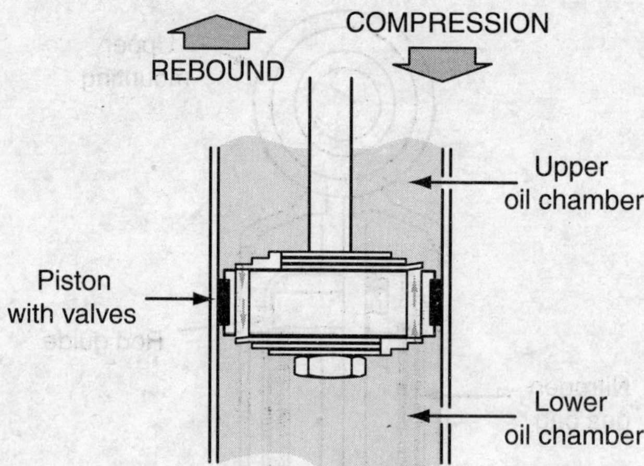

FIGURE 5-2 *Shock absorber action.*

When the shock absorber piston moves, oil is forced through the piston. Since the piston valves and orifices resist the flow of oil, friction and heat are created. The resistance of the oil moving through the piston must be calibrated as closely as possible to the spring's deflection rate or strength. Wheels and suspension systems deflect at many different speeds, depending on the type and size of bump and the vehicle speed. The resistance of a shock absorber piston increases with the square of its speed. For example, if the wheel deflection speed increases four times, the piston resistance is sixteen times as great. Therefore, if a wheel strikes a large bump at high speed, the wheel deflection and rebound can be effectively locked by the shock absorber. Shock absorber engineers prevent this action by precisely designing shock absorber valves and orifices to provide enough friction to prevent the spring from overextending on the rebound stroke. These piston valves and orifices must not create excessive friction, which slows the wheel from returning to its original position.

Shock absorber pistons have many different types of valves and orifices. In some pistons, small orifices control the oil flow during slow wheel and suspension movements. Stacked steel valves control the oil flow during medium speed wheel and suspension movements. During maximum wheel and suspension movements, larger orifices between the piston valves provide oil flow control. On other shock absorber pistons, the stacked steel valves alone provide oil flow control. Regardless of the piston orifice and valve design, the shock absorber must be precisely matched to absorb the spring's energy.

During fast upward wheel movement on the compression stroke, excessive pressure in the lower oil chamber forces the base valve open and thus allows oil to flow through this valve to the reservoir. The nitrogen gas provides a compensating space for the oil that is displaced into the reservoir on the compression stroke and when the oil is heated. Since the gas exerts pressure on the oil, cavitation, or foaming of the oil, is eliminated. When oil bubbles are eliminated in this way, the shock absorber provides continuous damping for wheel deflections as small as 0.078 in (2.0 mm). A rebound rubber is located on top of the piston. If the wheel drops downward into a hole, the shock absorber may become fully extended. Under this condition, the rebound rubber provides a cushioning action.

GAS-FILLED SHOCK ABSORBERS AND STRUTS

Gas-filled units are identified with a warning label. If a **gas-filled shock absorber** is removed and compressed to its shortest length, it should re-extend when it is released. Failure to re-extend indicates that shock absorber or strut replacement is necessary.

WARNING: New gas-filled shock absorbers are wired in the compressed position for shipping purposes. Exercise caution when cutting this wire strap because shock absorber extension may cause personal injury. After the upper shock absorber attaching bolt is installed, the wire strap can be cut to allow the unit to extend. Front gas-filled struts have an internal catch that holds them in the compressed position. This catch is released when the strut rod is held and the strut rotated 45° counterclockwise.

WARNING: Do not throw gas-filled shock absorbers or struts in the fire or apply excessive heat or flame to these units. These procedures may cause the unit to explode, resulting in personal injury.

CAUTION: When drilling worn-out shock absorbers or struts to relieve the gas pressure prior to disposal, drill the shock absorber only at the vehicle manufacturer's specified location.

HEAVY-DUTY SHOCK ABSORBER DESIGN

Some **heavy-duty shock absorbers** have a dividing piston in the lower oil chamber. The area below this piston is pressurized with nitrogen gas to 360 pounds per square inch (psi), or 2,482 kilopascals (kPa). Hydraulic oil is contained in the oil chamber above the dividing piston. The other main features of the heavy-duty shock absorber are:

1. High-quality seal for longer life.
2. Single tube design to prevent excessive heat buildup.
3. Rising rate valve to provide precise spring control under all conditions.

The operation of the heavy-duty shock absorber is similar to that of the conventional type (Figure 5-3).

SHOCK ABSORBER RATIOS

Most automotive shock absorbers are a double-acting-type that controls spring action during jounce and rebound wheel movements. The piston and valves in many shock absorbers are designed to provide more extension control than compression control. An average shock absorber may have 70 percent of the total control on the extension cycle, and thus 30 percent of the total control is on the compression cycle. Shock absorbers usually have this type of design because they must control the heavier sprung body weight on the extension cycle. The lighter unsprung axle, wheel, and tire weight are controlled by the shock absorber on the compression cycle. A shock absorber with this type of design is referred to as a 70/30 type. **Shock absorber ratios** vary from 50/50 to 80/20.

A shock absorber is mounted between the rear axle and the chassis on a front-wheel-drive car (Figure 5-4). Mounting bolts extend through hangers on the rear axle and chassis. These bolts also pass through the isolating bushings on each of the shock absorbers. The isolating bushings are very important for preventing vibration and noise. Front shock absorbers may be mounted in a similar way between the lower control arms and the chassis.

STRUT DESIGN, FRONT SUSPENSION

A strut-type front suspension is used on most front-wheel-drive cars and some rear-wheel-drive cars. Internal strut design is very similar to shock absorber design, and **struts** perform the same

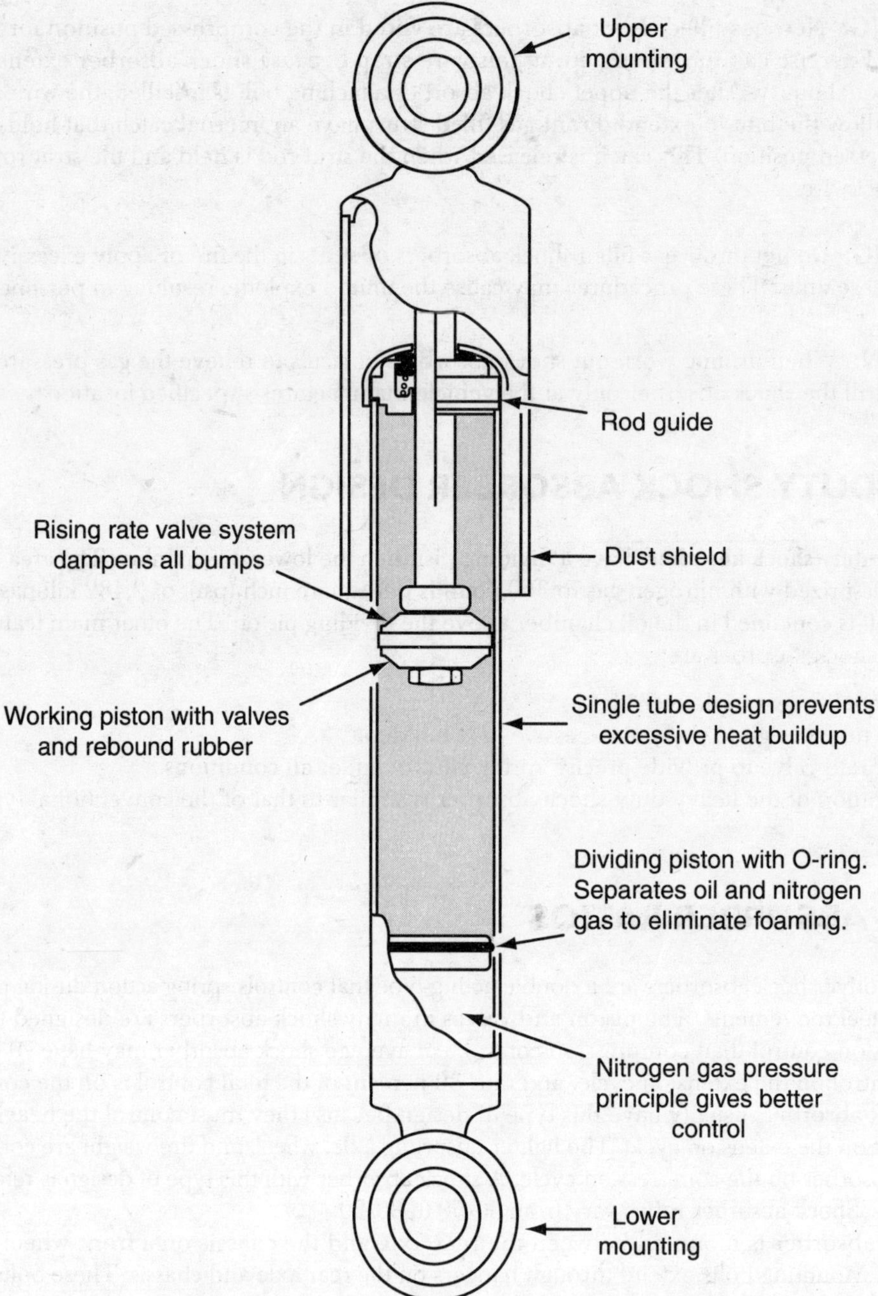

FIGURE 5-3 *Heavy-duty shock absorber.*

functions as shock absorbers. Some struts have a replaceable cartridge. In many strut-type suspension systems, the coil spring is mounted on the strut. The coil spring is largely responsible for proper curb riding height. A weak or broken coil spring reduces curb riding height and provides harsh riding. The lower end of the front suspension strut is bolted to the steering knuckle (Figure 5-5). An **upper strut mount** is attached to the strut, and this mount is bolted into the chassis strut tower. A lower spring seat is part of the strut assembly, and a lower insulator is

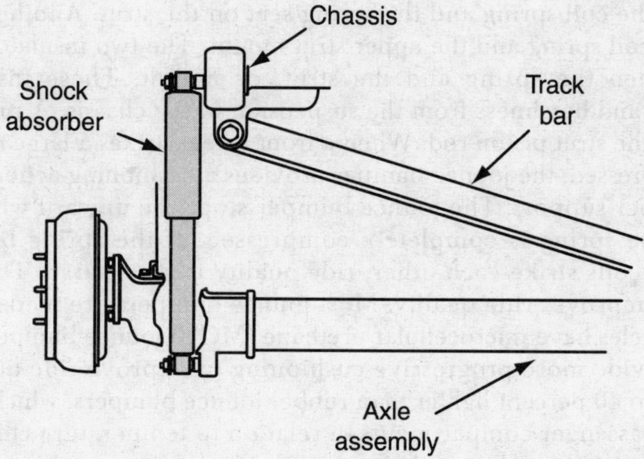

FIGURE 5-4 *Rear shock absorber mounting on a front-wheel-drive car.*

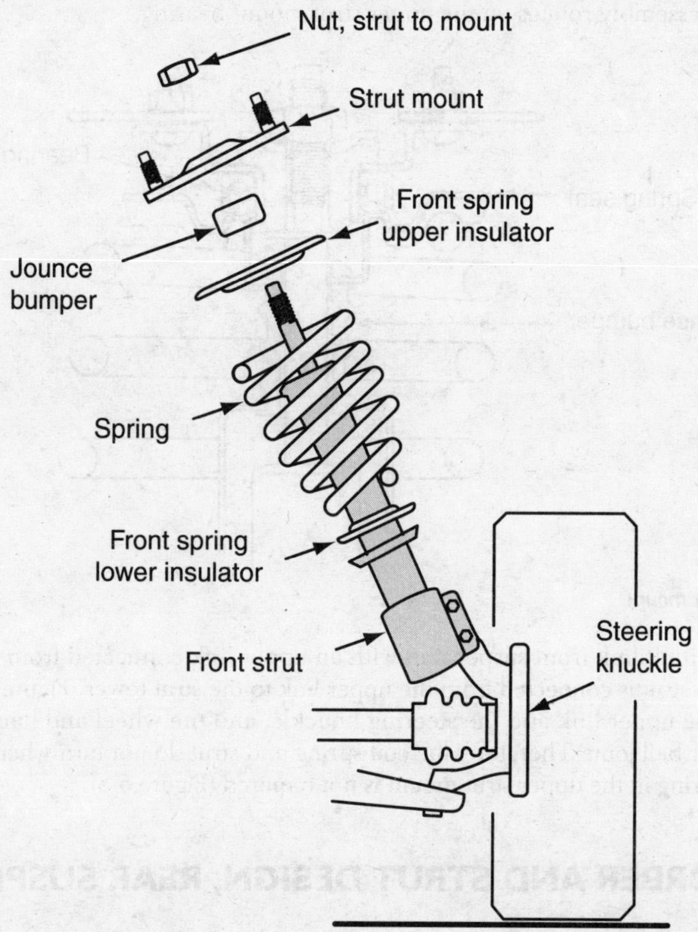

FIGURE 5-5 *Front strut assembly.*

positioned between the coil spring and the spring seat on the strut. Another **spring insulator** is located between the coil spring and the upper strut mount. The two insulators prevent metal-to-metal contact between the spring and the strut, or mount. These insulators reduce the transmission of noise and harshness from the suspension to the chassis. A rubber spring bumper is positioned around the strut piston rod. When a front wheel strikes a large road irregularity and the strut is fully compressed, the jounce bumper provides a cushioning action between the top of the strut and the upper support. The jounce bumper stops the upward wheel and suspension movement before the spring is completely compressed. If the spring becomes completely compressed and the coils strike each other, ride quality is very harsh. Therefore, the jounce bumper in the strut improves ride quality. Most jounce bumpers are made from butyl rubber. Some late model vehicles have microcellular urethane (MCU) jounce bumpers, which are lighter than rubber and provide more progressive cushioning to improve ride quality. MCU jounce bumpers are also 20 to 40 percent lighter than rubber jounce bumpers, which reduces road noise transmission to the passenger compartment. In relation to temperature changes, MCU jounce bumpers remain more stable and provide improved ride quality regardless of the temperature. The upper strut mount contains a bearing, upper spring seat, and jounce bumper (Figure 5-6).

When the front wheels are turned, the front strut and coil spring rotate with the steering knuckle. The strut-and-spring assembly rotates on the upper strut mount bearing.

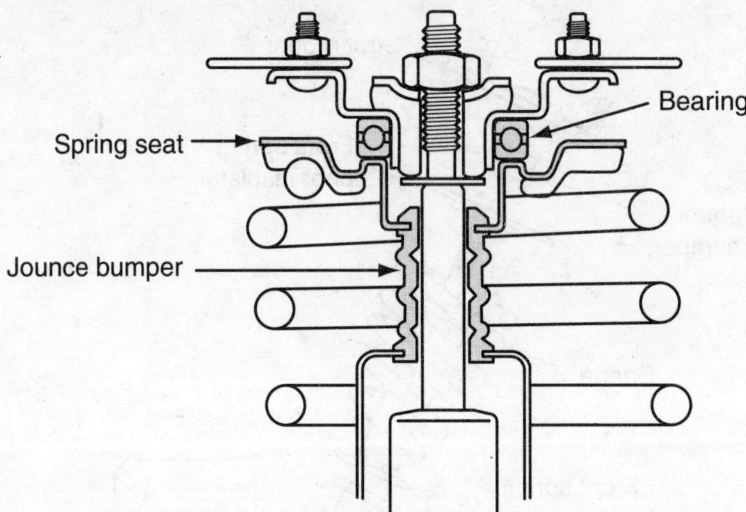

FIGURE 5-6 *Upper strut mount.*

Some cars have a multilink front suspension with an upper link connected from the chassis to the steering knuckle. The strut is connected from the upper link to the strut tower (Figure 5-7). A bearing is mounted between the upper link and the steering knuckle, and the wheel and knuckle turn on this bearing and the lower ball joint. Therefore, the coil spring and strut do not turn when the front wheels are turned, and a bearing in the upper strut mount is not required (Figure 5-8).

SHOCK ABSORBER AND STRUT DESIGN, REAR SUSPENSION

In some rear suspension systems, the lower end of the strut is bolted to the spindle, and the top of the strut is connected through a strut mount to the chassis. The rear coil springs are mounted separately from the struts. These springs are mounted between the lower control arms and the chassis (Figure 5-9).

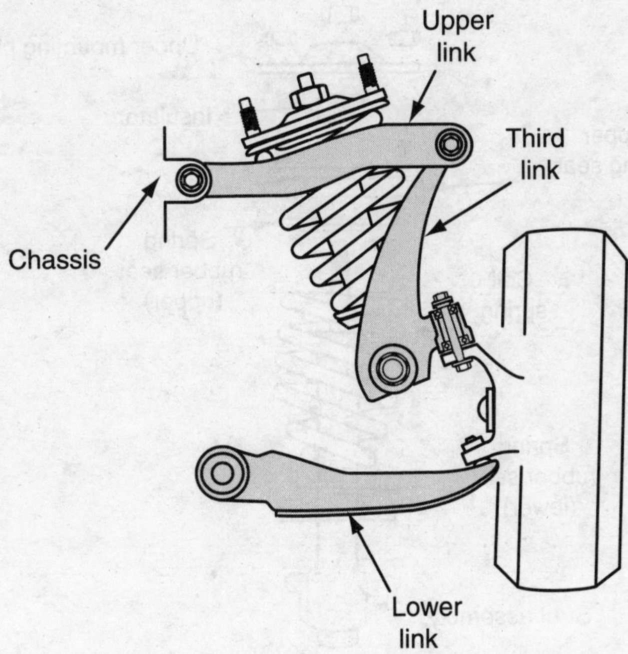

FIGURE 5-7 *Multilink front suspension with strut connected between the upper link and the strut tower.*

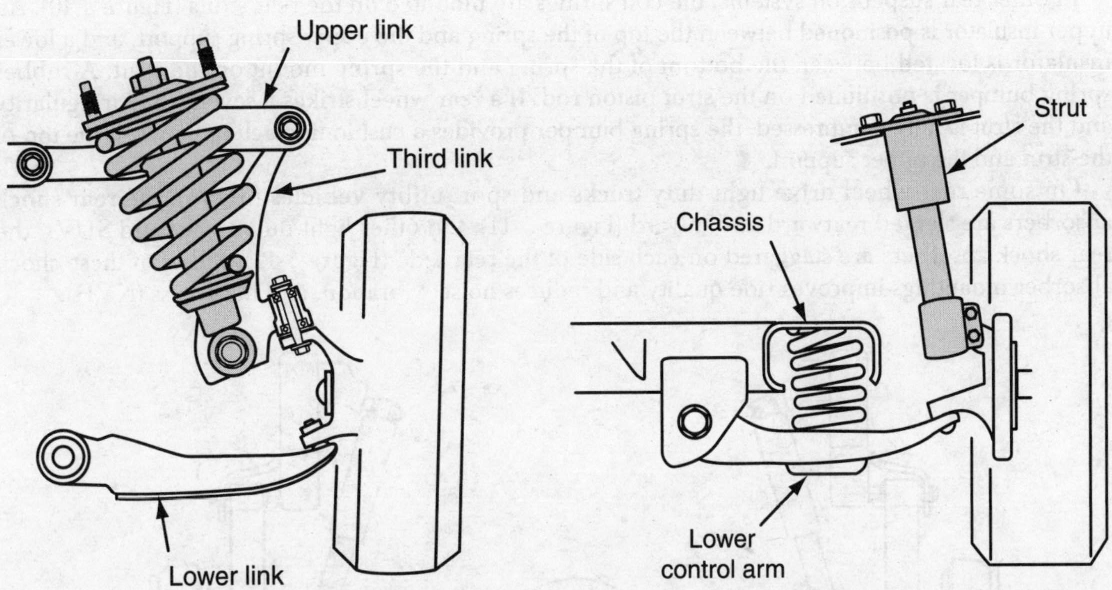

FIGURE 5-8 *Multilink front suspension with knuckle and wheel pivots at the upper link bearing and lower ball joint, and a nonrotating upper strut mount.*

FIGURE 5-9 *Rear suspension system with coil springs mounted separately from the struts.*

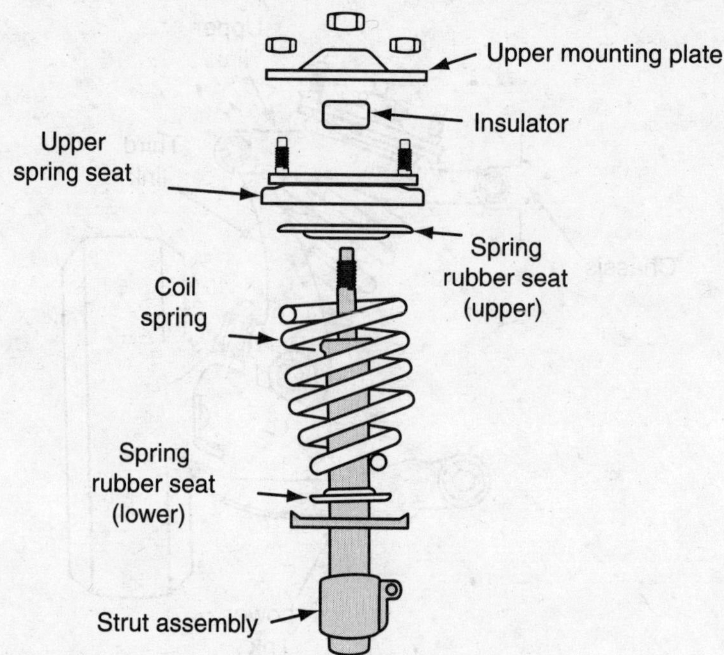

FIGURE 5-10 *Rear suspension system with coil springs mounted on the struts.*

In other rear suspension systems, the coil springs are mounted on the rear struts (Figure 5-10). An upper insulator is positioned between the top of the spring and the upper spring support, and a lower insulator is located between the bottom of the spring and the spring mount on the strut. A rubber spring bumper is positioned on the strut piston rod. If a rear wheel strikes a severe road irregularity and the strut is fully compressed, the spring bumper provides a cushioning action between the top of the strut and the upper support.

On some rear-wheel-drive light-duty trucks and sport utility vehicles (SUVs), the rear shock absorbers are slanted rearward and inward (Figure 5-11). On other light-duty trucks and SUVs, the rear shock absorbers are staggered on each side of the rear axle (Figure 5-12). Either of these shock absorber mountings improves ride quality and reduces noise, vibration, and harshness (NVH).

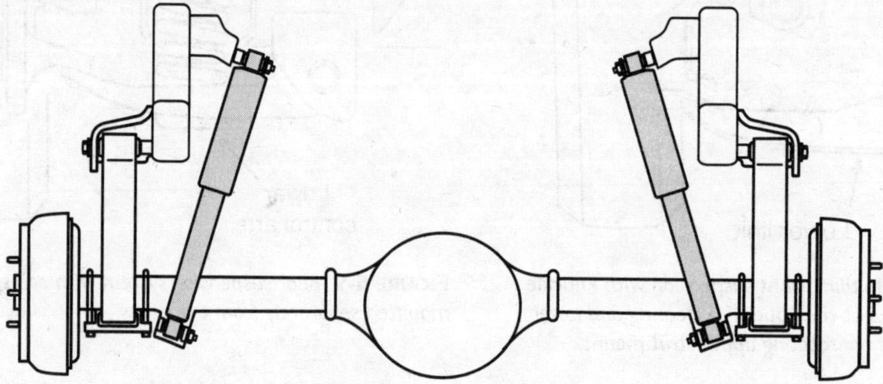

FIGURE 5-11 *Rear shock absorber mounting, sport utility vehicle (SUV).*

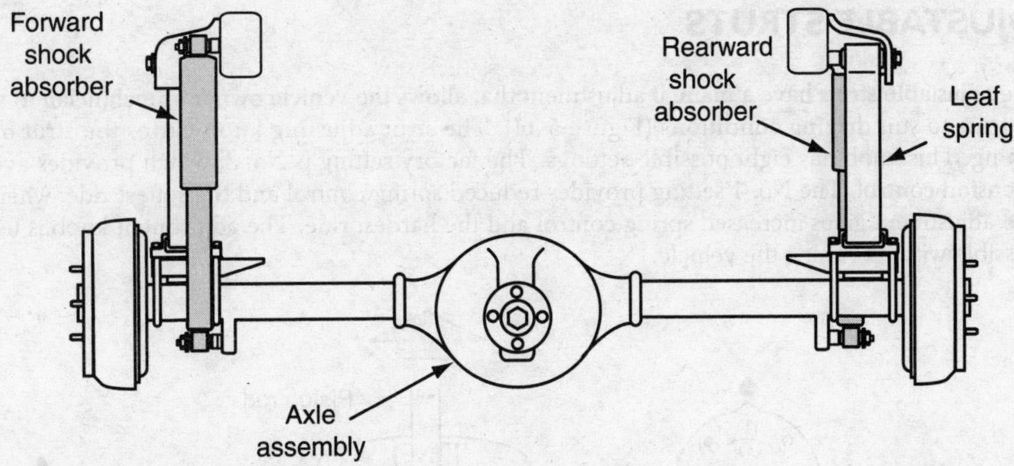

FIGURE 5-12 *Shock absorbers staggered on each side of the rear axle.*

TRAVEL-SENSITIVE STRUT

Some **travel-sensitive struts** contain narrow longitudinal grooves in the lower oil chamber (Figure 5-13). These grooves are parallel to the piston orifices, and some oil flows through the grooves as well as the orifices. Under normal driving and road conditions, the orifices and grooves are calibrated to provide normal spring damping and control. If the front wheel drops suddenly, such as when it strikes a large hole, the piston moves into the narrow portion of the oil chamber. Under this condition, all the oil must flow through the piston orifices, which greatly increases the strut's resistance to movement and the suspension damping action. This strut action prevents harsh impacts against the internal strut rebound rubber.

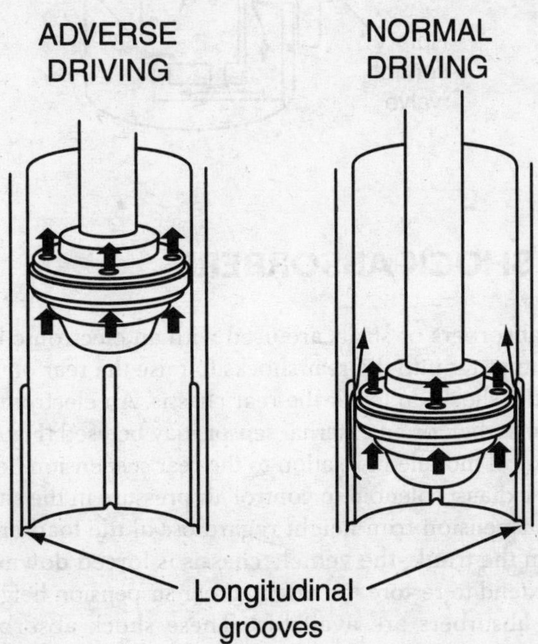

FIGURE 5-13 *Travel-sensitive strut.*

ADJUSTABLE STRUTS

Some **adjustable struts** have a manual adjustment that allows the vehicle owner or technician to adjust the struts to suit driving conditions (Figure 5-14). The strut adjusting knob varies the strut orifice opening. This knob has eight possible settings. The factory setting is No. 3, which provides average suspension control. The No. 1 setting provides reduced spring control and the softest ride, whereas a No. 8 adjustment gives increased spring control and the hardest ride. The adjustment knob is usually accessible without raising the vehicle.

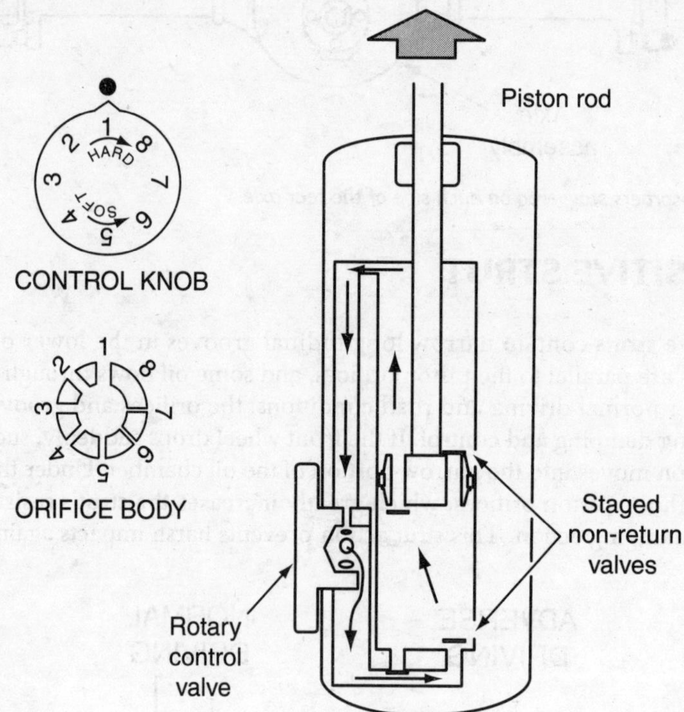

FIGURE 5-14 *Adjustable strut.*

LOAD-LEVELING SHOCK ABSORBERS

Load-leveling rear shock absorbers or struts are used with an electronic height control system. An onboard air compressor pumps air into the rear shocks to raise the rear of the vehicle, and an electric solenoid releases air from the shocks to lower the rear chassis. An electromagnetic height sensor may be contained in the shock absorber, or an external sensor may be used (Figure 5-15). This sensor sends a signal to an electronic control module in relation to the rear suspension height. The module controls the air compressor and the exhaust solenoid to control air pressure in the shock absorbers. This action maintains a specific rear suspension trim height regardless of the load on the rear suspension. If a heavy package is placed in the trunk, the vehicle chassis is forced downward. However, the **load-leveling shock absorbers** extend to restore the original rear suspension height.

Aftermarket air shock absorbers are available. These shock absorbers contain an air valve connection. A shop air hose may be used to supply the desired pressure in these air shock absorbers.

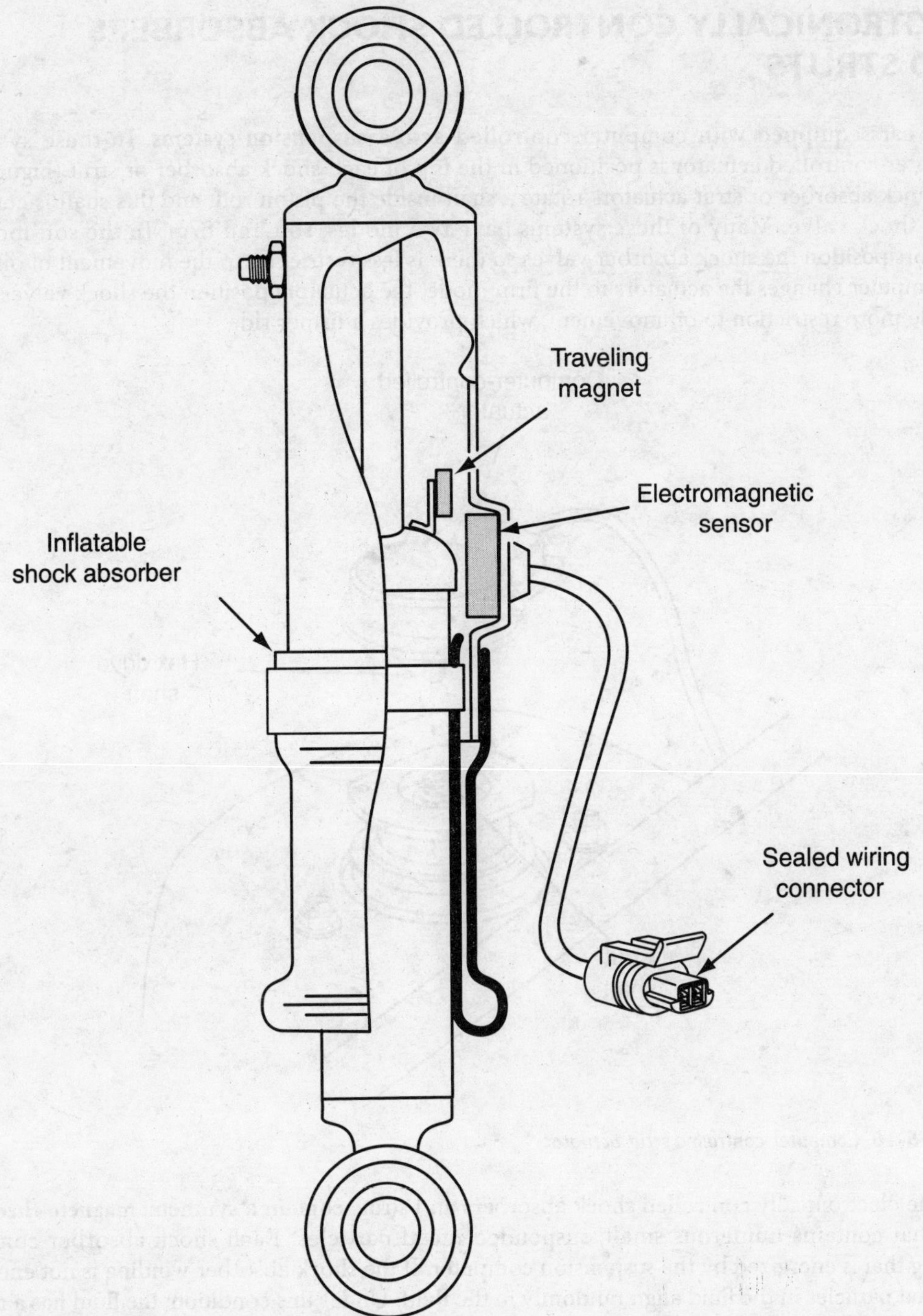

FIGURE 5-15 *Load-leveling strut.*

Aftermarket spring-assisted shock absorbers are also available. These are conventional shock absorbers with a small coil spring mounted over them. Upper and lower spring seats are attached near the top and bottom of these shock absorbers to support and retain the spring. The coil springs on the shock absorbers help the springs in the suspension system support the vehicle weight.

ELECTRONICALLY CONTROLLED SHOCK ABSORBERS AND STRUTS

Many cars equipped with computer-controlled **active suspension systems.** In these systems, a computer-controlled actuator is positioned in the top of each shock absorber or strut (Figure 5-16). The shock absorber or strut actuators rotate a shaft inside the piston rod, and this shaft is connected to the shock valve. Many of these systems have two modes, soft and firm. In the soft mode, the actuators position the shock absorber valves so there is less restriction to the movement of oil. When the computer changes the actuators to the firm mode, the actuators position the shock valves so they provide more restriction to oil movement, which provides a firmer ride.

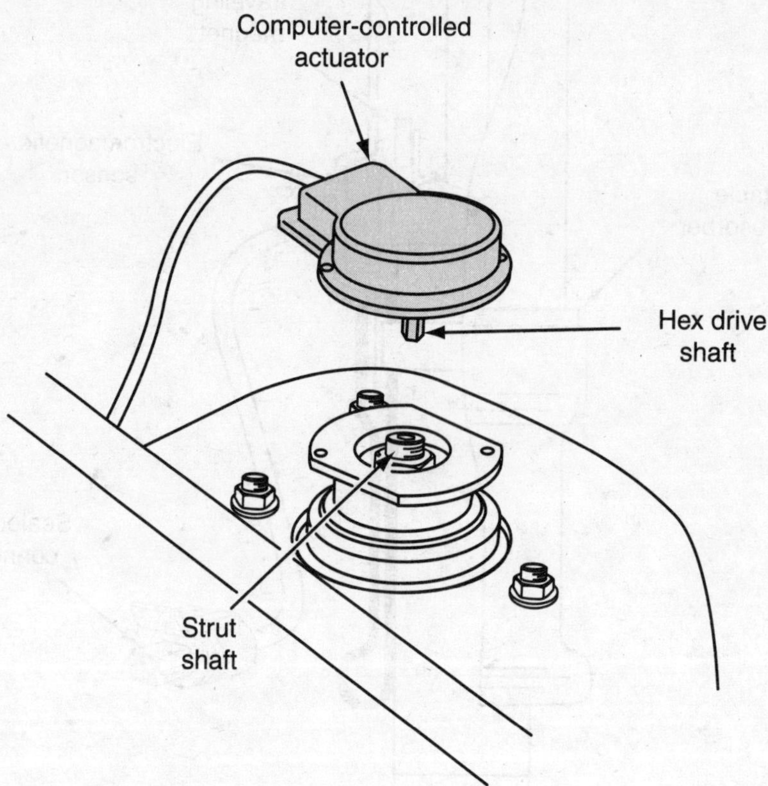

FIGURE 5-16 *Computer-controlled strut actuator.*

Some electronically controlled shock absorbers and struts contain a synthetic **magneto-rheological fluid** that contains numerous small, suspended metal particles. Each shock absorber contains a winding that is energized by the suspension computer. If the shock absorber winding is not energized, the metal particles in the fluid align randomly in the fluid. Under this condition, the fluid has a mineral oil–like consistency and the fluid moves easily through the shock absorber orifices. If the suspension computer energizes a shock absorber winding, the metal particles in the fluid are aligned into fibrous structures. When this occurs, the fluid has a jelly-like consistency for a firm ride (Figure 5-17). The computer can change the shock absorber damping characteristics in 1 millisecond (ms) and can also supply a varying amount of current through the shock absorber windings to provide a wide variety of shock absorber damping characteristics.

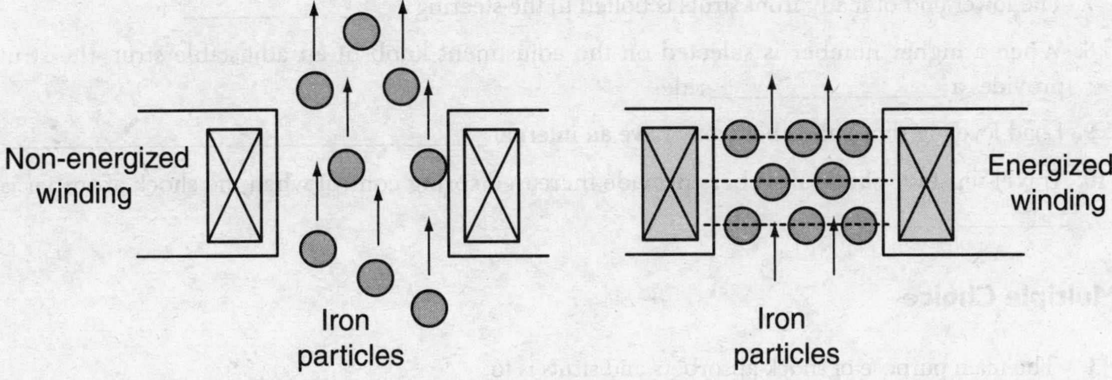

FIGURE 5-17 *Magneto-rheological fluid action in a strut or shock absorber.*

REVIEW QUESTIONS

Short Answer Essays

1. Describe spring action during jounce and rebound travel.
2. Describe uncontrolled spring action without a shock absorber.
3. Explain shock absorber operation.
4. Describe the vehicle safety hazards created by worn-out shock absorbers.
5. Explain shock absorber ratio.
6. Explain the purpose of the nitrogen gas charge in shock absorbers and struts.
7. Explain the differences between heavy-duty and conventional shock absorbers.
8. Identify the purposes of an upper strut mount.
9. Explain the purpose of strut and spring insulators.
10. Describe the purpose of the rubber spring bumper on a strut piston rod.

Fill-in-the-Blanks

1. Shock absorbers control spring action and prevent excessive spring ____________.
2. Shock absorber design is matched to the ________________ rate of the spring.
3. The valves in most shock absorbers are designed to vary the oil flow through the valve in relation to the amount of ________________ movement.
4. The nitrogen gas charge in a shock absorber prevents oil ________________ and ________________.
5. The single tube design in a heavy-duty shock absorber prevents excessive ________________ ________________.
6. A shock absorber with a 70/30 ratio provides more control on the ________________ cycle.

7. The lower end of many front struts is bolted to the steering ________________.
8. When a higher number is selected on the adjustment knob of an adjustable strut, the strut provides a ________________ ride.
9. Load-leveling shock absorbers may have an internal ________________ ________________.
10. Travel-sensitive shock absorbers provide increased spring control when the shock absorber is ________________.

Multiple Choice

1. The main purpose of shock absorbers and struts is to:
   A. Control spring action.
   B. Prevent fore-and-aft wheel movement.
   C. Reduce lateral wheel movement.
   D. Prevent wheel shimmy.

2. All of these statements about shock absorber design and operation are true EXCEPT:
   A. The oil flow through the orifices and valves is matched to the spring's strength and deflection rate.
   B. A typical shock absorber may have 70 percent of the total control on the extension cycle.
   C. During jounce wheel travel the piston moves upward in the shock absorber lower tube unit.
   D. A nitrogen gas charge in a shock absorber prevents oil foaming.

3. Compared to a conventional shock absorber, a heavy-duty shock absorber has:
   A. Triple layers of steel in the lower tube unit.
   B. Higher viscosity oil.
   C. A larger diameter piston rod.
   D. A high-quality seal for longer life.

4. All of these statements about gas-filled shock absorbers are true EXCEPT:
   A. A hydrogen gas charge is used in most shock absorbers and struts.
   B. Gas-filled shock absorbers and struts have an identification label.
   C. New gas-filled shock absorbers are wired in the compressed position.
   D. A gas-filled shock absorber provides continuous damping action with very little wheel movement.

5. The magneto-rheological fluid used in some shock absorbers and struts contains:
   A. Transmission fluid.
   B. Small, suspended metal particles.
   C. Anti-foaming agents.
   D. A dye for lead detection purposes.

6. During normal strut operation:
   A. Downward wheel movement is called wheel jounce.
   B. The strut prevents excessive wheel oscillations.
   C. When the wheel moves upward the strut piston also moves upward.
   D. The strut prevents wheel shimmy.

7. Travel-sensitive struts:
   A. Have an adjustment on the outside of the strut.
   B. Provide more resistance to oil movement when compressed.
   C. Provide more resistance to oil movement when driving on a smooth road surface.
   D. Bypass some of the oil past the piston when compressed.

8. Adjustable struts:
   A. May be adjusted with a control knob in the instrument panel.
   B. Provide five different settings.
   C. Provide softest ride with a No. 1 setting.
   D. Rotate the upper part of the strut to provide adjustable ride quality.

9. Load-leveling shock absorber systems:
   A. May be pressurized from an onboard air pressure tank.
   B. May have a suspension height sensor.
   C. Maintain lower rear suspension height when driving on smooth road surfaces.
   D. Prevent suspension bottoming on rough road surfaces.

10. Electronically controlled shock absorbers and struts:
    A. Contain an electronically controlled actuator in the top of each strut.
    B. Usually have 12 different modes of strut operation from soft to very firm.
    C. Have an electronically controlled actuator that rotates the strut piston rod.
    D. Have an actuator that positions the strut valves to provide more oil restriction in the soft mode.

FRONT SUSPENSION SYSTEMS

6

Upon completion and review of this chapter, you should be able to:

- Explain the causes of coil spring failure.
- Describe the design and spring rate of a linear-rate coil spring.
- Explain the difference between a regular-duty coil spring and a heavy-duty coil spring.
- Describe the functions of three different types of coils in a variable-rate coil spring.
- Explain basic torsion bar action as a front wheel strikes a road irregularity.
- Explain how friction and noise problems are reduced in a multiple-leaf spring.
- List the advantages of a front suspension system with ball joints compared to earlier I-beam front suspension systems.
- Describe two types of load-carrying ball joints, and explain the location of the control arm in each type.
- Explain how you would recognize a worn ball joint from a visual inspection of the ball joint wear indicator.
- Describe the mounting location and purpose of a stabilizer bar.
- Explain the purpose of a strut rod.

- List the two steering knuckle pivot points in a MacPherson strut front suspension system.
- Explain the advantage of a short-and-long arm front suspension system compared with a suspension system with equal-length upper and lower control arms.
- Describe two methods of attaching the spindles to the I-beams in a twin I-beam front suspension.
- Explain the effect of sagged front springs on caster angle and directional stability.
- Explain the effect of sagged front springs on camber angle.

INTRODUCTION

The front and rear suspension systems must perform several extremely important functions to maintain vehicle safety and owner satisfaction. The suspension system must supply steering control for the driver under all road conditions. Vehicle owners expect the suspension system to provide a comfortable ride. The suspension, together with the frame, must maintain proper vehicle tracking and directional stability. Another important purpose of the suspension system is to provide proper wheel alignment and minimize tire wear.

The impact of the front tires striking road irregularities must be absorbed and dissipated by the front suspension system. These impacts are distributed throughout the suspension, and this action isolates the vehicle passengers from road shock. The vehicle's ride characteristics are determined by the amount of impact energy that the suspension can absorb and by the rate at which the suspension dissipates these tire impacts. Ride characteristics are designed into the suspension system, and these characteristics are not adjustable. For example, the front suspension may be designed to provide a very soft ride in which all the tire impacts are absorbed and dissipated quickly by the suspension system. This type of suspension system provides a very comfortable ride, but it also allows excessive body lean during cornering, which reduces high-speed cornering and handling capabilities. Such vehicles as sports cars and sport utility vehicles (SUVs) are usually designed with a suspension system that provides a firm ride and absorbs and dissipates tire impacts more slowly. Although high-speed cornering and handling capabilities are improved, this type of suspension may transfer some road shock to the passenger compartment.

When the vehicle is driven over road irregularities, the front suspension system must allow the front wheels to move vertically while maintaining the tire's proper horizontal position in relation to the road surface. To provide this wheel action, the steering knuckle must be mounted between the upper and lower control arms on short-and-long arm (SLA) suspension systems or between the lower control arm and the lower end of the strut on MacPherson strut suspension systems. The upper and lower control arms must be pivoted on the inner ends; the steering knuckle pivots on the ball joints in SLA suspensions or on the lower ball joint and upper strut mount on MacPherson strut suspensions.

Coil springs absorb much of the shock from tire impacts with the road surface. When a front wheel strikes a road irregularity and moves upward, the coil spring compresses and absorbs energy during this movement. The coil spring immediately dissipates this energy as the spring moves back to its original state. Shock absorbers are installed in the front suspension system to dampen the oscillations of the coil springs.

A stabilizer bar is mounted on rubber insulating bushings and bolted to the chassis. The outer ends of the stabilizer bar are attached through links to the lower control arms. The stabilizer bar controls the amount of independent lower control arm movement. When one front wheel strikes a road irregularity and moves upward, the stabilizer bar transfers part of the lower control arm movement to the opposite lower control arm, which reduces and stabilizes body roll. Therefore, the stabilizer bar helps to define the suspension characteristics related to body roll.

All suspension components, including the frame and chassis, are designed or "tuned" to provide the ride and handling qualities that the manufacturer believes the average driver will desire. For example, the late model Explorer Sport Trac frame has been stiffened 40 percent more than the Explorer frame. To achieve this increased stiffness, the frame side rails are thicker than the ones on the Explorer, and a new tubular crossmember has been added to the frame. **Gussets** have also been welded into the corners where the crossmembers meet the side rails. This frame design is matched to the torsion bar suspension to provide improved vehicle agility on and off the road.

SUSPENSION SYSTEM COMPONENTS

Coil Springs

The coil spring is the most commonly used spring for front and rear suspension systems. Coil springs are actually a coiled-spring steel bar. When a vehicle wheel strikes a road irregularity, the coil spring compresses to absorb shock, and then recoils back to its original installed height. Many coil springs contain a steel alloy that contains different types of steel mixed with other elements such as silicon or chromium. Coil springs may be manufactured by a cold or hot coiling process. The hot coiling process includes procedures for tempering and hardening the steel alloy. Coil springs are designed to carry heavy loads, but they must be light in weight. Many coil springs have a vinyl coating, which increases corrosion resistance and reduces noise.

Coil spring failures may be caused by these conditions:

1. Constant overloading
2. Continual jounce and rebound action
3. Metal fatigue
4. A crack or nick on the surface layer or coating

Coil springs do not have much ability to resist lateral movement. However, when coil springs are used on the drive wheels, the suspension usually has special bars to prevent lateral movement.

Linear-Rate Coil Springs. Coil springs are classified into two general categories: linear rate and variable rate. **Linear-rate coil springs** have equal spacing between the coils and one basic shape with a consistent wire diameter. When the load is increased on a linear-rate spring, the spring compresses and the coils twist or deflect. As the load is removed from the spring, the coils unwind, or flex, back to their original position. The spring rate is the load required to deflect the spring 1 inch. Linear-rate coil springs have a constant spring rate, regardless of the load. For example, if 200 pounds deflect the spring 1 inch, 400 pounds deflect the spring 2 inches. The spring rate on linear springs is usually calculated between 20 and 60 percent of the total spring deflection.

Variable-Rate Coil Springs. Variable-rate coil springs have a variety of wire sizes and shapes. The most common variable-rate coil springs have a consistent wire diameter with a cylindrical shape and unequally spaced coils (Figure 6-1).

The **inactive coils** at the end of the spring introduce force into the spring when the wheel strikes a road irregularity. When the **transitional coils** are compressed to their point of maximum load-carrying capacity, these coils become inactive. The **active coils** operate during the complete range of

FIGURE 6-1 *Variable rate coil springs have consistent wire diameter and unequally spaced coils.*

spring loading. When a stationary load is applied to a variable-rate coil spring, the inactive coils theoretically support the load. If the load is increased, the transitional coils support the load until they reach maximum load-carrying capacity, and the active coils carry the remaining overload. This spring action provides automatic load adjustment while maintaining vehicle height.

Some variable-rate coil springs have a tapered wire in which the active coils have the larger diameter, and the inactive coils have the smaller diameter. Other variable-rate spring designs include truncated cone, double cone, and barrel shape. A variable-rate spring does not have a standard spring rate. This type of spring has an average spring rate based on the load at a predetermined spring deflection. It is impossible to compare variable spring rates and linear spring rates because of this difference in spring rates. Variable-rate coil springs usually have more load-carrying capacity than linear-rate springs in the same application.

Light-Weight Coil Springs

A few sports cars are presently equipped with titanium coil springs. This type of coil spring reduces the weight on the front springs by 39 percent and 28 percent on the rear springs compared to steel coil springs. Decreasing the weight of the coil springs reduces the **unsprung weight** and improves ride control. The unsprung vehicle weight tends to force the wheel downward during rebound wheel travel. Higher unsprung weight drives the wheel downward with greater force and increases the impact force between the tire and the road surface, resulting in a harsh ride. To compensate for the high unsprung weight, the shock absorber damping rate must be increased. This suspension design reduces ride quality. When the unsprung weight is reduced, the wheel is forced downward with less force, reducing the shock absorber damping rate and improving ride quality.

Heavy-Duty Coil Springs. **Heavy-duty coil springs** are designed to carry 3 to 5 percent greater loads than regular-duty coil springs. The wire diameter may be up to 0.100 inch greater in a heavy-duty spring than in a regular-duty coil spring. This larger-diameter wire increases the load-carrying capacity of the spring. The free height of a heavy-duty coil spring is shorter than a regular-duty coil spring for the same application (Figure 6-2).

Selecting Replacement Springs. When replacement coil springs are required, the technician must select the correct spring. The original part number is usually on a tag wrapped around one of the coils. However, this tag may have fallen off if the spring has been in service for very long. Some aftermarket suppliers stamp the part number on the end of the coil spring. If the original part number is available, the replacement springs may be ordered with the same part number. Most vehicle manufacturers recommend that both front or rear springs be replaced at the same time. The replacement springs must have the same type of ends as the springs in the vehicle. Coil spring ends may be square tapered, square untapered, or tangential (Figure 6-3).

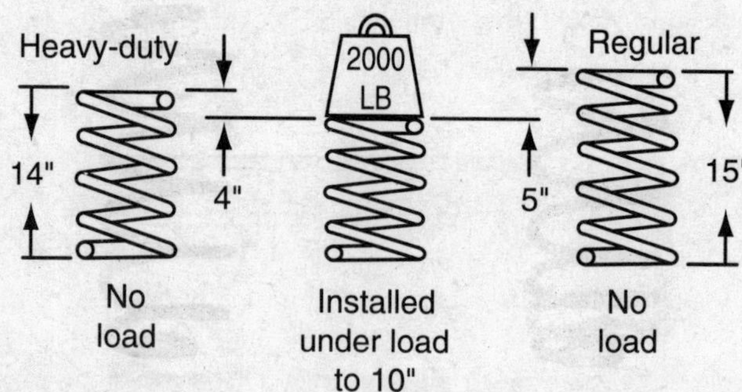

FIGURE 6-2 *Comparison of heavy-duty and regular-duty coil springs.*

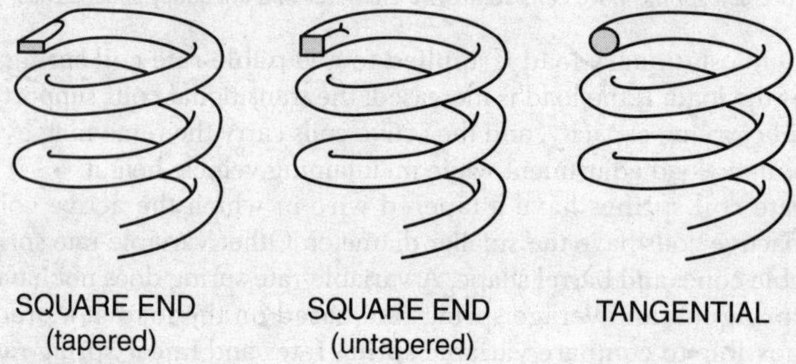

FIGURE 6-3 *Types of coil spring ends.*

Full-wire open-end springs have the ends cut straight off, and sometimes these ends are flattened, squared, or ground to a D-shape. **Taper-wire closed-end springs** are ground to a taper and wound to ensure squareness. **Pigtail spring ends** are wound to a smaller diameter. Springs are generally listed for front or rear suspensions.

Regular-duty coil springs are a close replacement for the original spring in the vehicle, and these springs may replace several different original equipment (OE) springs in the same vehicle. Linear-rate coil springs are usually found in regular-duty, heavy-duty, and sport suspension packages. Heavy-duty coil springs are required when the vehicle is carrying a continuous heavy load, such as trailer towing.

Variable-rate coil springs are generally used when automatic load leveling is required under increased loads. Variable-rate coil springs maintain the correct vehicle height under various loads and provide increased load-carrying capacity compared to heavy-duty coil springs. The technician must select the correct spring to meet the requirements of the vehicle and load conditions.

WARNING: A very large amount of energy is stored in a compressed coil spring. Always follow the spring service procedures in the vehicle manufacturer's service manual to avoid personal injury.

WARNING: Never disconnect a suspension component that quickly releases the tension on a compressed coil spring. This action may cause personal injury.

Torsion Bars

In some front suspension systems, torsion bars replace the coil springs. During wheel jounce, the torsion bar twists. During wheel rebound, the torsion bar unwinds back to its original position. A torsion bar may be thought of as a straight, flattened coil spring. One end of the heat-treated alloy steel torsion bar is attached to the vehicle frame, and the opposite end is connected to the lower control arm. Some light-duty trucks and sport utility vehicles (SUVs) are presently equipped with longitudinal torsion bars in the front suspension (Figure 6-4). Transversely mounted torsion bars were used in some front suspensions on older cars.

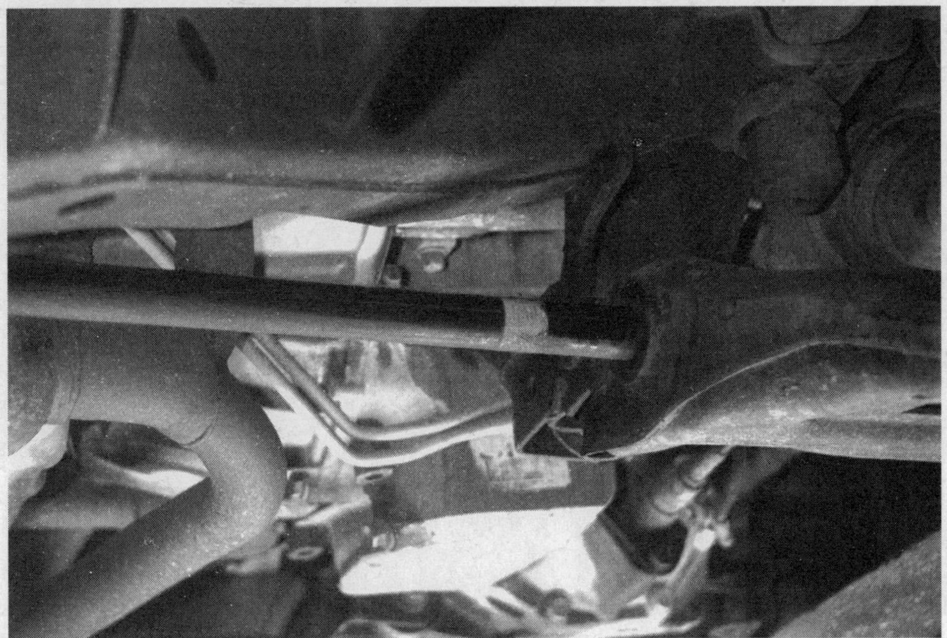

FIGURE 6-4 *Longitudinal torsion bar.*

Because the lower control arm moves up and down as the wheel strikes road irregularities, this control arm action twists the torsion bar. The bar's natural resistance to twisting causes it to return to its original position. During the manufacturing process, torsion bars are prestressed to provide fatigue strength. These bars are directional. Torsion bars are marked right or left, and they must be installed on the appropriate side of the vehicle. Left and right on a vehicle is always viewed from the driver's seat.

A torsion bar is capable of storing a higher maximum energy compared with a loaded coil or leaf spring. Shorter, thicker torsion bars have increased load-carrying capacity compared with longer, thinner bars. Since torsion bars require less space compared with coil or leaf springs, they are usually found on front suspensions. However, a few rear suspensions have torsion bars. Torsion bars have a riding height adjustment screw at the end where they are attached to the frame.

Multiple-Leaf Springs

Leaf springs may be multiple-leaf or mono-leaf. **Multiple-leaf springs** have a series of flat steel leaves of varying lengths that are clamped together. A center bolt extends through all the leaves to maintain the leaf position in the spring. The upper leaf is called the main leaf, and this leaf has an eye on each end. An insulating bushing is pressed into each main leaf eye. The front bushing is attached to the frame, and the rear bushing is connected through a shackle to the frame. The shackle provides fore-and-aft movement as the spring compresses (Figure 6-5).

The main leaf is the longest leaf in the spring, and the other leaves get progressively shorter. Each spring leaf is curved in the manufacturing process. If this curve were doubled, it would form an ellipse. Therefore, leaf springs are referred to as semielliptical or quarter elliptical. Most leaf springs are semielliptical. The ellipse designation refers to how much of the ellipse the spring actually describes.

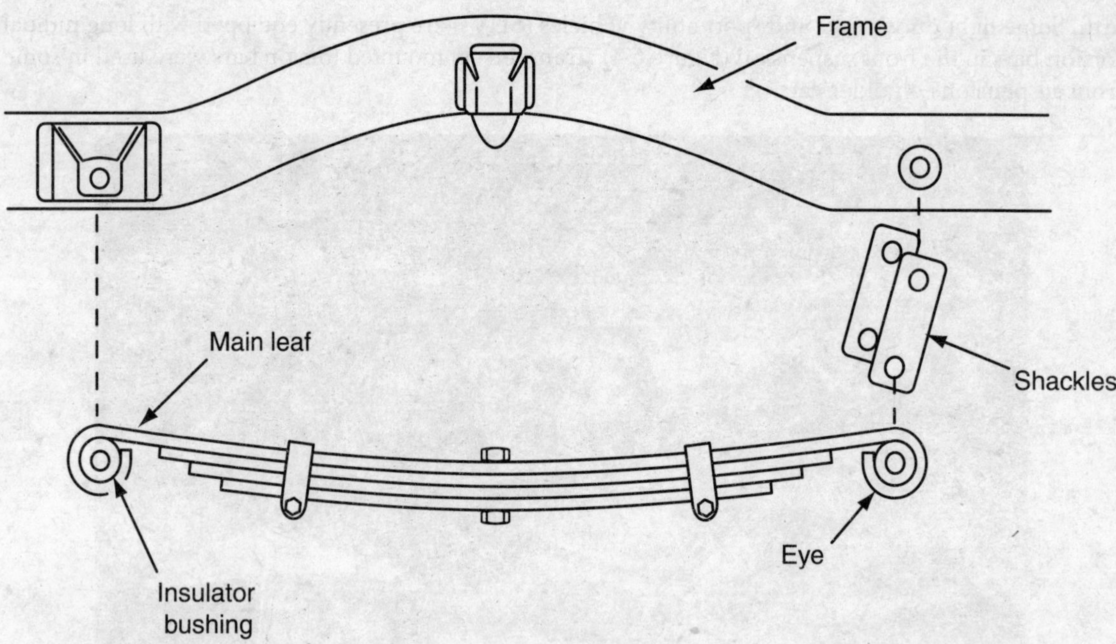

FIGURE 6-5 *Leaf spring design.*

As a leaf spring compresses, it becomes progressively stiffer. When a leaf spring is compressed, the length of the leaves changes, and the leaves slide on each other. This sliding action could be a source of noise and friction. These noise and friction problems are reduced by interleaves, or spacers, made from zinc and plastic placed between the steel leaves. The head on the spring center bolt fits into an opening in the axle to position the axle properly and provide proper vehicle tracking. If the center bolt is broken, the axle position may shift and alter vehicle tracking and alignment. Leaf springs are usually mounted at right angles to the axle. They provide excellent resistance to lateral movement.

Mono-Leaf Springs

Some leaf springs contain a single steel leaf, and these springs may be referred to as **mono-leaf springs.** The single leaf is thicker in the center and becomes gradually thinner toward the outer ends. This design provides a variable spring rate for a smooth ride and adequate load-carrying capacity. Mono-leaf springs do not have a friction and noise problem as the spring compresses. Some cars, such as the Corvette and front-wheel-drive Oldsmobile Cutlass Supreme, use a fiberglass-reinforced plastic mono-leaf spring in place of a steel spring to reduce weight (Figure 6-6). The mono-leaf spring may be mounted longitudinally or transversely, and this type of spring may be used in front or rear suspensions.

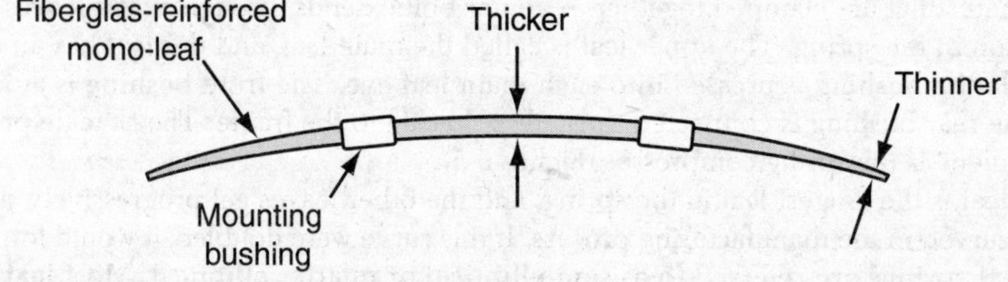

FIGURE 6-6 *Transversely mounted fiberglass mono-leaf spring.*

Ball Joints

The ball joints act as pivot points that allow the front wheels and spindles, or knuckles, to turn between the upper and lower control arms. Compared with the earlier I-beam and kingpin-type front suspension systems, ball-joint suspension systems are much simpler. A front suspension with ball joints reduces the number of load-carrying bearing surfaces. Compared with an I-beam front suspension with kingpins, a front suspension with ball joints has these advantages:

1. Reduced space requirements
2. Reduced unsprung weight
3. Easier alignment
4. More dependable steering control
5. Improved safety
6. Improved tire life
7. Reduced steering effort
8. Improved ride quality
9. Simplified service–no kingpin reaming or honing
10. Simplified lubrication

WARNING: Worn ball joints may suddenly pull apart, resulting in loss of steering control and possibly a collision! Refer to the procedures in the Shop Manual Chapter 6 for measuring ball joint wear.

Load-Carrying Ball Joint

Ball joints may be grouped into two classifications, load carrying and non-load carrying. Ball joints may be manufactured with forged, stamped, cold-formed, or screw-machined housings. The coil spring is seated on the control arm to which the load-carrying ball joint is attached. For example, when the coil spring is mounted between the lower control arm and the chassis, the lower ball joint is a load-carrying joint (Figure 6-7). In a torsion bar suspension, the **load-carrying ball joint** is mounted on the control arm to which the torsion bar is attached. A load-carrying ball joint supports the vehicle weight.

In a load-carrying ball joint, the vehicle weight forces the ball stud into contact with the bearing surface in the joint. Load-carrying ball joints may be compression loaded or tension loaded. If the control arm is mounted above the lower end of the knuckle and rests on the knuckle, the ball joint is

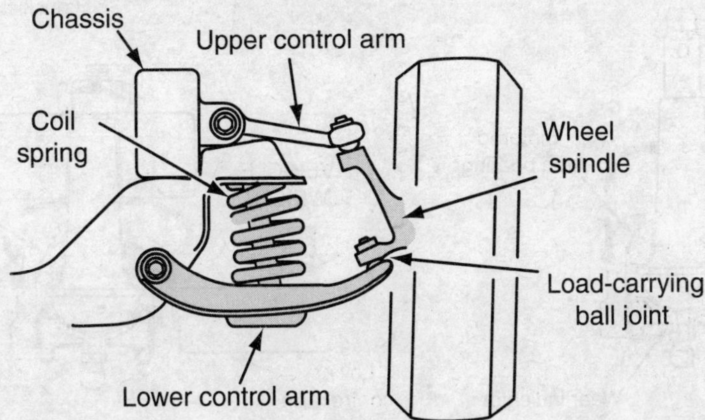

FIGURE 6-7 *Load-carrying ball joint mounted on the control arm on which the spring is seated.*

compression loaded. In this type of ball joint, the vehicle weight is pushing downward on the control arm. This weight is supported on the tire and wheel, which are attached to the steering knuckle. Since the ball joint is mounted between the control arm and the steering knuckle, the vehicle weight squeezes the ball joint together (Figure 6-8). In this type of ball-joint mounting, the ball joint is mounted in the lower control arm and the ball joint stud faces downward (Figure 6-9).

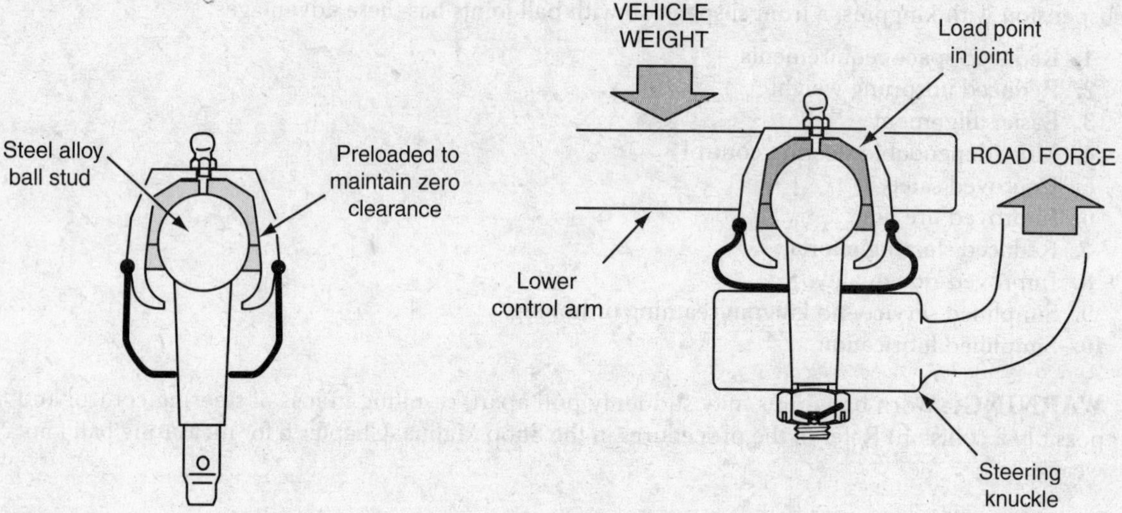

FIGURE 6-8 *Compression-loaded ball joint.*

FIGURE 6-9 *Compression-loaded ball joint mounting.*

When the lower control arm is positioned below the steering knuckle, the vehicle weight is pulling the ball joint away from the knuckle (Figure 6-10). This type of ball joint mounting is referred to as **tension loaded.** This type of ball joint is mounted in the lower control arm with the ball-joint stud facing upward into the knuckle (Figure 6-11).

Since the load-carrying ball joint supports the vehicle weight, this ball joint wears faster compared with a non-load-carrying ball joint. Many load-carrying ball joints have built-in **wear indicators.** These ball joints have an indicator on the grease nipple surface that recedes into the housing as the joint wears.

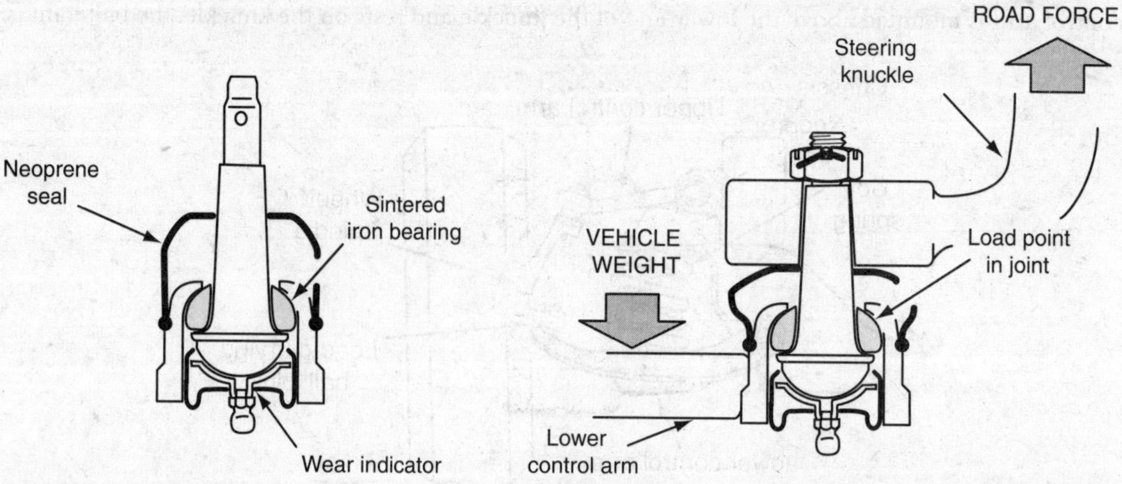

FIGURE 6-10 *Tension-loaded ball joint.*

FIGURE 6-11 *Tension-loaded ball joint mounting.*

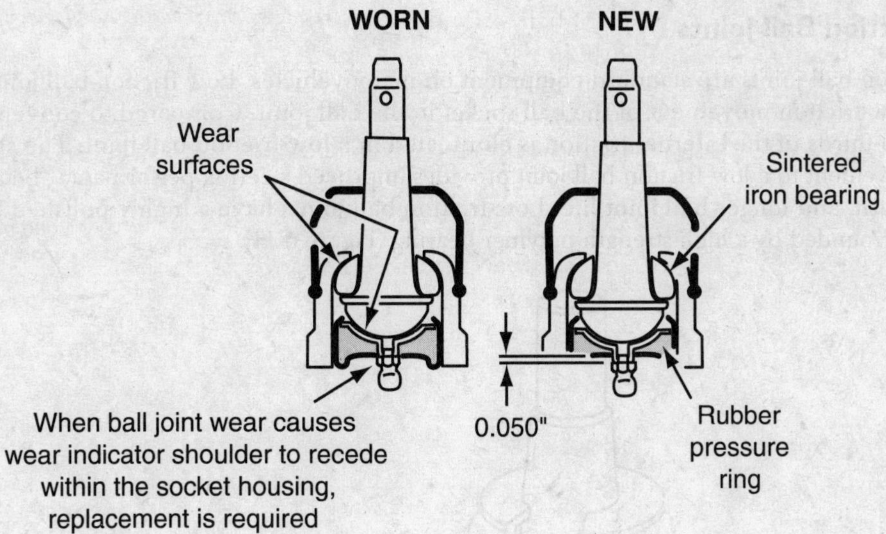

FIGURE 6-12 *Ball joint wear indicator.*

If the ball joint is in good condition, the grease nipple shoulder extends a specified distance out of the housing. If the grease nipple shoulder is even with or inside the ball-joint housing, the ball joint is worn and replacement is necessary (Figure 6-12).

Most states have safety inspection procedures for testing ball joints and other safety-related components. These safety inspection procedures include specifications. Always follow the guidelines when performing safety inspections.

Non-Load-Carrying Ball Joint

A **non-load-carrying ball joint** may be referred to as a stabilizing or follower ball joint. A non-load-carrying ball joint is designed with a preload, which provides damping action (Figure 6-13). This ball joint preload provides improved steering quality and vehicle stability.

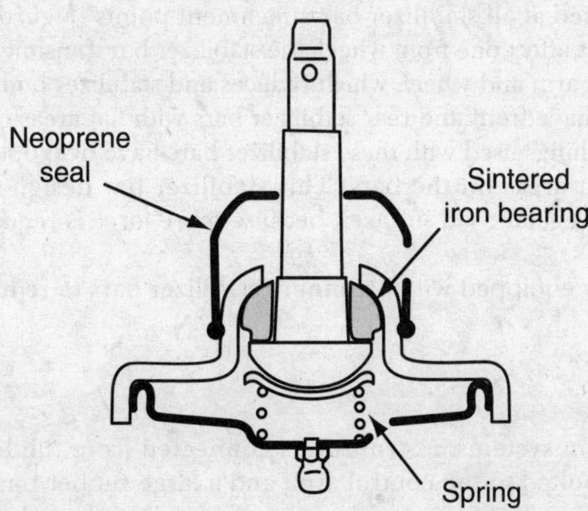

FIGURE 6-13 *Non-load-carrying ball joint.*

Low-Friction Ball Joints

Low-friction ball joints are standard equipment on many vehicles. Low-friction ball joints provide precise low-friction movement of the ball socket in the ball joint. Compared to conventional ball joints, two-thirds of the internal friction is eliminated in a low-friction ball joint. The smooth ball socket movement in a low-friction ball joint provides improved steering performance, better steering wheel return, and longer ball joint life. Low-friction ball joints have a highly polished ball socket surface surrounded by a high-strength polymer bearing (Figure 6-14).

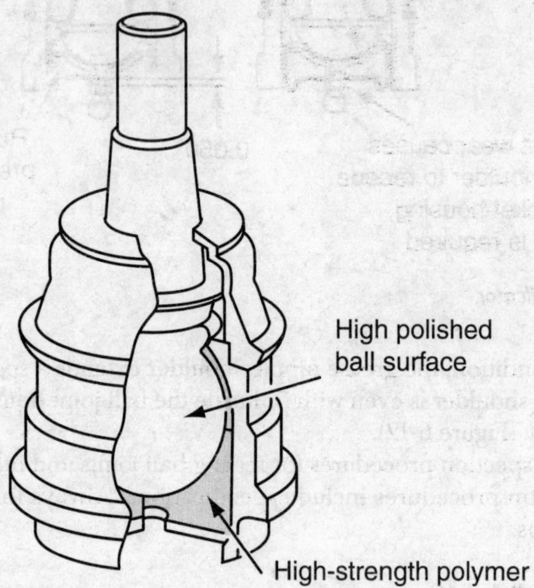

FIGURE 6-14 *Low-friction ball joint.*

Stabilizer Bar

The stabilizer bar is attached to the crossmember and interconnects the lower control arms. Rubber insulating bushings are used at all stabilizer bar attachment points (Figure 6-15). When jounce and rebound wheel movements affect one front wheel, the stabilizer bar transmits part of this movement to the opposite lower control arm and wheel, which reduces and stabilizes body roll.

Some current vehicles have front and rear stabilizer bars with flat areas on the bars in the bushing contact locations. The bushings used with these stabilizer bars have oval openings in the center of the bushing to match the flat areas on the bars. This stabilizer bar design reduces body roll when cornering or driving on irregular road surfaces, because more force is required to twist the stabilizer bar.

Some vehicles are now equipped with aluminum stabilizer bars to reduce unsprung weight and improve ride quality.

Strut Rod

On some front suspension systems, a strut rod is connected from the lower control arm to the chassis. The strut rod is bolted to the control arm, and a large rubber bushing surrounds the strut rod in the chassis opening. The outer end of the strut rod is threaded and steel washers are positioned on each side of the strut rod bushing. Two nuts tighten the strut rod into the bushing

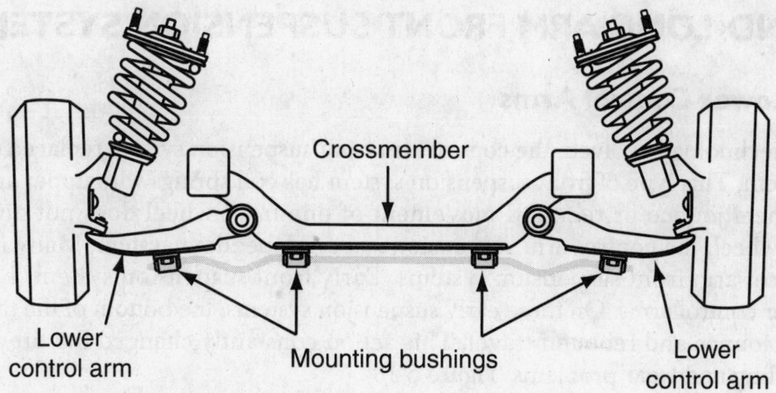

FIGURE 6-15 *Stabilizer bar with mounting bushings.*

(Figure 6-16). The strut rod prevents fore-and-aft movement of the lower control arm. In some suspension systems, the position of the strut rod nuts provides proper front wheel adjustment.

Some strut rods are presently manufactured from tubular steel to reduce strut rod and unsprung weight.

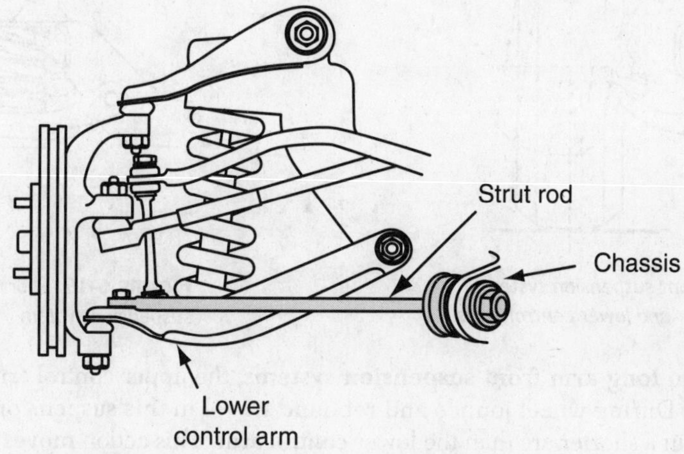

FIGURE 6-16 *Strut, or radius, rod and bushings.*

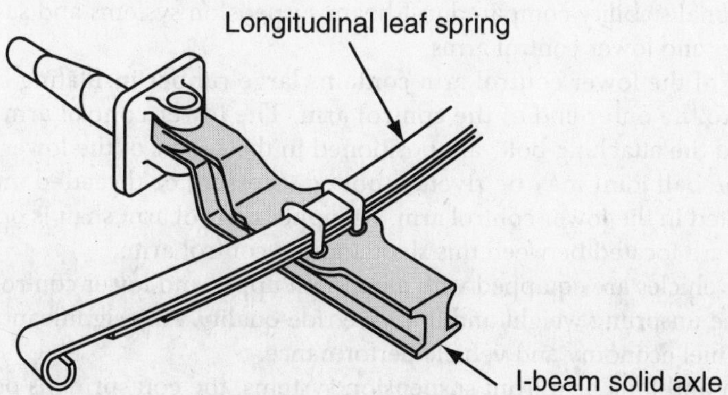

FIGURE 6-17 *I-beam front suspension with longitudinally mounted leaf springs.*

SHORT-AND-LONG ARM FRONT SUSPENSION SYSTEMS

Upper and Lower Control Arms

As automotive technology evolved, the control arm front suspension system replaced the I-beam front suspension system. This type of front suspension system has coil springs with upper and lower control arms. Since wheel jounce or rebound movement of one front wheel does not directly affect the opposite front wheel, the control arm suspension is an independent system. Many rear-wheel-drive cars have control arm front suspension systems. Early front suspension systems had equal-length upper and lower control arms. On these early suspension systems, the bottom of the tire moved in and out with wheel jounce and rebound travel. This action constantly changed the tire tread width and caused tire scuffing and wear problems (Figure 6-18).

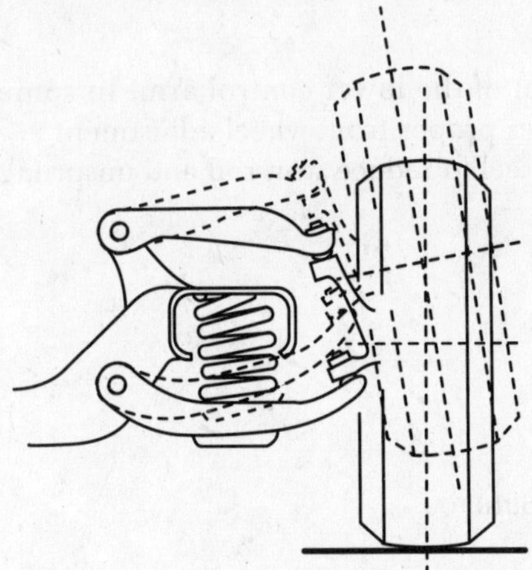

FIGURE 6-18 *Early front suspension system with equal length upper and lower control arms.*

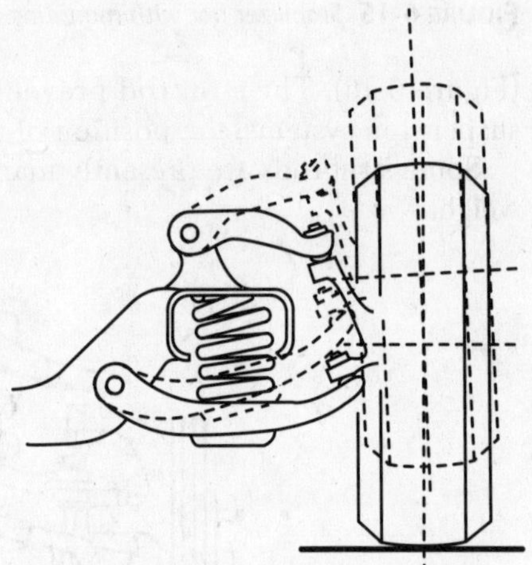

FIGURE 6-19 *Short-and-long arm front suspension system.*

In later **short-and-long arm front suspension systems,** the upper control arm is shorter than the lower control arm. During wheel jounce and rebound travel in this suspension system, the upper control arm moves in a shorter arc than the lower control arm. This action moves the top of the tire in and out slightly, but the bottom of the tire remains in a more constant position (Figure 6-19). This short-and-long arm front suspension system provides reduced tire tread wear, improved ride quality, and better directional stability compared to I-beam suspension systems and suspension systems with equal-length upper and lower control arms.

The inner end of the lower control arm contains large rubber insulating bushings, and the ball joint is attached to the outer end of the control arm. The lower control arm is bolted to the front crossmember, and the attaching bolts are positioned in the center of the lower control arm bushings (Figure 6-20). The ball joint may be riveted, bolted, pressed, or threaded into the control arm. A spring seat is located in the lower control arm. An upper control arm shaft is bolted to the frame, and rubber insulators are located between this shaft and the control arm.

Many current vehicles are equipped with aluminum upper and lower control arms and/or steering knuckles to reduce unsprung weight and improve ride quality. Any significant weight reduction also helps to improve fuel economy and vehicle performance.

On some short-and-long arm front suspension systems, the coil spring is positioned between the upper control arm and the chassis (Figure 6-21). In these suspension systems, the upper ball joint is compression loaded.

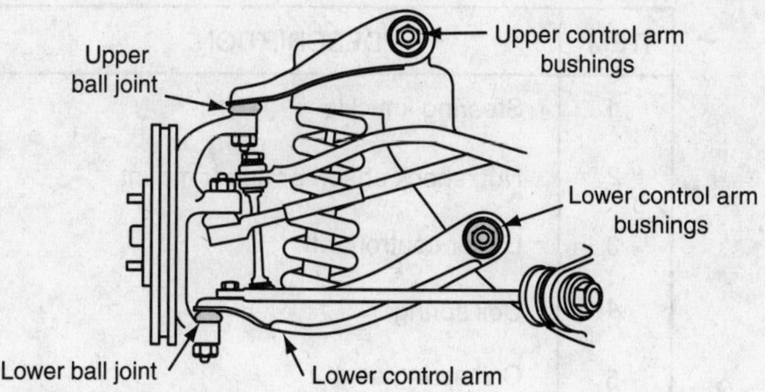

FIGURE 6-20 *Ball joints and complete short-and-long arm front suspension system.*

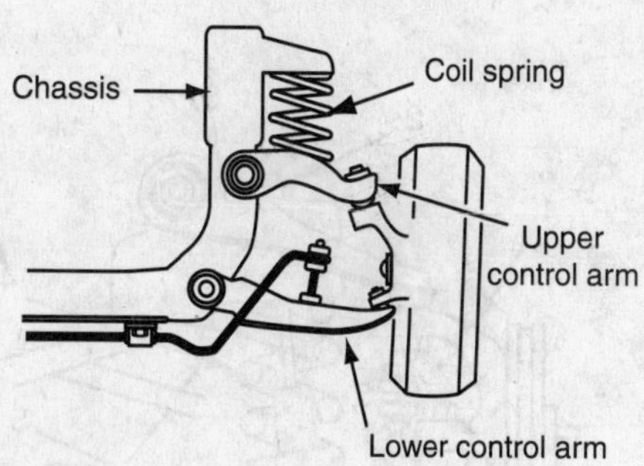

FIGURE 6-21 *Short-and-long arm front suspension with the coil spring between the upper control arm and the chassis.*

Steering Knuckle

The upper and lower ball joint studs extend through openings in the steering knuckle. Nuts are threaded onto the ball joint studs to retain the ball joints in the knuckle, and the nuts are secured with cotter pins. The wheel hub and bearings are positioned on the steering knuckle extension, and the wheel assembly is bolted to the wheel hub. When the steering wheel is turned, the steering gear and linkage turn the steering knuckle. During this turning action, the steering knuckle pivots on the upper and lower ball joints. The upper and lower control arms must be positioned properly to provide correct tracking and wheelbase between the front and rear wheels. The control arm bushings must be in satisfactory condition to position the control arms properly.

Coil Spring and Shock Absorber

The coil spring is positioned between the lower control arm and the spring seat in the frame. A spring seat is located in the lower control arm, and an insulator is positioned between the top of the coil spring and the spring seat in the frame. The shock absorber is mounted in the center of the coil spring, and the lower shock absorber bushing is bolted to the lower control arm. The top of the shock absorber extends through an opening in the frame above the upper spring seat. Washers, grommets, and a nut retain the top of the shock absorber to the frame. Side roll of the front suspension is controlled by a steel stabilizer bar, which is mounted to the lower control arms and the frame with rubber bushings.

On some later model short-and-long arm front suspension systems, the lower end of the coil spring is mounted on a seat attached to the shock absorber. A rubber bushing containing a metal bar is installed in the lower end of the shock absorber. This bushing is bolted to the lower control arm (Figure 6-22 and Figure 6-23). The upper end of the coil spring is seated on an upper shock absorber mount. The rod in the center of the shock absorber extends through this mount, and a nut on the threaded end of the shock absorber rod retains the mount on the shock absorber. Bolts in the top of the upper shock absorber mount extend through the upper control arm.

The upper control arm is mounted high in the suspension system, and the upper end of the knuckle has a “goose neck” shape. The lower control arm is made from stamped steel to reduce weight. The rear lower control arm bushing is mounted vertically and carries only fore-and-aft loads. This mounting allows the use of a softer rear bushing in the lower control arm. The horizontal front lower control arm bushing and the lower shock absorber mounting are aligned with the wheel center. This provides a direct path for lateral cornering loads. This design allows the use of a hard front lower control arm bushing.

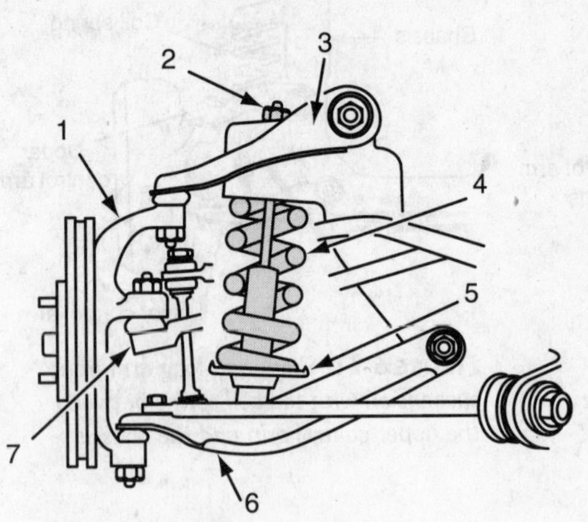

FIGURE 6-22 *Short-and-long arm front suspension system with coil spring mounted on the shock absorber.*

ITEM	DESCRIPTION
1	Steering knuckle
2	Nut, shock absorber upper mount
3	Upper control arm
4	Coil spring
5	Coil spring seat
6	Lower control arm
7	Tie-rod end

FIGURE 6-23 *Component identification in short-and-long arm suspension with the coil spring mounted on the shock absorber.*

When servicing this suspension system, a special spring compressing tool must be used to compress all the spring tension before loosening the nut on top of the shock absorber rod (Figure 6-24 and Figure 6-25). After this nut is removed, the compressing tool is operated to gradually release the spring tension, and then the upper mount may be removed. (Refer to Chapter 5 in the Shop Manual for strut and coil spring service.)

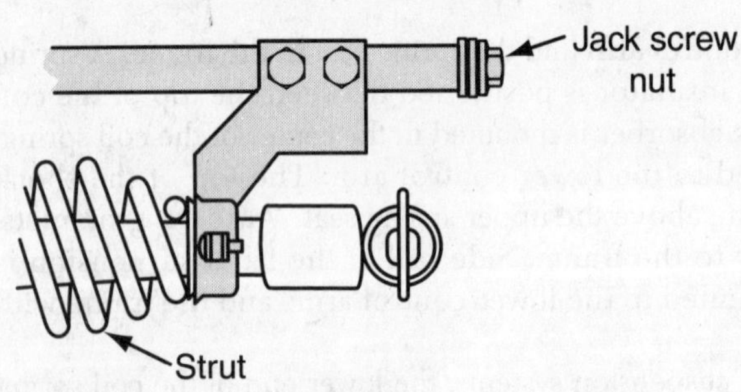

FIGURE 6-24 *Lower end of spring compressing tool.*

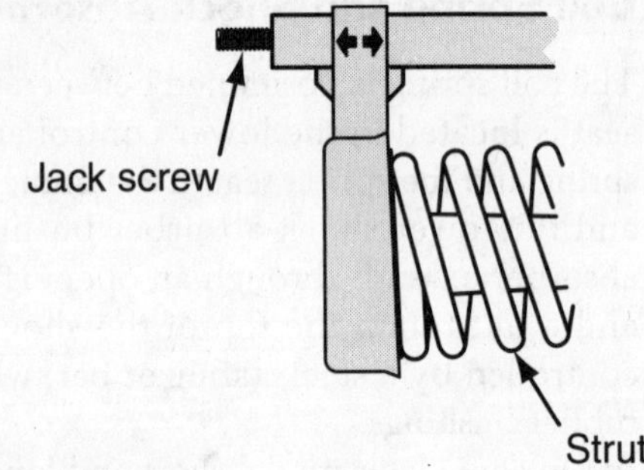

FIGURE 6-25 *Upper end of spring compressing tool.*

In the short-and-long arm front suspension system on the Trailblazer SUV, the coil spring is mounted over the shock absorber; the coil spring tension is applied against the upper mount and the lower spring seat on the shock absorber (Figure 6-26). A special yoke attaches to the lower end of the shock absorber, and the lower end of this yoke pivots on a bolt in the lower control arm (Figure 6-27). This type of suspension system provides a more positive shock absorber and spring mounting because the rubber bushing-type mounting between the shock absorber and the lower control arm is not required. The steering knuckle pivots on the upper and lower ball joints in the control arms. Therefore, the shock absorber and coil spring do not have to turn when the knuckle turns, which allows the use of a more rigid upper spring mount. This suspension design provides improved vehicle handling and ride characteristics.

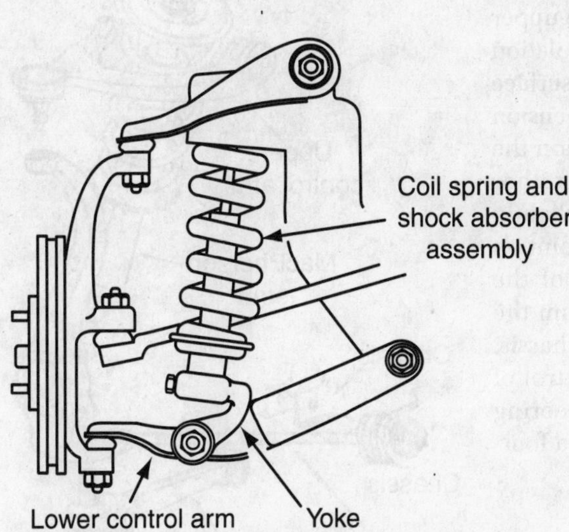

FIGURE 6-26 *Short-and-long arm front suspension with yoke-type shock absorber mounting.*

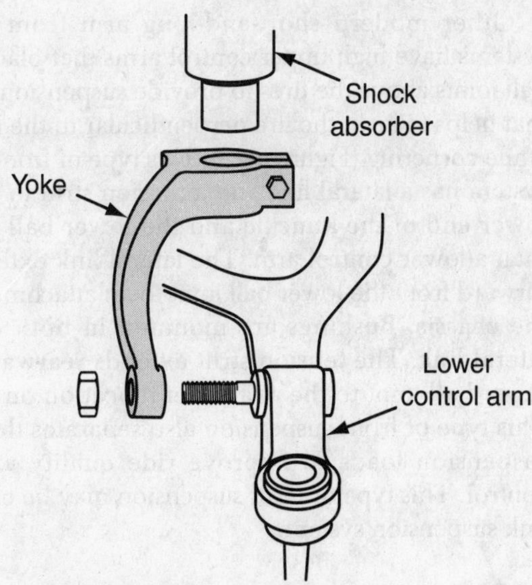

FIGURE 6-27 *Shock absorber with yoke attachment to lower control arm.*

CAUTION: Never loosen the nut on top of the shock absorber rod until a coil spring compressing tool is used to compress all the spring tension. Failure to follow this procedure may cause the spring tension to suddenly release, resulting in personal injury.

Improved Designs in Short-and-Long Arm Front Suspension Systems

Some vehicles now have a reverse-L front suspension system. In these suspension systems, the rear attachment point on the lower control arm extends rearward and attaches to the engine cradle at a point farther toward the rear of the vehicle (Figure 6-28). The lower control arm has an L-shaped design. A firm bushing is installed at the location where the shorter forward leg of the lower control arm attaches to the cradle to control lateral control arm movement and quicken steering response. A more compliant bushing is installed between the longer rear leg and the rear attachment point to absorb the impact of longitudinal forces caused by road irregularities. This type of suspension separates the control of suspension loads into fore-and-aft control and side-to-side control to improve ride and steering quality.

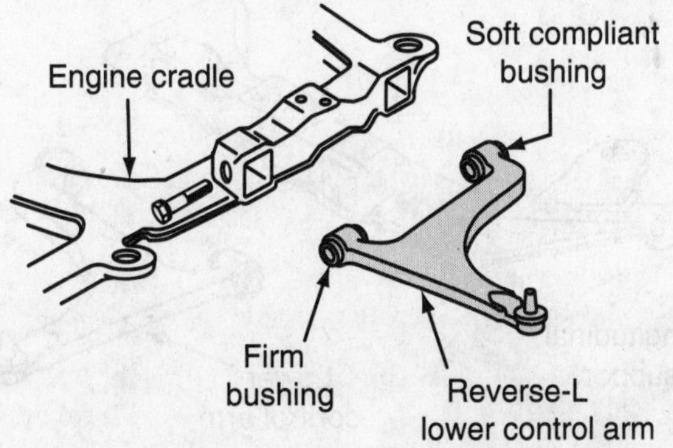

FIGURE 6-28 *Reverse-L front suspension system with firm, front lower control arm bushing and more compliant rear, lower control arm bushing.*

Other modern short-and-long arm front suspension systems have high upper control arms that place the upper ball joints above the tires to provide suspension articulation that helps to keep the tire perpendicular to the road surface while cornering (Figure 6-29). This type of front suspension system has a lateral link and a tension strut to position the lower end of the knuckle and the lower ball joint rather than a lower control arm. The lateral link extends slightly forward from the lower ball joint to an attachment point on the chassis. Bushings are mounted in both ends of the lateral link. The tension strut extends rearward from the lower ball joint to the attachment location on the chassis. This type of front suspension also separates the control of suspension loads to improve ride quality and steering control. This type of front suspension may be called a four-link suspension system.

FIGURE 6-29 *Front suspension system with lateral link and tension strut in place of lower control arm.*

MACPHERSON STRUT FRONT SUSPENSION SYSTEM DESIGN

Lower Control Arms and Support

When smaller front-wheel-drive cars became popular, most of these cars had **MacPherson strut front suspension systems.** In these suspension systems, the lower end of the strut is bolted to the top of the steering knuckle, and the lower end of the knuckle is attached to the ball joint in the lower control arm. An upper strut mount connects the top of the strut to the chassis. An upper control arm is not required in this type of suspension system, because the strut supports the top of the steering knuckle. Since the upper control arm is not required in these suspension systems, they are more compact and therefore very suitable for smaller cars.

On some MacPherson strut front suspension systems, a steel support is positioned longitudinally on each side of the front suspension. These supports are bolted to the unitized body. The inner ends of the lower control arms contain large insulating bushings with a bolt opening in the bushing center. The control arm retaining bolts extend through the center of these bushings and openings in the support (Figure 6-30).

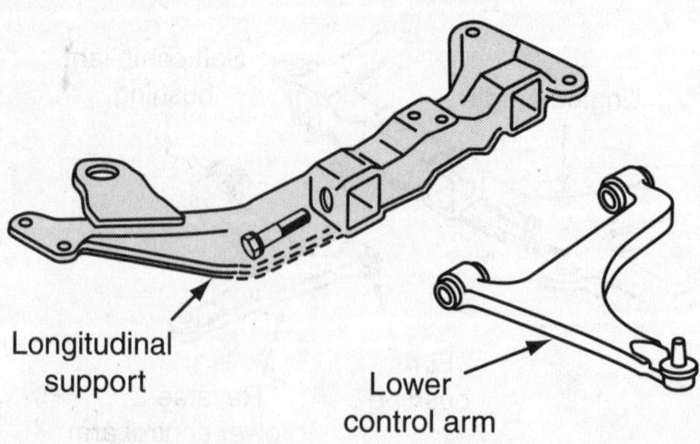

FIGURE 6-30 *Lower control arm and support.*

Road irregularities cause the tire and wheel to move up and down vertically, and the lower control arm bushings pivot on the mounting bolts during this movement. When the vehicle is driven over road irregularities, vibration and noise are applied to the tire and wheel. The control arm bushings help prevent the transfer of this noise and vibration to the support, the unitized body, and the passenger compartment. Proper location of the support and lower control arm is important to provide correct vehicle tracking. The supports also carry the engine and transaxle weight. Large rubber mounts are positioned between the supports and the engine and transaxle. These mounts absorb engine vibration.

Stabilizer Bar

A stabilizer bar is connected between the two lower control arms. This bar is attached to the lower control arms with retaining bolts, small rubber bushings, steel washers, and sleeves. Large rubber bushings and clamps connect the stabilizer bar to the unitized body (Figure 6-31). The outer ends of the stabilizer bar move up and down with the lower control arms, and the bushings prevent noise transfer to the body and passenger compartment.

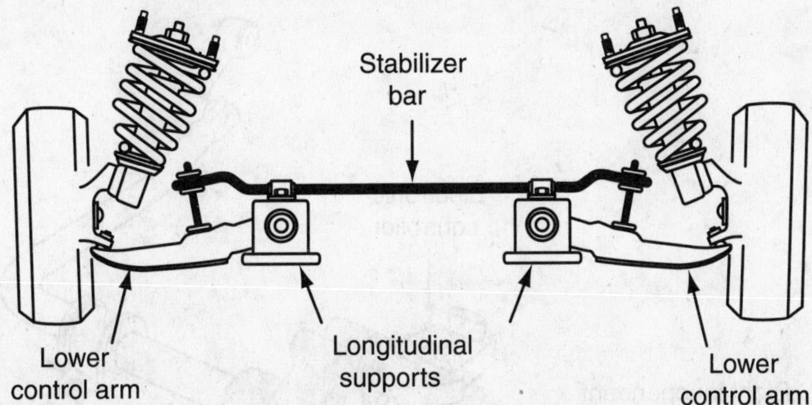

FIGURE 6-31 *Stabilizer bar connected between the two lower control arms.*

In some suspension systems links are connected between the ends of the stabilizer bar and a bracket on the strut (Figure 6-32). An aftermarket electronically controlled stabilizer bar is available for off-road vehicle operation (Figure 6-33). In this type of stabilizer bar system the driver may press a switch in the instrument panel, and the electronic control disconnects one side of the stabilizer bar from the opposite side, thus making this component ineffective. When the stabilizer bar is disconnected electronically, full vertical wheel travel is allowed on rough terrain. The driver can press the control switch again to return the stabilizer bar to normal operation for stabilized control of body roll during on-road operation.

Lower Ball Joint

The lower ball joint is attached to the outer end of the lower control arm. Methods used to attach the ball joint to the control arm include bolting, riveting, pressing, and threading. A threaded stud extends from the top of the lower ball joint. This stud fits snugly into a hole in the bottom of the steering knuckle. When the ball joint stud is installed in the steering knuckle opening, a nut and cotter pin retain the ball joint (Figure 6-34).

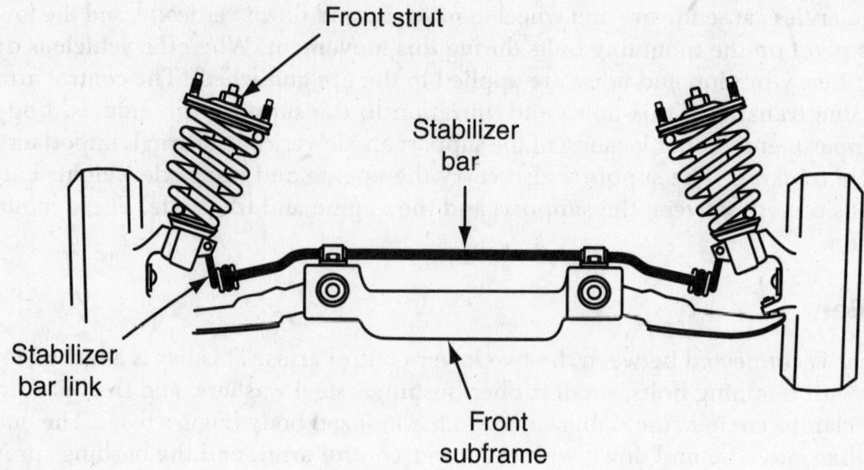

FIGURE 6-32 *Stabilizer bar connected to the front strut.*

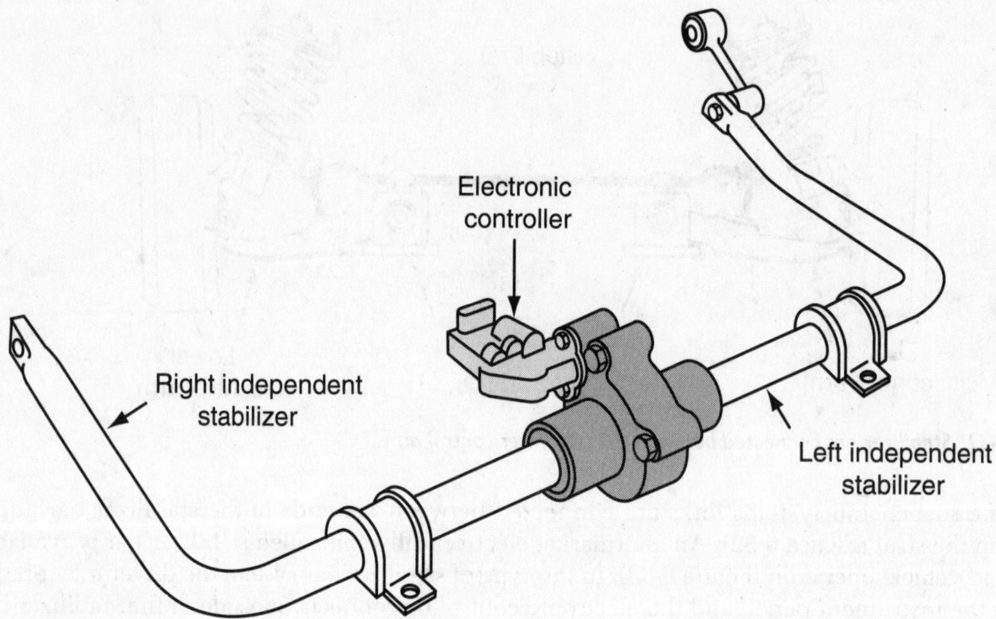

FIGURE 6-33 *Electronically controlled stabilizer bar.*

Steering Knuckle and Bearing Assembly

The front wheel bearing assembly is bolted to the outer end of the steering knuckle, and the brake rotor and wheel rim are retained on the studs in the wheel bearing assembly. This front wheel bearing assembly is a complete, nonserviceable, sealed unit. The front drive shaft is splined into the center of the wheel bearing hub. Thus, drive axle torque is applied to the front wheel. A tie-rod end connects the steering linkage from the steering gear to the steering knuckle. The top end of the steering knuckle is bolted to the lower end of the strut (Figure 6-35).

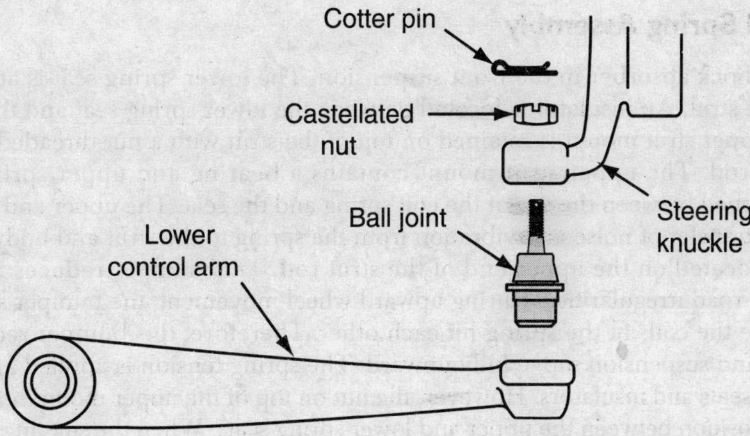

FIGURE 6-34 *Lower ball joint.*

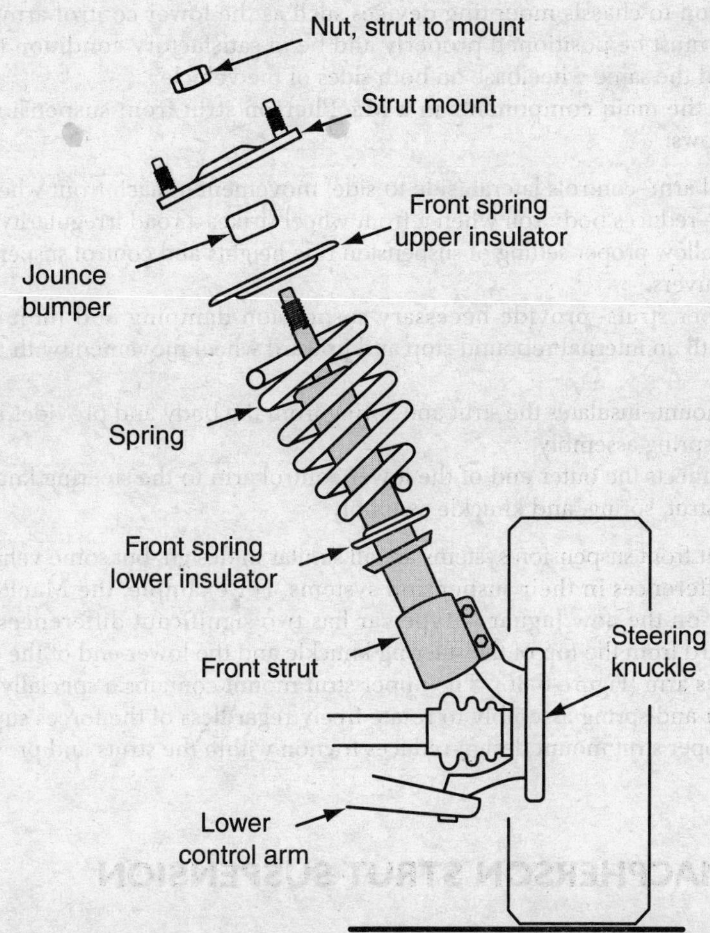

FIGURE 6-35 *Complete MacPherson strut front suspension system.*

Strut and Coil Spring Assembly

The strut is the shock absorber in the front suspension. The lower spring seat is attached near the center area of the strut. An insulator is located between the lower spring seat and the bottom of the coil spring. An upper strut mount is retained on top of the strut with a nut threaded onto the upper end of the strut rod. The upper strut mount contains a bearing and upper spring seat, and an insulator is positioned between the top of the coil spring and the seat. The upper and lower insulators help prevent the transfer of noise and vibration from the spring to the strut and body.

A bumper is located on the upper end of the strut rod. This bumper reduces harshness while driving on severe road irregularities. During upward wheel movement, the bumper strikes the upper spring seat before the coils in the spring hit each other. Therefore, this bumper reduces harshness when the wheel and suspension move fully upward. The spring tension is applied against the upper and lower spring seats and insulators. However, the nut on top of the upper mount holds the spring in the compressed position between the upper and lower spring seats. When the steering wheel is turned, the steering linkage turns the steering knuckles to the right or left. During this front wheel turning action, the strut-and-spring assembly pivots on the lower ball joint and the upper strut mount bearing.

All the suspension-to-chassis mounting devices such as the lower control arm bushings and the upper strut mount must be positioned properly and be in satisfactory condition to provide correct vehicle tracking and the same wheelbase on both sides of the vehicle.

The purpose of the main components in a MacPherson strut front suspension system may be summarized as follows:

1. Lower control arm–controls lateral (side-to-side) movement of each front wheel.
2. Stabilizer bar–reduces body roll when a front wheel strikes a road irregularity.
3. Coil springs–allow proper setting of suspension ride heights and control suspension travel during driving maneuvers.
4. Shock absorber struts–provide necessary suspension damping and limit downward wheel movement with an internal rebound stop and upward wheel movement with an external jounce bouncer.
5. Strut upper mount–insulates the strut and spring from the body and provides a bearing pivot for the strut-and-spring assembly.
6. Ball joint–connects the outer end of the lower control arm to the steering knuckle and acts as a pivot for the strut, spring, and knuckle assembly.

MacPherson strut front suspension systems are all similar in design, but some vehicle manufacturers provide unique differences in their suspension systems. For example, the MacPherson strut front suspension system on the new Jaguar X-type car has two significant differences: an arm extends several inches inward from the top of the steering knuckle and the lower end of the strut is attached to the inner end of this arm (Figure 6-36). The upper strut mount contains a specially designed bearing that allows the strut-and-spring assembly to rotate freely regardless of the forces supplied to the front suspension. This upper strut mount design reduces friction within the struts and provides very smooth steering action.

MODIFIED MACPHERSON STRUT SUSPENSION

A modified MacPherson strut front suspension is used on some older vehicles. This type of suspension has MacPherson struts with coil springs positioned between the lower control arms and the frame (Figure 6-37). The struts in these systems may be gas-filled or oil-filled.

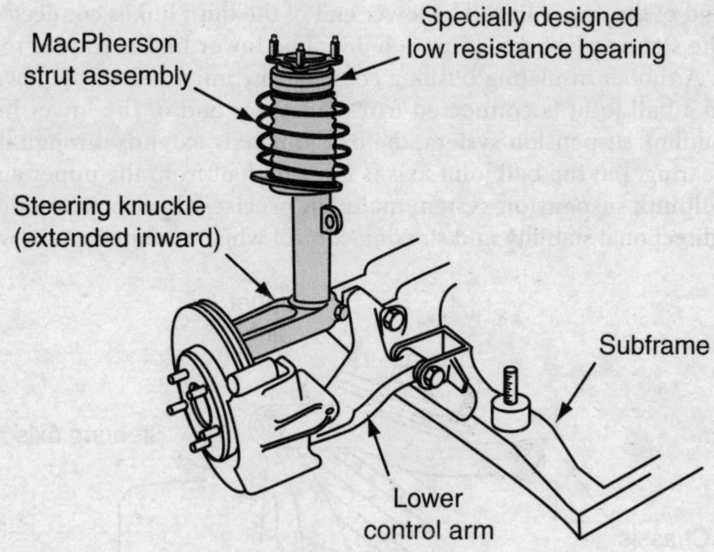

FIGURE 6-36 *MacPherson strut front suspension system on Jaguar X-type car.*

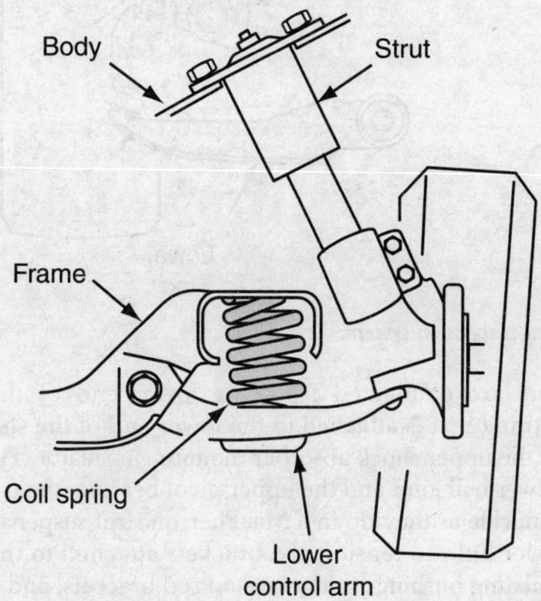

FIGURE 6-37 *Modified MacPherson strut front suspension system.*

HIGH-PERFORMANCE FRONT SUSPENSION SYSTEMS

Multilink Front Suspension System

High-performance suspension systems are usually installed on sports cars. In these cars, the driver expects improved steering quality, especially when driving and cornering at higher speeds.

In a **multilink front suspension,** a short upper link is attached to the chassis with a bracket, and the outer end of this upper link is connected to a third link. Large rubber insulating bushings are mounted in each end of the upper link. The lower end of the third link is connected through a heavy pivot bearing to the steering knuckle (Figure 6-38). The lower link is similar to the conventional lower control arm. A rubber insulating bushing connects the inner end of the lower link to the front crossmember, and a ball joint is connected from the outer end of the lower link to the steering knuckle. In the multilink suspension system, the ball joint axis extends through the lower ball joint and upper pivot bearing, but the ball joint axis is independent from the upper and third links. The extra links in a multilink suspension system maintain precise wheel position during cornering to provide excellent directional stability and steering control while minimizing tire wear.

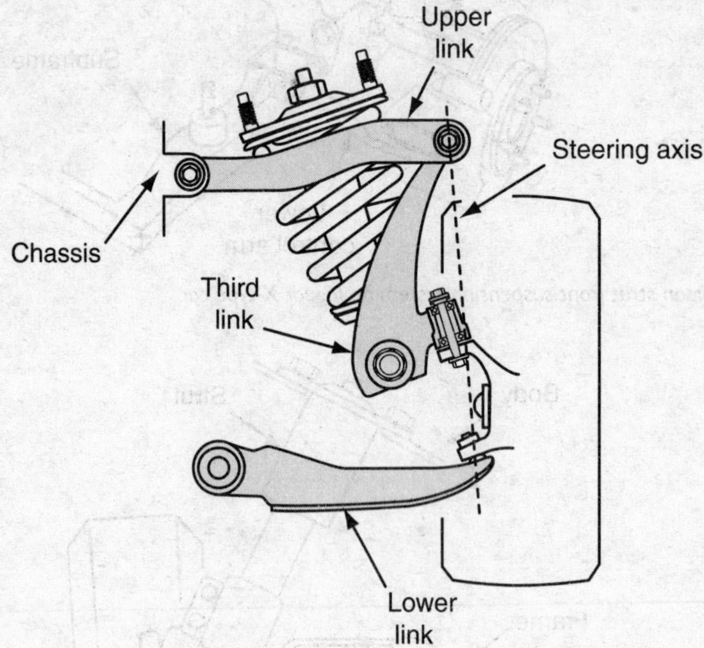

FIGURE 6-38 *Multilink front suspension system.*

The shock absorbers are connected from the lower end of the third link to the fender reinforcement. A coil spring seat is attached to the lower end of the shock absorber, and the upper spring seat is located on the upper shock absorber mounting insulator (Figure 6-39). Since the steering knuckle pivots on the lower ball joint and the upper pivot bearing, the coil spring and shock absorber do not rotate with the knuckle as they do in a MacPherson strut suspension. Tension or strut rods are connected from the lower links to tension rod brackets attached to the chassis. A stabilizer bar is mounted on rubber insulating bushings in the tension rod brackets, and the outer ends of this bar are attached to the third link.

Double Wishbone Front Suspension System

Double wishbone suspension systems provide increased suspension rigidity and maintain precise wheel position under all driving conditions to supply improved directional stability and steering control. In the double wishbone front suspension system, the upper and lower control arms are manufactured from lightweight, high-strength aluminum alloys designed for maximum strength and rigidity. These lighter control arms decrease the unsprung weight of the vehicle, which improves traction and ride quality. Since the upper and lower control arms have a wishbone shape, the term "double wishbone" is used for this type of suspension. Suspension rigidity is also increased by positioning the ball joints and steering

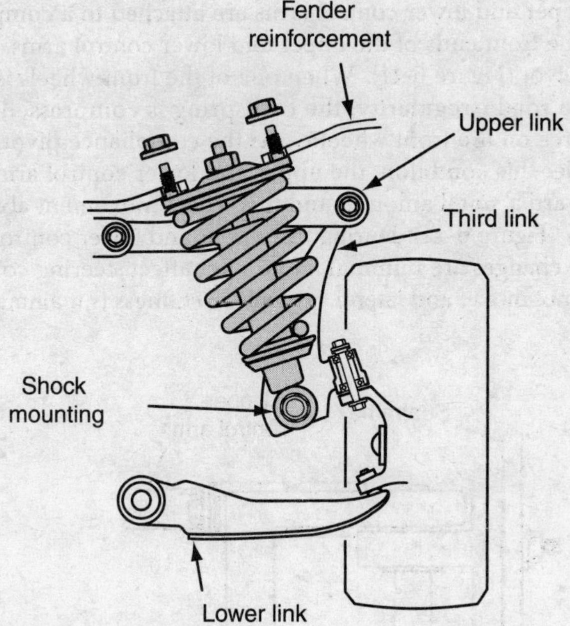

FIGURE 6-39 *Complete multilink suspension system.*

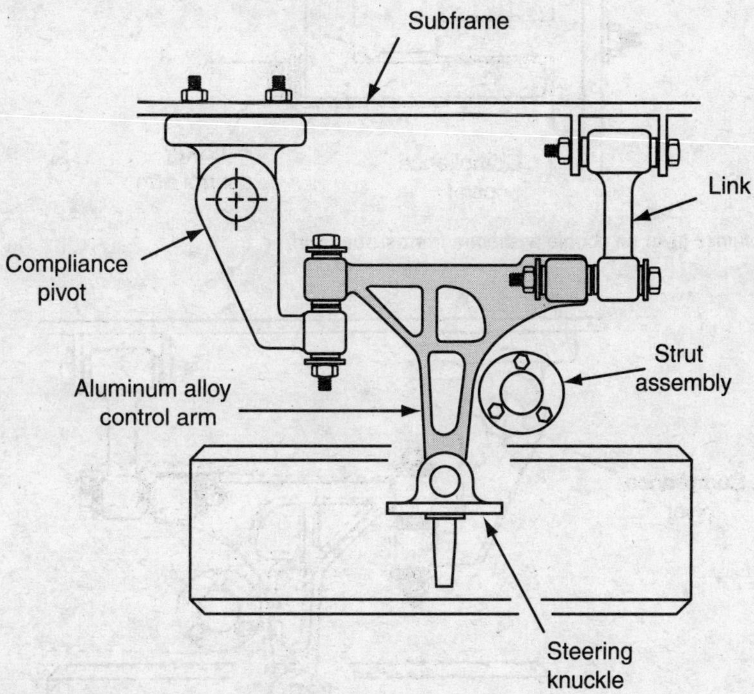

FIGURE 6-40 *Double wishbone front suspension.*

knuckle inside the wheel profile (Figure 6-40). On each side of the car, the front suspension is attached to the chassis by a cast aluminum subframe. This design also reduces vehicle weight. The double wishbones are attached to the chassis at the most efficient locations to maintain precise wheel position and provide improved ride quality.

The front ends of the upper and lower control arms are attached to a compliance pivot assembly. Bushings are mounted in the front ends of the upper and lower control arms, and these bushings are bolted to the compliance pivot (Figure 6-41). When one of the front wheels is subjected to rearward force by hard braking or a road irregularity, the coil spring is compressed and the ride height is lowered. This rearward force on the front wheel twists the compliance pivot, allowing both control arms to pivot slightly. Under this condition, the upper and lower control arm movement allows the front wheel to move rearward a small amount, and this wheel movement absorbs energy to significantly improve ride quality (Figure 6-42). During this upper and lower control arm movement, track width and wheel geometry changes are minimal and do not affect steering control. While cornering, the compliance pivot does not move, and lateral suspension stiffness is maintained to supply excellent steering control.

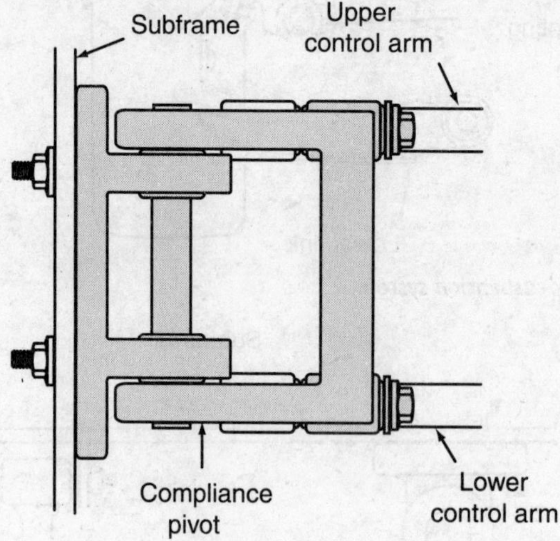

FIGURE 6-41 *Compliance pivot on double wishbone front suspension.*

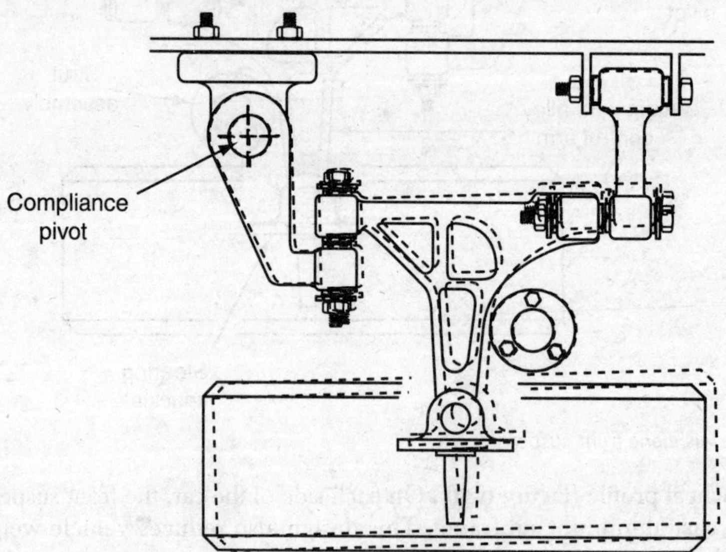

FIGURE 6-42 *Compliance pivot action.*

Multilink Front Suspension with Compression and Lateral Lower Arms

Some lateral multilink front suspensions have compression and lateral lower arms. The lateral arm prevents front wheel movement, and the compression arm prevents fore-and-aft front wheel movement. A rubber insulating bushing in the inner end of the lateral arm is bolted to the chassis. A second rubber insulating bushing near the outer end of the lateral arm is bolted to the damper fork. The upper end of the damper fork is bolted to the front strut (Figure 6-43 and Figure 6-44). A ball joint in the outer end of the lateral arm is bolted into the steering knuckle. A rubber insulating bushing in the inner end of the compression arm is bolted to the chassis, and a ball joint in the outer end of this arm is bolted into the steering knuckle.

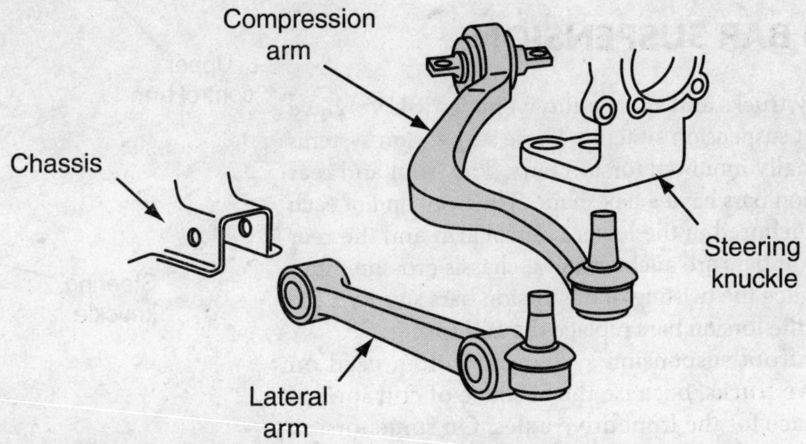

FIGURE 6-43 *Multilink front suspension with lateral and compression lower arms.*

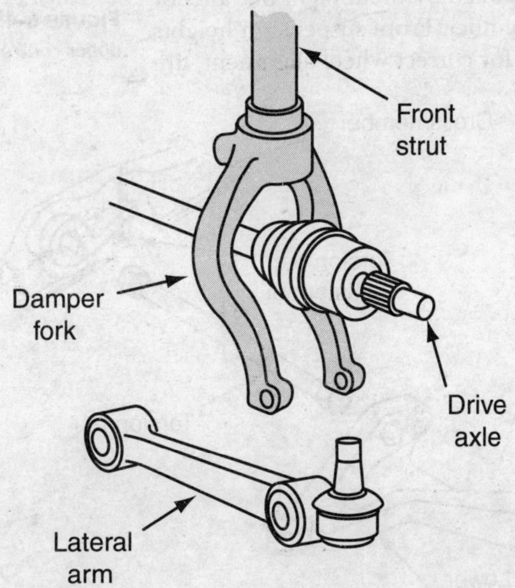

FIGURE 6-44 *Multilink front suspension damper fork.*

The upper control arm is mounted higher so it is above the front tire. The higher upper control arm and the lateral and compression lower arms provide excellent suspension stability and steering control, especially during high-speed cornering or when driving on irregular road surfaces. A ball joint in the outer end of the upper control arm is attached to the top of the knuckle, and two shafts in the inner end of this arm are bolted into the strut tower (Figure 6-45). There are no provisions for camber or caster adjustments on this multilink front suspension.

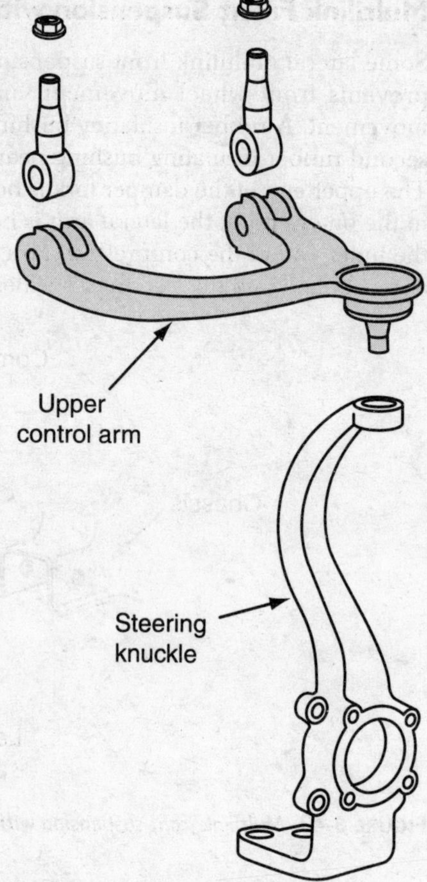

FIGURE 6-45 *Mutilink front suspension upper control arm.*

TORSION BAR SUSPENSION

Some light-duty trucks and sport utility vehicles (SUVs) have torsion bar front suspension systems. These suspension systems have longitudinally mounted torsion bars. The front and rear ends of the torsion bars have a hex shape. The front end of each torsion bar is anchored in the lower control arm and the rear end of the torsion bars are anchored to a chassis crossmember (Figure 6-46). Since the twisting of the torsion bars supports the vehicle weight, the torsion bars replace the coil springs.

Torsion bar front suspension systems are often used on four-wheel-drive trucks, because the absence of coil springs allows more space for the front drive axles. On some torsion bar front suspension systems the torsion bars are anchored into the upper control arms rather than the lower control arms.

Vehicle ride height is controlled by the torsion bar anchor adjusting bolts in the crossmember. Front suspension heights must be within specifications for correct wheel alignment, tire

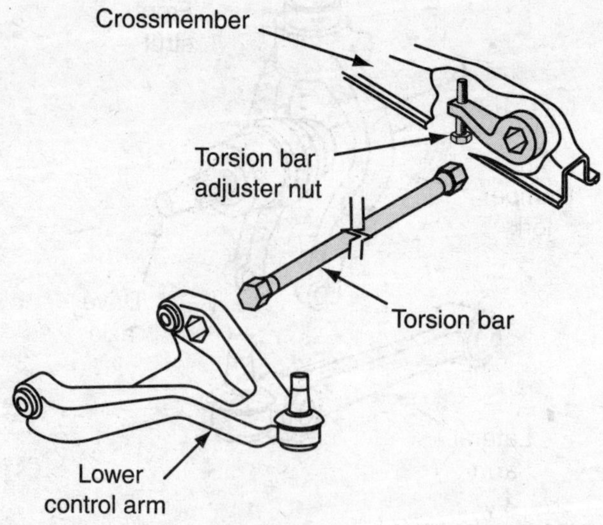

FIGURE 6-46 *Torsion bar mounting.*

wear, satisfactory ride, and accurate bumper heights. A conventional stabilizer bar is connected between the lower control arms and the crossmember. Ball joints are located in the upper and lower control arms, and both ball joints are bolted into the steering knuckle. The shock absorbers are connected between the lower control arms and the crossmember support, and the inner ends of the lower control arms are bolted to the crossmember through an insulating bushing (Figure 6-47).

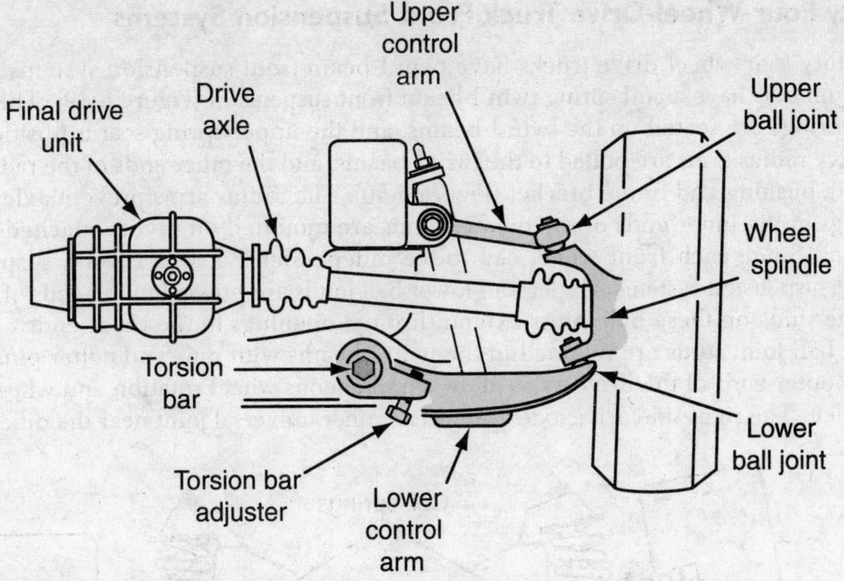

FIGURE 6-47 *Front suspension system with longitudinal torsion bars.*

Twin I-Beam Suspension Systems

Some Ford trucks are equipped with twin I-beam front suspension systems. In this type of suspension system, each front wheel is connected to a separate I-beam. The outer ends of the I-beam are connected to the spindles, and the inner ends of the beams are connected through a rubber pivot bushing to the chassis (Figure 6-48). Coil springs are positioned between the I-beams and the chassis to support the

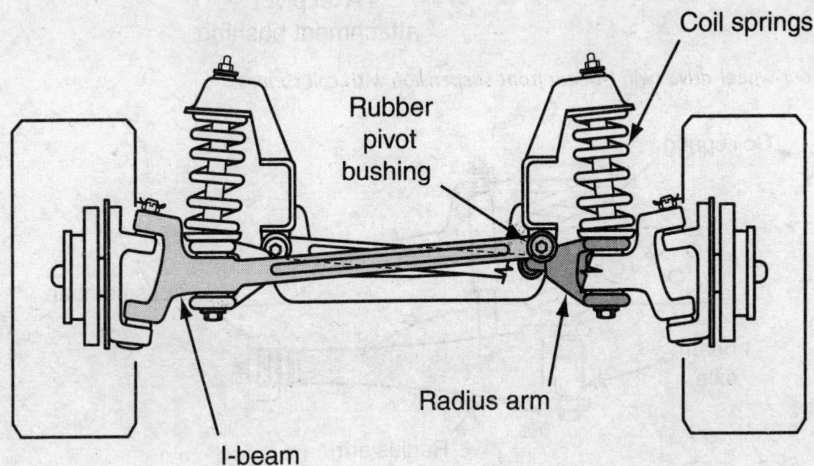

FIGURE 6-48 *Twin I-beam front suspension.*

vehicle weight. Radius arms are connected rearward from each I-beam to the chassis to prevent longitudinal wheel movement. Since each front wheel can move independently in a twin I-beam suspension system, the problems associated with straight I-beam systems are greatly reduced.

In some I-beam front suspension systems, kingpins are used to attach the I-beams to the spindles. In other I-beam suspension systems, ball joints connect the I-beams to the spindles.

Light-Duty Four-Wheel-Drive Truck Front Suspension Systems

Ford light-duty four-wheel-drive trucks have twin I-beam front suspension systems. F-150 four-wheel-drive models have a coil spring twin I-beam front suspension (Figurc 6-49). The lower ends of the coil springs are seated on the twin I-beams, and the upper spring seat is positioned on the chassis. Heavy radius arms are bolted to the twin I-beams, and the other ends of the radius arms are mounted in a bushing and frame bracket (Figure 6-50). The radius arms prevent axle movement. The bushings in the inner ends of the twin I-beams are mounted on pivots attached to the front crossmember. Since each front wheel can move independently, twin I-beam suspensions are independent suspension systems. Upper and lower ball joints are pressed in the ends of the steering knuckle. The studs on these ball joints extend through openings in the outer ends of the twin I-beams. The ball joint studs are retained in the twin I-beams with nuts and cotter pins. Universal joints in the outer ends of the drive axles allow simultaneous wheel rotation and wheel turning to the right or left. The right-side drive axle also has an inner universal joint near the differential.

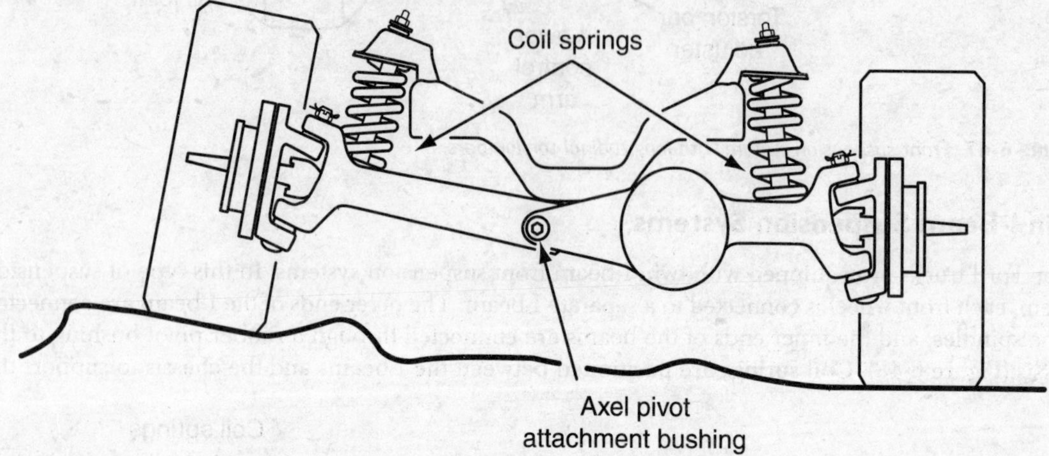

FIGURE 6-49 *Four-wheel-drive twin I-beam front suspension with coil springs.*

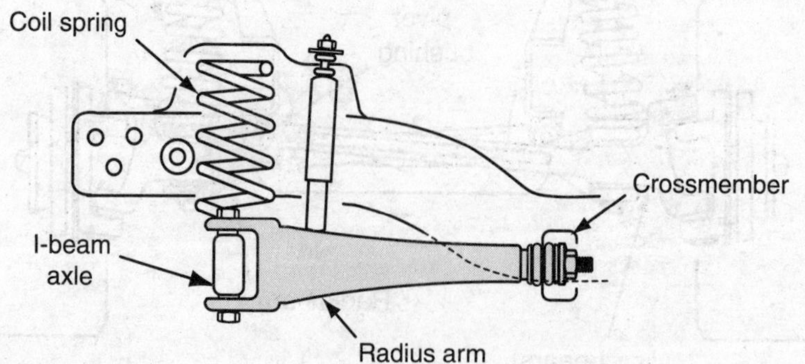

FIGURE 6-50 *Radius arms on a twin I-beam front suspension system with coil springs.*

Ford F-250 and F-350 four-wheel-drive trucks have a leaf spring twin I-beam front suspension system (Figure 6-51). U-bolts retain the leaf springs to the twin I-beams. A bushing in the front of the leaf spring eye is bolted into a frame bracket. The bushing in the rear spring eye is connected to the frame through a conventional spring shackle (Figure 6-52). Since the leaf springs maintain the axle position, the radius arms are not required.

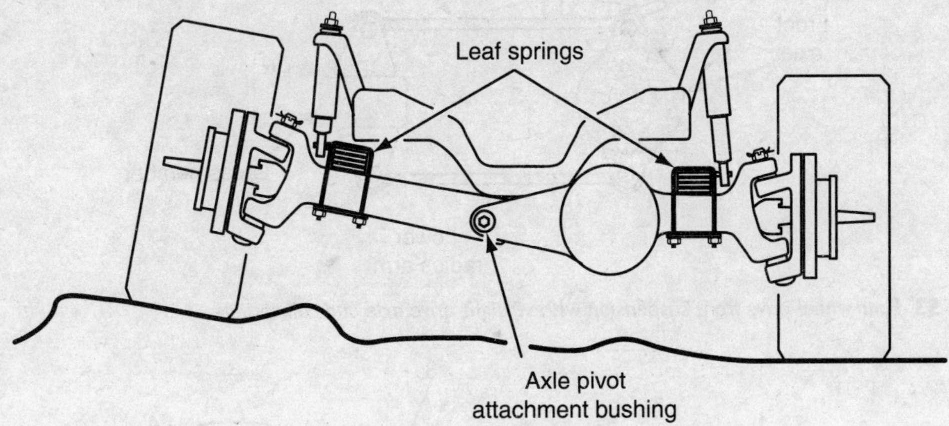

FIGURE 6-51 *Four-wheel-drive twin I-beam front suspension system with leaf springs.*

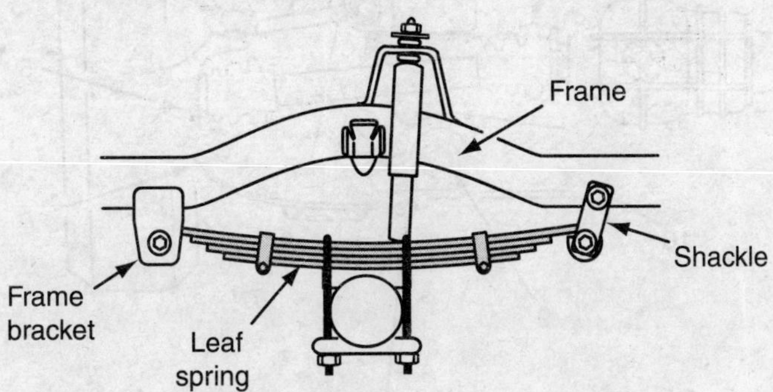

FIGURE 6-52 *Leaf spring mounting, four-wheel-drive twin I-beam front suspension.*

Some light-duty four-wheel-drive trucks have a straight front drive axle housing and a coil spring suspension system (Figure 6-53). Upper and lower radius rods control fore-and-aft drive axle movement, and a track bar controls lateral axle movement. Ball joints connect the steering knuckles to the outer ends of the drive axle housing.

Other light-duty four-wheel-drive trucks have a torsion bar front suspension system with upper and lower control arms (Figure 6-54 and Figure 6-55). The front of the torsion bars have hex-shaped ends that are mounted in a matching hex in the lower control arm. The hex-shaped rear ends of the torsion bars are mounted in adjusting arms that are retained in the torsion bar crossmember. An adjusting bolt in this crossmember contacts the outer end of each adjusting arm (Figure 6-56). Rotation of this adjusting bolt changes the tension on the torsion bar to adjust the curb riding height. On this type of torsion bar front suspension system, the front wheel bearing hubs are a prelubricated, sealed, nonserviceable assembly (Figure 6-57).

Twin I-beam front suspension systems have recently been replaced with short-and-long arm or torsion bar suspension systems, because these systems are lighter weight and provide improved ride quality.

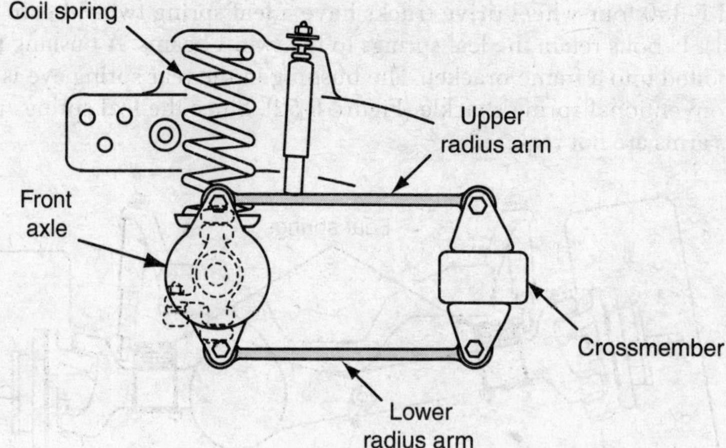

FIGURE 6-53 *Four-wheel-drive front suspension with straight drive axle and coil springs.*

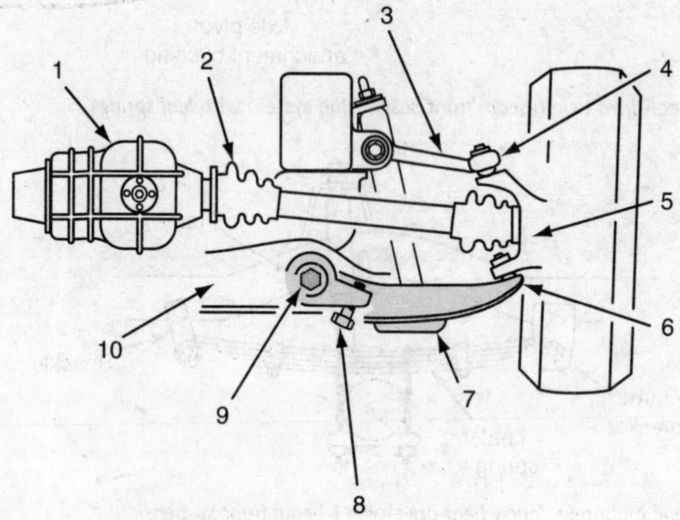

FIGURE 6-54 *Four-wheel-drive light-duty truck torsion bar front suspension.*

CURB RIDING HEIGHT

Regular inspection and proper maintenance of suspension systems are extremely important to maintain vehicle safety. The curb riding height is determined mainly by spring condition. Other suspension components such as control arm bushings will affect curb riding height if they are worn. Since incorrect curb riding height affects most of the other suspension angles, this measurement is critical. Sagged springs change the normal operating arc of the lower ball joint. This action causes excessive lateral movement of the tire during wheel jounce and rebound with resulting tire wear (Figure 6-58).

The curb riding height must be measured at the vehicle manufacturer's specified location, which varies depending on the type of suspension system. When the vehicle is on a level floor or an alignment rack, measure the curb riding height from the floor to the manufacturer's specified location on the chassis.

ITEM	DESCRIPTION
1	Final drive unit
2	Drive axle
3	Upper control arm
4	Upper ball joint
5	Steering knuckle
6	Lower ball joint
7	Lower control arm
8	Torsion bar adjuster
9	Torsion bar
10	Crossmember

FIGURE 6-55 *Component identification light-duty four-wheel-drive truck torsion bar front suspension.*

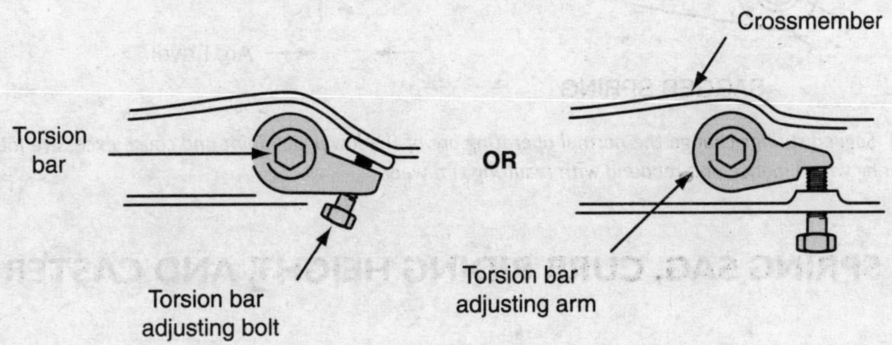

FIGURE 6-56 *Torsion bar adjusting arm and adjusting bolt.*

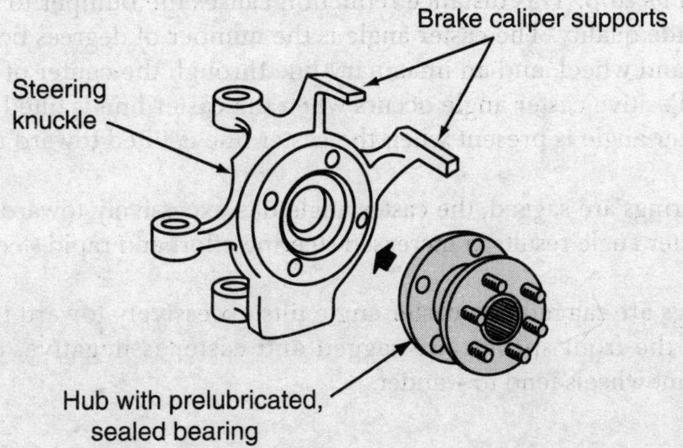

FIGURE 6-57 *Four-wheel-drive torsion bar front suspension with sealed non-serviceable front wheel bearing hubs.*

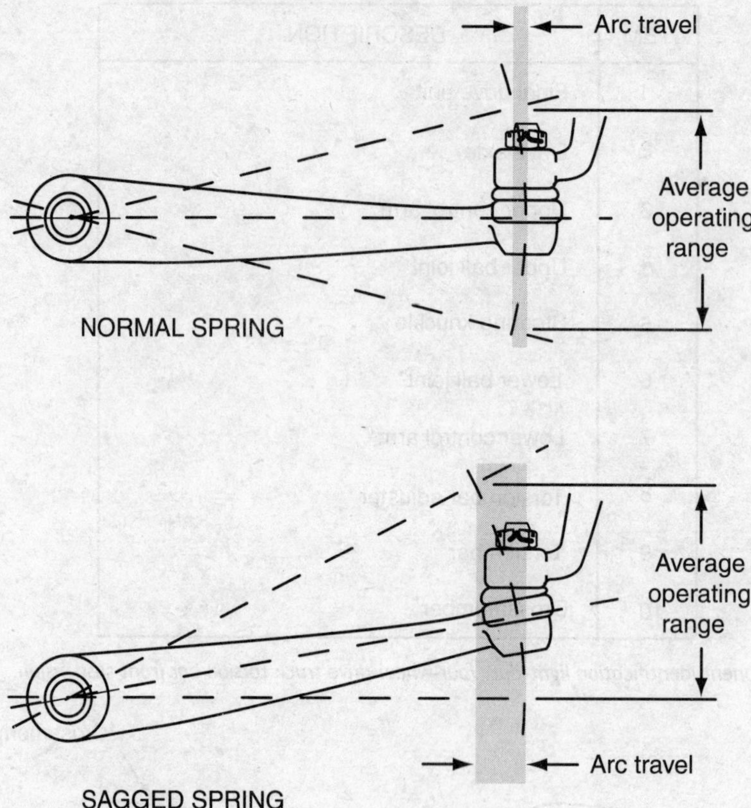

FIGURE 6-58 *Sagged springs change the normal operating arc of the lower ball joint and cause excessive lateral tire movement during wheel jounce and rebound with resulting tire wear.*

FRONT SPRING SAG, CURB RIDING HEIGHT, AND CASTER ANGLE

Sagged springs cause insufficient curb riding height. Therefore, the distance is reduced between the rebound bumper and its stop. This distance reduction causes the bumper to hit the stop frequently with resulting harsh ride quality. The caster angle is the number of degrees between the true vertical centerline of the tire and wheel, and an imaginary line through the center of the upper strut mount and lower ball joint. Positive caster angle occurs when the caster line is tilted toward the rear of the vehicle. Negative caster angle is present when the caster line is tilted toward the front of the vehicle (Figure 6-59).

When both rear springs are sagged, the caster angle tilts excessively toward the rear of the vehicle (Figure 6-60). This caster angle results in increased steering effort and rapid steering wheel return after a turn.

If both front springs are sagged, the caster angle tilts excessively toward the front of the vehicle (Figure 6-61). When the front springs are sagged and caster is negative, directional stability is decreased, and the front wheels tend to wander.

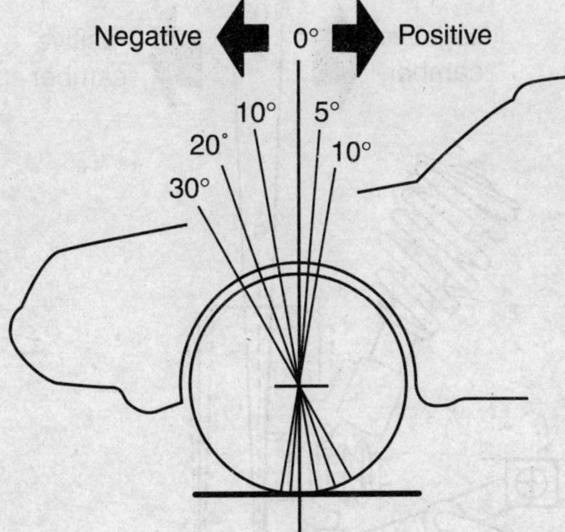

FIGURE 6-59 *Positive and negative caster.*

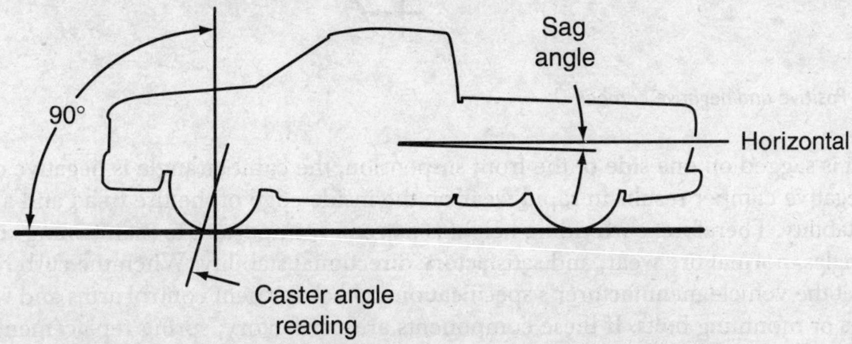

FIGURE 6-60 *Effects of rear spring sag and incorrect curb riding height on caster angle.*

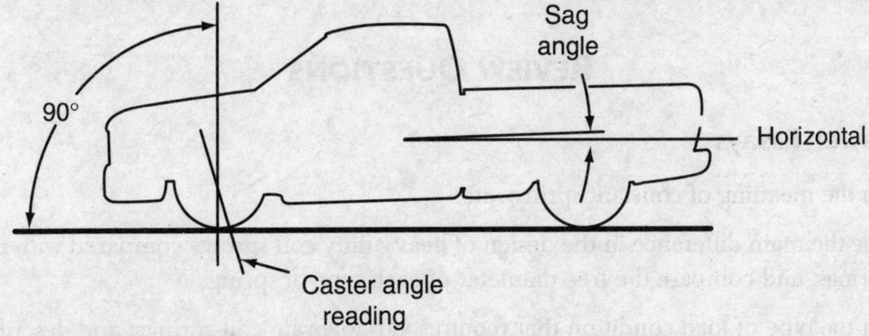

FIGURE 6-61 *Effects of front spring sag on caster angle.*

SPRING SAG, CURB RIDING HEIGHT, AND CAMBER ANGLE

Positive camber occurs when the camber line is tilted outward from the vertical centerline of the wheel. If the camber line is tilted inward from the vertical centerline of the wheel, the camber is said to be negative (Figure 6-62).

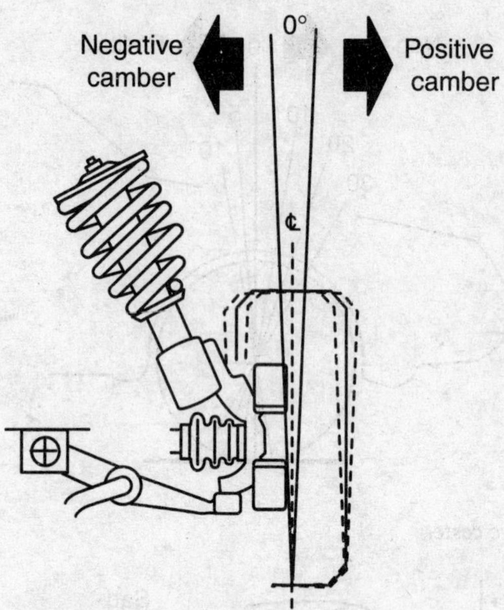

FIGURE 6-62 *Positive and negative camber.*

If a spring is sagged on one side of the front suspension, the camber angle is negative on that side. Excessive negative camber results in rapid wear on the inside edge of the tire tread and a decrease in directional stability. Therefore, curb riding height is extremely important to maintaining correct wheel alignment angles, normal tire wear, and satisfactory directional stability. When the curb riding height does not meet the vehicle manufacturer's specifications, check for bent control arms and worn control arm bushings or mounting bolts. If these components are satisfactory, spring replacement is required to correct the curb riding height.

REVIEW QUESTIONS

Short Answer Essays

1. Explain the meaning of constant spring rate.
2. Describe the main difference in the design of heavy-duty coil springs compared with regular-duty coil springs, and compare the free diameter of each type of spring.
3. Explain the type of load condition that requires variable-rate coil springs, and describe the load-carrying advantage of these springs.
4. Describe the design of taper-wire closed-end springs.
5. Explain torsion bar action during wheel jounce and rebound.
6. Describe the action of a leaf spring as it compresses.
7. Explain the position of the lower control arm when the lower ball joint is compression loaded.

8. Describe the position of the wear indicator when a ball joint is worn.
9. Explain the basic purpose of the lower control arms.
10. Describe the effect of sagged front springs on caster angle and directional stability.

Fill-in-the-Blanks

1. Heavy-duty coil springs are designed to carry ____________ to ____________ percent greater loads than regular-duty coil springs.
2. A variable-rate coil spring provides automatic ____________ adjustment.
3. In a variable-rate spring, the ____________ coils operate during the complete range of spring loading.
4. The load-carrying ball joint is attached to the control arm on which the ____________ ____________ is seated.
5. If the lower control arm is mounted above the steering knuckle and rests on the knuckle, the lower ball joint is ____________ ____________.
6. When the grease nipple shoulder is extended from the ball joint housing, the ball joint is ____________.
7. When one front wheel strikes a road irregularity, the stabilizer bar reduces ____________ ____________.
8. The strut rod prevents ____________ and ____________ lower control arm movement.
9. When the front springs are sagged, the positive caster is ____________.
10. If a front spring is sagged, the camber angle moves toward a ____________ position.

Multiple Choice

1. A 400-pound load deflects a linear-rate coil spring 1 inch. An 800-pound load will deflect this coil spring:
   A. 1.5 inches.
   B. 2 inches.
   C. 3 inches.
   D. 4 inches.
2. Heavy-duty coil springs have:
   A. The same wire diameter as a regular-duty coil spring.
   B. A shorter free height compared to a regular-duty coil spring.
   C. A 10 percent increase in load carrying capacity.
   D. A high aluminum content in the spring material.
3. A car's rear coil springs keep breaking. This problem is likely due to:
   A. Continual driving on rough road surfaces.
   B. Continual driving on curved roads.

C. Excessive air pressure in the rear tires.
D. Constant overloading of the rear suspension.

4. All of these statements about coil springs are true EXCEPT:
A. It is impossible to compare variable-rate and linear-rate coil springs.
B. Heavy-duty rear springs are required if the rear suspension is continually carrying a heavy load.
C. A variable-rate coil spring has a standard spring rate.
D. A variable-rate coil spring may have unequally spaced coils.

5. While discussing a torsion bar front suspension system:
A. One end of the torsion bar is attached to the upper control arm.
B. A suspension height adjustment is positioned on the end of the torsion bar connected to the control arm.
C. Torsion bars may be mounted longitudinally or transversely in a front suspension system.
D. Torsion bars eliminate the need for shock absorbers in the front suspension system.

6. While discussing leaf springs:
A. A fiberglass mono-leaf spring is heavier than a steel mono-leaf spring.
B. Some mono-leaf springs are mounted transversely.
C. In a multiple-leaf spring, the lower leaf is called the main leaf.
D. A multiple-leaf spring has the same stiffness regardless of how much it is compressed.

7. All these statements about ball joints are true EXCEPT:
A. A load-carrying ball joint wears faster than a non-load-carrying ball joint.
B. A non-load-carrying ball joint is designed with a preload.
C. Wear indicators may be positioned in the side of the ball-joint housing.
D. Low-friction ball joints have a highly polished ball socket surrounded by a high-strength polymer bearing.

8. While discussing MacPherson strut suspension systems:
A. During a turn, the strut, spring, and knuckle rotate on the upper strut mount.
B. The lower end of the coil spring is seated on the lower control arm.
C. The strut is welded into the knuckle and these components are replaced as an assembly.
D. The inner ends of the lower control arms are bolted to the vehicle frame.

9. While discussing short-and-long arm front suspension systems:
A. The coil springs are positioned between the upper and lower control arms.
B. Compared with a suspension system with equal length control arms, the short-and-long design reduces track width change and tire wear.
C. The outer ends of the stabilizer bar may be attached to the steering knuckles.
D. The coil spring is retained in the lower control arm with a clamp and bolt.

10. While discussing sagged springs:
A. Sagged front springs cause harsh riding.
B. Sagged front springs cause excessive positive caster on the front wheels and increased directional stability.
C. Sagged rear springs cause excessive negative caster on the front wheels.
D. Sagged rear springs cause excessive positive camber on the front wheels.

Rear Suspension Systems

7

Upon completion and review of this chapter, you should be able to:

- Describe a live-axle rear suspension system.
- List the advantages and disadvantages of a live-axle leaf-spring rear suspension system.
- Describe the movement of the rear axle housing during vehicle acceleration.
- Explain how the differential torque is absorbed in a live-axle coil-spring rear suspension system.
- Explain the purpose of a tracking bar in a live-axle coil-spring rear suspension system.
- Explain the difference between a semi-independent and an independent rear suspension system.
- Describe how individual rear wheel movement is provided in a semi-independent rear suspension system.
- Explain the difference between a MacPherson strut and a modified MacPherson strut rear suspension.
- Explain the advantage of attaching the differential housing to the chassis in an independent rear suspension system.

- Explain how differential and suspension vibration, noise, and shock are insulated from the chassis in a multilink independent rear suspension system.
- Explain how the top of the knuckle is supported in a multilink independent rear suspension system.
- Describe the effect of sagged rear springs on caster angle and steering.

INTRODUCTION

The **rear suspension system** plays a very important part in ride quality and in the control of suspension and differential noise, vibration, and shock. Although the front wheels actually steer the vehicle, the rear suspension is also vital to steering control. The rear suspension must also provide adequate tire life and maintain tire traction on the road surface. Rear suspension systems described in this chapter include live-axle, semi-independent, and independent. **Live-axle rear suspension systems** are found on rear-wheel-drive (RWD) trucks and vans, a few RWD cars, and some four-wheel-drive (4WD) cars. Most front-wheel-drive (FWD) vehicles have semi-independent or independent rear suspensions. Independent rear suspensions are also found on RWD cars and 4WD cars.

NOISE, VIBRATION, HARSHNESS

Original equipment manufacturers (OEMs) have made significant improvements in reducing vehicle noise, vibration, and harshness (NVH) because many customers prefer a quieter-running vehicle with reduced vibration and ride harshness. The suspension system plays a significant role in reducing NVH. Many of the suspension features described in this chapter are designed to reduce NVH. These features include track bars and braces, proper car riding height, hydraulic suspension system mounts, independent rear suspension systems, and large rubber insulating bushings on suspension system mountings.

However, the technician must understand that reducing NVH involves many mechanical and body/chassis components on the vehicle. For example, the 2001 Oldsmobile Aurora has an optimized body structure, which is the major reason for reduced NVH. In this body design, lateral tie bars that connect the front longitudinal rails provide a stiffer front end. At the rear of the car, one-piece side rings with integral quarters eliminate rear pillar seams and provide a more precise door fit. The instrument panel and steering column are integrated solidly into the body structure by a cast magnesium beam. The door hinges are through-bolted and thick spacer blocks are installed on these bolts to provide a very solid door attachment. Because the entire body is stronger and more rigid, the suspension can provide excellent ride quality and steering control without having to compensate for unwanted body flexing. In addition, appropriate body cavities like the dash panel are filled with expandable baffles to eliminate noise. The five-layer noise buffer in the dash panel contains these materials:

1. Fiberglass insulation mat
2. Viscoelastic energy-absorbing layer
3. Double steel panel
4. Single one-piece dash mat

A cast foam floor carpet system reduces noise transmitted through the floor pan and wheel wells. The door pillar and rocker panel cavities contain over 20 noise blockers.

Many engine refinements reduce vibration. For example, many engines now have a deep skirt block with the main bearings bolted through the sides of the block and also vertically. Many engines now have cast oil pans and rocker covers rather than stamped steel components. The main bearing caps are contained in a one-piece casting on many engines to increase bottom end strength and reduce engine vibration. Some V-8 engines have a rubber intake manifold valley stuffer attached to the underside of the intake manifold to reduce vibration. Other vehicles have a slip yoke vibration damper mounted on the front of the drive shaft to reduce driveline vibration. Therefore, reducing NVH is a total vehicle concept.

Vibration Theory

Vibrations have these three elements:

1. Source–the cause of the vibration
2. Path–where the vibration travels through the vehicle
3. Responder–the component where the vibration is felt

For example, if the vehicle has an unbalanced tire, this is the vibration source. The vibration path is the steering and suspension system through which the vibration travels. The responder is the steering wheel because this component is where the customer feels the vibration (Figure 7-1). When diagnosing vibration problems, locate and correct the source of the vibration. In the previous example of the unbalanced tire, installing a rigid brace from the steering column to the instrument panel and chassis may reduce the vibration experienced by the customer, but this does not solve the problem. To eliminate the problem, also diagnose the unbalanced tire condition and then balance the tire-and-wheel assembly.

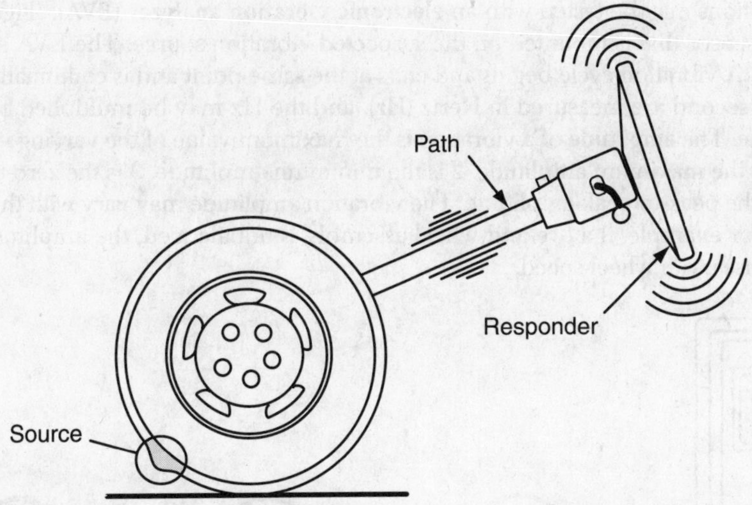

FIGURE 7-1 *Vibration source, path, and responder.*

Vibration may also produce noise. If a vehicle has a broken or improperly positioned tailpipe hanger that allows the tailpipe to contact the chassis, the customer may complain about a vibrating noise. The floor panel acts as a large speaker and amplifies the vibrating noise. The vibration path is through the exhaust system and chassis to the floor panel. The responder is the chassis and floor panel. In this case, after diagnosing the broken or improperly positioned tailpipe hanger, replace or reposition it so the vibration transfer path is eliminated.

Clamp a yardstick to a table top with 18 in (45 cm) hanging over the edge of the table (Figure 7-2). If the outer end of the yardstick is pulled upward or downward and then released, the end of the yardstick repeatedly vibrates up and down. Each vibration **cycle** begins at the midpoint with the yardstick straight. From this point, the vibration cycle continues to the lowest point of travel and then moves up through the midpoint to the highest point of travel. The vibration cycle then returns to the midpoint where it begins over again.

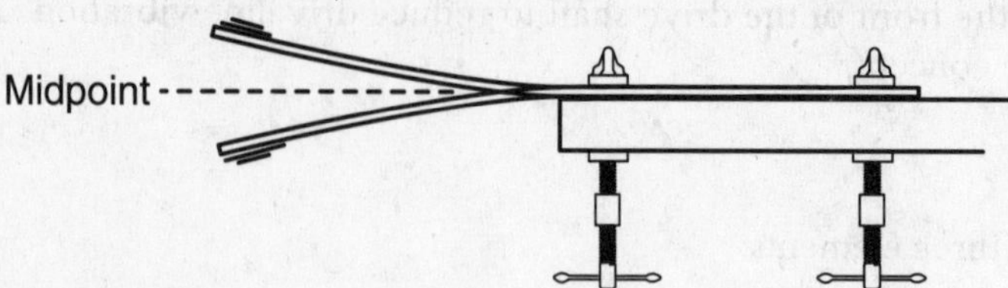

FIGURE 7-2 *Theory of vibration cycles.*

If the end of the vibrating yardstick completed 10 cycles per second, this is called the **frequency** of the vibration. To calculate the cycles per minute multiply the cycles per second by 60. In this example the 10 × 60 = 600 cycles per minute.

If the yardstick is clamped to the table top with an 8 in (20 cm) overhang, the end of the yardstick will vibrate much faster when the end of the yardstick is pulled upward or downward. Under this condition, the end of the yardstick may vibrate at a frequency of 30 cycles per second or 1800 cycles per minute.

Many vehicle vibrations are caused by an out-of-balance rotating component or engine firing pulses improperly isolated from the passenger compartment. Customers usually complain about vibrations that are felt in the steering wheel, instrument panel, frame or chassis, or the front or rear seat.

Vehicle vibrations may be tested with an **electronic vibration analyzer (EVA)**. (Figure 7-3). The EVA has a vibration sensor that is mounted on the suspected vibration source. The EVA senses and records vibration cycles. A vibration cycle begins and ends at the same point and is continually repeated (Figure 7-4). Cycles per second are measured in **Hertz (Hz)**, and the Hz may be multiplied by 60 to obtain the cycles per minute. The **amplitude** of a vibration is the maximum value of the varying vibration. In Figure 7-5, 1 represents the maximum amplitude, 2 is the minimum amplitude, 3 is the zero-to-peak amplitude, and 4 indicates the peak-to-peak amplitude. The vibration amplitude may vary with the rotating speed of a component. For example, if a tire-and-wheel assembly is unbalanced, the amplitude of the resulting vibrations increases with wheel speed.

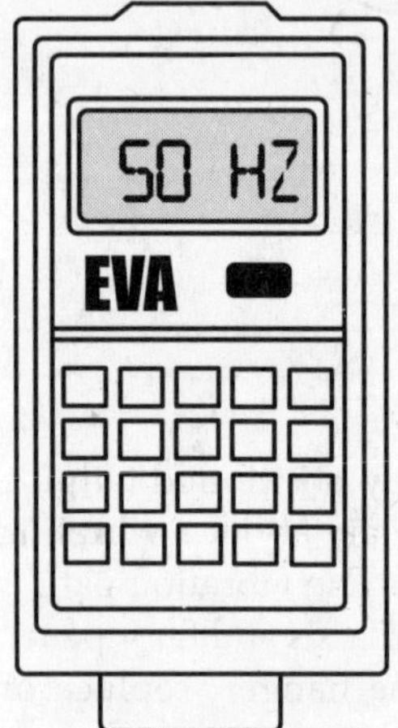

FIGURE 7-3 *Electronic vibration analyzer (EVA).*

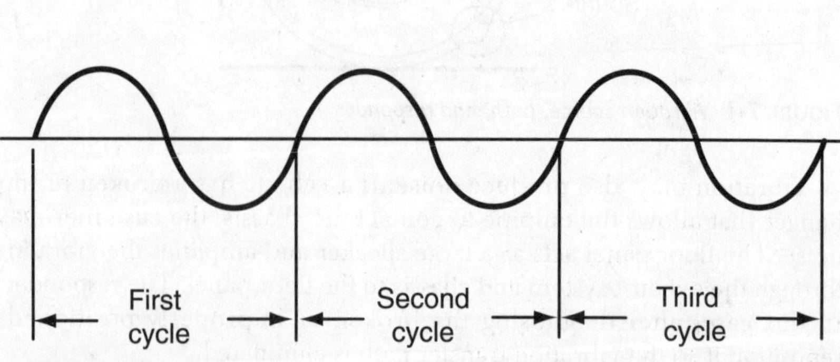

FIGURE 7-4 *Vibration cycles.*

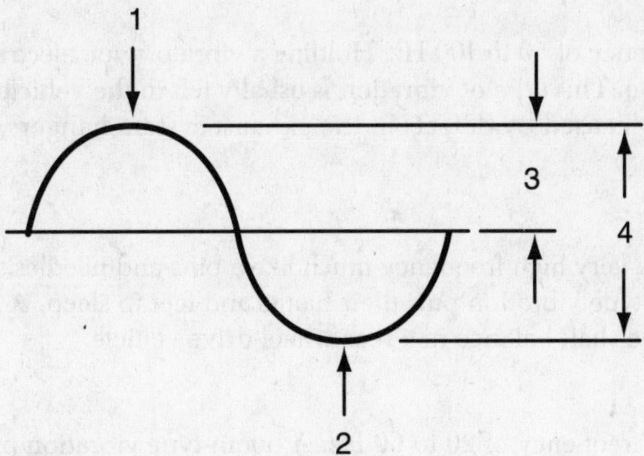

FIGURE 7-5 *Amplitude of vibration cycles.*

All objects have **natural vibration frequencies**. The natural frequency of a front suspension system is 10 to 15 Hz. The suspension system design determines the natural frequency. The natural frequency of the suspension system is the same at all vehicle speeds.

The vibration frequency caused by an unbalanced tire-and-wheel assembly increases with wheel speed. When the vibration frequency caused by the wheel balance problem intersects with the natural frequency of the suspension system, the suspension system begins to vibrate. This intersection point is called the **resonance**.

Vibration Classifications and Terminology

Vibrations that can be felt are:

1. Shake
2. Roughness
3. Buzz
4. Tingling

Vibrations that result in noise may be classified as:

1. Boom
2. Moan or drone
3. Howl
4. Whine

Shake

A shake is a vibration with a low frequency of 5 to 20 Hz, and is sometimes experienced in the steering wheel, seat, or console. Customers may refer to shake as shimmy, wobble, shudder, waddle, or hop. Most cases of a shake vibration are caused by brake rotors and drums or unbalanced tire-and-wheel assemblies. These defects cause a shake-type vibration that is vehicle-speed sensitive. The engine, clutch, or transmission may cause a shake-type vibration that is engine-speed sensitive.

Roughness

Roughness is a vibration with a higher frequency of 20 to 50 Hz. Holding a jigsaw to cut a piece of wood produces a roughness-type vibration. A roughness vibration may be caused by a defective wheel bearing. Prior to causing a roughness vibration, the defective wheel bearing would cause a howl.

Buzz

A buzz has a faster frequency of 50 to 100 Hz. Holding a vibrator-type electric razor produces a feeling similar to a buzz vibration. This type of vibration is usually felt in the vehicle floor or the seat. A buzz-type vibration is usually caused by defects in the exhaust system hangers, A/C compressor, or the engine.

Tingling

A tingling vibration has a very high frequency much like a pins-and-needles sensation. Customers may complain that a tingling-type vibration puts their hands and feet to sleep. A tingling vibration may be caused by improper drive shaft balance in a rear-wheel-drive vehicle.

Boom

A boom noise has a low frequency of 20 to 60 Hz. A boom-type vibration produces a noise similar to a bowling ball rolling down a bowling alley. A customer may describe a boom-type vibration as droning, growling, humming, rumbling, roaring, or moaning. A boom-type noise and vibration may be caused by engine backfiring resulting from ignition defects.

Moan or Drone

A moan or drone is a tone with a higher frequency of 60 to 120 Hz. A moan or drone produces a noise similar to a bumblebee in flight. Moan or drone may be caused by defects in the exhaust system or defective engine or transmission mounts.

Howl

A howl is a noise with frequency of 120 to 300 Hz, and this sound is much like the wind howling. A howling noise may be caused by worn differential bearings.

Whine

A whine is a high-pitched sound with a frequency of 300 to 500 Hz, and this sound is similar to a vacuum cleaner. A whine problem may be caused by meshing gears in the transmission of differential. When diagnosing vibration problems, the technician should match the vibration frequency to the rotating speed of a component, to help locate the component responsible for the vibration.

LIVE-AXLE REAR SUSPENSION SYSTEMS

Leaf-Spring Rear Suspension

A leaf spring is mounted longitudinally on each side of the rear suspension on some rear-wheel-drive cars and trucks (Figure 7-6). These relatively flat springs provide excellent lateral stability and reduce side sway, which contribute to a well-controlled ride with very good handling characteristics. However, leaf-spring rear suspension systems have a lot of **unsprung weight**, and leaf springs require a considerable amount of space.

The **semielliptical springs** have steel leaves and zinc or plastic interleaves to reduce corrosion, friction, and noise. A large rubber bushing is installed in the front eye of the main spring leaf, and a bolt retains this bushing to the front spring hanger (Figure 7-7). The rear spring shackle is bolted to a rubber bushing in the rear main leaf eye, and the upper shackle bolt extends through a similar rubber bushing in the rear spring hanger (Figure 7-8). Some rear spring shackles contain threaded steel bushings or a slipper mount in which the end of the spring slides through the shackle. Shackle insulating bushings help prevent the transfer of noise and road shock from the suspension to the chassis and vehicle interior. When a rear wheel strikes a road irregularity, the spring is compressed

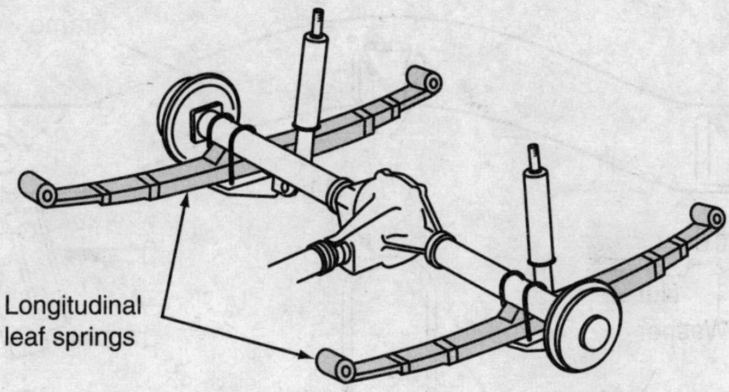

FIGURE 7-6 *Leaf-spring rear suspension system.*

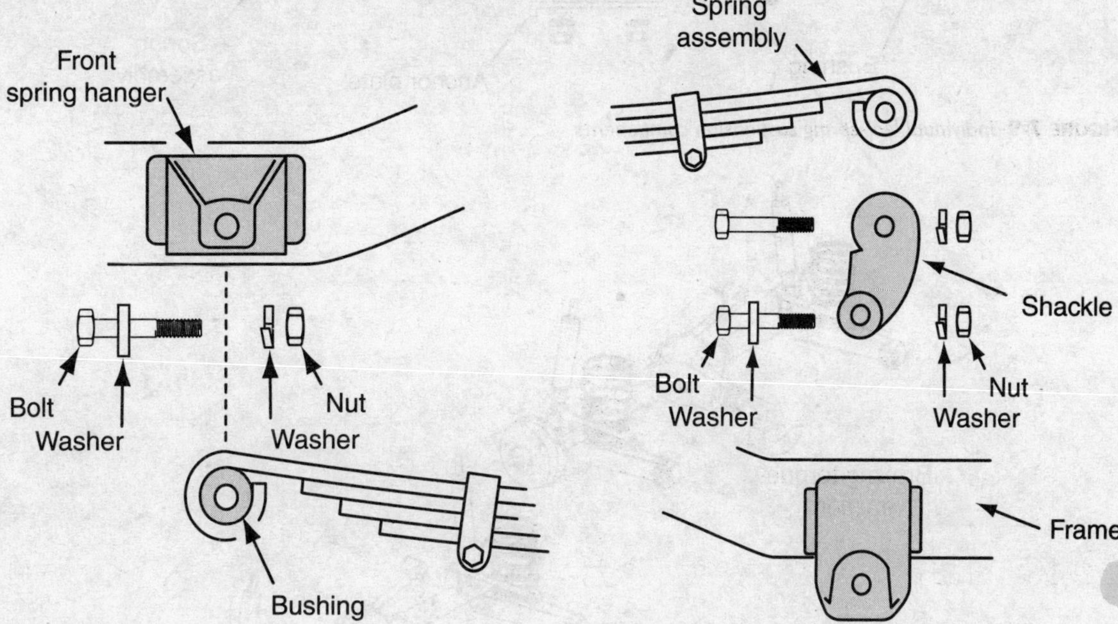

FIGURE 7-7 *Rear leaf-spring eye bushing.*

FIGURE 7-8 *Rear leaf-spring shackle.*

and the spring length changes. The rear shackle provides fore-and-aft movement with variations in spring length.

Because the differential axle housing is a one-piece unit, jounce and rebound travel of one rear wheel affects the position of the other rear wheel. This action increases tire wear and decreases ride quality and traction.

The differential axle housing is mounted above the springs, and a spring plate with an insulating clamp and U-bolts retains the springs to the rear axle housing (Figure 7-9). The shock absorbers are mounted between the spring plates and the frame.

The vehicle **sprung weight** is supported by the springs through the rear axle housing and wheels. When the vehicle accelerates, the rear wheels turn counterclockwise when viewed from the left vehicle side. One of Newton's laws of motion states that for every action there is an equal and opposite reaction. Therefore, when the wheels turn counterclockwise (when viewed from the left), the rear axle housing tries to rotate clockwise. This rear axle torque action is absorbed by the rear springs and the chassis moves downward (Figure 7-10). Engine torque supplied through the driveshaft to the differential

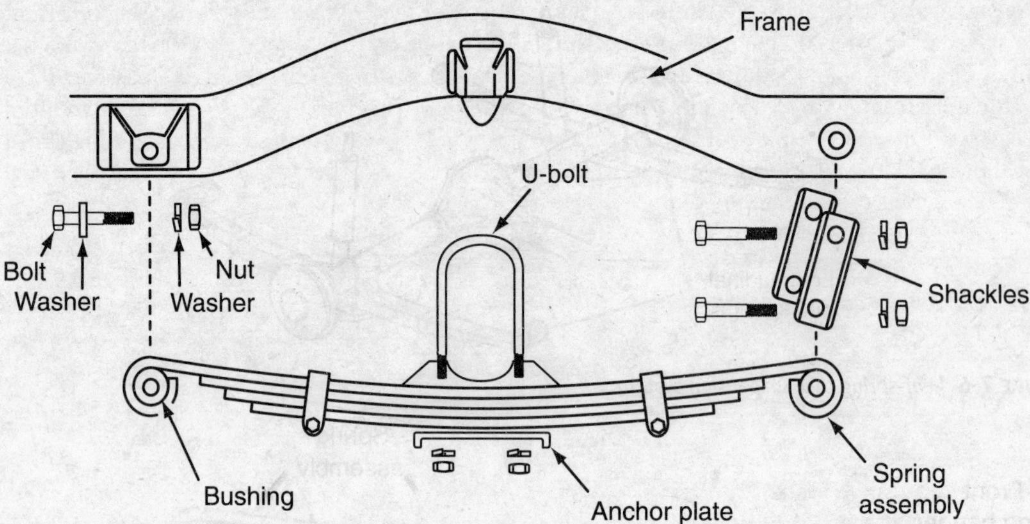

FIGURE 7-9 *Individual leaf-spring suspension components.*

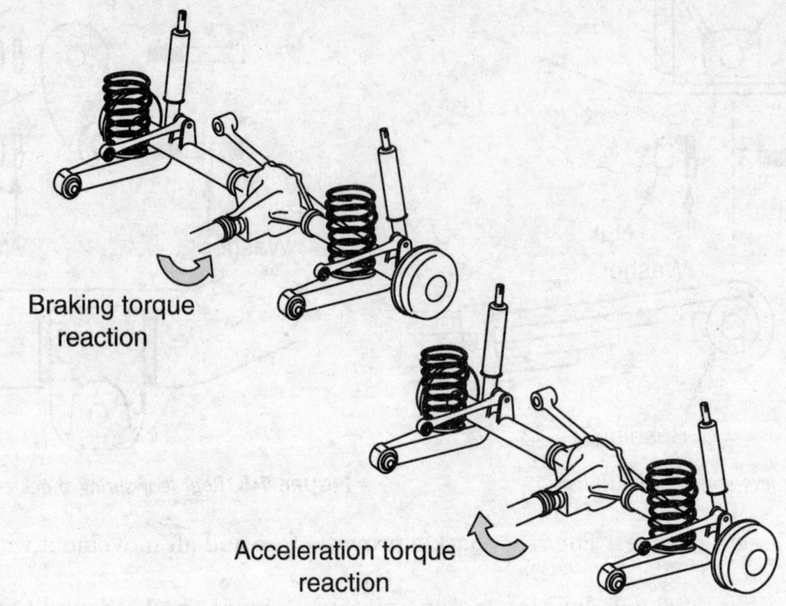

FIGURE 7-10 *Rear axle torque action during acceleration and deceleration.*

tends to twist the differential housing and the springs. This twisting action may be referred to as **axle windup**. Many leaf springs have a shorter distance from the center bolt to the front of the spring compared to the distance from the center bolt to the rear of the spring. This type of leaf spring is referred to as an **asymmetrical leaf spring**, and the shorter distance from the center bolt to the front of the spring resists axle windup. A **symmetrical leaf spring** has the same distance from the center bolt to the front and rear of the spring.

When braking and decelerating, the rear axle housing tries to turn counterclockwise. This rear axle torque action applied to the springs lifts the chassis. This action may be called **braking and deceleration torque**.

During hard acceleration, the entire power train twists in the opposite direction to engine crankshaft and drive shaft rotation. The engine and transmission mounts absorb this torque. However, the twisting action of the drive shaft and differential pinion shaft tends to lift the rear wheel on the passenger's side of the vehicle. Extremely hard acceleration may cause the rear wheel on the passenger's side to lift off the road surface. Once this rear wheel slips on the road surface, engine torque is reduced, and the leaf spring forces the wheel downward. When this rear tire contacts the road surface, engine torque increases and the cycle repeats. This repeated lifting of the differential housing is called **axle tramp**, and this action occurs on live-axle rear suspension systems. Axle tramp is more noticeable on live-axle leaf-spring rear suspension systems in which the springs have to absorb all the differential torque. For this reason, only engines with moderate horsepower were used with this type of rear suspension. Rear suspension and axle components such as spring mounts, shock absorbers, and wheel bearings may be damaged by axle tramp. Mounting one rear shock absorber in front of the rear axle and the other rear shock behind the rear axle helps reduce axle tramp.

In some cars with higher torque engines, a long torque arm is bolted to the rear axle housing (Figure 7-11). This torque arm helps prevent differential rotation during hard acceleration and braking. The front of this torque arm is mounted in a rubber insulator and bracket that is bolted to the back of the transmission housing. This long torque arm helps prevent differential rotation when high torque is delivered from the engine to the differential. The center bearing assembly on the drive shaft is bolted to the long torque arm. This rear suspension system has a track bar (tie-rod) connected from the left side of the rear axle housing to the chassis to help prevent lateral rear axle movement. A track bar brace is connected from the chassis end of the track bar to the other side of the chassis to provide extra rigidity.

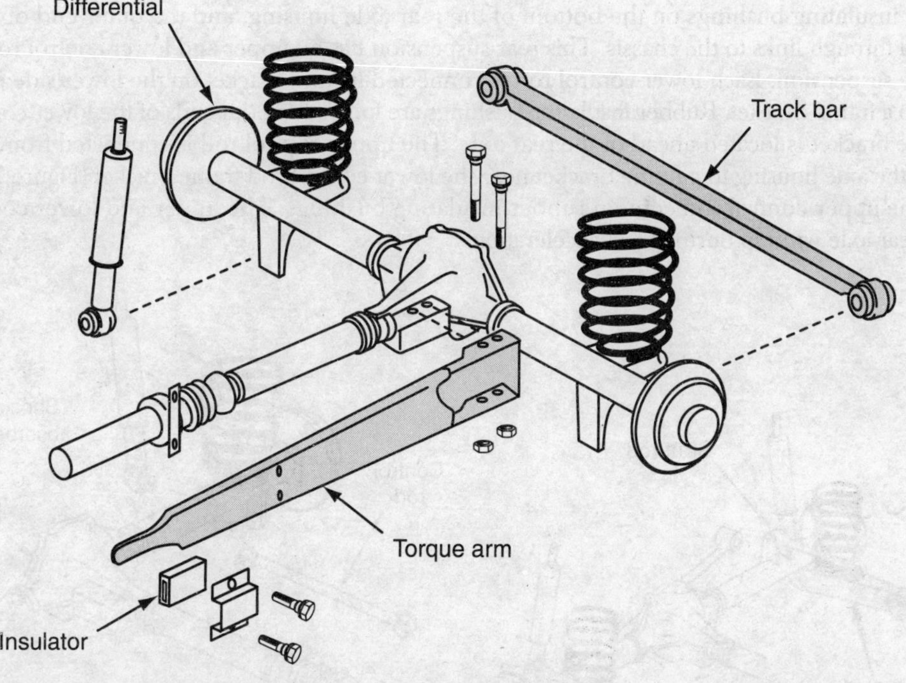

FIGURE 7-11 *Rear suspension system with long torque arm and track bar.*

Coil-Spring Rear Suspension

WARNING: Compressed coil springs contain a large amount of energy. Never disconnect any suspension component that suddenly releases the coil-spring tension. This action may result in personal injury and vehicle damage.

WARNING: Always follow the vehicle manufacturer's recommended rear suspension service procedures in the service manual to avoid personal injury.

Some rear-wheel-drive cars have a coil-spring rear suspension. Upper and lower suspension arms with insulating bushings are connected between the differential housing and the frame (Figure 7-12). The upper arms control lateral movement, and the lower trailing control arms absorb differential torque. In some rear suspension systems, the upper arms are replaced with strut rods. The front of the upper and lower arms contains large rubber bushings. When strut rods are used in place of the upper arms, both ends of these rods contain large rubber bushings to prevent noise and vibration transfer from the suspension to the chassis. The coil springs are usually mounted between the lower suspension arms and the frame, whereas the shock absorbers are mounted between the back of the suspension arms and the frame.

Some rear suspension systems have a **track bar** connected from one side of the differential housing to the chassis to prevent lateral chassis movement. Large rubber insulating bushings are positioned in each end of the track bar.

Some late model sport utility vehicles (SUVs) have a rear suspension system with coil springs and shock absorbers mounted separately from the springs (Figure 7-13). Notice that a control rod is mounted in rubber insulating bushings on the bottom of the rear axle housing, and the outer end of this bar is connected through links to the chassis. This rear suspension has an upper and lower control rod on each side of the suspension. Each lower control rod is connected from a bracket on the lower side of the axle housing to a frame bracket. Rubber insulating bushings are located in both ends of the lower control rods. The frame bracket is located ahead of the rear axle. The upper control rod is connected from a bracket on top of the axle housing to a frame bracket near the lower control rod frame bracket (Figure 7-14). Both ends of the upper control rod contain rubber insulating bushings. The upper and lower control rods prevent rear axle windup during hard acceleration.

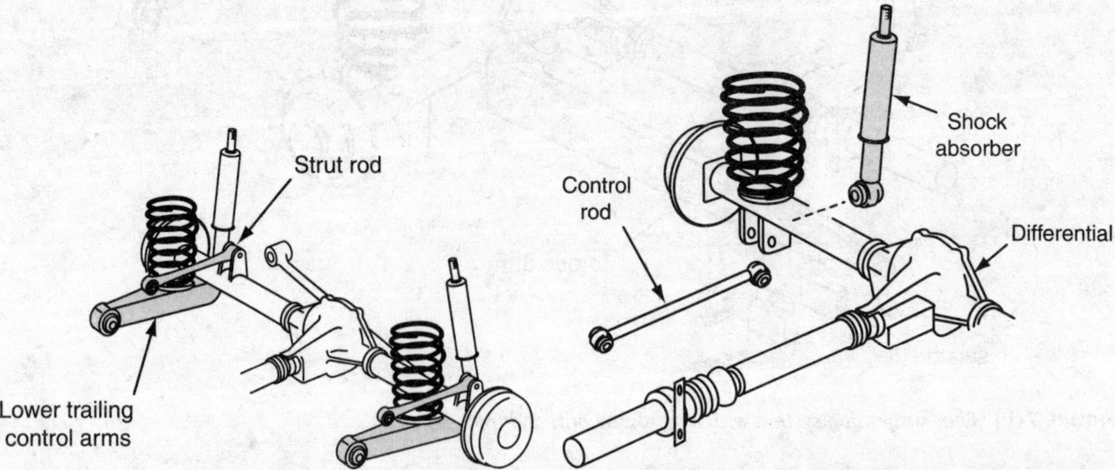

FIGURE 7-12 *Live-axle coil-spring rear suspension.*

FIGURE 7-13 *Rear suspension system with coil springs and shock absorbers mounted separately.*

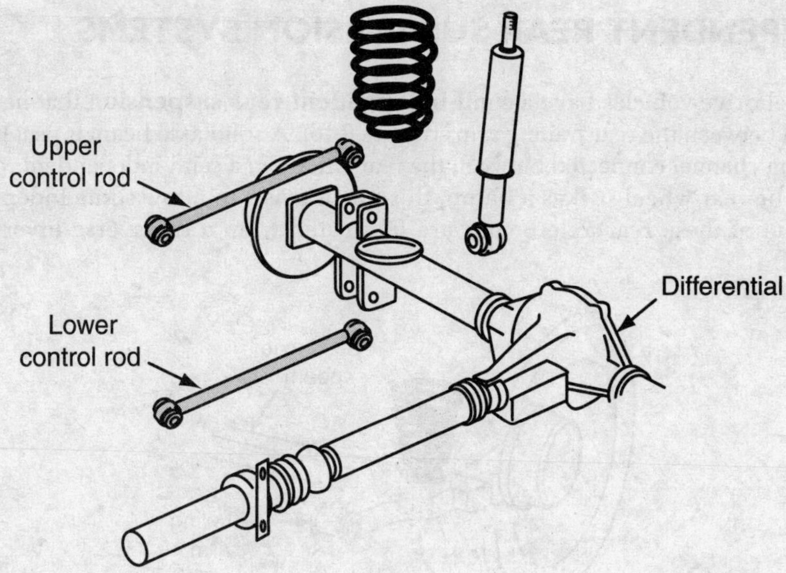

FIGURE 7-14 *Rear suspension system with upper and lower control rods.*

This SUV rear suspension also has a track bar connected from a bracket on the rear of the axle housing to a frame bracket on the opposite side of the vehicle. The track bar prevents lateral rear axle movement. A rear axle brace is also connected from the track bar frame bracket to another frame bracket on the opposite side of the vehicle (Figure 7-15). The rear axle brace prevents any movement of the track bar frame bracket during off-road or severe driving conditions. The dual rear axle rods on each side of this suspension with the track bar and brace provide a very stable rear axle position during hard acceleration and severe driving conditions. This rear axle stability improves tire life, ride comfort, and steering control.

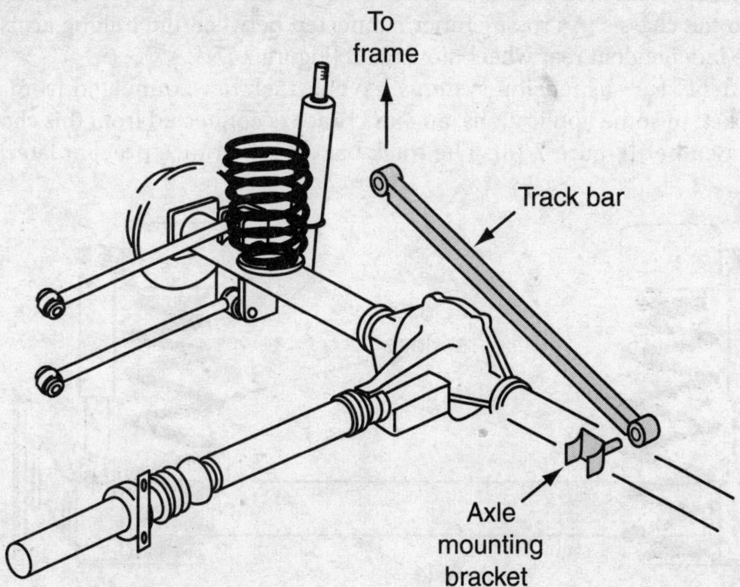

FIGURE 7-15 *Track bar and brace.*

SEMI-INDEPENDENT REAR SUSPENSION SYSTEMS

Many front-wheel-drive vehicles have a **semi-independent rear suspension** that has a **solid axle beam** connected between the rear trailing arms (Figure 7-16). A solid axle beam is usually a transverse inverted U-section channel connected between the rear wheels in a semi-independent rear suspension system. When one rear wheel strikes a bump, this beam twists to allow some independent wheel movement. Some of these rear axle beams are fabricated from a transverse inverted U-section channel.

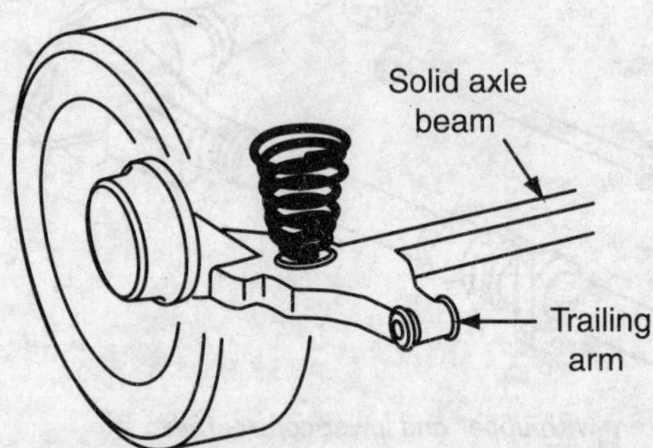

FIGURE 7-16 *Semi-independent rear suspension system.*

In some rear suspension systems, the inverted U-section channel contains an integral tubular stabilizer bar. When one rear wheel strikes a road irregularity and the wheel moves upward, the inverted U-section channel twists, which allows some independent rear wheel movement. The trailing arms are connected to chassis brackets through rubber insulating bushings. In some semi-independent rear suspension systems, the coil springs are mounted on the rear struts, the lower spring seat is located on the strut, and the upper spring seat is positioned on the upper strut mount.

In other semi-independent rear suspension systems, the coil springs are mounted separately from the shock absorbers. Coil-spring seats are located on the trailing arms, and the shock absorbers are connected from the trailing arms to the chassis. A crossmember connected between the trailing arms provides a twisting action and some independent rear wheel movement (Figure 7-17).

Some semi-independent rear suspension systems have a track bar connected from a rear axle bracket to a chassis bracket. In some applications, an extra brace is connected from this chassis bracket to the rear upper crossmember (Figure 7-18). The track bar and the brace prevent lateral rear axle movement.

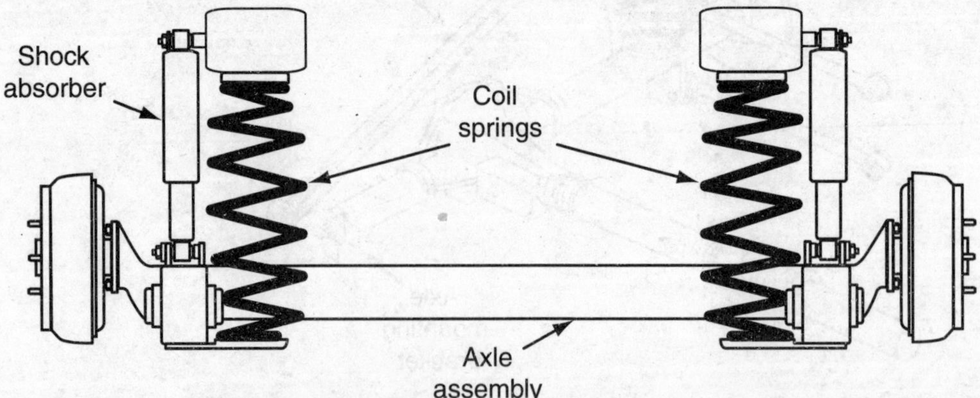

FIGURE 7-17 *Semi-independent rear suspension system with coil springs and shock absorbers mounted separately.*

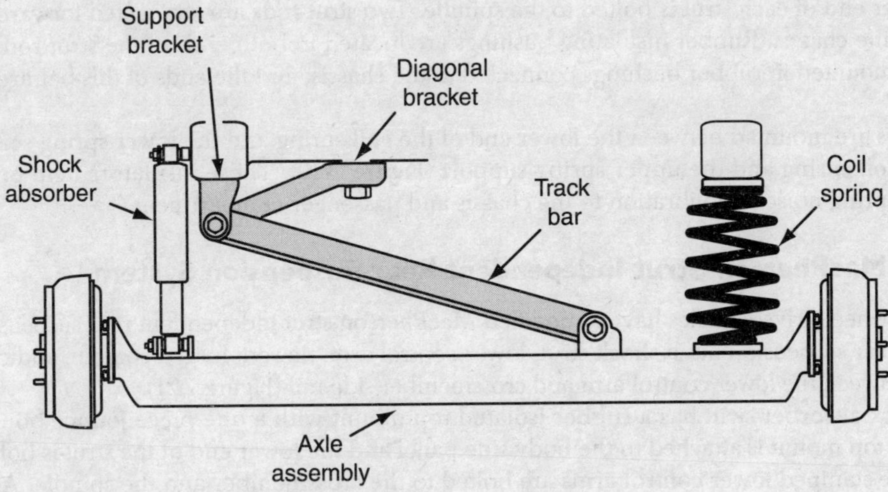

FIGURE 7-18 *Semi-independent rear suspension with track bar and brace.*

INDEPENDENT REAR SUSPENSION SYSTEMS

MacPherson Strut Independent Rear Suspension System

In an **independent rear suspension** system, each rear wheel can move independently from the opposite rear wheel. Independent rear suspension systems may be found on front-wheel-drive and rear-wheel-drive vehicles. When rear wheel movement is independent, ride quality, tire life, steering control, and traction are improved. In a MacPherson strut rear suspension system, the coil springs are mounted on the rear struts. A lower spring seat is located on the strut, and the upper spring seat is positioned on the upper strut mount. This upper strut mount is bolted into the inner fender reinforcement. Dual lower control arms on each side of the suspension are connected from the chassis to the lower end of the spindle (Figure 7-19).

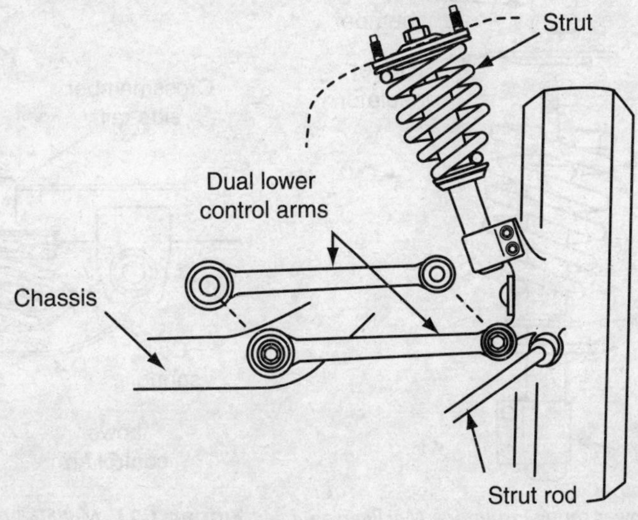

FIGURE 7-19 *MacPherson strut independent rear suspension system.*

The lower end of each strut is bolted to the spindle. Two strut rods are connected forward from the spindles to the chassis. Rubber insulating bushings are located in both ends of the strut rods. A stabilizer bar is mounted in rubber bushings connected to the chassis, and the ends of this bar are linked to the struts.

Insulators are mounted between the lower end of the coil spring and the lower spring seat, and the top of the coil spring and the upper spring support (Figure 7-20). These insulators help prevent the transfer of spring noise and vibration to the chassis and passenger compartment.

Modified MacPherson Strut Independent Rear Suspension System

Some front-wheel-drive vehicles have a modified MacPherson strut independent rear suspension. Each side of the rear suspension has a shock strut, lower control arm, tie-rod, forged spindle, and coil spring mounted between the lower control arm and crossmember side rail (Figure 7-21).

The shock absorber strut has a rubber isolated top mount with a one-piece jounce bouncer dust shield. This top mount is attached to the body side panel and the lower end of the strut is bolted to the spindle. The stamped lower control arms are bolted to the crossmember and the spindle. A tie-rod is connected from the spindle to the underbody. The purpose of each rear suspension component may be summarized as follows:

1. Stamped lower control arm–controls the lateral (side-to-side) wheel movement and contains the lower spring seat.
2. Tie-rod–controls fore-and-aft wheel movement and positions the spindle properly.
3. Shock absorber strut–reacts to braking forces and provides suspension damping. A strut internal rebound stop provides rebound control, and an external jounce bumper supplies jounce control.
4. Coil spring–controls suspension travel, provides ride height control, and acts as a metal-to-metal jounce stop.

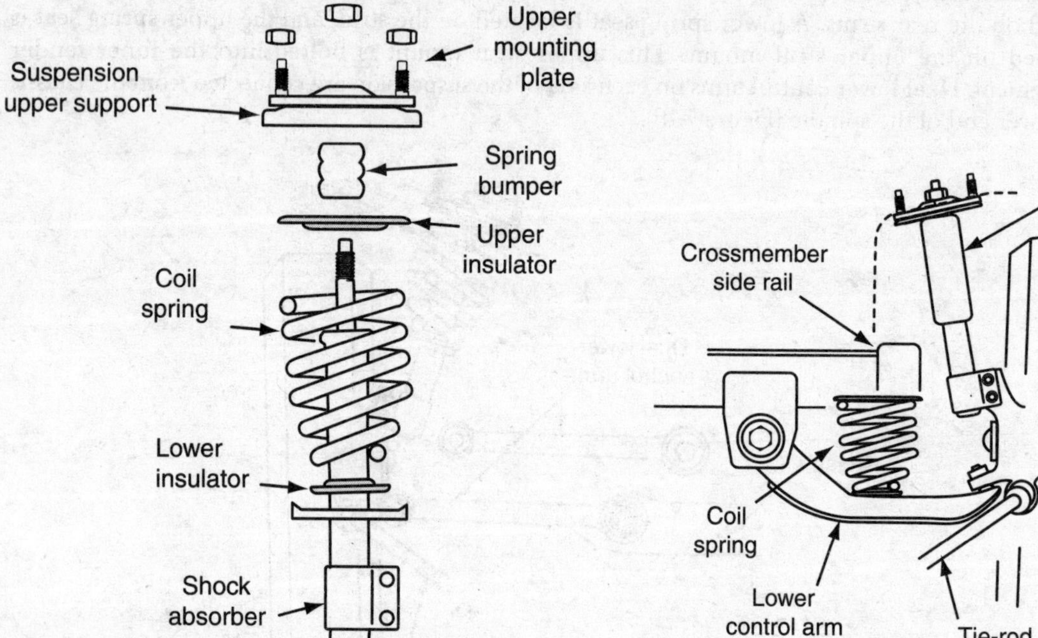

FIGURE 7-20 *Upper and lower spring insulators, MacPherson strut independent rear suspension.*

FIGURE 7-21 *Modified MacPherson strut independent rear suspension.*

5. Forged spindle–supports the wheel bearings and attaches to the lower control arms, tie-rod, brake assembly, and strut.
6. Suspension bushings–insulate the chassis and passenger compartment from road noise and vibration.
7. Suspension fasteners–connect components such as the spindle and strut. These fasteners must always be replaced with equivalent quality parts, and each fastener must be tightened to the specified torque.

Independent Rear Suspension with Lower Control Arm and Ball Joint

Some front-wheel-drive cars have an independent rear suspension system with a ball joint pressed into the outer end of the lower control arm. The ball joint contains a conventional wear indicator. The upper end of the ball joint stud is bolted into the knuckle (Figure 7-22). The inner end of the lower control arm is connected to the chassis through two rubber insulating bushings (Figure 7-23).

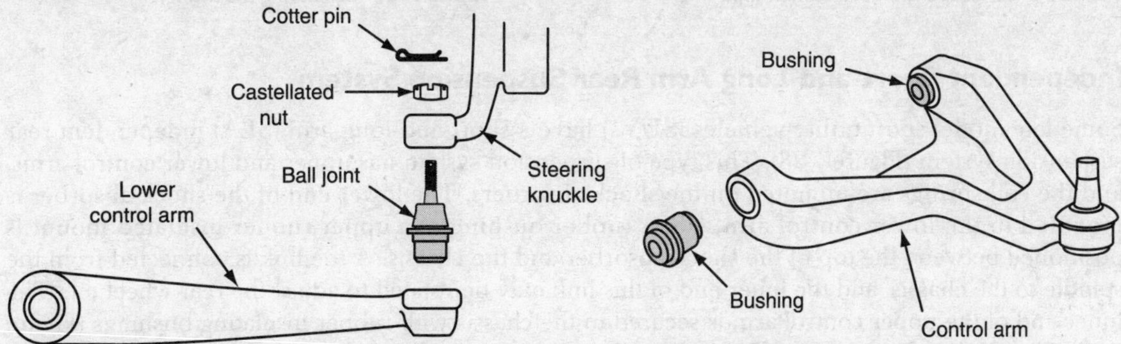

FIGURE 7-22 *Lower control arm and ball joint.*

FIGURE 7-23 *Lower control arm bushings.*

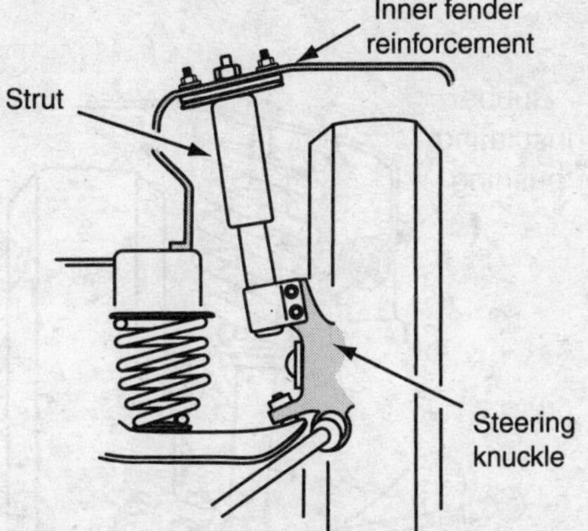

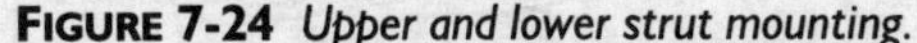

FIGURE 7-24 *Upper and lower strut mounting.*

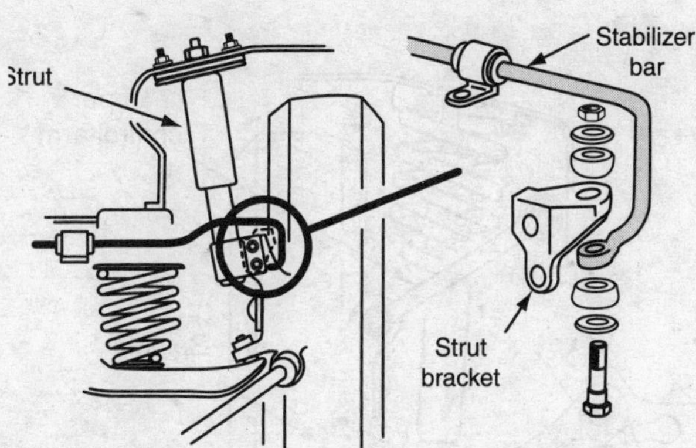

FIGURE 7-25 *Stabilizer bar mounting.*

The lower end of the strut is bolted to the knuckle, and the upper strut mount is bolted to the inner fender reinforcement (Figure 7-24). A stabilizer bar is mounted in bushings attached to the chassis, and the outer ends of this bar are linked to brackets connected to the strut (Figure 7-25).

A suspension adjustment link is connected from the lower control arm to the knuckle (Figure 7-26). This link provides a **rear wheel toe** adjustment. A coil-spring seat is located in the lower control arm and the coil spring is mounted between this seat and an upper seat in the chassis (Figure 7-27). Upper and lower insulators are mounted between the coil spring and the seats.

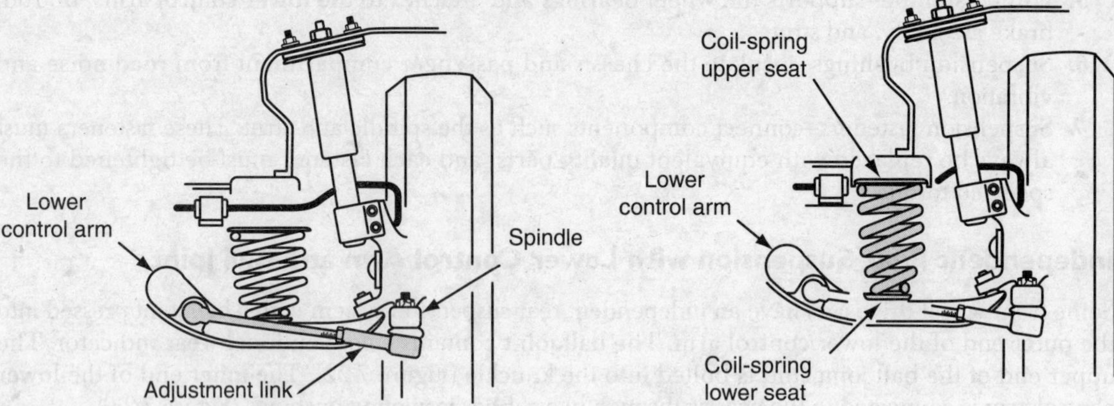

FIGURE 7-26 *Suspension adjustment link.*

FIGURE 7-27 *Coil-spring mounting.*

Independent Short-and-Long Arm Rear Suspension System

Some late model sport utility vehicles (SUVs) have a short-and-long arm (SLA) independent rear suspension system (Figure 7-28). This type of suspension system has upper and lower control arms, and the coil springs are mounted on the shock absorbers. The lower end of the shock absorber is mounted to the lower control arm with a rubber bushing. An upper rubber-insulated mount is positioned between the top of the shock absorber and the chassis. A toe link is connected from the spindle to the chassis, and the inner end of this link may be rotated to adjust the rear wheel toe. The inner end of the upper control arm is secured to the chassis with rubber insulating bushings (Figure 7-29). The SLA independent rear suspension system design allows the rear floor in the SUV to be lowered 5 in. This body design allows extra cargo space and more headroom in the rear of the vehicle if the optional third seat is installed.

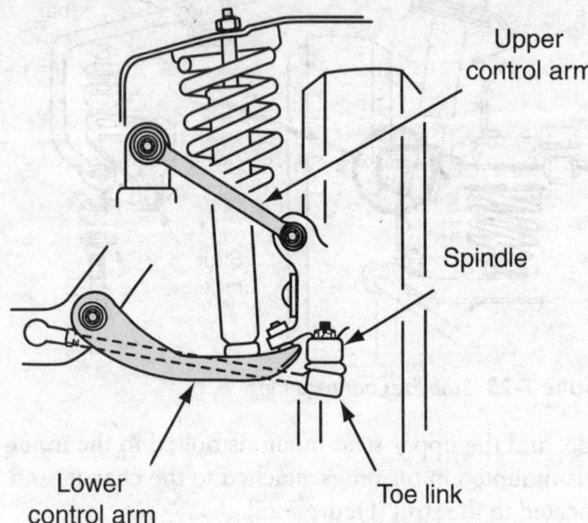

FIGURE 7-28 *Short-and-long arm independent rear suspension system.*

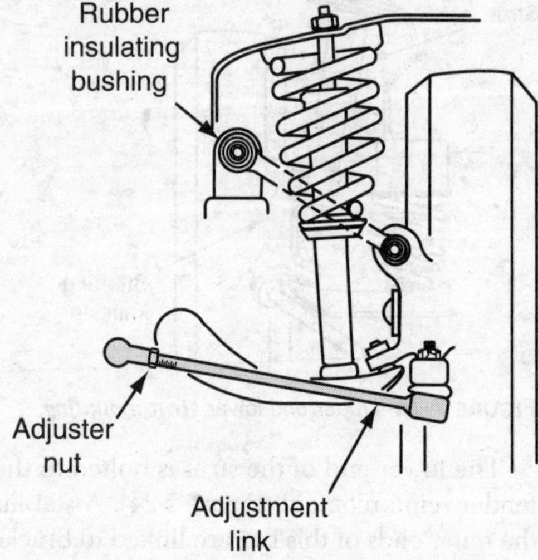

FIGURE 7-29 *Upper control arm, short-and-long arm independent rear suspension system.*

Independent Rear Suspension System with Rear Axle Carrier

Some import rear-wheel-drive cars have an independent rear suspension with a large rear axle carrier extending across the width of the chassis. A large extension on the rear axle carrier is bolted to the top of the differential, and the outer ends of this carrier are connected through heavy insulating bushings to chassis brackets (Figure 7-30).

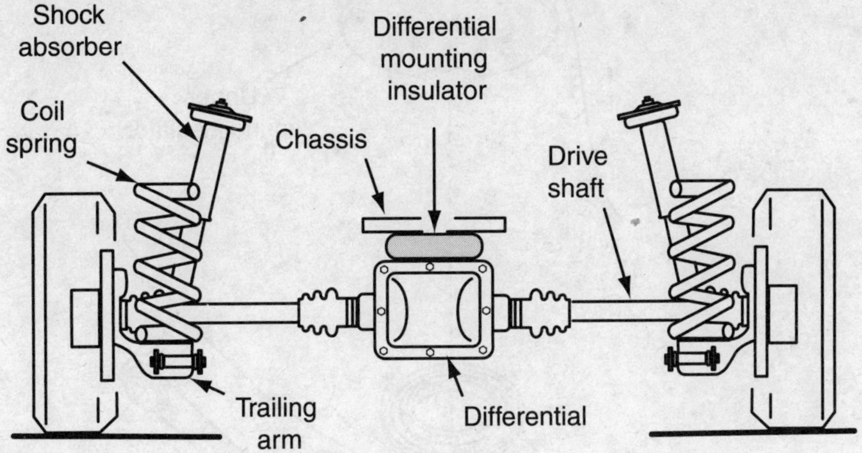

FIGURE 7-30 *Independent rear suspension with rear axle carrier.*

A large final drive mount extends from the rear of the differential housing, and this mount is bolted to the chassis. When the differential is attached to the chassis, rather than being connected to the suspension, the unsprung weight is reduced. Two rubber insulating bushings connect the large trailing arms to the rear axle carrier. The rear axle carrier provides very stable differential and wheel position, which improves steering control, ride quality, and tire life. Lower coil-spring seats are located on the trailing arms, and upper coil-spring seats are positioned in the chassis.

Shock absorbers are connected from the back of the trailing arms to the chassis. The rear wheel bearings are mounted in the outer ends of the trailing arms. Drive axles with inner and outer drive joints are connected from the differential to the rear wheels. When the drive axles have inner and outer joints, rear wheel camber change is minimized during wheel jounce and rebound. On some early independent rear suspension systems in rear-wheel-drive cars, the drive axles had only inner joints. With this type of rear suspension and drive axle, camber change was excessive during wheel jounce and rebound, and this action caused wear on the tire edges.

A stabilizer bar is bolted to the rear axle carrier through rubber insulating bushings. The outer ends of this bar are linked to the trailing arms.

Multilink Independent Rear Suspension System

Many vehicles have a **multilink independent rear suspension system**. A typical multilink rear suspension system has upper and lower control arms and additional links connected from the rear knuckles to the chassis to stabilize the rear wheel position. The suspension components are attached to the rear frame. The lower control arm is connected from the rear frame to the lower end of the knuckle. A large bushing is mounted in the inner end of the control arm at the frame attachment location (Figure 7-31). The coil springs are mounted between the lower control arms and the rear chassis, and insulators are positioned on the upper and lower ends of the springs. The upper control arms are connected from the rear frame to the top of the knuckle. The inner end of each upper control

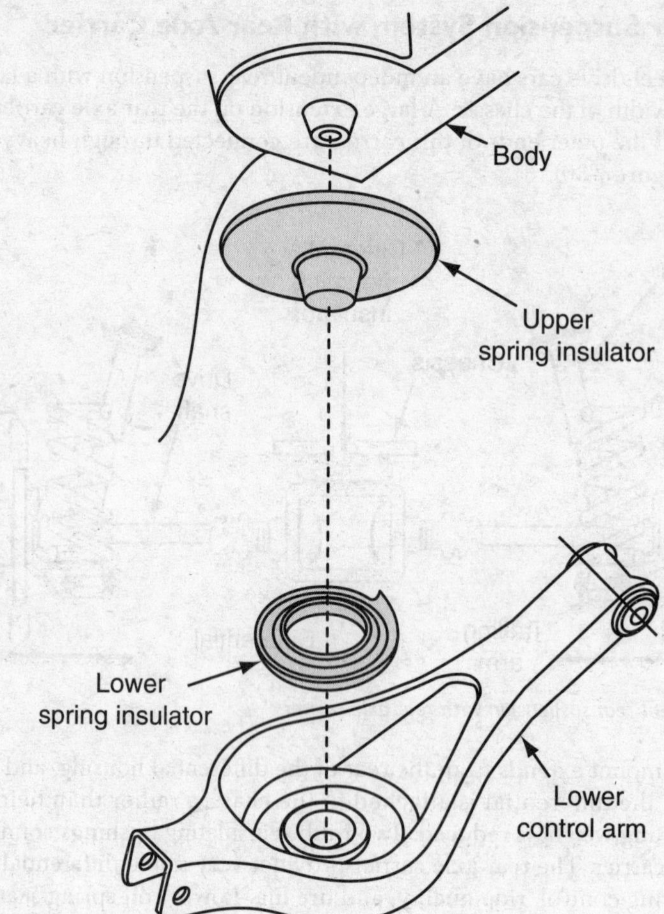

FIGURE 7-31 *Lower control arm with upper and lower spring insulators.*

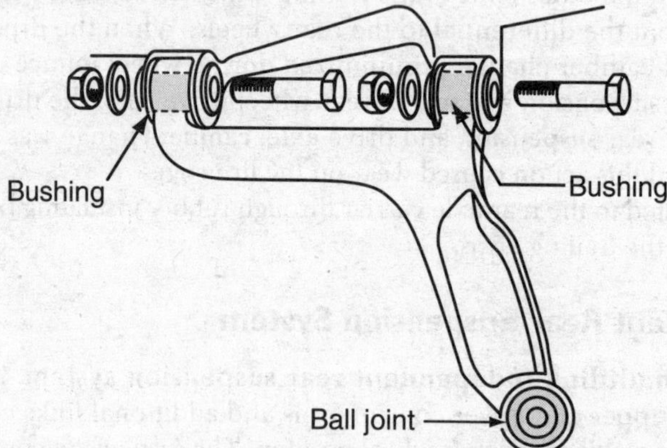

FIGURE 7-32 *The upper control arm is connected from the frame to the top of the knuckle.*

arm has two attachment points to frame, and large insulating bushings are installed at these attachment locations (Figure 7-32). A ball joint in the outer end of each upper control arm connects the control arm to the top end of the knuckle.

A trailing arm in connected from the lower end of the knuckle to the frame. Large insulating bushings are mounted at each trailing arm attachment location (Figure 7-33). The trailing arm prevents fore-and-aft wheel movement. An adjustment link is also connected from the lower end of the knuckle to the frame through insulating bushings (Figure 7-34). The adjustment link and lower control arm prevent lateral wheel movement, and this link also provides a method of rear wheel toe adjustment. This type of rear suspension may be called a **five-link suspension** because there are five attachments points between each knuckle and the frame. The lower control arm, trailing arm, and adjustment link each have one attachment location, and the upper control arm has two attachment points. A five-link rear suspension provides a very stable rear wheel position, which improves steering control and rear tire tread life.

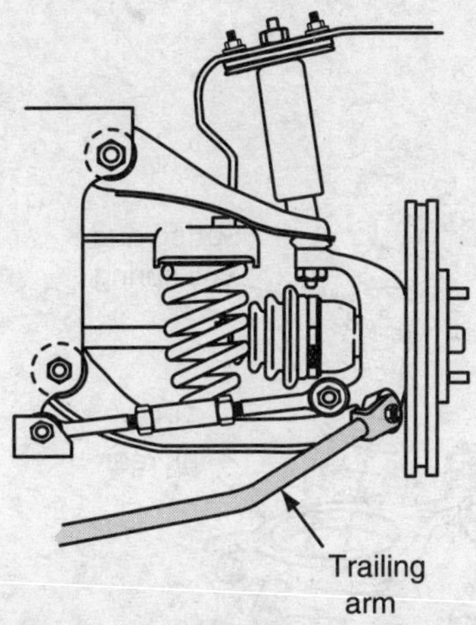

FIGURE 7-33 *The trailing arm is connected from the lower end of the knuckle to the frame.*

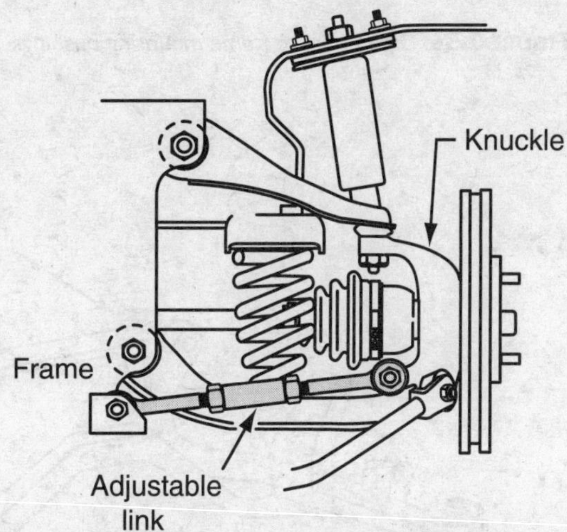

FIGURE 7-34 *Adjustment link.*

The shock absorbers are connected from the rear knuckles to the chassis (Figure 7-35). Two bolts retain the upper insulating shock absorber mount to the chassis. In this rear-wheel-drive car, the top of the differential is bolted to the upper part of the rear frame. Two large insulating bushings are mounted between the differential and the frame (Figure 7-36). Mounting the differential to the frame reduces the unsprung weight, which improves ride quality, because the unsprung weight forces the wheels downward during wheel rebound, which contributes to harsh ride quality.

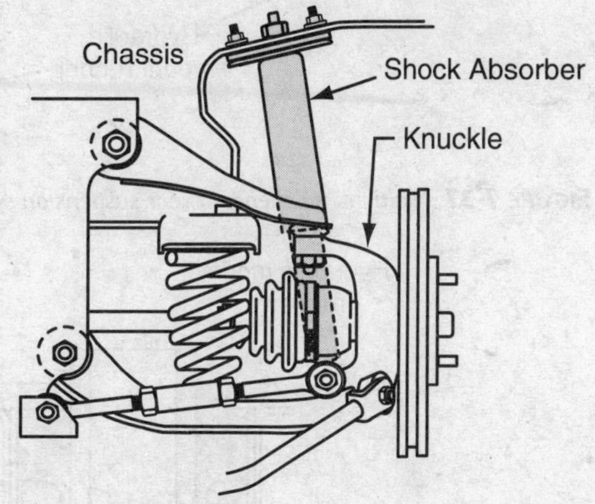

FIGURE 7-35 *Shock absorber mounting.*

Some multilink rear suspension systems have four hydraulic mounts mounted between the rear suspension member or frame and the chassis. The differential is bolted to the rear frame. These hydraulic mounts contain a silicone oil that helps prevent noise, vibration, and shock transfer from the differential and suspension to the chassis and vehicle interior (Figure 7-37).

The rear suspension member is connected to the outer shell of the hydraulic mounts, and the inner shell is attached to the chassis. Silicone oil fills the area between the inner and outer shells in each mount (Figure 7-38). Noise, vibration, and shock are transferred from the differential and suspension

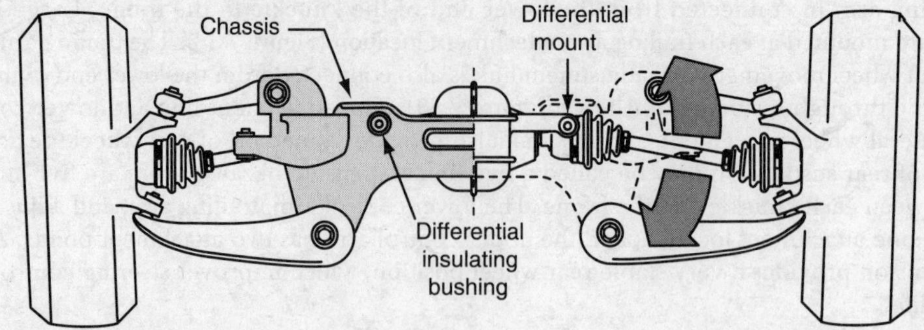

FIGURE 7-36 *Differential to frame mounting bushings.*

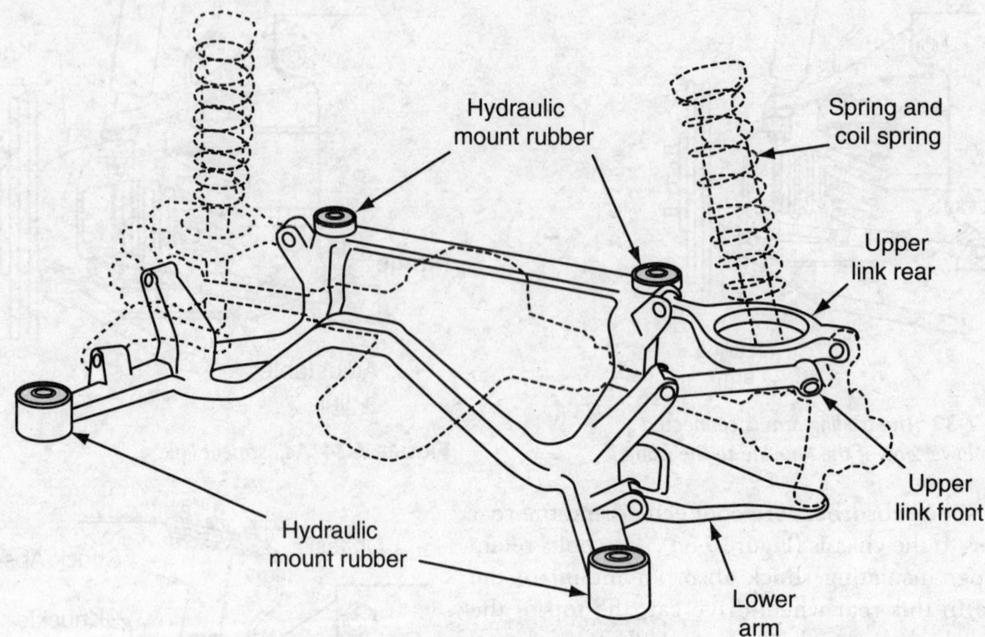

FIGURE 7-37 *Multilink independent rear suspension system with hydraulic mounts.*

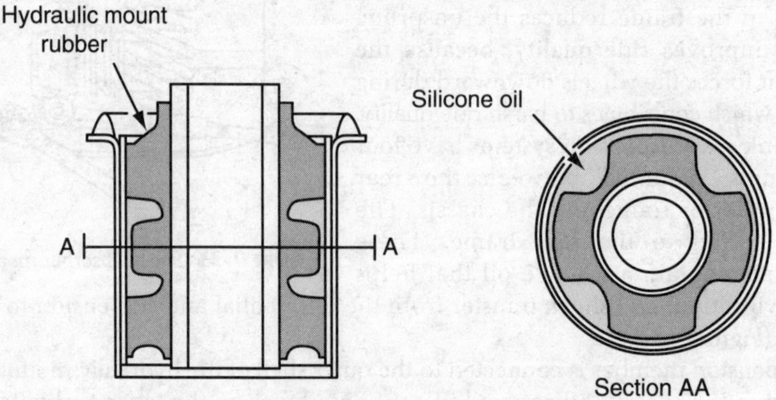

FIGURE 7-38 *Hydraulic mount design.*

to the rear suspension member, but the silicone oil in the hydraulic mounts prevents the transfer of these undesirable forces to the chassis and vehicle interior. These hydraulic mounts have superior noise and vibration dampening characteristics compared to rubber bushings.

A rear upper link is connected from each side of the rear suspension member to the top of the knuckles. Both ends of this rear upper link contain rubber insulating bushings. The lower end of the shock absorber strut extends through a circular opening in the rear upper link. A front upper link is also connected from the rear suspension member to the knuckle. The top of the knuckle is supported by the front and rear upper links, rather than being supported by the shock absorber strut. The coil springs are mounted on the shock absorber struts, and the lower spring seat is attached to the strut. An upper spring seat is attached to the top of the shock absorber strut, and this upper seat is bolted into the inner fender reinforcement. The lower end of the shock absorber strut is connected to the back of the lower control arm. Lower control arms are connected from the rear suspension member to the lower end of the knuckles.

Some multilink rear suspension systems have a lower control arm and a toe control arm parallel to the lower control arm (Figure 7-39). A bolt in the outer end of the lower control arm extends through a bushing in the lower end of the steering knuckle. A ball joint in the outer end of the toe control arm is bolted into the lower end of the knuckle. Rubber insulating bushings are pressed into the inner ends of the toe control arm and lower control arm. Bolts extend through these bushings and openings in the chassis. The rear end of the trailing arm is bolted to a bushing in the knuckle, and a bushing in the front end of this arm is bolted to the chassis. The trailing arm, lower control arm, and toe control arm prevent lateral and fore-and-aft wheel movement and provide excellent suspension rigidity when cornering or driving on irregular road surfaces. An eccentric cam bolt on the inner end of the toe control arm provides a rear wheel toe adjustment (Figure 7-40).

A bushing in the upper end of the knuckle is bolted to the outer end of the upper control arm (Figure 7-41). Front and rear bushings in the inner ends of the upper control arm are bolted to brackets that are in turn bolted to the chassis.

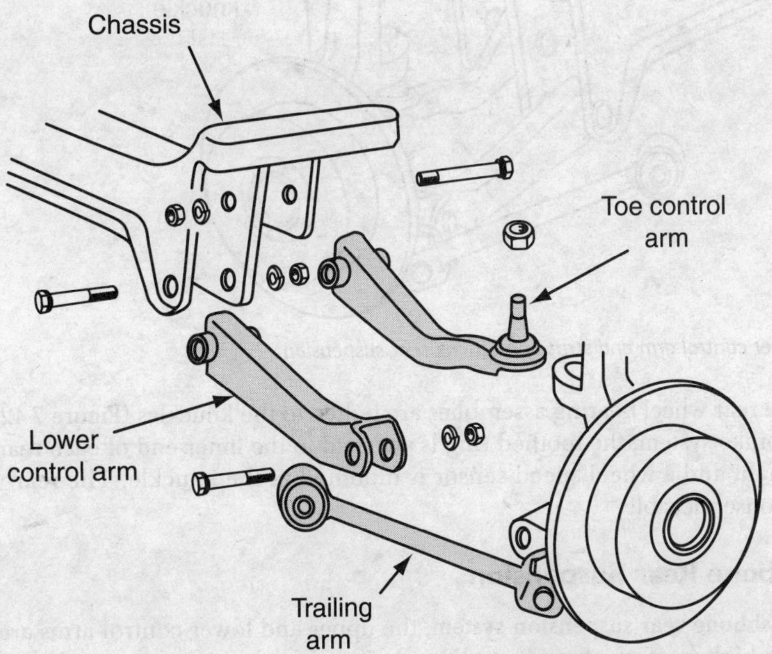

FIGURE 7-39 *Multilink rear suspension with parallel lower control arm and toe control arm.*

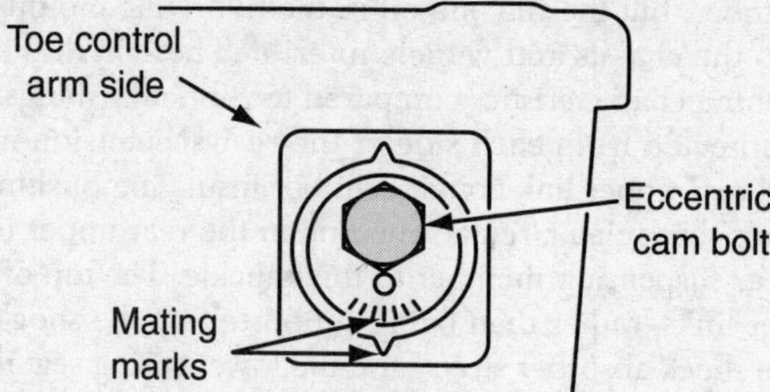

FIGURE 7-40 *Eccentric cam bolt on inner end of toe control arm.*

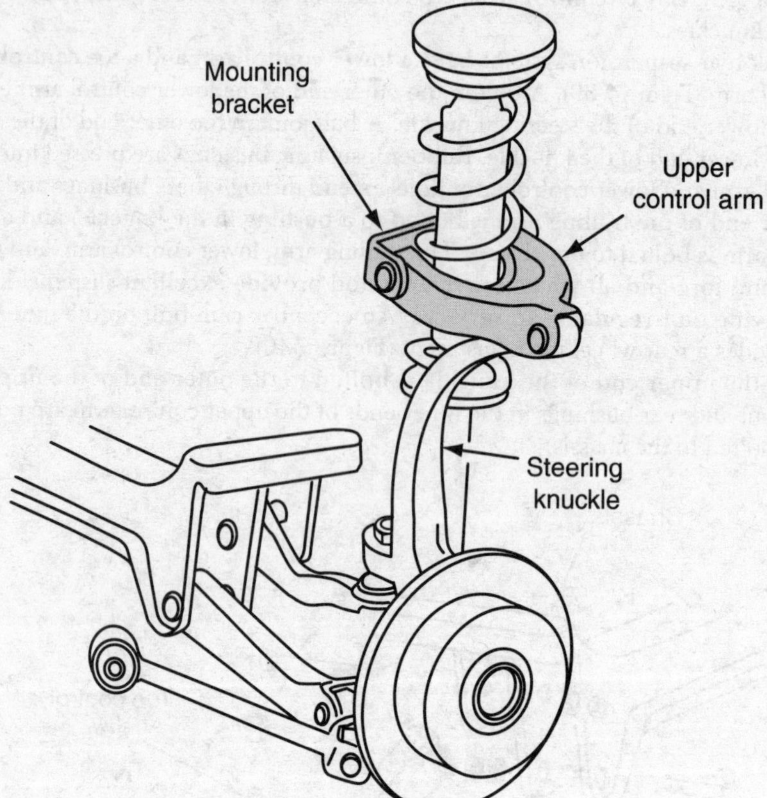

FIGURE 7-41 *Upper control arm and strut in multilink rear suspension.*

The one-piece rear wheel bearing assemblies are bolted to the knuckles (Figure 7-42). If the vehicle has an antilock brake system, the toothed ring is attached to the inner end of each rear wheel bearing and stub axle shaft, and a wheel-speed sensor is mounted in the knuckle. The rear wheel bearings assemblies are nonserviceable.

Double Wishbone Rear Suspension

In the **double wishbone rear suspension system**, the upper and lower control arms are manufactured from lightweight, high-strength aluminum alloys designed for maximum strength and rigidity. These lighter control arms decrease the unsprung weight, which helps improve traction and ride quality.

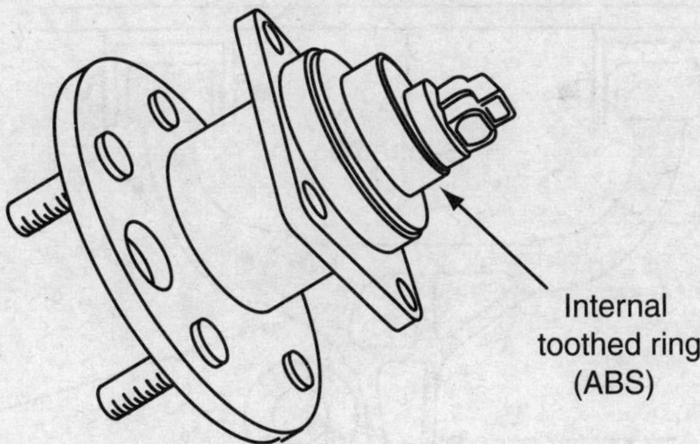

FIGURE 7-42 *One-piece rear wheel bearing assembly.*

Suspension rigidity is also increased by positioning the ball joints and steering knuckle inside the wheel profile (Figure 7-43). Since the upper and lower control arms have a wishbone shape, the term "double wishbone" suspension system is used for this type of rear suspension. On each side of the car, the rear suspension is attached to the chassis by a cast aluminum subframe (Figure 7-44). This design also helps reduce vehicle weight and transmits suspension loads to the chassis at the most efficient locations.

Some independent rear suspension systems experience undesirable toe changes during wheel jounce and rebound. These toe changes cause vehicle instability during cornering and acceleration. In the double wishbone rear suspension system, the control arm design and the pivot locations on the rear toe control arm provide minimal change in toe-in during wheel jounce (Figure 7-45). This action results in extremely stable steering while cornering, accelerating, or driving on irregular road surfaces. The toe control arm may be lengthened or shortened to adjust rear wheel toe. An eccentric cam on the rear upper control arm bolt provides a rear wheel camber adjustment (Figure 7-46 and Figure 7-47).

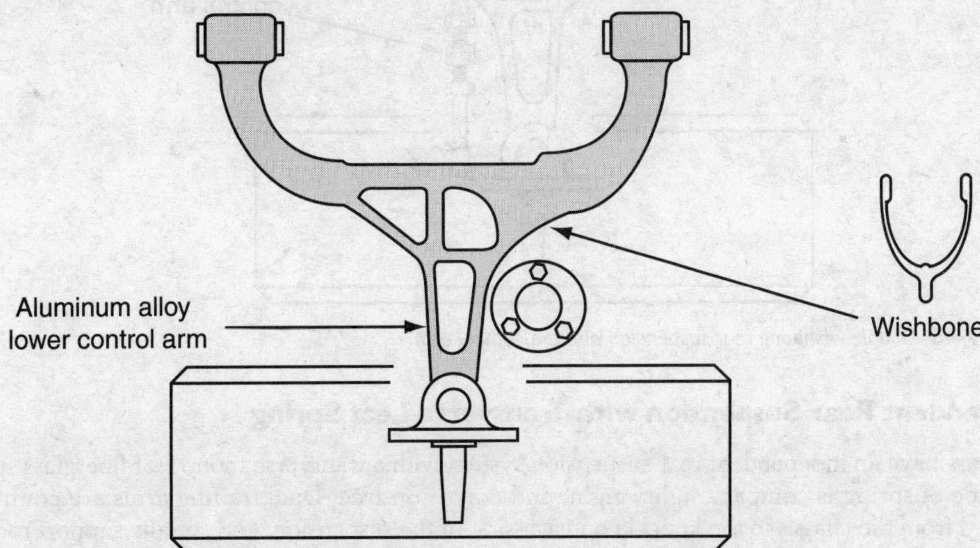

FIGURE 7-43 *Double wishbone rear suspension.*

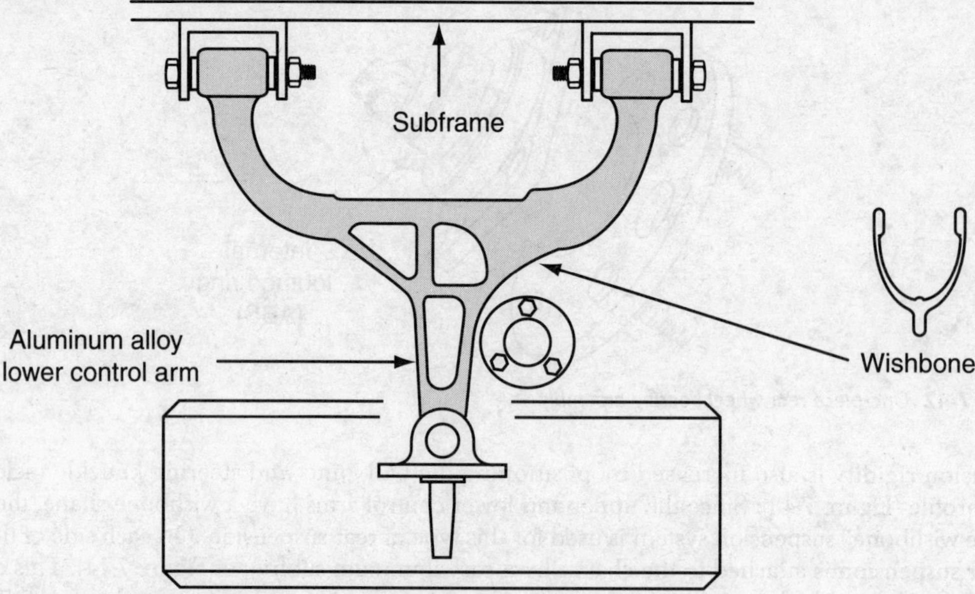

FIGURE 7-44 *Double wishbone rear suspension and subframe.*

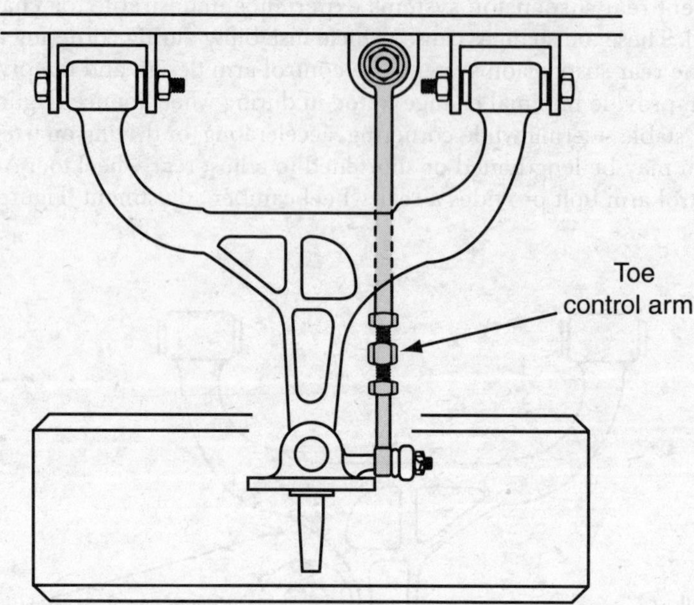

FIGURE 7-45 *Double wishbone rear suspension and toe control arm.*

Independent Rear Suspension with Transverse Leaf Spring

Some cars have an independent rear suspension system with a transverse mono-leaf fiberglass spring. This type of spring is compact, lightweight, and corrosion-free. Dual trailing arms are connected rearward from the chassis to the knuckle on each side of the suspension, and spindle support rods are attached from the center of the suspension to the bottom of the knuckle. Tie rods are connected from the rear of the knuckle to the center of the suspension (Figure 7-48).

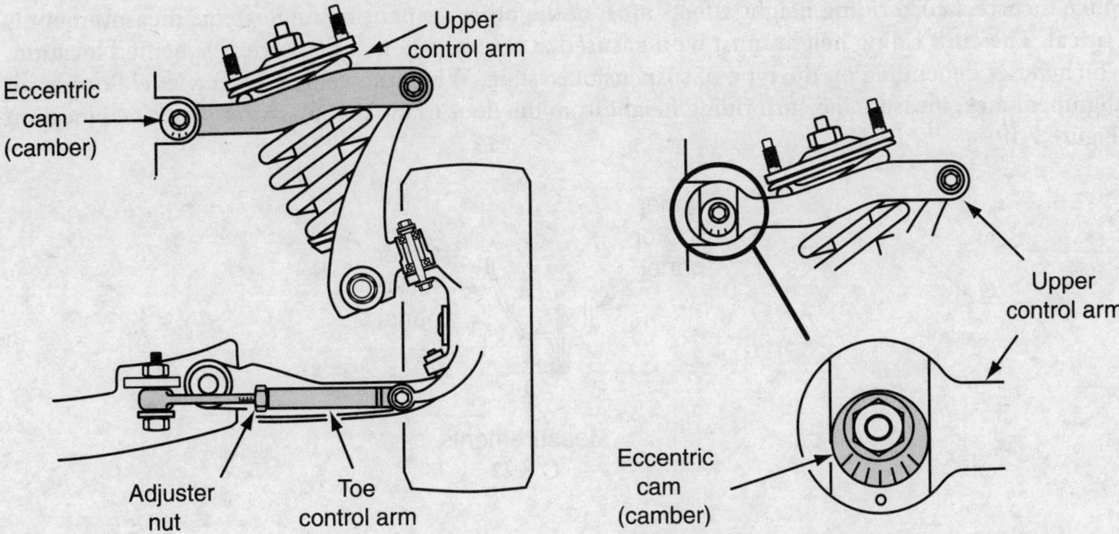

FIGURE 7-46 *Rear suspension camber and toe adjustments.*

FIGURE 7-47 *Eccentric cam for camber adjustment on rear upper control arm bolt.*

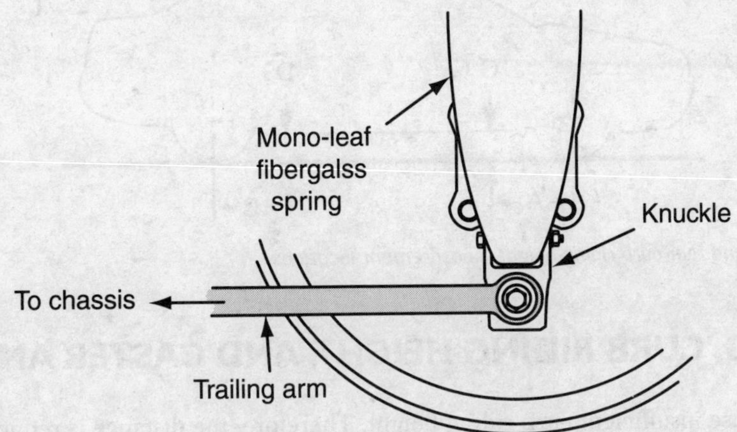

FIGURE 7-48 *Independent rear suspension with mono-leaf transverse fiberglass spring.*

Other independent rear suspension systems have a multiple-leaf transversely mounted rear spring. In these suspension systems, heavy control arms extend rearward from the chassis to the knuckles, and strut rods are connected from the bottom of the knuckles to the center of the suspension. The shock absorbers are connected from the lower end of the knuckles to the chassis. A suspension member connects the differential housing to the chassis. All suspension component mounting locations are insulated with rubber bushings.

CURB RIDING HEIGHT

Regular inspection and proper maintenance of suspension systems is extremely important to maintaining vehicle safety. The curb riding height is determined mainly by spring condition. Other suspension components such as control arm bushings will affect curb riding height if they are worn.

Since incorrect curb riding height affects most of the other suspension angles, this measurement is critical. The curb riding height must be measured at the vehicle manufacturer's specified location, which varies depending on the type of suspension system. When the vehicle is on a level floor or an alignment rack, measure the curb riding height from the floor to the manufacturer's specified location (Figure 7-49).

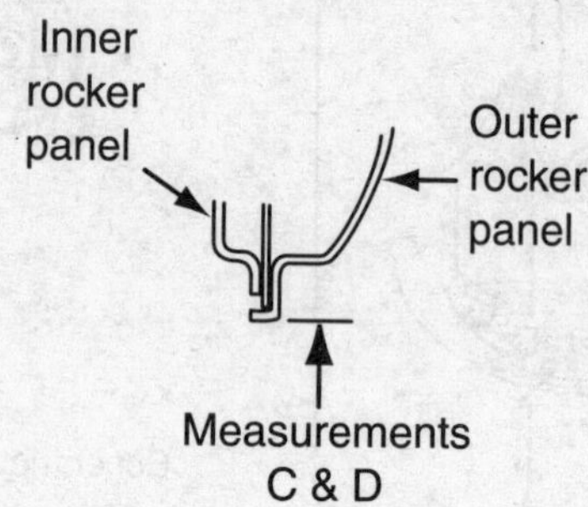

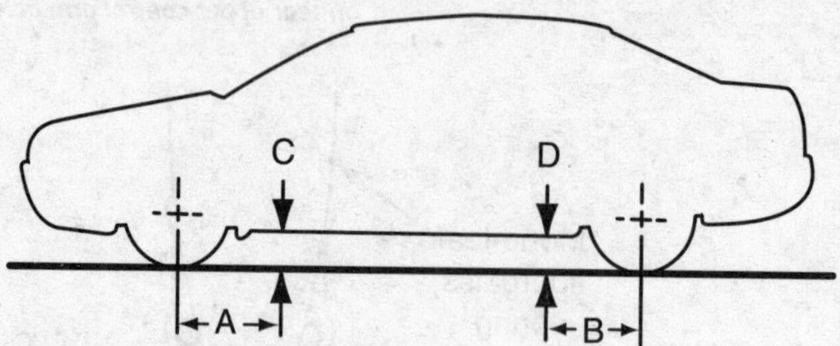

FIGURE 7-49 *Front and rear curb riding height measurement locations.*

SPRING SAG, CURB RIDING HEIGHT, AND CASTER ANGLE

Sagged springs cause insufficient curb riding height. Therefore, the distance is reduced between the rebound bumper and its stop. This distance reduction causes the bumper to hit the stop frequently with resulting harsh ride quality.

When both rear springs are sagged, the **caster angle** tilts excessively toward the rear of the vehicle. This type of angle is called positive caster. Rear spring sag and excessive positive caster increase steering effort and cause rapid steering wheel return after a turn is completed.

REVIEW QUESTIONS

Short Answer Essays

1. Describe a live-axle rear suspension system.
2. Explain the disadvantages of a live-axle leaf-spring rear suspension.
3. Describe the purpose of a leaf-spring shackle.

4. Explain the differential torque action during acceleration, and describe how this torque is absorbed in a live-axle coil-spring rear suspension.
5. Define axle tramp.
6. Describe the purpose of a tracking bar.
7. Explain the difference between a semi-independent and an independent rear suspension system.
8. Explain the advantages of an independent rear suspension compared with a live-axle rear suspension.
9. Describe the advantage of mounting the differential to the chassis in a RWD car with an independent rear suspension.
10. Describe the components that position the upper end of the knuckle in a multilink rear suspension.

Fill-in-the-Blanks

1. A live-axle leaf-spring rear suspension provides excellent ________________ stability.
2. During braking and deceleration, the front of the differential is twisted ______________.
3. Axle tramp occurs during hard ______________.
4. In many live-axle coil-spring rear suspensions, the differential torque is absorbed by the trailing lower ________________ ________________.
5. In a modified MacPherson strut independent rear suspension, the coil-spring seat is located on the ________________ ________________.
6. In a multilink independent rear suspension, the rear suspension member supports the suspension and the ______________.
7. In a multilink rear suspension, the rear suspension member is insulated from the chassis by _____-____________ ______________.
8. A fiberglass mono-leaf rear spring is compact, lightweight, and ________________ free.
9. When the rear springs are sagged, the caster angle on the front suspension becomes more _____-__________.
10. If the rear springs are sagged, the ______________ ______________ is increased.

Multiple Choice

1. Rear axle tramp is caused by:
   A. Irregular road surfaces.
   B. A bent rear control arm.
   C. Engine torque transmitted through the drive shaft.
   D. Improper rear wheel alignment.

2. All of these statements about a live-axle leaf-spring rear suspension are true EXCEPT:
   A. During acceleration the front of the differential twists upward.
   B. The differential torque in a live-axle rear suspension is applied to the springs.
   C. While decelerating and braking, the front of the differential twists downward.
   D. This type of rear suspension has a small amount of unsprung weight.

3. Rear axle tramp occurs during:
   A. Hard acceleration.
   B. Deceleration.
   C. High speed driving.
   D. Cornering at high speed.

4. In a semi-independent rear suspension system, some individual wheel movement is provided by:
   A. The U-section channel and integral stabilizer bar.
   B. The struts.
   C. The trailing arms.
   D. The track bar and brace.

5. In a semi-independent rear suspension system:
   A. The track bar and brace absorb differential torque.
   B. The trailing arms prevent lateral wheel movement.
   C. The lower coil spring seats may be on the trailing arms.
   D. The lower end of the shock absorbers may be attached to the track bar.

6. In a MacPherson strut independent rear suspension system:
   A. The spring seats are positioned on the struts.
   B. The upper spring seat is positioned in a chassis support.
   C. The lower end of each strut is attached to the strut rod.
   D. The ends of the coil spring are in direct contact with the spring seats.

7. All of these statements about modified MacPherson strut suspension systems are true EXCEPT:
   A. The lower control arms prevent lateral wheel movement.
   B. The tie rods control fore-and-aft wheel movement.
   C. The strut is bolted to the lower end of the spindle.
   D. The upper strut mount is retained on top of the strut.

8. In an independent rear suspension with a lower control arm and ball joint:
   A. The ball joint is pressed into the tie rod.
   B. The strut is bolted to the top of the knuckle.
   C. The lower coil-spring seat is mounted on the strut.
   D. The suspension adjustment link is connected from the lower control arm to the chassis.

9. Sagged rear springs may cause:
   A. Slow steering wheel return after turning a corner.
   B. Decreased steering effort.
   C. Decreased positive caster on the front wheels.
   D. Harsh ride quality.

10. The adjustment link in a multilink rear suspension:

A. Provides a rear wheel caster adjustment.

B. Provides a rear wheel toe adjustment.

C. Reduces fore-and-aft rear wheel movement.

D. Absorbs engine torque transmitted through the drive shaft.

COMPUTER-CONTROLLED SUSPENSION SYSTEMS

8

Upon completion and review of this chapter, you should be able to:

- List the conditions that cause a programmed ride control (PRC) system to switch from the normal to the firm mode.
- Explain how the firm ride condition is obtained in PRC struts.
- Describe the major components in an electronic air suspension system.
- Explain how air is forced into and exhausted from the air springs in an air suspension system.
- Describe how an electronic air suspension system corrects low suspension trim height.
- Explain the operation of an electronic air suspension system while driving the car with the doors closed and the brake pedal applied.
- Describe the normal operation of the warning lamp in an electronic air suspension system.
- Explain the three modes in the air suspension system on some modern four-wheel-drive sport utility vehicles (SUVs).
- Describe how unnecessary rear suspension height corrections are prevented on irregular road surfaces with an air suspension system.

- Describe the design of the struts and air springs in an automatic air suspension system.
- Describe the design of an electronic rotary height sensor.
- Explain speed-leveling capabilities and the advantage of this function in a suspension control module.
- Explain the operation of an automatic ride control (ARC) system in relation to transfer case modes.
- Describe the inputs in an electronic suspension control (ESC) system.
- Explain the advantages of an ESC system with magneto-rheological fluid in the shock absorbers compared to other computer-controlled suspension systems.
- Briefly explain the operation of the rear electronic level control system that is combined with the road sensing suspension system.
- Briefly explain the operation of the speed sensitive steering system that is combined with the road sensing suspension system.
- Explain the operation of a stability control system.
- Explain the advantages of a traction control system.

INTRODUCTION

We are all aware of the ever accelerating electronics revolution in the 1990s and early 2000s. Most industries have felt the impact of this revolution, and the automotive industry is no exception. Computers have greatly influenced the way vehicles are designed and built. Most systems on the automobile, including the suspension system, have been impacted by the computer. Many drivers like a soft, comfortable ride while driving normally on the highway. However, many of these same drivers prefer a firm ride during hard cornering, severe braking, or fast acceleration. A firm ride under these driving conditions reduces body sway and front end dive or lift. Prior to the age of electronics, cars were designed to provide either a soft, comfortable ride or a firm ride. Drivers who wanted a firm ride selected a sports car with a suspension designed to supply the type of ride and handling characteristics they desired. Car buyers who wanted a softer ride purchased a family sedan with a suspension designed to provide a softer, more comfortable ride.

Thanks to computer control, suspension system manufacturers can now provide a soft ride during normal highway driving, and then almost instantly switch to a firm ride during hard cornering, braking, fast acceleration, and high-speed driving. The computer-controlled suspension system allows the same car to meet the demands of both the driver who desires a soft ride, and the driver who wants a firm ride. Because computer-controlled suspension systems reduce body sway during hard cornering, these systems provide improved steering control.

Some computer-controlled suspension systems also supply a constant vehicle riding height regardless of the vehicle passenger or cargo load. This action maintains the vehicle's cosmetic appearance as the passenger and/or cargo load is changed. Maintaining a constant riding height also supplies more constant suspension alignment angles, which may provide improved steering control.

PROGRAMMED RIDE CONTROL SYSTEM

System Design

The **programmed ride control (PRC) system** is available on some Ford cars. Some import cars have a similar system. The damping action of the front and rear struts and shocks is automatically controlled by the PRC system to provide improved ride and handling characteristics under various driving conditions. The main components in the PRC system are (Figure 8-1):

1. Steering sensor
2. Brake sensor
3. Speed sensor
4. Struts and shocks with electric actuators
5. Control module
6. Electronic engine control IV (EEC IV) powertrain control module (PCM)
7. Firm and plush shock relays
8. Mode select switch
9. Mode indicator light

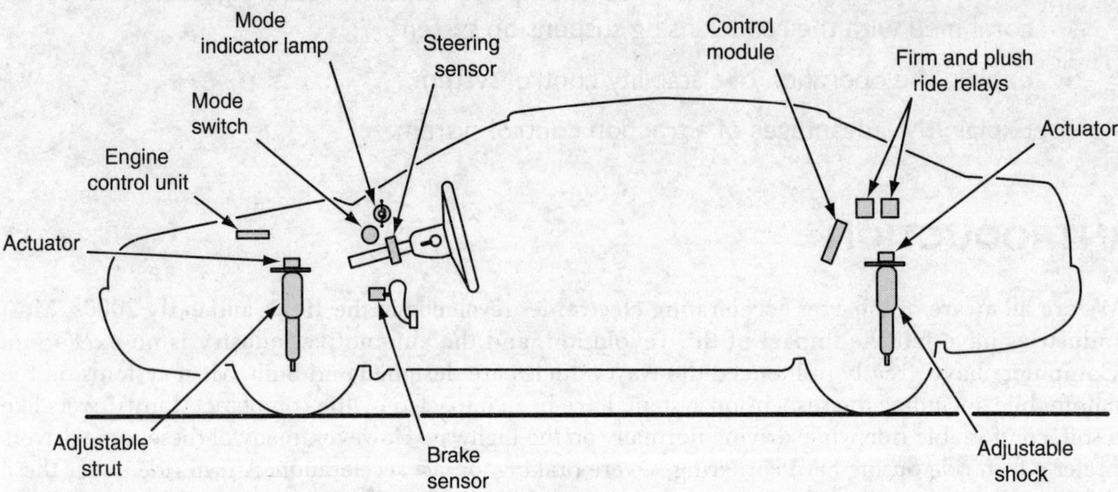

FIGURE 8-1 *Programmed ride control (PRC) system components.*

Steering Sensor

The **steering sensor** is mounted on the steering column. This sensor contains a pair of **light-emitting diodes (LEDs)** and a matching pair of **photo diodes**. A slotted disc attached to the steering shaft rotates between the LEDs and photo diodes when the steering wheel is turned (Figure 8-2). This disc contains 20 slots spaced at 9° intervals. A signal is sent from the steering sensor to the control module in relation to the amount and speed of steering wheel rotation.

Brake Sensor

The brake sensor is a normally open (NO) switch mounted in the brake control valve assembly (Figure 8-3). When the brake fluid pressure reaches 400 pounds per square inch (psi) or 2,758 kilopascals (kPa), the **brake pressure switch** closes and sends a signal to the control module.

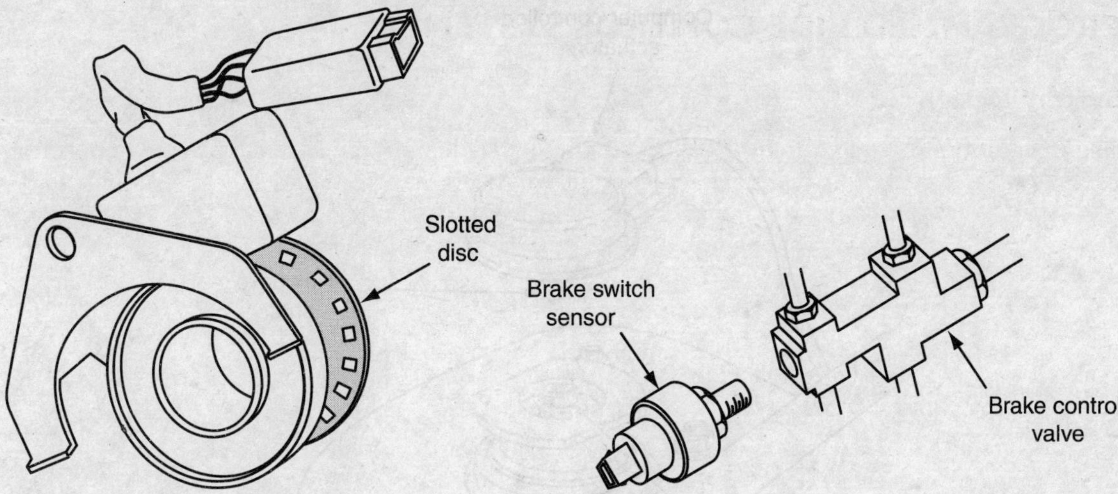

FIGURE 8-2 *Steering sensor.*

FIGURE 8-3 *Brake switch.*

Vehicle Speed Sensor

The vehicle speed sensor is usually mounted in the speedometer cable outlet of the transaxle or transmission (Figure 8-4). This sensor sends a vehicle speed signal to the control module. This signal is also used by the PCM in the EEC IV system.

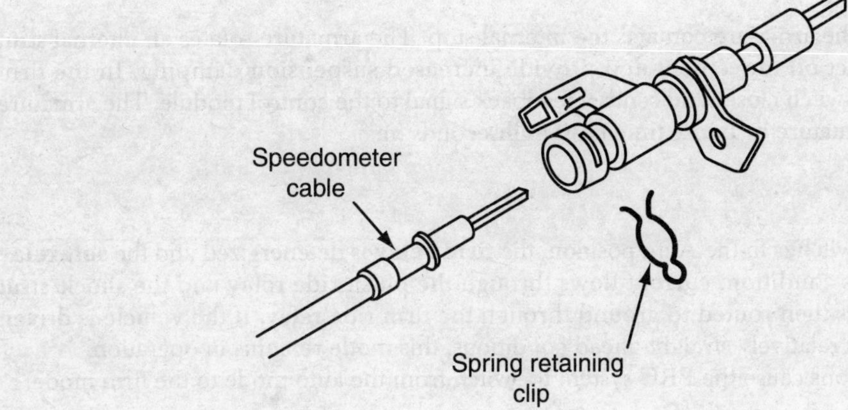

FIGURE 8-4 *Vehicle speed sensor.*

Strut and Shock Actuators

An **actuator** is positioned in the top of each strut and shock (Figure 8-5). Each actuator contains a single pole armature, a pair of permanent magnets, and a position switch. When current is applied through the plush relay to the armature, the magnetic fields of the armature and the permanent magnets repel each other (Figure 8-6). This action causes clockwise armature rotation until the armature hits the internal stop. Under this condition, the leaf-spring switch is open in the position sensor circuit and no signal is returned to the PRC control module.

If current is applied through the firm relay to the armature, there is an attraction between the magnetic fields of the armature and permanent magnets. This attraction causes counterclockwise

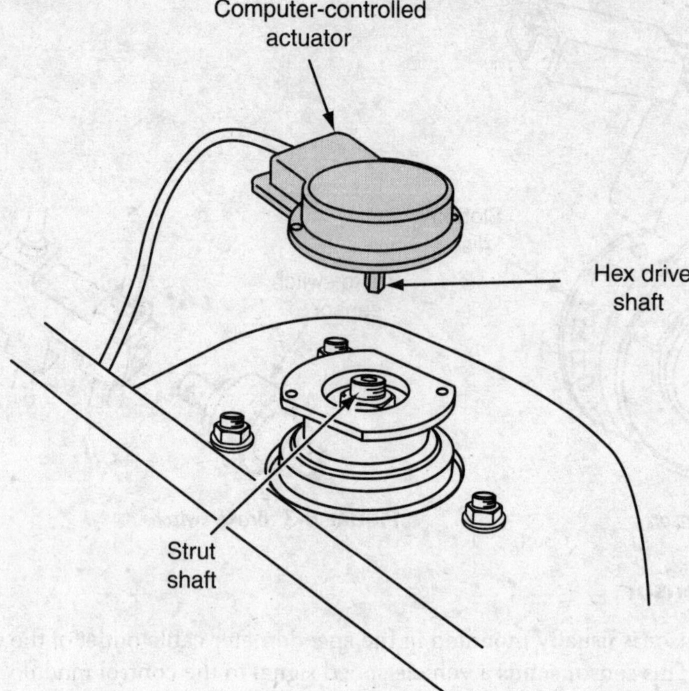

FIGURE 8-5 *Strut actuator.*

armature rotation until the armature contacts the internal stop. The armature rotates an internal strut or shock valve to restrict oil movement and provide increased suspension damping. In the firm position, the leaf-spring switch closes and sends a feedback signal to the control module. The armature movement is 60° and armature response time is 30 milliseconds (ms).

Operation

When the mode select switch is in the Auto position, the **firm relay** is de-energized and the **soft relay** is energized. Under this condition, current flows through the plush ride relay and the shock/strut actuators. This current is then routed to ground through the firm ride relay. If the vehicle is driven under normal speed and relatively straight-ahead conditions, this mode remains in operation.

The following conditions cause the PRC system to switch from the auto mode to the firm mode:

1. Vehicle speed above 83 miles per hour (mph) or 133 kilometers per hour (km/h)
2. Engine acceleration at 90 percent throttle opening or 8 psi (55 kPa) turbo boost pressure
3. Lateral vehicle acceleration above 0.35 g
4. Brake pressure of 400 psi (2,758 kPa) or more

The vehicle acceleration signal is sent from the **throttle position sensor (TPS)** to the powertrain control module (PCM) in the EEC IV system. This signal is relayed to the PRC control module. Lateral vehicle acceleration is sensed by the steering sensor.

When the PRC control module receives an input signal that requires firm ride control, the control module energizes the firm relay and de-energizes the soft relay. This action results in current flow from the firm ride relay through the shock/strut actuators, and the soft ride relay to ground. Therefore, shock/strut actuator current is reversed and the armature in each actuator moves the shock/strut valves to the Firm position.

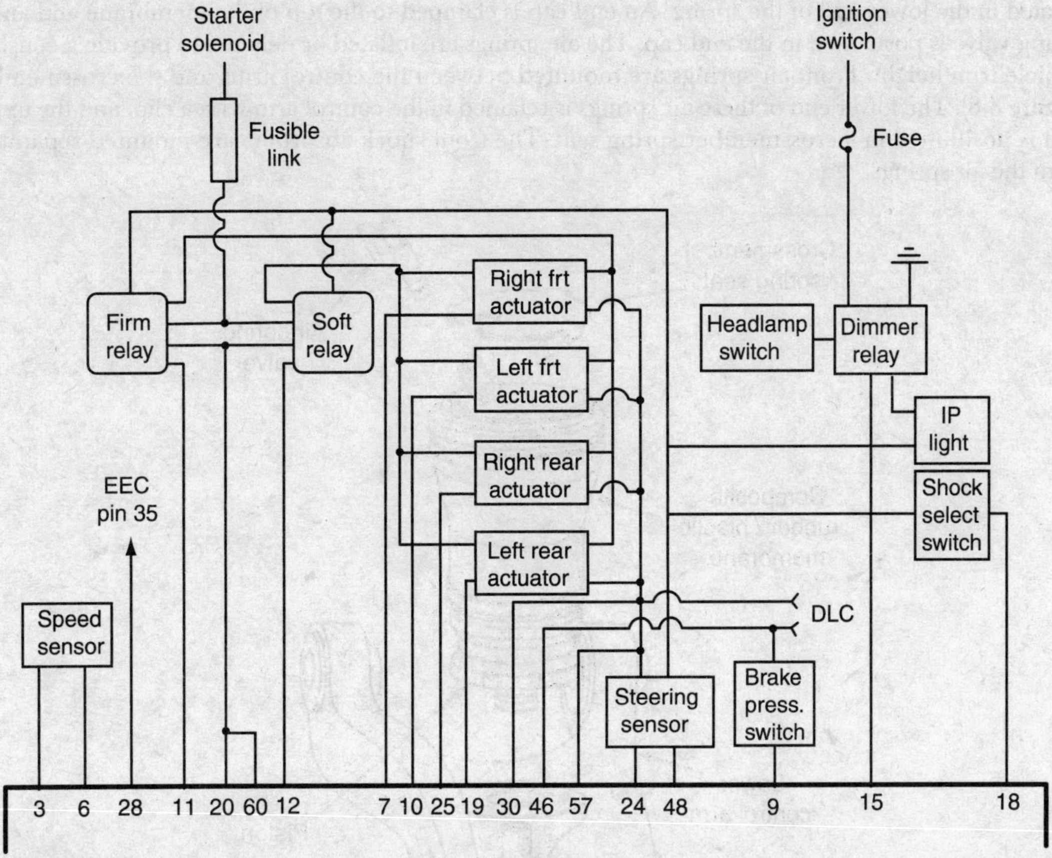

FIGURE 8-6 *Firm relay, strut actuators, and other PRC system components.*

The mode indicator light in the tachometer glows when the PRC system is in the Firm mode (Figure 8-7). During the first 80 seconds after the ignition switch is turned on, the PRC system does not respond to changes in vehicle direction. This action allows the PRC control module to calculate the straight-ahead position.

If the mode select switch is placed in the Firm position, the system remains in the firm mode continually. In this mode, the mode indicator light remains on. In the firm mode, the shocks/struts provide approximately three times the damping action on the extension stroke compared to the normal mode.

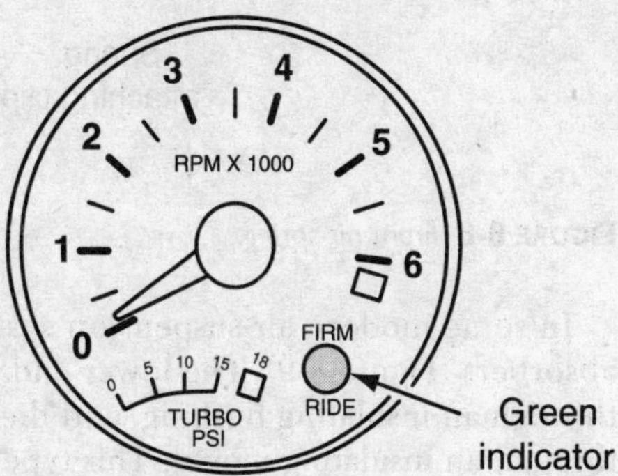

FIGURE 8-7 *Mode indicator light.*

ELECTRONIC AIR SUSPENSION SYSTEM COMPONENTS

Air Springs

In an air suspension system, the **air springs** replace the coil springs in conventional suspension systems. These air springs have a composite rubber and plastic membrane that is clamped to a piston located in the lower end of the spring. An end cap is clamped to the top of the membrane and an air spring valve is positioned in the end cap. The air springs are inflated or deflated to provide a constant vehicle trim height. Front air springs are mounted between the control arms and the crossmember (Figure 8-8). The lower end of these air springs is retained in the control arm with a clip, and the upper end is positioned in a crossmember spring seat. The front shock absorbers are mounted separately from the air springs.

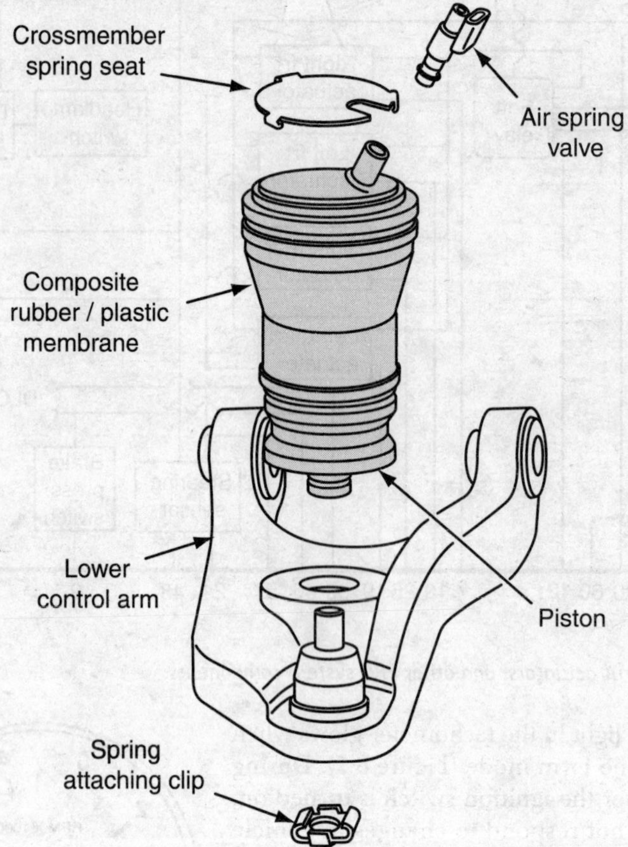

FIGURE 8-8 *Front air spring.*

In some modern air suspension systems the air springs are mounted and sealed on the shock absorbers (Figure 8-9). The lower end of the shock absorber is attached to the lower control arm through an insulating bushing, and the upper end of the shock absorber is attached to the chassis through an insulating mount. This type of air suspension system has aluminum front lower control arms and spindles, and forged steel upper control arms. Ball joints are mounted in the outer ends of the upper and lower control arms. The aluminum suspension components reduce the unsprung weight and improve ride quality. Reducing vehicle weight also improves fuel economy. The upper and lower ball joints are an integral part of the control arms, and these ball joints cannot be replaced separately.

CAUTION: The ball joint studs in the upper ball joints do not have a press fit in the steering knuckle. When loosening these ball joint nuts, a hex holding feature on the ball joint stud prevents the stud from rotating when loosening the ball joint nuts. If the upper ball joint stud rotate in the aluminum knuckle the knuckle opening may be damaged.

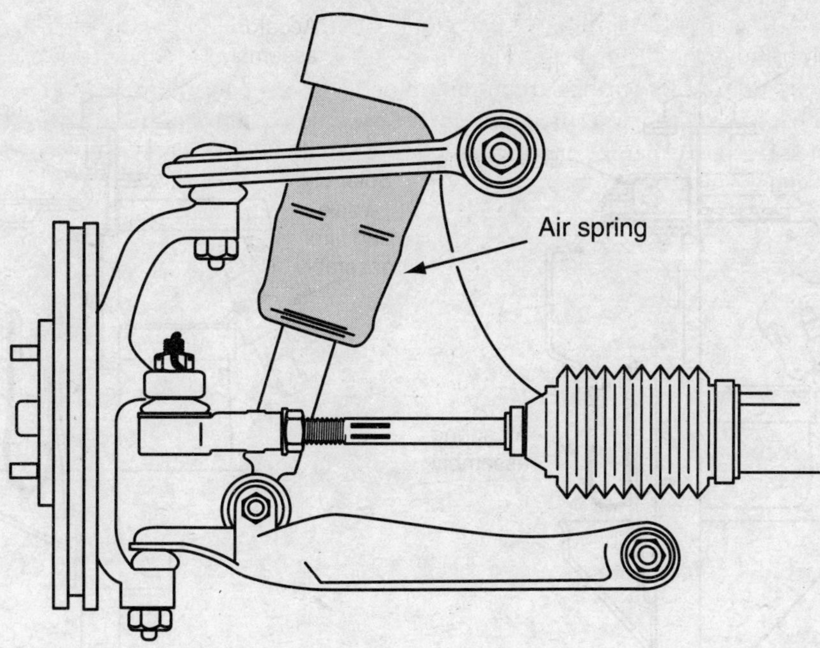

FIGURE 8-9 *Air spring mounted on the shock absorber.*

Other vehicles have the air springs mounted over the front and rear struts, and these struts contain a solenoid actuator that varies the strut valve opening to control ride firmness (Figure 8-10 and Figure 8-11). These strut actuators are similar to the ones explained previously in this chapter on the PRC system. Some of these air suspension systems that control ride firmness are not driver adjustable. The suspension module controls the strut firmness automatically in relation to the module inputs. This type of system may be called an automatic air suspension system. Some vehicles with solenoid actuators in the struts have up to four suspension modes that may be selected by the driver. One premium luxury car has these driver selectable suspension modes:

1. Comfort–provides a smooth luxurious ride.
2. Automatic–the suspension computer provides the best possible combination of comfort and handling based on speed, driver style, and road conditions.
3. Dynamic–stiffest, lowest, sportiest, most aerodynamic suspension mode.
4. Life–for rougher roads, steep approaches, and deep snow. This mode is used only for low speed driving.

When the driver selects a suspension mode, the suspension module positions the strut actuators to provide the desired ride quality, and this module also adjusts the air spring pressure to provide the appropriate ride height.

This type of air suspension system dramatically reduce body roll and pitch that occurs during cornering and hard braking. Because this air suspension system lowers the ride height at higher speeds, it improves aerodynamic efficiency.

The rear air springs are similar to the front air springs and also have similar mountings. Some rear air springs are mounted between the rear suspension arms and the frame with the shock absorbers mounted separately from the air springs (Figure 8-12). Other rear air springs are mounted over the rear shock absorbers, and the shock absorbers are mounted between the lower control arms and the frame. Some modern air suspension systems on four-wheel-drive vehicles have rear knuckles with **cross-axis ball joints**. The lower cross-axis ball joint is a round insulating bushing mounted in the lower

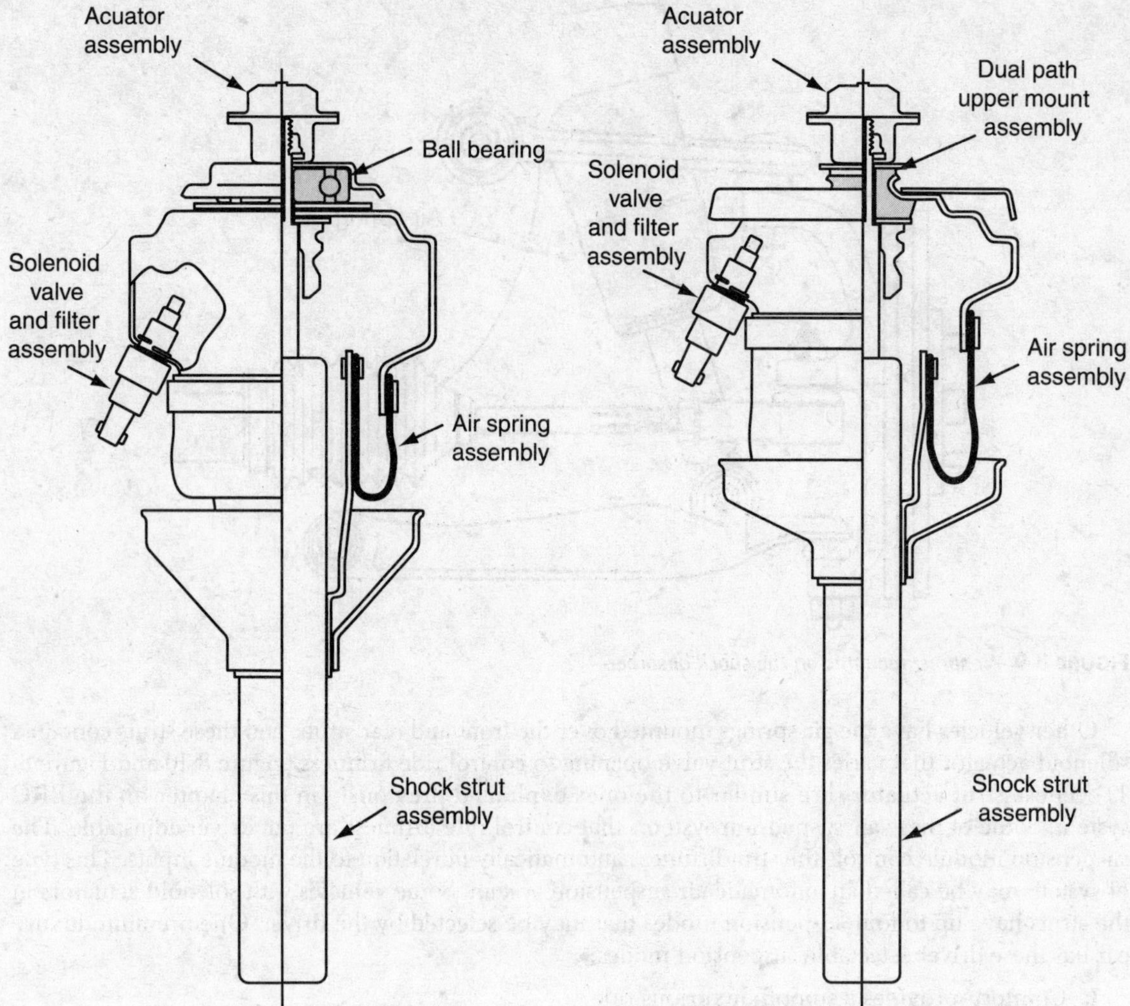

FIGURE 8-10 *Front air spring and strut assembly.*

FIGURE 8-11 *Rear air spring and strut assembly.*

control arm, and a bolt attaches this bushing to the lower end of the knuckle. The upper cross-axis ball joint is a round insulating bushing mounted in the top of the knuckle, and a bolt attaches this bushing to the upper control arm (Figure 8-13). In this rear suspension system the upper and lower control arms are made from aluminum. An adjustable toe link is connected from the knuckle to the frame to provide a rear toe adjustment. Rear wheel camber can be adjusted by installing a camber adjustment kit in place of the upper knuckle-to-control arm retaining bolt.

Air Spring Valves

An **air spring solenoid valve** is mounted in the top of each air spring (Figure 8-14). These valves are an electric solenoid-type valve that is normally closed. When the valve winding is energized, plunger movement opens the air passage to the air spring. Under this condition, air may enter or be exhausted from the air spring. Two O-ring seals are located on the end of the valves to seal them into the air spring cap. The valves are installed in the air spring cap with a two-stage rotating action similar to a radiator pressure cap.

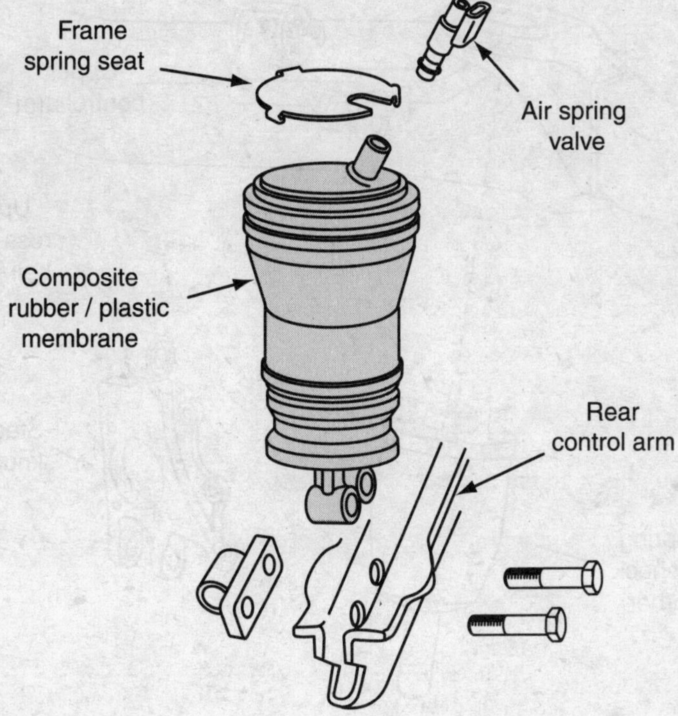

FIGURE 8-12 *Rear air spring mounting.*

Air Compressor

A single piston in the air compressor is moved up and down in the cylinder by a crankshaft and connecting rod (Figure 8-15). The armature is connected to the crankshaft, and therefore the rotating action of the armature moves the piston up and down. Armature rotation occurs when 12 V are supplied to the compressor input terminal. Intake and discharge valves are located in the cylinder head. An air dryer that contains a silica gel is mounted on the compressor. This silica gel removes moisture from the air as it enters the system.

Nylon air lines are connected from the compressor outlets to the air spring valves. The compressor operates when it is necessary to force air into one or more air springs to restore the vehicle trim height.

An air **vent valve** is located in the compressor cylinder head (Figure 8-16). This normally closed electric solenoid valve allows air to be vented from the system. When it is necessary to exhaust air from an air spring, the air spring valve and vent valve must be energized at the same time with the compressor shut off. Air exhausting is necessary if the vehicle trim height is too high.

Compressor Relay

When the compressor relay is energized, it supplies 12 V through the relay contacts to the compressor input terminal (Figure 8-17). The relay contacts open the circuit to the compressor if the relay is deenergized. An electronic relay is used in some air suspension systems.

Control Module

The control module is a microprocessor that operates the compressor, vent valve, and air spring valves to control the amount of air in the air springs and maintain the trim height. The control module

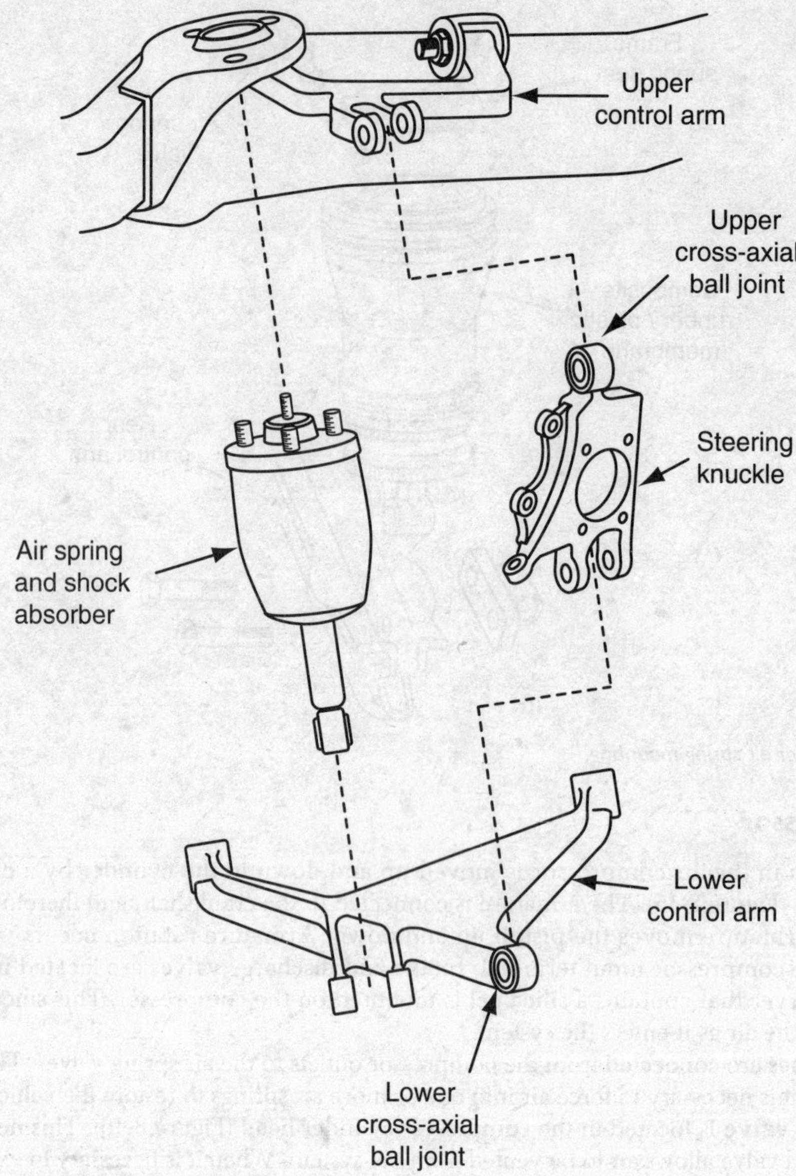

FIGURE 8-13 *Rear air suspension system with cross-axis ball joints and air spring mounted over the shock absorber.*

is located in the trunk (Figure 8-18) on some models. On other models the module is mounted under the instrument panel above the parking brake.

The control module turns on the suspension service indicator light in the roof panel or instrument panel to alert the driver when a suspension defect occurs. Diagnostic capabilities are designed into the suspension module. On some vehicles the suspension module is called a vehicle dynamics module (VDM). On many air suspension systems the suspension module is interconnected via data links to some of the other onboard computers and the data link connector (DLC) under the dash. A scan tool may be connected to the DLC to diagnose the air suspension and other electronic systems on the vehicle. The data links allow data transmission between the on-board computers and the DLC. For example, the vehicle speed sensor (VSS) signal may be sent through connecting wires to the power-

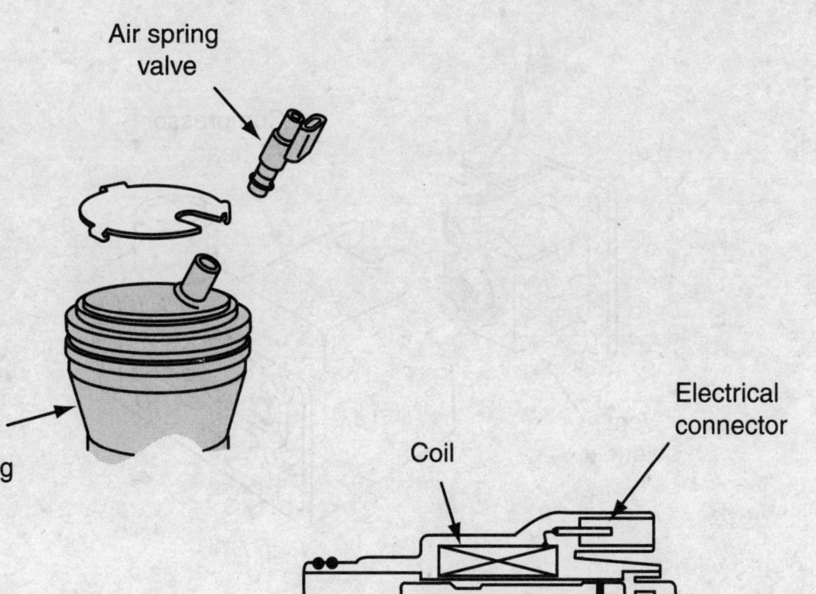

FIGURE 8-14 *Air spring valve.*

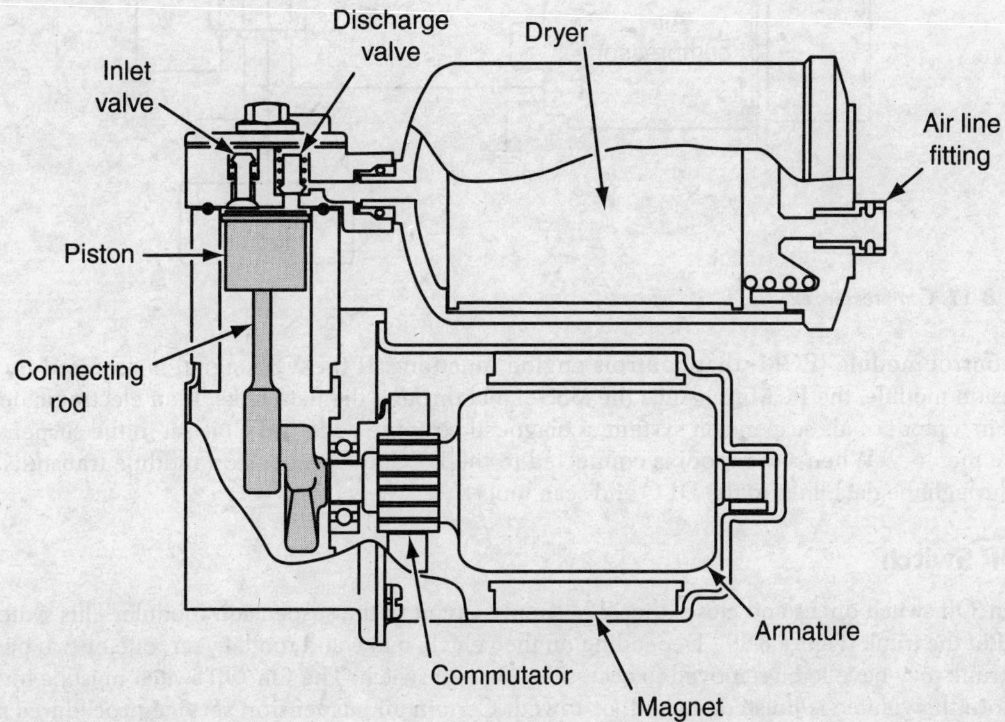

FIGURE 8-15 *Air compressor.*

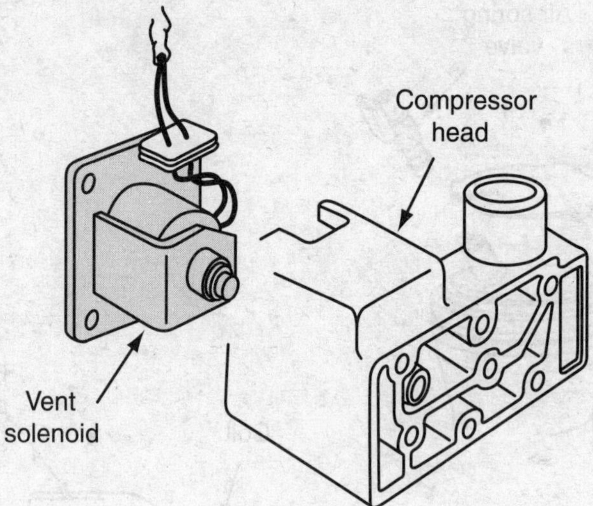

FIGURE 8-16 *Air vent valve.*

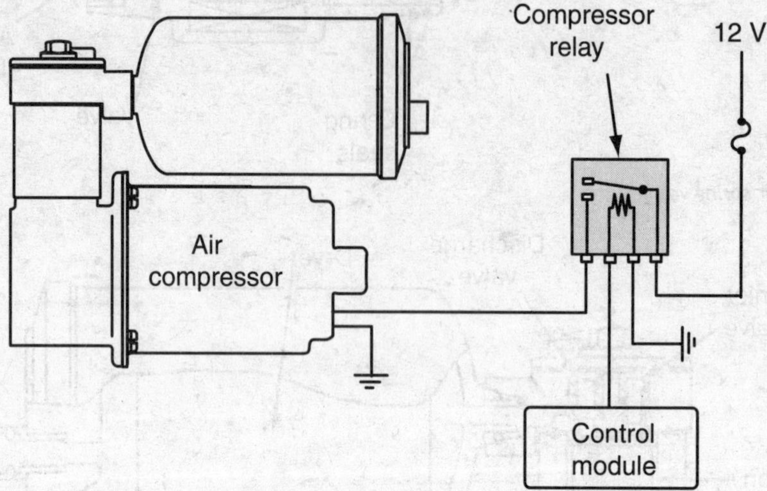

FIGURE 8-17 *Compressor relay.*

train control module (PCM) that controls engine functions. If the VSS signal is required by the suspension module, the PCM transmits the VSS signal through the data links. If an electronic defect occurs in a modern air suspension system, a diagnostic trouble code (DTC) is set in the suspension module memory. When a scan tool is connected to the DLC, the suspension module transmits the DTC through the data links to the DLC and scan tool.

On/Off Switch

The On/Off switch opens and closes the 12 V supply circuit to the suspension module. This switch is located in the trunk (Figure 8-19). Depending on the vehicle make and model year, one or two panels in the trunk may have to be removed to access the On/Off switch. The On/Off switch must be turned off before the vehicle is hoisted, jacked, or towed. Certain air suspension service procedures may require this switch to be placed in the Off position.

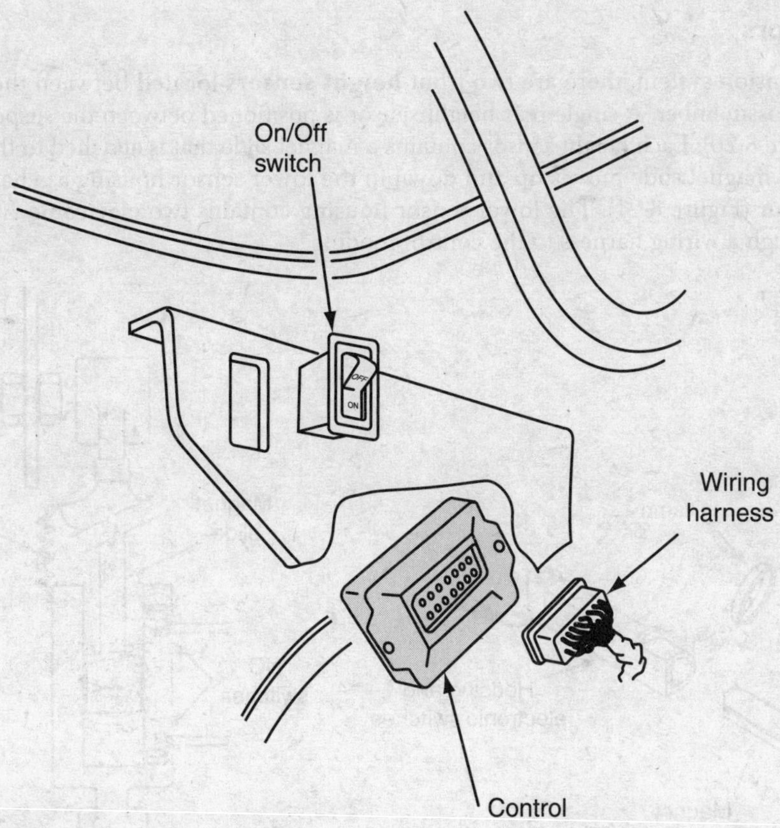

FIGURE 8-18 *Control module.*

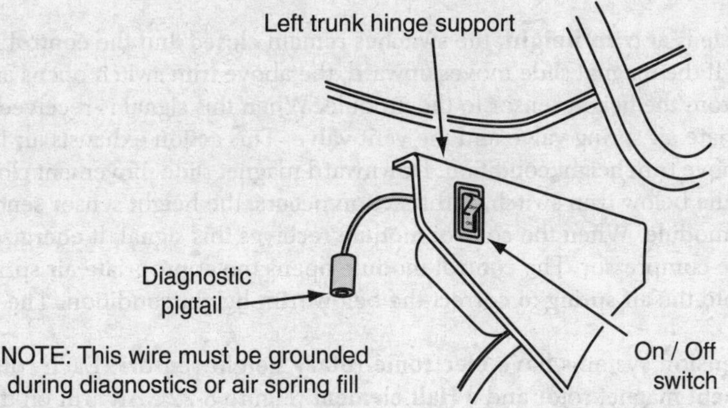

FIGURE 8-19 *On/Off switch.*

WARNING: If the vehicle is hoisted, jacked, or towed with the electronic air suspension switch in the On position, personal injury or vehicle damage may occur.

Height Sensors

In the air suspension system, there are two front **height sensors** located between the lower control arms and the crossmember. A single rear height sensor is positioned between the suspension arm and the frame (Figure 8-20). Each height sensor contains a magnet slide that is attached to the upper end of the sensor. This magnet slide moves up and down in the lower sensor housing as changes in vehicle trim height occur (Figure 8-21). The lower sensor housing contains two electronic switches that are connected through a wiring harness to the control module.

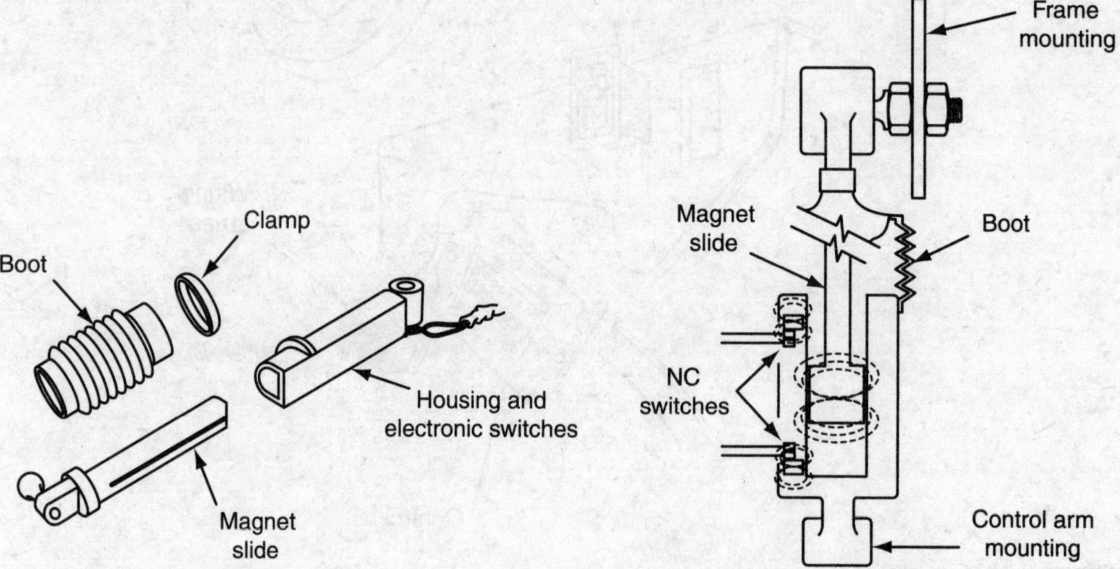

FIGURE 8-20 *Height sensor.*

FIGURE 8-21 *Rear height sensor mounting.*

When the vehicle is at **trim height,** the switches remain closed and the control module receives a trim height signal. If the magnet slide moves upward, the above trim switch opens and a **lower vehicle command** is sent from the height sensor to the module. When this signal is received by the module, it opens the appropriate air spring valve and the vent valve. This action exhausts air from the air spring and corrects the above trim height condition. Downward magnet slide movement closes the above trim switch and opens the below trim switch. If this action occurs, the height sensor sends a **raise vehicle command** to the module. When the control module receives this signal, it energizes the compressor relay and starts the compressor. The control module opens the appropriate air spring valve, and this action forces air into the air spring to correct the below trim height condition. The height sensors are serviced as a unit.

Some air suspension systems have **electronic rotary height sensors**. Each rotary height sensor contains a permanent magnet rotor and a **Hall element** (Figure 8-22). An arm on the height sensor is attached to the rotor. The height sensor body is mounted on the chassis and a linkage is connected from the sensor arm to the suspension (Figure 8-23). Suspension movement rotates the permanent magnet rotor and changes the voltage signal in the Hall element. The voltage signal from a rotary height sensor is proportional to trim height, above trim height, and below trim height.

CAUTION: Never attempt to probe the electronic switches in slide-type height sensors. This action may damage the sensor.

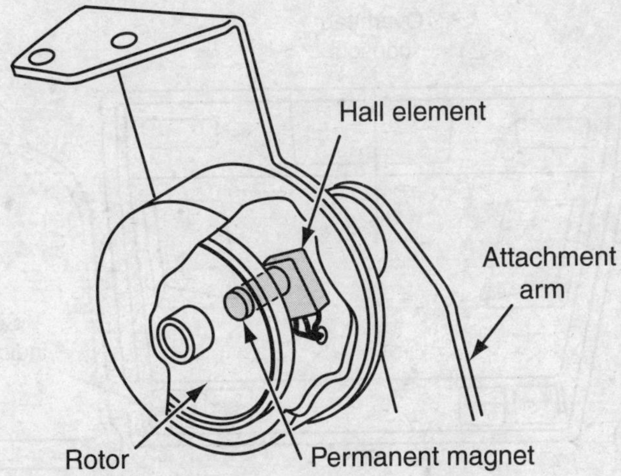

FIGURE 8-22 *Electronic rotary height sensor.*

FIGURE 8-23 *Height sensor mounting.*

Warning Lamp

When the control module senses a system defect, the module turns on the air suspension warning lamp in the roof console or instrument panel to inform the driver that a problem exists (Figure 8-24). If the air suspension system is working normally, the warning lamp will be on for one second when the ignition switch is turned from the Off to the Run position. After this time, the warning lamp should remain off. This lamp does not operate with the ignition switch in the start position. The warning lamp is used during the self-diagnostic procedure and the spring fill sequence.

On some vehicles the air suspension warning light is replaced with a CHECK SUSPENSION message in the instrument panel message center. The suspension module provides a CHECK SUSPENSION message if an electrical defect occurs in the air suspension system. An AIR SUSPENSION SWITCHED OFF message appears in the message center if the air suspension switch is in the Off position.

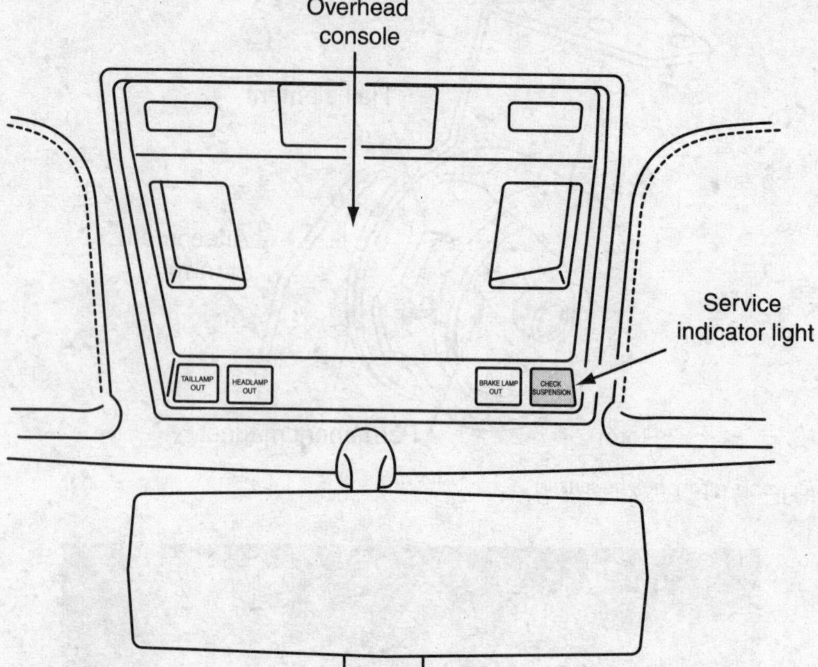

FIGURE 8-24 *Air suspension warning light.*

ELECTRONIC AIR SUSPENSION SYSTEM OPERATION

The operation of an air suspension system varies depending on the vehicle make and model year. The following section discusses typical air suspension operation.

Ignition Switch Off

The electronic air suspension system is fully operational for one hour after the ignition switch is turned from the Run to the Off position. During this time, lower vehicle commands are completed unless a height sensor was providing a high signal when the ignition switch was turned off. After a one-hour period, raise vehicle commands are acted upon and lower vehicle commands are ignored. The air compressor run time is limited to 15 seconds for rear springs and 30 seconds for front springs.

Ignition Switch in Run Position

When the ignition system has been in the Run position for less than 45 seconds, raise vehicle commands are completed immediately, but lower vehicle commands are ignored. If the ignition switch has been in the Run position for more than 45 seconds, the operation is as follows:

1. If a door is opened with the brake pedal released, raise vehicle commands are completed immediately, but lower vehicle commands are serviced after the door is closed. This action prevents an open door from catching on curbs or other objects.
2. If the doors are closed and the brake pedal is released, all commands are serviced by a 45-second averaging method to prevent excessive suspension height corrections on irregular road surfaces.

3. If the brake is applied and a door is open, raise vehicle commands are completed immediately, but lower vehicle commands are ignored.
4. When the doors are closed and the brake pedal is applied, all commands are ignored by the control module. If a command to raise the rear suspension is in progress under these conditions, this command will be completed. This action prevents correction of front end jounce while braking.

General Operation

When a height sensor sends a raise vehicle command to the control module and the other input signals are acceptable, the module grounds the compressor relay winding and starts the compressor. The module also opens the appropriate air spring valve to allow air flow into the air spring (Figure s8-25).

The rear air valve solenoids always operate together, but the front solenoids may be energized independently. When the correct chassis trim height is obtained, the control module opens the circuit from the compressor relay winding to ground and de-energizes the air spring valve. This action shuts off the compressor and traps the air in the air spring.

If a lower vehicle request is sent from a height sensor to the control module and the other input signals are acceptable, the control module opens the air vent valve and appropriate air spring valve. When this action occurs, air is released from the air spring until the correct trim height is obtained. The trim height signal from the height sensor to the module causes the module to close the air vent valve and the air spring valve.

Specific Control Module Operation

Commands are completed by the module in this order: rear up, front up, rear down, front down. When the ignition switch is in the Run position and a command cannot be completed within three minutes, the module turns on the air suspension warning lamp. This lamp remains on until the ignition switch is turned off. On some older models all the control module memory is erased when the ignition switch is turned off. Therefore, the warning lamp may not indicate a defect immediately if the ignition switch is turned from the Off to the Run position. When a system defect causes the module to illuminate the warning lamp with the ignition in the Run position, other commands may be completed by the module. Commands from the front and rear height sensors are never completed simultaneously.

If an electrical defect occurs in a modern air suspension system, a diagnostic trouble code (DTC) is set and retained in the suspension module memory. In these systems, DTCs are transmitted via the data links to the data link connector (DLC) under the instrument panel, and the DTCs may be displayed on a scan tool connected to the DLC.

AIR SUSPENSION SYSTEM DESIGN VARIATIONS

Rear Load-Leveling Air Suspension System

Some vehicles have air suspension on only the rear wheels, and these systems may be referred to as rear load-leveling air suspension systems. These air suspension systems have basically the same air springs, compressor and relay, On/Off switch, and rear height sensor as the air suspensions described previously. If additional weight is placed in the trunk, the rear height sensor signals the suspension control module to raise the rear suspension height to the specified trim height. When the extra weight is removed from the trunk, the suspension height is higher than specified, and the air suspension system lowers the rear trim height to the specified height.

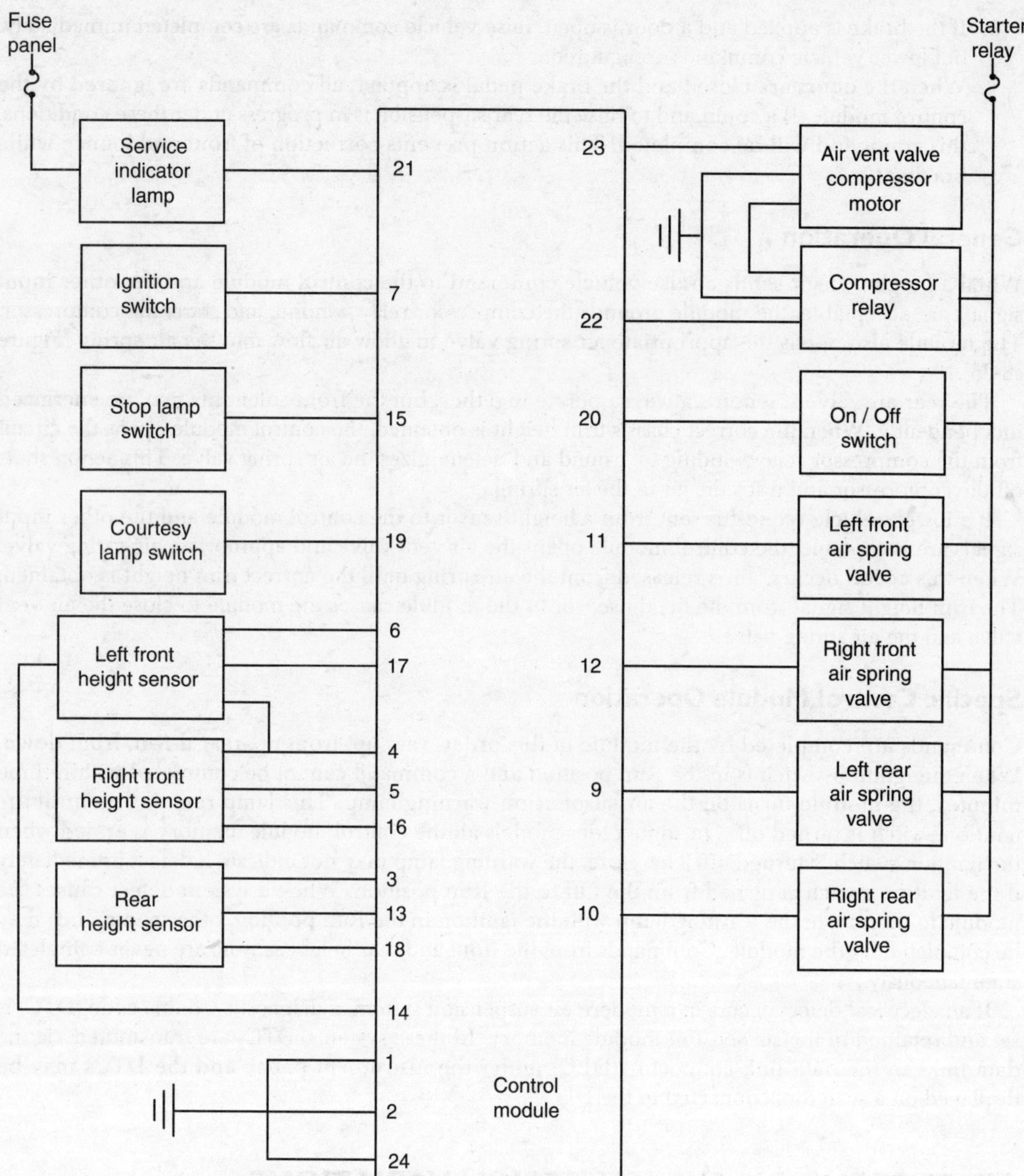

FIGURE 8-25 *Air suspension wiring diagram.*

Air Suspension System with Speed Leveling Capabilities

Some vehicles have an air suspension system on the front and rear wheels that is similar to the air suspension systems described earlier in this chapter. However, these systems have an input signal from the vehicle speed sensor (VSS) to the suspension module. On some vehicles the signal from the VSS is sent to the powertrain control module (PCM) that controls engine functions. The PCM transmits the VSS signal through the data links from the PCM to the suspension module. When the VSS signal indicates the vehicle is traveling above 65 mph (105 km/h), the suspension module opens the vent valve and spring solenoid valves to lower the suspension height a specific amount. Under this condition the vehicle is more dynamically efficient and this improves high-speed vehicle stability and fuel economy.

Special Air Suspension System Features on Four-Wheel-Drive Vehicles

Some four-wheel-drive vehicles with a conventional front torsion bar suspension and a leaf-spring rear suspension also have an air suspension system on all four wheels. These front and rear suspension systems maintain the specified ride height during two-wheel-drive operation. The air suspension system has the same components as described previously, except this air suspension system has front and rear air shock absorbers in place of air springs. An air solenoid is connected in the air line to each air shock absorber (Figure 8-26). The air shock absorbers also contain electrical solenoids that rotate the shock absorber valves and vary the ride firmness (Figure 8-27). This type of air suspension may be called an automatic ride control (ARC) system.

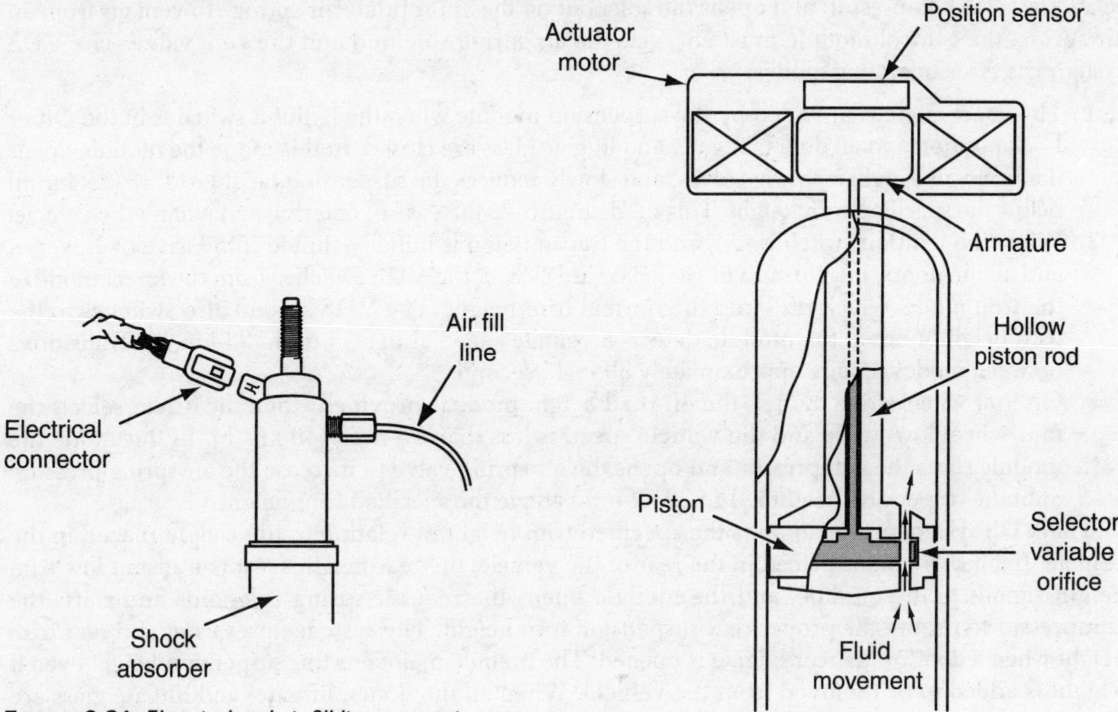

FIGURE 8-26 *Electrical and air fill line connections to the shock absorber.*

FIGURE 8-27 *Strut actuator.*

When driving on a smooth road surface in two-wheel drive, the suspension module positions the shock absorber valves to provide a soft ride. If the vehicle is driven on a rough road surface, the suspension's computer switches the shock absorber valves to the firm mode. When the driver selects four-wheel high mode, the suspension module starts the compressor and opens the air shock absorber valves, and increases the air shock absorber pressure until the suspension trim height is raised 1 in. (25.4 mm). If the vehicle speed exceeds 58 mph (93 km/h), the module returns the suspension height to the specified trim height. If the driver selects the four-wheel low mode, the suspension module operates the compressor and air shock absorber valves to increase the trim height 2 in. (50.8 mm). If the vehicle speed exceeds 30 mph (48 km/h in the four-wheel low mode), the module adjusts the suspension height to 1 in. (25.4 mm) above the specified trim height.

VEHICLE DYNAMIC SUSPENSION SYSTEM

Some SUVs are equipped with a **vehicle dynamic suspension (VDS)** system that is similar to the air suspension systems described previously in this chapter. The VDS system has these components:

1. Off/On service switch
2. Two front height sensors
3. One rear height sensor
4. Compressor with internal vent solenoid and air dryer
5. Control module
6. Air lines
7. Front and rear combined air springs and shock absorbers
8. Four air spring solenoids
9. Compressor relay

When increased air pressure is required in an air spring, the control module closes the compressor relay, starts the compressor, and opens the solenoid on the appropriate air spring. To vent air from an air spring, the control module must energize the air spring solenoid and the vent valve. The VDS system has three operating modes:

1. The kneel mode is provided by the suspension module when the ignition switch is in the Off or Lock position and all doors, liftgate, and liftgate glass are closed. In this mode the module opens the vent valve and air spring valves, and slowly reduces the suspension height to 1 in. (25.4 mm) below the specified trim height. This mode improves the ease of entering and exiting the vehicle.
2. When the ignition switch is On, and the transmission is initially shifted into Drive or Reverse, and all the doors, liftgate, and liftgate glass are closed, the VDS switches from the kneel mode to the trim mode, which provides the normal trim height. The VDS system also switches to the trim height mode if the module detects a vehicle speed above 15 mph (24 km/h). Transitions between modes require approximately 30 to 45 seconds.
3. On four-wheel-drive models the off-road height mode is provided when the driver selects the four-wheel low mode and the vehicle speed is less than 25 mph (40 km/h). In this mode the module starts the compressor and opens the air spring valve to increase the air spring pressure until the suspension height is 1 in. (25.4 mm) above the specified trim height.

The VDS system also maintains the specified trim height in relation to the weight placed in the vehicle. If a heavy load is placed in the rear of the vehicle, the rear height sensors transmit low trim height signals to the module, and the module opens the rear air spring solenoids and starts the compressor to restore the proper rear suspension trim height. The system stores front and rear trim height when a door or the rear liftgate is opened. The module maintains this suspension height even if weight is added to or removed from the vehicle. When all the doors, liftgate, and liftgate glass are closed, the system returns to normal operation. The VDS system makes limited height adjustments for 40 minutes after the ignition switch is turned Off.

ELECTRONIC SUSPENSION CONTROL (ESC) SYSTEM

General Description

The **electronic suspension control (ESC) system** controls damping forces in the front struts and rear shock absorbers in response to various road and driving conditions. The ESC system changes shock and strut damping forces in 1 to 12 milliseconds, whereas other suspension damping systems require a much longer time interval to change damping forces. It requires about 200 milliseconds to blink your eye. This gives us some idea how quickly the ESC system reacts. On some older models the ESC system may be called a continuously variable road sensing suspension (CVRSS).

The ESC module receives inputs regarding vertical acceleration, wheel-to-body position, speed of wheel movement, vehicle speed, and lift/dive (Figure 8-28). The CVRSS module evaluates these inputs and controls a solenoid in each shock or strut to provide suspension damping control. The solenoids in the shocks and struts can react much faster compared with the strut actuators explained previously in some systems.

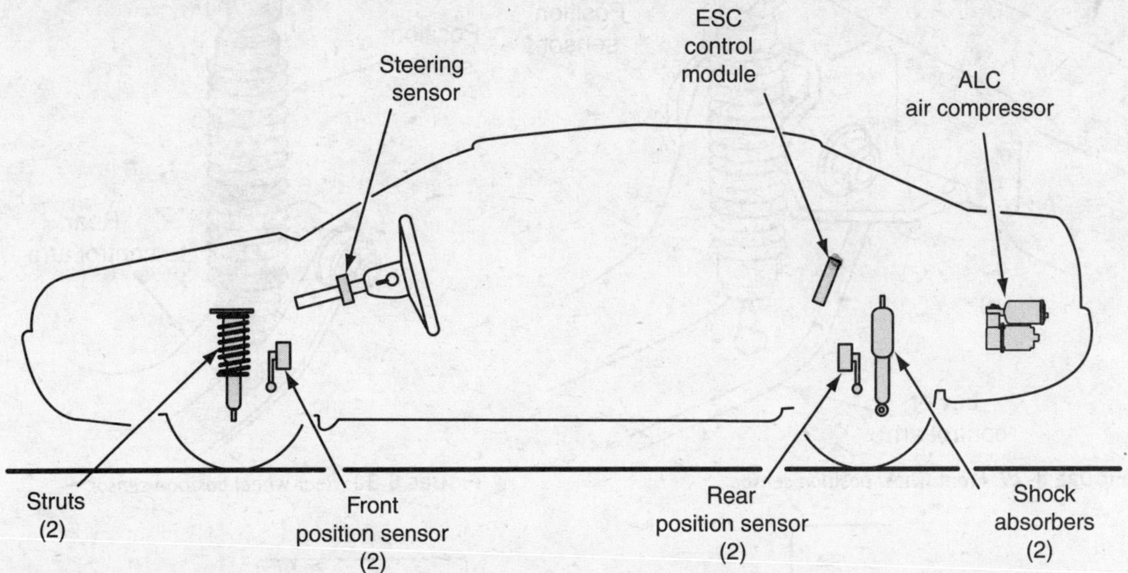

FIGURE 8-28 *Electronic suspension control (ESC) system.*

The ESC module also controls the speed-dependent steering system called MagnaSteer® and the automatic level control (ALC). This MagnaSteer® system is similar to the electronic variable orifice (EVO) steering explained in Chapter 12 under conventional and electronic rack-and-pinion steering gears. The ALC system controls the air pressure in the rear air shock absorbers to maintain the proper rear suspension height. The ALC system is similar to the rear load-leveling suspension system explained previously in this chapter.

Inputs

Position Sensors. A **wheel position sensor** is mounted at each corner of the vehicle between a control arm and the chassis (Figures 8-29 and 8-30). These sensor inputs provide analog voltage signals to the ESC module regarding relative wheel-to-body movement and the velocity of wheel movement (Figure 8-31). The rear position sensor inputs also provide rear suspension height information to the ESC module, and this information is used by the module to control the rear suspension trim height. All four position sensors have the same design. The wheel position sensors may be linear-type or rotary-type.

Accelerometer. An **accelerometer** is mounted on each corner of the vehicle. These inputs send information to the ESC module in relation to vertical acceleration of the body. The front accelerometers are mounted on the strut towers (Figure 8-32), and the rear accelerometers are located on the rear chassis near the rear suspension support (Figure 8-33). All four accelerometers are similar in design, and they send analog voltage signals to the ESC module (Figure 8-34). On some later model

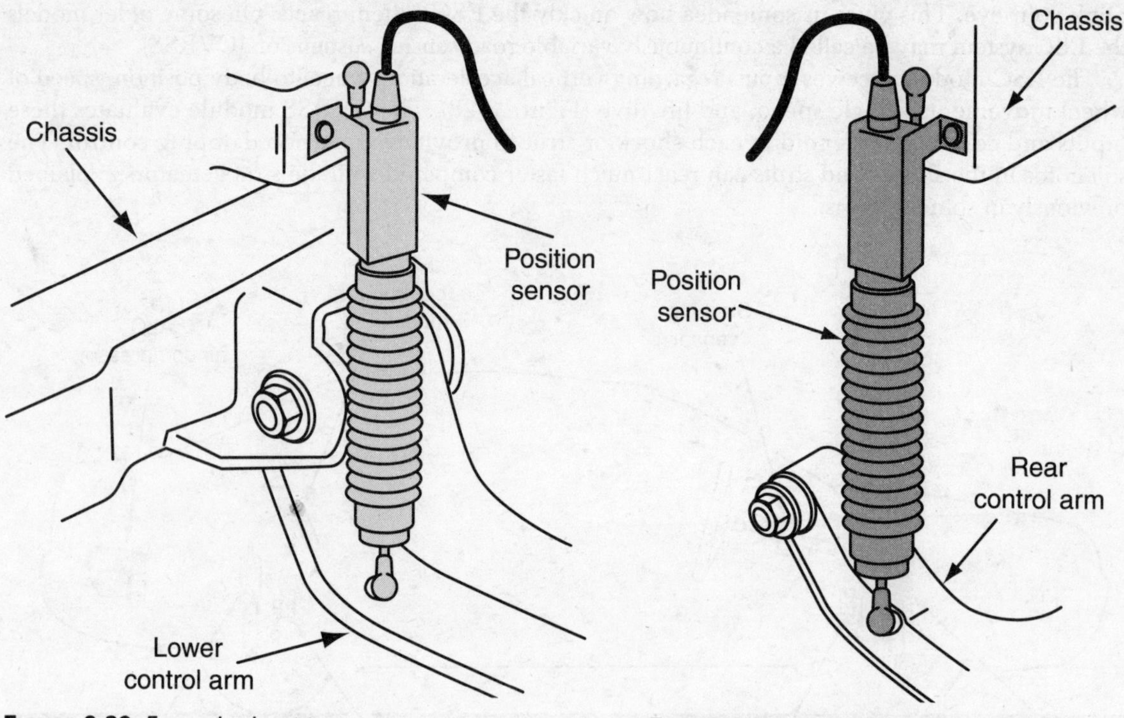

FIGURE 8-29 *Front wheel position sensor.*

FIGURE 8-30 *Rear wheel position sensor.*

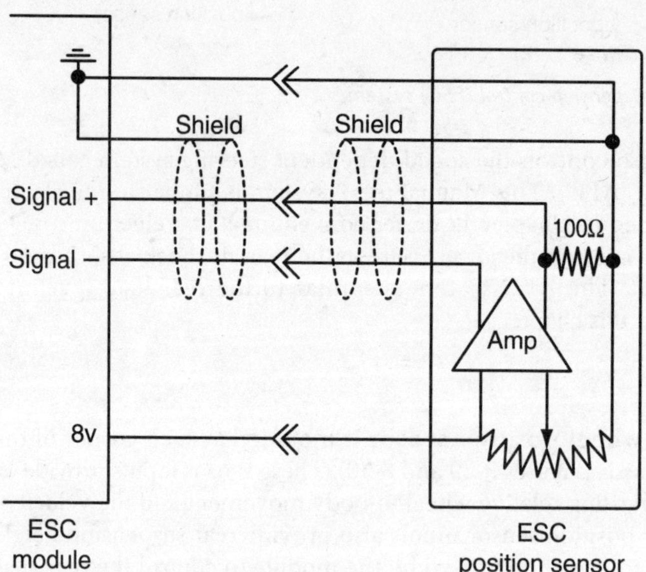

FIGURE 8-31 *Position sensor internal design and wiring diagram.*

vehicles, the four accelerometers are replaced by a single accelerometer under the driver's seat. On other late-model vehicles the accelerometer(s) are eliminated.

Vehicle Speed Sensor. The **vehicle speed sensor (VSS)** is mounted in the transaxle. This sensor sends a voltage signal to the powertrain control module (PCM) in relation to vehicle speed (Figure 8-35). The VSS signal is transmitted via data links from the PCM to the ESC module.

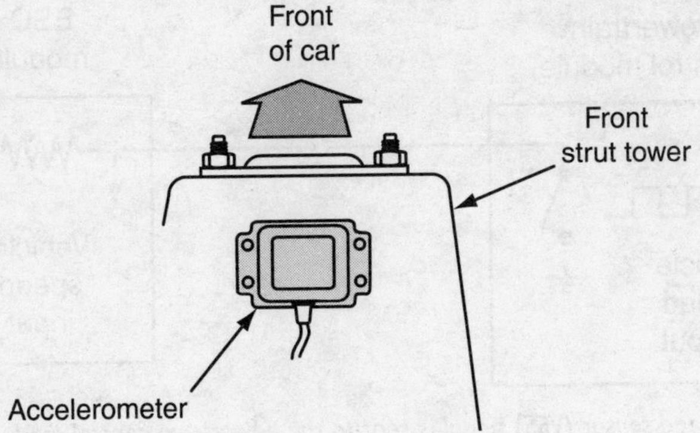

FIGURE 8-32 *Front accelerometer mounting location.*

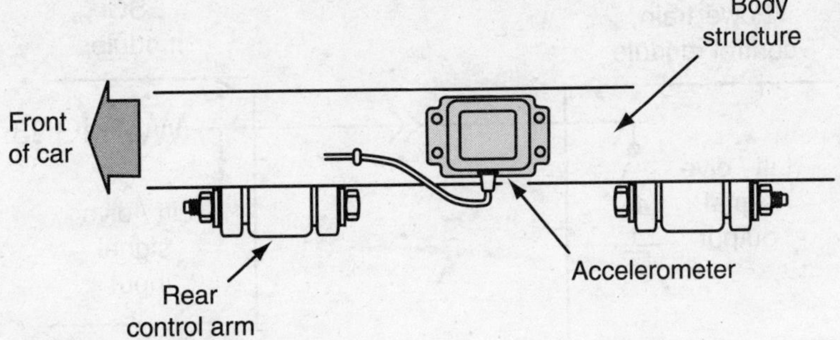

FIGURE 8-33 *Rear accelerometer position.*

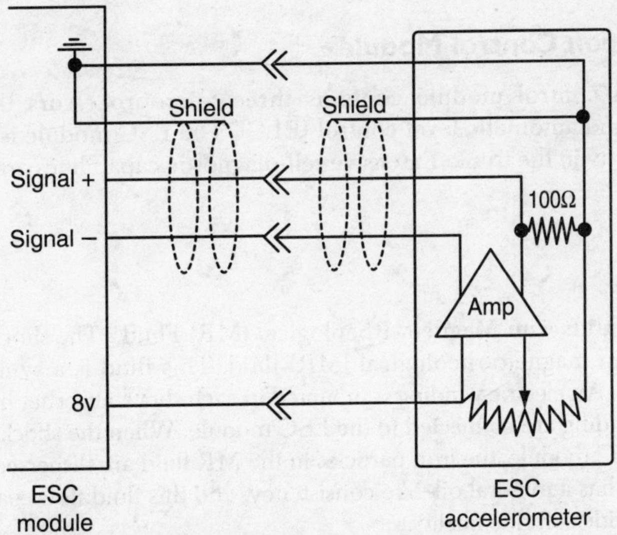

FIGURE 8-34 *Accelerometer internal design and wiring diagram.*

Lift/Dive Input. The **lift/dive input** is sent from the PCM to the ESC module (Figure 8-36). Suspension lift information is obtained by the PCM from the throttle position, vehicle speed, and transaxle gear input signals. The PCM calculates suspension dive information from the rate of vehicle speed change when decelerating.

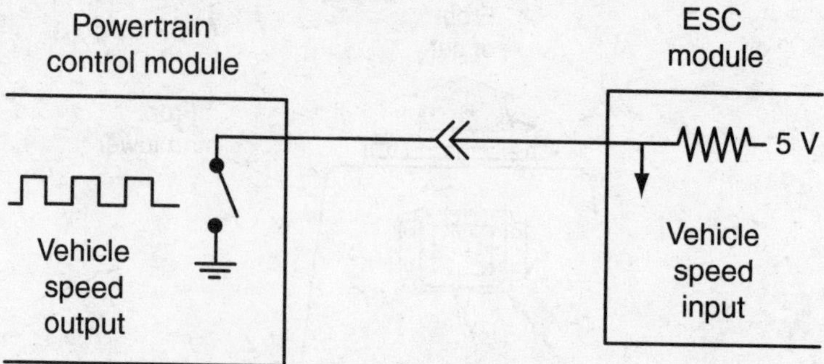

FIGURE 8-35 *The vehicle speed sensor (VSS) signal is sent to the powertrain control module (PCM) and transmitted to the ESC module.*

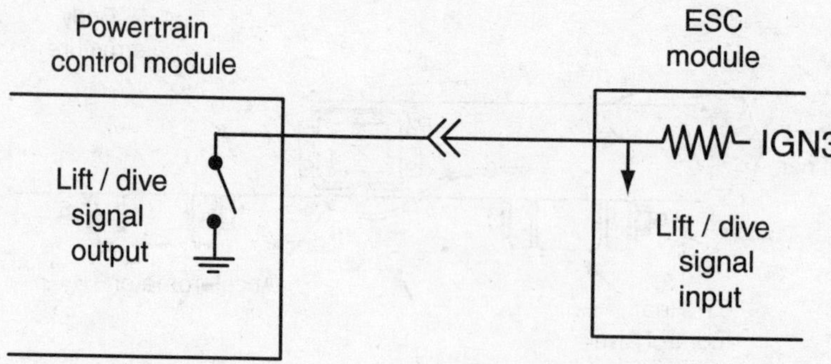

FIGURE 8-36 *The lift-dive signal is sent from the powertrain control module (PCM) to the ESC module.*

Electronic Suspension Control Module

Electronic suspension control module contains three microprocessors that control the ESC, Magnsateer® system, and automatic level control (ELC). The ESC module is mounted on the right side of the electronics bay in the trunk. Extensive self-diagnostic capabilities are programmed into the ESC module.

Outputs

Shock Absorbers and Struts with Magneto-Rheological (MR) Fluid. The shock absorbers or struts in the ESC system contain magneto-rheological (MR) fluid. This fluid is a synthetic fluid containing suspended iron particles. An electric winding is mounted in each shock absorber housing, and the ends of each shock absorber winding are connected to the ESC module. When the shock absorber windings are not energized by the ESC module, the iron particles in the MR fluid are dispersed randomly. Under this condition the MR fluid has a mineral oil–like consistency, and this fluid flows easily through the shock absorber orifices to provide soft ride quality.

When the ESC module energizes the shock absorber windings, the magnetic field around the winding aligns the iron particles in the MR fluid into thick fibrous structures. In this condition the MR fluid has a jelly-like consistency that does not flow easily through the shock absorber orifices (Figure 8-37). This fluid change provides firm ride quality. Based on the wheel position sensor and other inputs, the ESC module can energize each individual shock absorber winding many times per second with a **pulse width modulated (PWM)** signal. Therefore the ESC system with magneto-rheological fluid in the shock

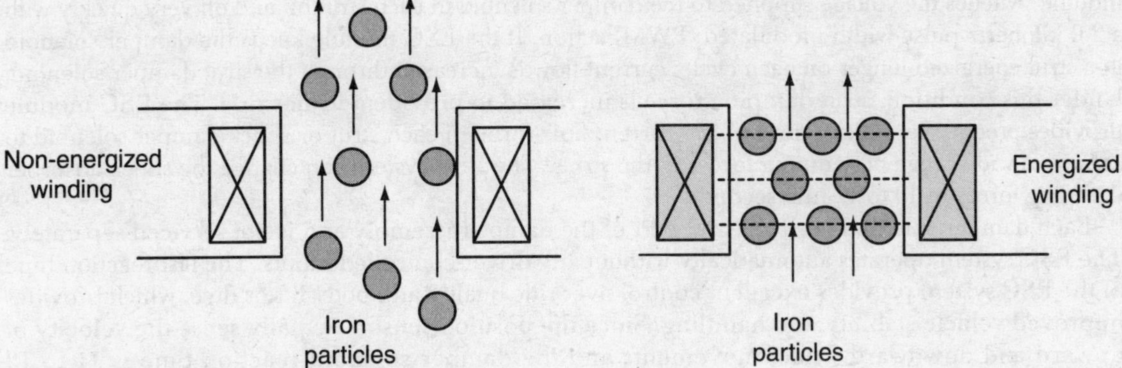

FIGURE 8-37 *Magneto-rheological fluid action in a strut or shock absorber.*

absorbers or struts provides an almost infinite variation in shock absorber damping. The ESC system can change the damping characteristics of the MR fluid in 1 millisecond.

The ESC system with MR fluid in the shock absorbers or struts provides greatly improved control of pitch and body roll motions, which supplies better road-holding capabilities, steering control, ride quality, and safety.

Damper Solenoid Valves. On some older models each strut or shock damper contains a solenoid that is controlled by the ESC module. Each **damper solenoid valve** provides a wide range of damping forces between soft and firm levels. Strut or shock absorber damping is controlled by the amount of current supplied to the damper solenoid in each strut or shock absorber. Battery voltage and ignition voltage are supplied through separate fuses to the ESC module (Figure 8-38). If the damper solenoids are not energized, the struts provide minimum damping force. When the damper solenoids are energized, the struts provide increased damping force for a firmer ride. The ESC

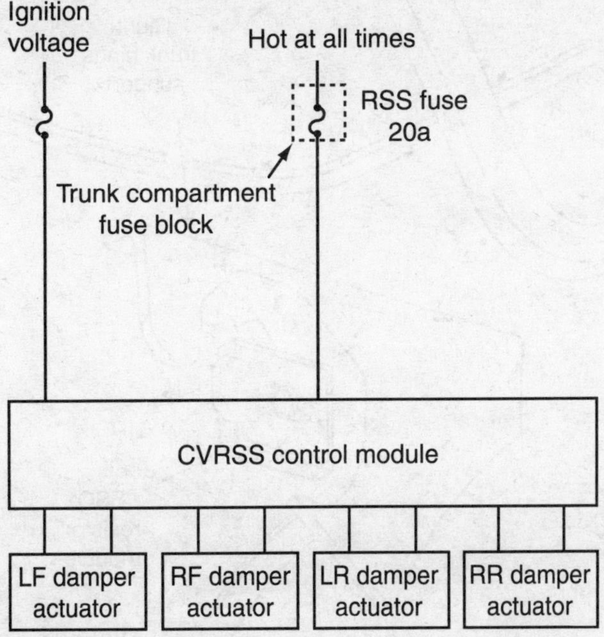

FIGURE 8-38 *Strut damper solenoid circuit.*

module switches the voltage supplied to the damper solenoid in each strut on and off very quickly with a 2.0 kilohertz pulse width modulated (PWM) action. If the ESC module keeps the damper solenoid in a strut energized longer on each cycle, current flow is increased through the strut damper solenoid. Under this condition, strut damping force is increased to provide a firmer ride. The ESC module provides precise, variable control of the current flow through each strut or shock damper solenoid to achieve a wide range of damping forces in the struts. The ESC system can change the shock absorber damping forces in 10 to 12 milliseconds.

Each damper solenoid is an integral part of the damper assembly and is not serviced separately. The ESC system operates automatically without any driver-controlled inputs. The fast reaction time of the ESC system provides excellent control over ride quality and body lift or dive, which provides improved vehicle stability and handling. Since the position sensors actually sense the velocity of upward and downward wheel movements and the damper solenoid reaction time is 11 to 12 milliseconds, the ESC module can react to these position sensor inputs very quickly. For example, if a road irregularity drives a wheel upward, the ESC module switches the damper solenoid to the firm mode before that wheel strikes the road again during the downward movement.

Resistor Module. In some older models, the resistor module contains four resistors encapsulated in a ceramic material. This resistor module is mounted in the right rear quarter panel inside the trunk (Figure 8-39).

When the ESC module switches a damper solenoid on, the module provides a direct ground for the solenoid, and full voltage is dropped across the solenoid winding to energize the solenoid very quickly. Under this condition, a higher current flow is supplied through the damper solenoid winding and the ESC module to ground. Since it is undesirable to maintain this higher current flow through the damper solenoid for any longer than necessary, the ESC module switches a resistor in the resistor module into the damper solenoid circuit after this circuit is energized for 15 milliseconds. On later model vehicles, the resistor module is discontinued because the ESC module controls the strut damper solenoids with a PWM signal.

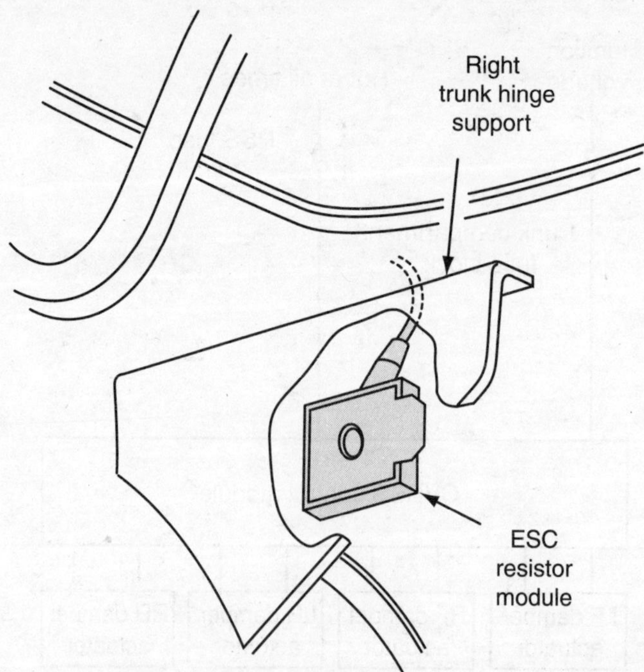

FIGURE 8-39 *Resistor module mounting location.*

This resistor reduces the voltage drop across the damper solenoid, which lowers the current flow. This lower current flow is high enough to hold the damper solenoid in the On mode. Each damper solenoid circuit is basically the same.

Rear Automatic Level Control

The **automatic level control** (ALC) system maintains the rear suspension trim height regardless of the rear suspension load. If a heavy object is placed in the trunk, the rear wheel position sensors send below trim height signals to the ESC module. When this signal is received, the ESC module grounds the ALC relay winding and closes the relay contacts that supply voltage to the compressor motor (Figure 8-40).

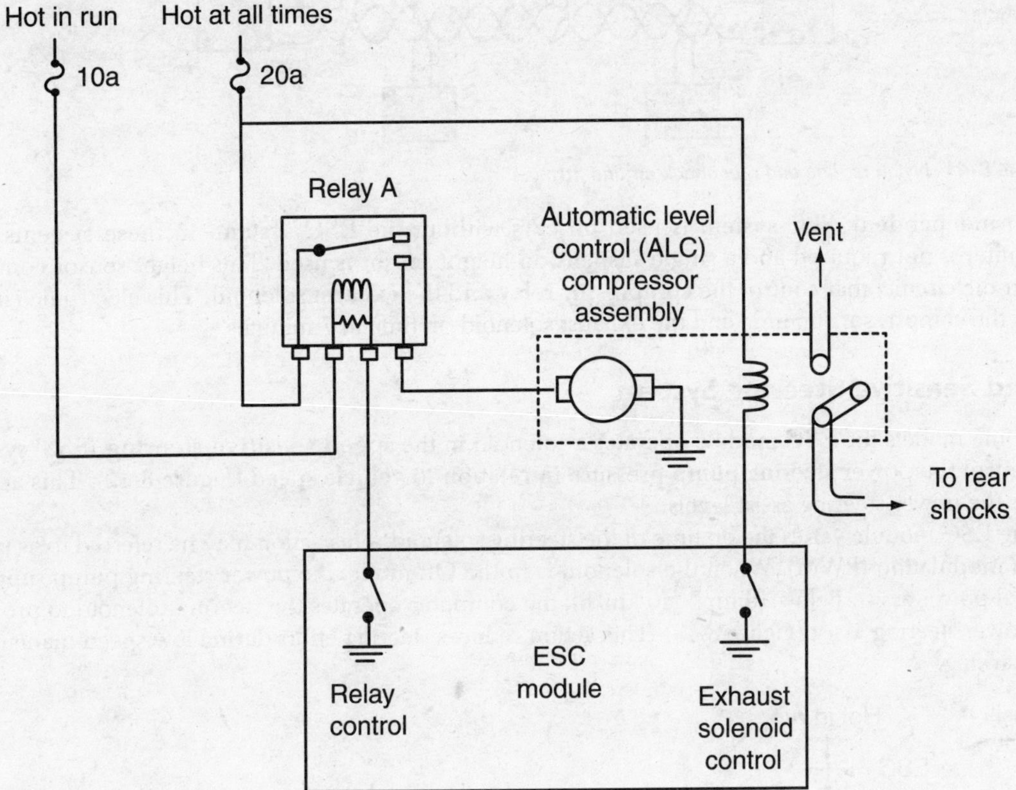

FIGURE 8-40 *Rear automatic level control (ALC).*

Once the compressor starts running, it supplies air through the nylon lines to the rear air shocks and raises the rear suspension height (Figure 8-41). When trim height signals are received from the rear wheel position sensors, the ESC module opens the compressor relay winding circuit and stops the compressor.

If a heavy object is removed from the trunk, the rear wheel position sensors send above trim height signals to the ESC module. Under this condition, the ESC module energizes the exhaust solenoid in the compressor assembly, and this action releases air from the rear air shocks. When the rear wheel position sensors send rear suspension trim height signals to the ESC module, this module shuts off the exhaust solenoid.

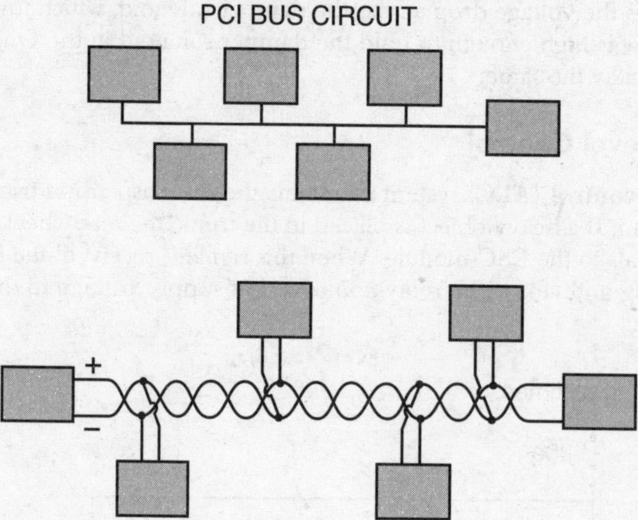

FIGURE 8-41 *Nylon air line and rear shock air line fitting.*

An independent ALC system is used on cars without the ESC system. In these systems, the computer is not required and a single suspension height sensor is used. This height sensor contains electronic circuits that control the compressor relay and the exhaust solenoid. This electronic circuit limits the compressor run time and the exhaust solenoid on time to 7 minutes.

Speed Sensitive Steering System

On some models the ESC module operates a solenoid in the **speed sensitive steering (SSS) system** to control the power steering pump pressure in relation to vehicle speed (Figure 8-42). This action varies the power steering assist levels.

The ESC module varies the on time of the steering solenoid. This action may be referred to as pulse width modulation (PWM). When the solenoid is in the Off mode, the power steering pump supplies normal power assist. Below 10 mph (16 km/h), the computer operates the steering solenoid to provide full power steering assist (Figure 8-43). This action reduces steering effort during low-speed maneuvers and parking.

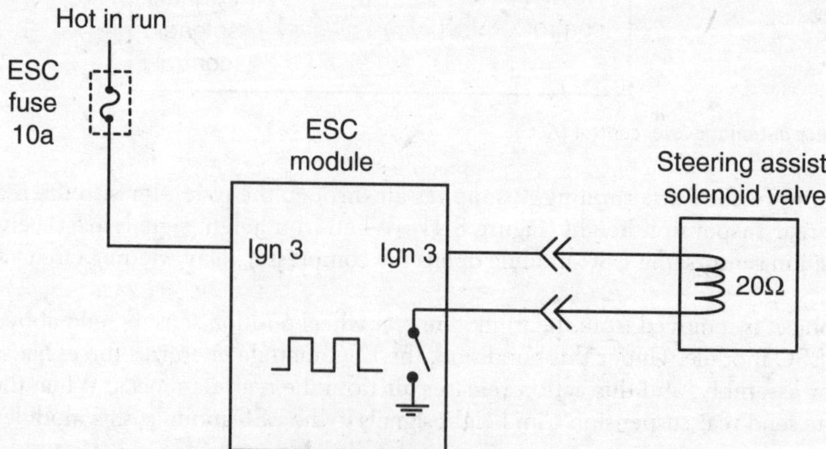

FIGURE 8-42 *Steering solenoid and ESC module wiring diagram.*

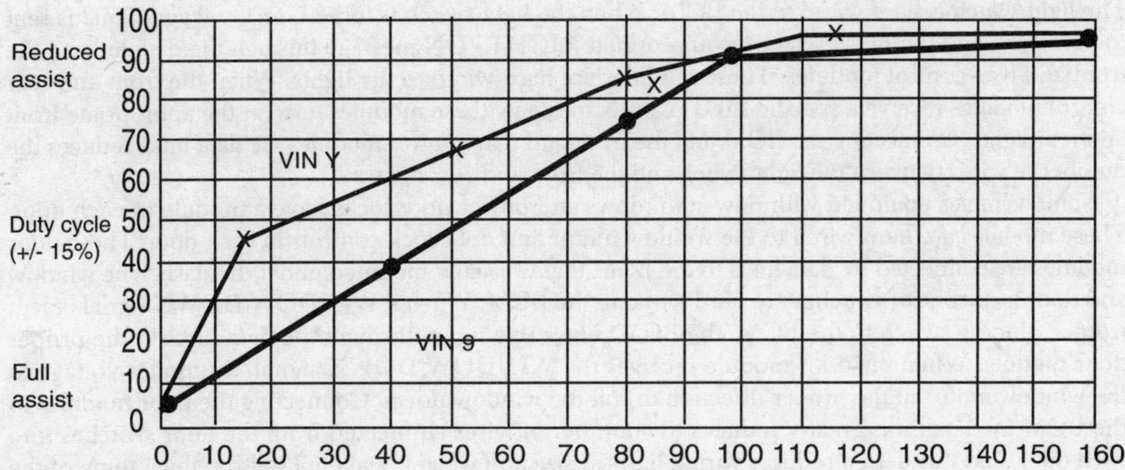

FIGURE 8-43 *Power steering assist in relation to vehicle speed.*

As the vehicle speed increases, the ESC module operates the steering solenoid so the power steering assist is gradually reduced to provide increased road feel and improved handling.

On later model cars, the speed sensitive steering (SSS) is called speed dependent steering or MagnaSteer®. The module that controls the MagnaSteer® is contained in the electronic brake and traction control module (EBTCM).

INTEGRATED ELECTRONIC SYSTEMS AND DATA LINKS

Advantages of Integrated Electronic Systems and Data Links

With the rapid advances in electronic technology, there is a trend toward integrating some computer-controlled automotive systems. Rather than having a separate computer for each electronic system, several of these systems may be controlled by one computer. Vehicles without any integrated electronic systems may have many individual modules and computers. Because computers must have some protection from excessive temperature changes, extreme vibration, magnetic fields, voltage spikes, and oil contamination, it becomes difficult for engineers to find a suitable mounting place for this large number of computers. Integration of several electronic systems into one computer solves some of these computer mounting problems and reduces the length of wiring harness. The (ESC) system explained in this chapter is an example of an integrated electronic system with suspension ride control, suspension level control, and speed sensitive steering controlled by one computer.

Another method of reducing the number of wires on a vehicle is to interconnect many of the on-board computers with data links. Some input sensor signals may be required by several computers. For example, on some vehicles the VSS signal is required by the PCM, suspension computer, transmission computer, cruise control module, and throttle control module. On many vehicles the VSS is hard-wired to the PCM, and then the PCM relays the VSS signal to the other computers via the data links.

Many vehicles now have a front control module mounted near the front of the vehicle and a rear control module mounted near the rear of the vehicle. These vehicles also have a body computer module (BCM). The BCM, PCM, front and rear control modules, and other modules are interconnected by data links. On some models the BCM is called a generic electronic module (GEM).

The light switch is hard wired to the BCM. When the light switch is turned on, a voltage signal is sent to the BCM, and the BCM relays the appropriate LIGHTS ON message through the data links to the front and rear control modules. These modules are hard wired to the lights. When the front and rear control modules receive a specific LIGHTS ON message, these modules turn on the appropriate front and rear lights. Connecting the BCM and the front and rear control modules via data links reduces the number of wires between the light switch and the front and rear lights.

Some vehicles equipped with power windows and power door locks have a module in each door. These modules are hard wired to the window motor and door lock controls in each door. These door modules are connected by data links to the BCM that is usually mounted under the dash. The window and door lock control switches are hard wired to the BCM. When a WINDOW DOWN signal is sent from a window switch to the BCM, the BCM relays this signal through the data links to the proper door module. When the door module receives the WINDOW DOWN signal, it supplies voltage to the window motor in the proper direction to roll the window down. Connecting the door modules to the BCM by data links greatly reduces the number of wires connected from the door switches into each door, and this design reduces wiring harness size and weight. Data links also reduce some of the problems associated with wiring harnesses.

Types of Data Links

One type of data link system introduced in the early 1980s is the Chrysler Collision Detection (CCD) network. The CCD system has a twisted pair of wires connected between the PCM, BCM, transmission control module (TCM), air bag control module (ACM), electro-mechanical instrument cluster (MIC), and vehicle theft security system (VTSS) module. On some models the CCD system is also connected to the data link connector (DLC), allowing the computers in the system to communicate with a scan tool connected to the DLC. The data link system may be called a data bus. The CCD system operates at 2.5 V.

Another type of data link system introduced in the 1980s is the universal asynchronous receive and transmit (UART) system. The UART data links are connected between various on-board computers and the DLC. The UART system operates at 5 V and transmits data at 8.2 kilobits per second. When sending data, the UART system toggles the voltage from 5 V to ground at a fixed bit pulse width. At rest the UART data link system has 5 V.

With the implementation of on-board diagnostic II (OBDII) systems in 1996, improved communication was required between the PCM, other computers, and the scan tool. Class 2 data links were installed to meet this demand. Class 2 data links transmit data at 10.4 kilobits per second, and transmit data by toggling the voltage from 0 to 7 V. At rest this data link system has zero volts. The programmable communication interface (PCI) data links were also introduced on some vehicles to increase the data communication requirements. The PCI data link system is a single wire system. Figure 8-44 illustrates a comparison between PCI and CCD data link systems. The PCI system operates between 0 V and 6 V to 8 V. Communication on a data link system is accomplished by sending a group of 0 and 1 signals (Figure 8-45). A long voltage pulse at a high voltage and a short pulse at a low voltage represent a 0 signal. Conversely, a short pulse at a high voltage and a long pulse at a low voltage indicate a 1 signal (Figure 8-46).

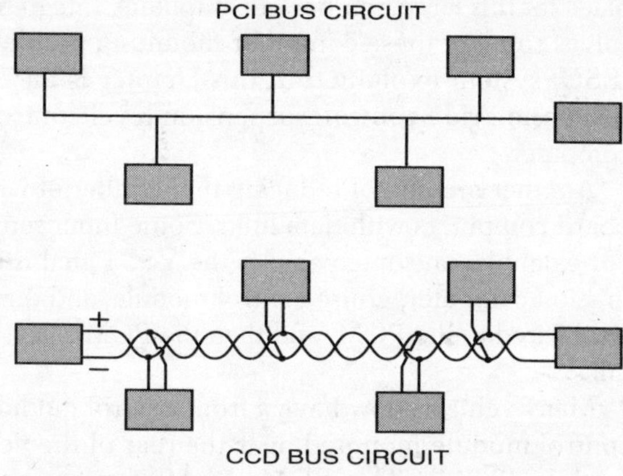

FIGURE 8-44 *Comparison between PCI and CCD data link systems.*

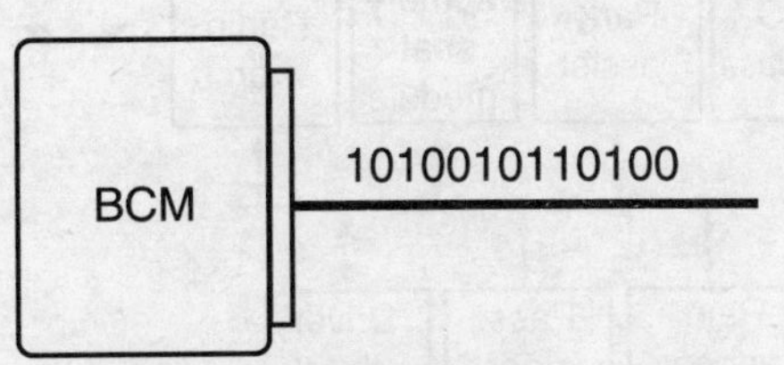

FIGURE 8-45 *A data link system transmits data by using a group of 0 and 1 signals.*

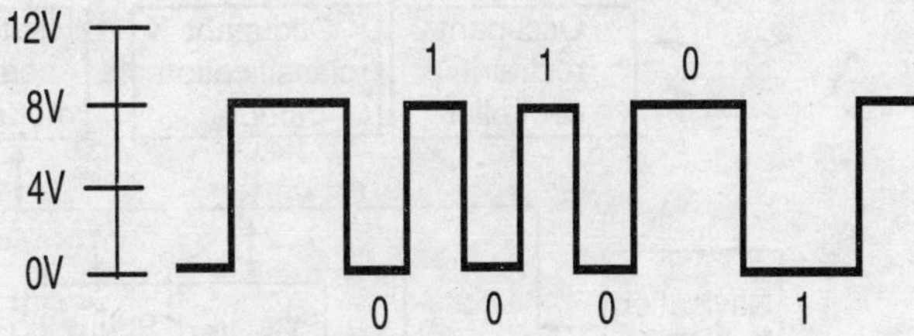

FIGURE 8-46 *Voltage level and duration required for 0 and 1 signals.*

Many vehicles are now equipped with controller area network (CAN) data link systems. A local area network (LAN) data link system is similar to the CAN system, and the LAN system is used on a significant number of vehicles. Some vehicles have a low-speed LAN system and a separate high-speed LAN system (Figure 8-47). The low-speed LAN system interconnects modules for applications such as door locks, window motors, HVAC, and radio. The low-speed LAN system is a single-wire system. The high-speed LAN system interconnects modules such as the PCM, transmission, antilock brake modules, and suspension modules. The high-speed LAN system is a two-wire system that operates at 500 kilobits per second. The greatly increased data transmission speed capabilities of the LAN system enhances the communication between various computers in the system and the scan tool. Other high-speed data link systems on modern vehicles include FlexRay and local interconnect network (LIN). The data link systems on a current sport utility vehicle (SUV) are shown in Figure 8-48.

Some luxury vehicles presently have a media oriented systems transport (MOST) data link system in which the computers are interconnected by fiber-optic data links. The MOST system transmits data at 22.6 megabits per second. This high data transmission speed is required on vehicles with navigation systems, CD changers, video systems, and satellite radios. The MOST system greatly reduces the number of wires in the wiring harnesses, but is more expensive compared to a system with data link wires.

VEHICLE STABILITY CONTROL

Many vehicles manufactured in recent years are equipped with a vehicle stability control system. A **vehicle stability control system** provides improved control if the vehicle begins to swerve sideways because of slippery road surfaces, excessive acceleration, or a combination of these two conditions.

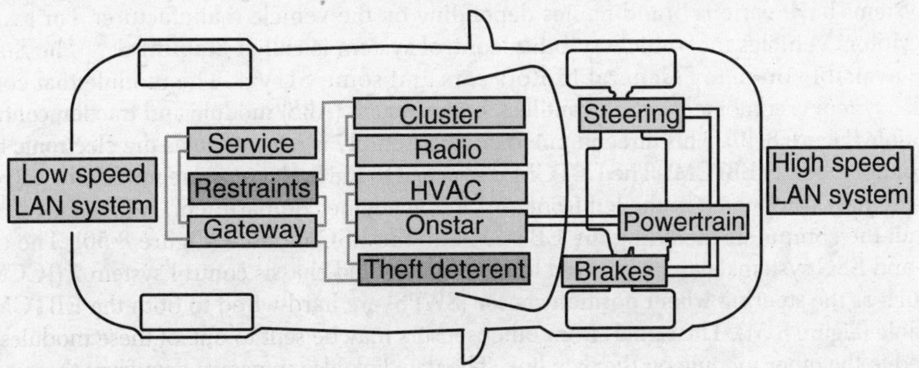

FIGURE 8-47 *Low-speed LAN and high-speed LAN data link systems.*

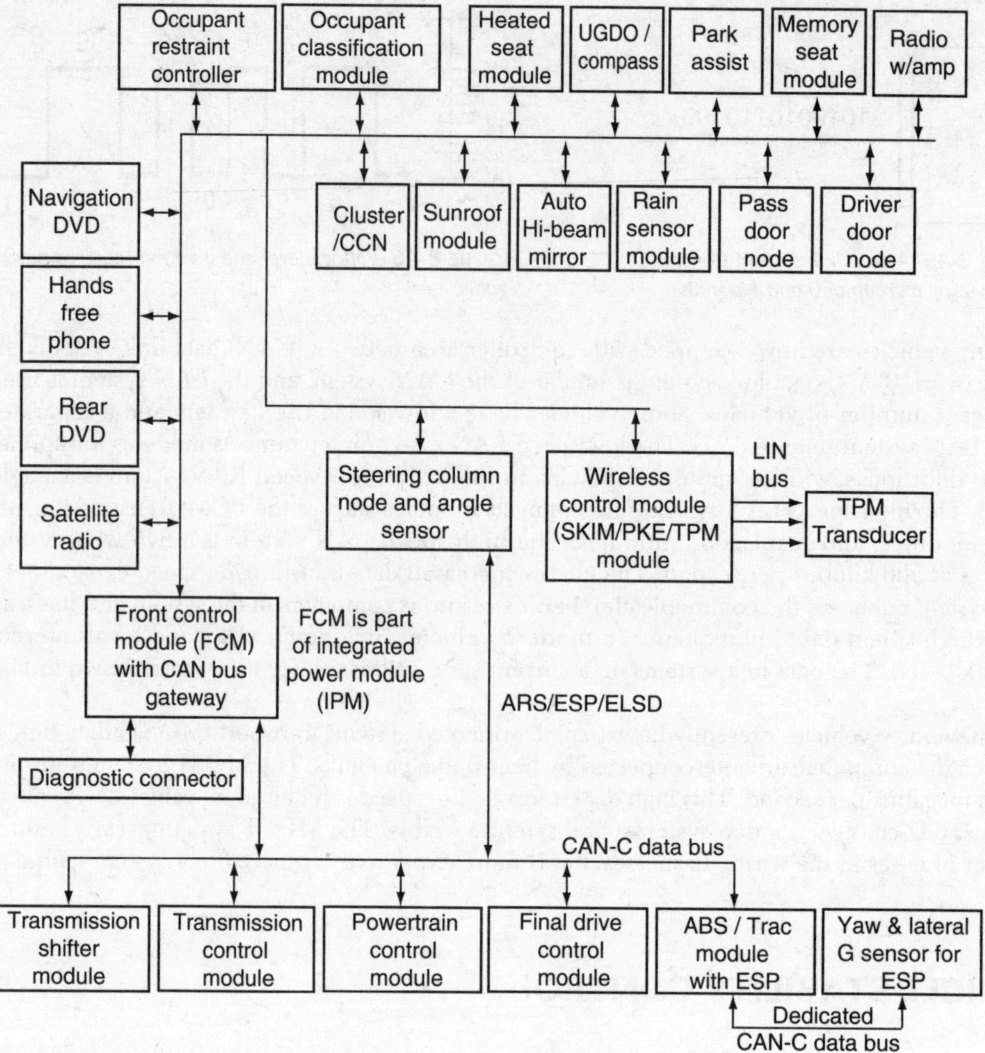

FIGURE 8-48 *Data link systems on a current SUV.*

Therefore, a vehicle stability control system provides increased vehicle safety. Vehicle stability control systems have various brand names depending on the vehicle manufacturer. For example, on General Motors vehicles the vehicle stability control system is called **Stabilitrak®**. The Stabilitrak® system is available on many General Motors cars and some SUVs. The module that controls the Stabilitrak® system is combined with the **antilock brake system (ABS)** module and **traction control system (TCS)** module (Figure 8-49). This three-in-one module assembly is referred to as the **electronic brake and traction control module (EBTCM)**. The EBTCM is attached to the **brake pressure modulator valve (BPMV)** and this assembly is mounted in the left front area in the engine compartment. A data link is connected between all the computers including the EBTCM and the ESC module (Figure 8-50). The combined EBTCM and ESC systems may be referred to as the integrated chassis control system 2 (ICCS2). Some sensors such as the **steering wheel position sensor (SWPS)** are hard-wired to both the EBTCM and the ESC module (Figure 8-51). The signals from other sensors may be sent to one of these modules and then transmitted to the other module on the data link. The data link also transmits data from these modules to the instrument panel cluster (IPC) during system diagnosis. This allows the IPC to display diagnostic information.

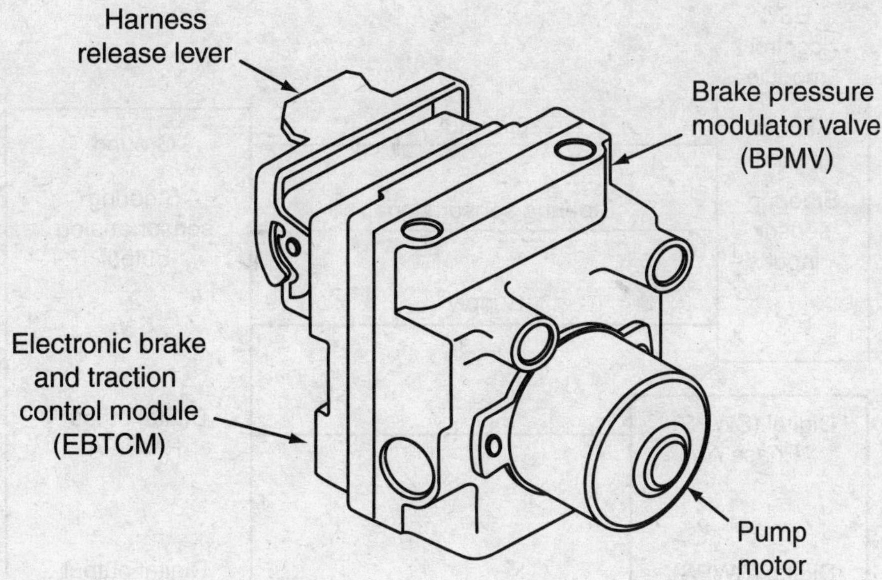

FIGURE 8-49 *The electronic brake and traction control module (EBTCM) contains the antilock brake system (ABS), traction control system, and stability control modules.*

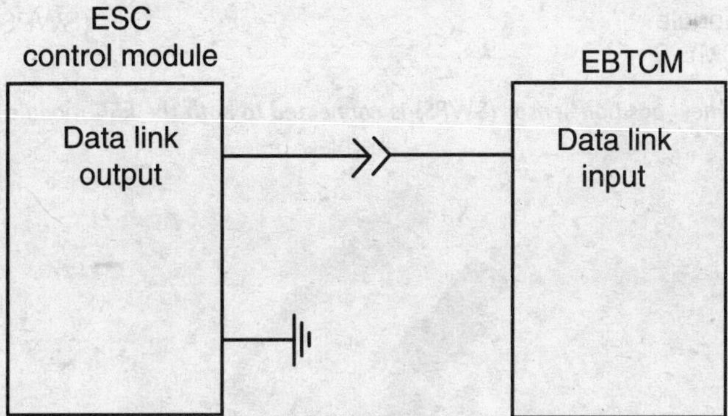

FIGURE 8-50 *Data link between the EBTCM and ESC modules.*

This book is concerned with suspension and steering systems. Because the stability control system operates in cooperation with the ABS and TCS systems, a brief description of these systems is necessary.

Antilock Brake System (ABS) Operation

Wheel speed sensors are mounted at each wheel. In this ABS system, the wheel speed sensors are integral with the front or rear wheel bearing hubs. These wheel bearing hubs with the integral wheel speed sensors are nonserviceable (Figure 8-52). Each wheel speed sensor contains a toothed ring that rotates past a stationary electromagnetic wheel speed sensor. This sensor contains a coil of wire surrounding a permanent magnet. As the toothed ring rotates past the sensor, an alternating current (AC) voltage is produced in the sensor. This voltage signal from each wheel speed sensor is sent to the EBTCM. As wheel speed increases, the frequency of AC voltage produced by the wheel speed sensor

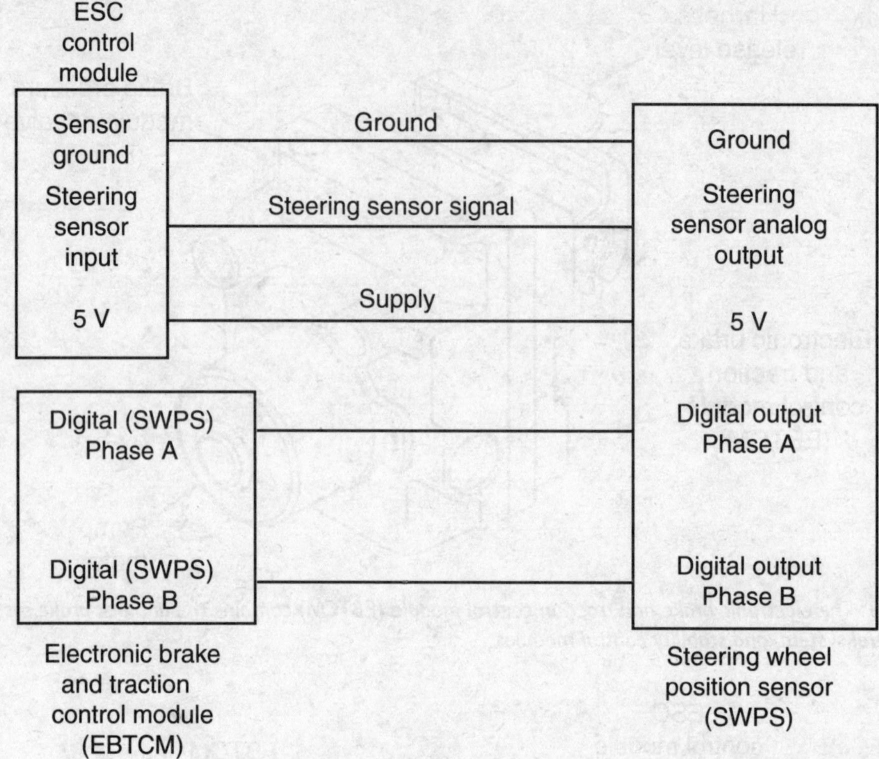

FIGURE 8-51 *The steering wheel position sensor (SWPS) is connected to both the ESC module and the EBTCM.*

FIGURE 8-52 *Wheel speed sensor.*

increases proportionally. During a brake application, the wheels slow down, and the frequency of AC voltage in the wheel speed sensors also decreases. If a wheel is nearing a lockup condition during a hard brake application, the frequency of the AC voltage from that wheel speed sensor becomes very slow. The EBTCM detects impending wheel lockup from the frequency of AC voltage signals sent from the wheel speed sensors.

The brake pressure modulator valve (BPMV) contains a number of electrohydraulic valves. These valves are operated electrically by the EBTCM. These valves in the BPMV are connected hydraulically in the brake system. A **hold valve** and a **release valve** are connected in the brake line to each wheel (Figure 8-53). If a wheel speed sensor signal indicates an impending wheel lockup condition, the EBTCM energizes the normally open hold solenoid connected to the wheel that is about to lock up. This action closes the solenoid and isolates the wheel caliper from the master cylinder to prevent any further increase in brake pressure. If the wheel speed sensor signal still indicates an impending wheel lockup, the EBTCM keeps the hold solenoid closed and opens the normally closed release solenoid momentarily. This action reduces wheel caliper pressure to reduce brake application force and prevent wheel lockup. The EBTCM pulses the hold and the release solenoids on and off to supply maximum braking force without wheel lockup.

When the hold and the release valves are pulsated during a prolonged antilock brake function, the brake pedal fades downward as brake fluid flows from the release valves into the accumulators. To maintain brake pedal height during an antilock brake function, the EBTCM starts the pump in the BPMV at the beginning of an antilock function. When the pump motor is started, the pump supplies brake fluid pressure to the hold valves and wheel calipers. Pump motor pressure is also supplied back to the master cylinder. Under this condition, the driver may feel a firmer brake pedal and pedal pulsations and may hear the clicking action of the hold and the release solenoids.

ANTILOCK and BRAKE warning lights are mounted in the instrument panel. Both of these lights are illuminated for a few seconds after the engine starts. If the amber ANTILOCK light is on with the engine running, the EBTCM has detected an electrical fault in the ABS system. Under this condition, the EBTCM no longer provides an ABS function, but normal power-assisted brake operation is still available. When the red BRAKE warning light is illuminated with the engine running, the parking brake may be on, the master cylinder may be low on brake fluid, or there may be a fault in the ABS system.

Traction Control System (TCS) Operation

The EBTCM detects drive wheel spin by comparing the two drive wheel speed sensor signals. Wheel spin on both drive wheels is detected by comparing the wheel speed sensor signals on the drive wheels and non-drive wheels. If a wheel speed sensor signal informs the EBTCM that one or both drive wheels are spinning, the EBTCM enters the traction control mode. First, the EBTCM requests the PCM to reduce the amount of engine torque supplied to the drive wheels. The PCM reduces engine torque by retarding the ignition spark advance and shutting off the fuel injectors of a very short time. The PCM then sends a signal back to the EBTCM regarding the amount of torque delivered to the drive wheels. If one or both drive wheels continue to spin on the road surface, the EBTCM energizes the normally closed prime valve, closes the normally open isolation valve, and starts the pump in the BPMV. Under this condition, the prime valve opens and the pump begins to move brake fluid from the master cylinder through the prime valve to the pump inlet. The closed isolation valve prevents the pump pressure from being applied back to the master cylinder. Under this condition, the pump pressure is supplied through the normally open hold valve to the brake caliper on the spinning wheel. This action stops the wheel from spinning. If both drive wheels are spinning on the road surface, the EBTCM operates both prime valves and isolation valves to supply brake fluid pressure to both drive wheel brake calipers. During a TCS function, the EBTCM pulses the

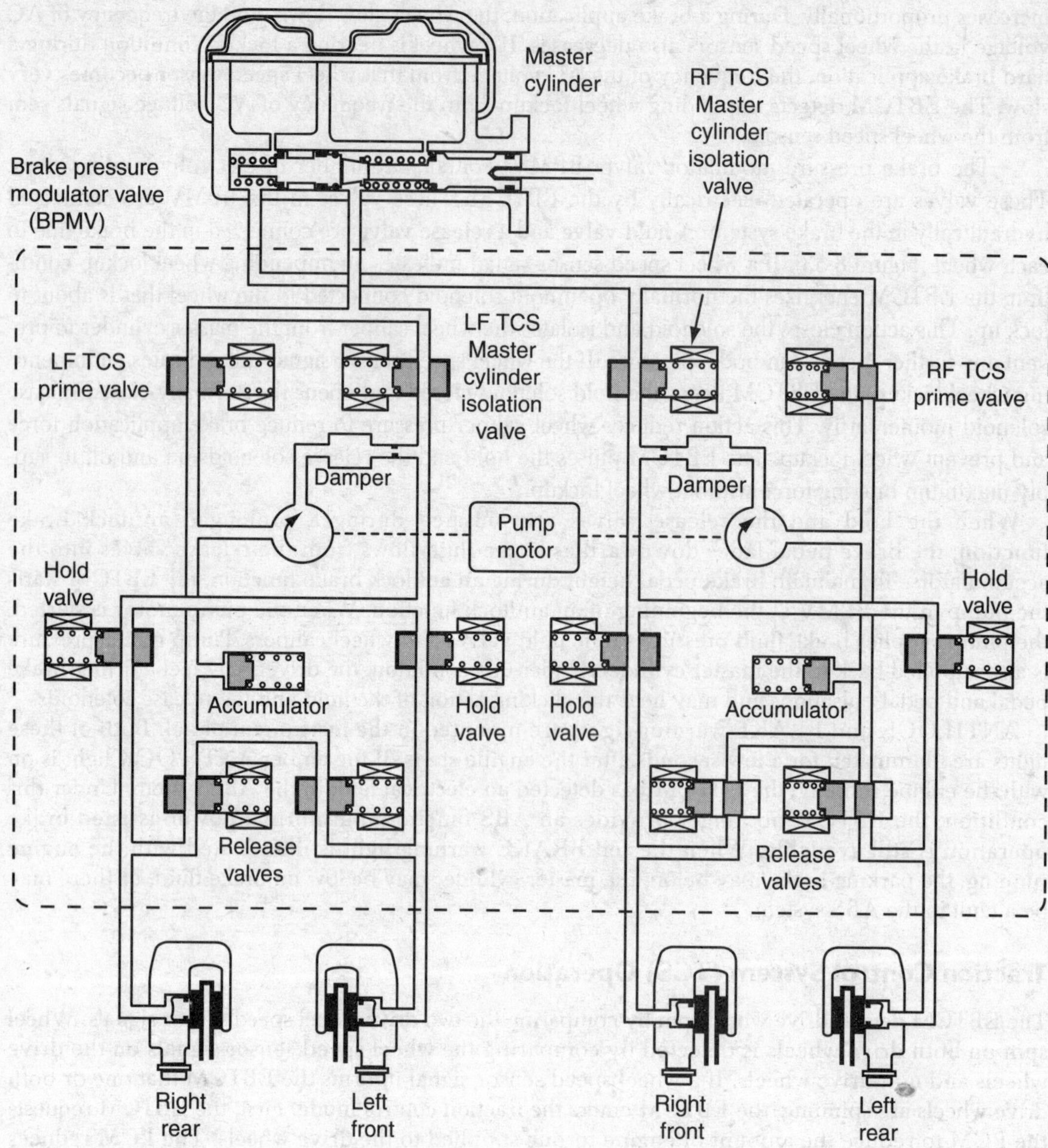

FIGURE 8-53 *Brake pressure modulator valve (BPMV).*

hold and the release solenoids on and off to control wheel caliper pressure. The EBTCM limits the traction control function to a short time period to prevent overheating brake components. During a TCS function, these messages may be displayed in the driver information center (DIC):

1. TRACTION ENGAGED is displayed after the TCS is in operation for 3 seconds.
2. TRACTION SUSPENDED is displayed if the EBTCM has discontinued the TCS function to prevent brake component overheating.
3. TRACTION OFF is displayed if the driver places the TCS switch on the instrument panel in the Off position.
4. TRACTION READY is displayed if the TCS switch is turned from Off to On.

During a TCS function, the EBTCM sends a signal through the data link to the powertrain control module (PCM). When this signal is received, the PCM disables some of the fuel injectors to reduce engine torque. This action also helps to prevent drive wheel spin. The PCM disables the two injectors at the beginning of the firing order and in the center of the firing order. Depending on the speed of drive wheel spin, the PCM may disable every second injector in the firing order. The injectors are disabled for a very short time period. The TCS system improves drive wheel traction, and this system also prevents the tendency for the vehicle to swerve sideways when one drive wheel is spinning. Therefore, the TCS system increases vehicle safety.

Vehicle Stability Control

To provide stability control, the EBTCM uses two additional input signals from the **lateral accelerometer** and the **yaw rate sensor**. The lateral accelerometer is mounted under the front passenger's seat (Figure 8-54). The EBTCM sends a 5 V reference voltage to the lateral accelerometer. If the vehicle is driven straight ahead, the chassis has zero lateral acceleration. Under this condition, the lateral accelerometer provides a 2.5 V signal to the EBTCM. If the vehicle begins to swerve sideways because of slippery road conditions, high-speed cornering, or erratic driving, the lateral accelerometer signal to the EBTCM varies from 0.25V to 4.75 V, depending on the direction and severity of the swerving action.

FIGURE 8-54 *Lateral accelerometer.*

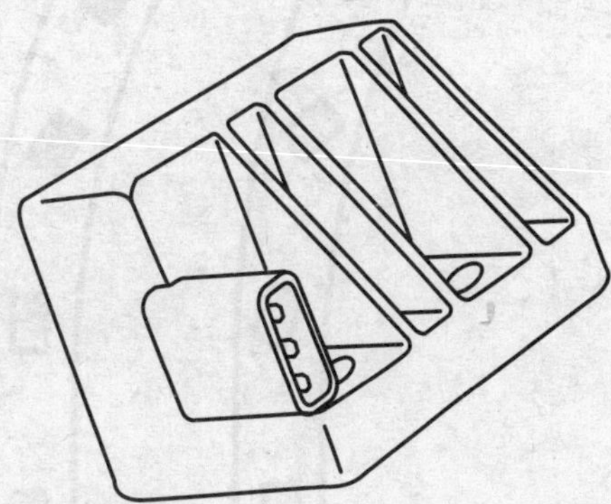

FIGURE 8-55 *Yaw rate sensor.*

The yaw rate sensor is mounted under the rear package shelf (Figure 8-55). Some yaw rate sensors contain a precision metal cylinder whose rim vibrates in elliptical shapes. The vibration and rotation of this metal cylinder is proportional to the rotational speed of the vehicle around the center of the cylinder. On some models the lateral accelerometer and yaw rate sensors are combined in a single sensor. The sensor mounting location varies depending on the vehicle make and model year.

The EBTCM sends a 5 V reference voltage to the yaw rate sensor. If the vehicle chassis experiences zero yaw rate, the yaw rate sensor sends a 2.5 V signal to the EBTCM module. If the vehicle begins to swerve sideways, the yaw rate sensor provides a 0.25 V to 4.75 V signal to the EBTCM, depending on the direction and severity of the swerve. The EBTCM also uses the wheel speed sensor signals for stability control. If the vehicle begins to swerve sideways, the EBTCM energizes the normally closed prime valve and closes the normally open isolation valve connected to the appropriate front wheel; then it starts the pump in the BPMV. Under this condition, the prime valve opens and the pump begins to move brake fluid from the master cylinder through the prime valve to the pump inlet. The closed isolation valve prevents the pump pressure from being applied back to the master cylinder. Under this condition, the pump pressure is supplied through the normally open hold valve to the brake caliper on the appropriate front wheel. Applying the brake on the front wheel pulls the vehicle out of the swerve and prevents the complete loss of steering control. If the EBTCM detects an electrical fault in the stability control system, STABILITY REDUCED is displayed in the DIC. If the EBTCM enters the stability control mode, STABILITY ENGAGED is indicated in the DIC.

In Figure 8-56, two vehicles driving side-by-side are negotiating a lane change to the left. The vehicle on the right has vehicle stability control, and the vehicle on the left does not have this system.

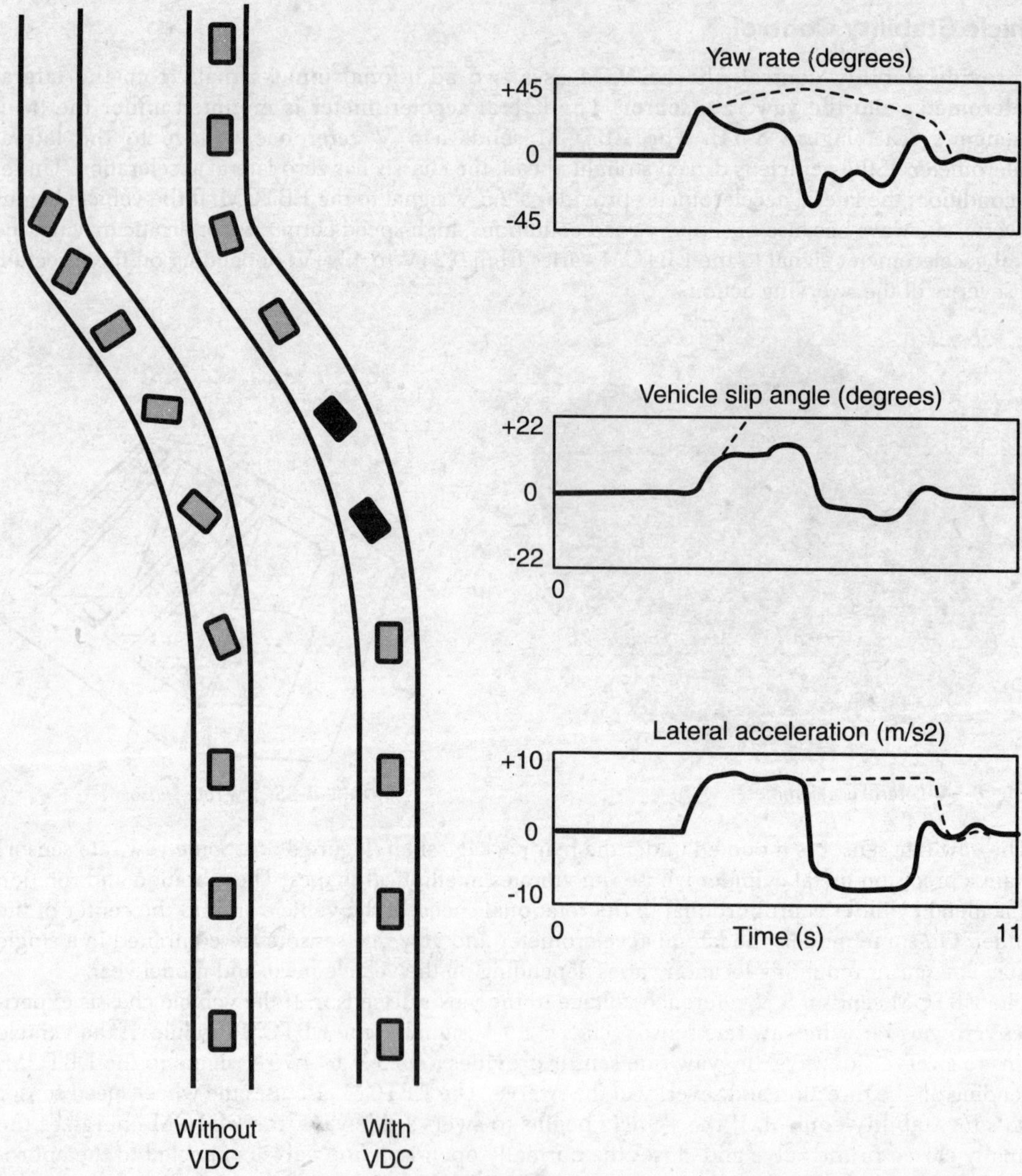

FIGURE 8-56 *Comparison during a turn between a vehicle with a stability control system and a vehicle with no stability control system.*

As the vehicle on the left begins to turn, the rear of the vehicle begins to swing around. When the vehicle on the right starts to turn, the rear of the vehicle swerves slightly and the right front brake is applied by the vehicle stability control system to prevent this swerve. Further into the turn, the driver attempts to steer the car on the left, but this car enters into an uncontrolled swerve with loss of steering control. As the car on the right continues into the turn, the rear of the vehicle swerves slightly, but the vehicle stability control system again applies the right front brake momentarily to prevent this swerve. The car with the stability control system completes the turn while maintaining directional stability, but the vehicle without stability control goes into an uncontrolled swerve with complete loss of directional control. The vehicle stability control system improves vehicle safety! The other charts in Figure 8-56 indicate that yaw rate, vehicle slip angle, and lateral acceleration are greatly reduced on a vehicle with a stability control system.

ACTIVE ROLL CONTROL SYSTEMS

Two independent automotive component manufacturers have developed active roll control systems in response to concerns about sport utility vehicles (SUVs) that roll over more easily compared with cars because of the SUVs' higher center of gravity. The active roll control systems were developed in response to this concern. The active roll control system contains a control module, accelerometer, speed sensor, fluid reservoir, electrohydraulic pump, pressure control valve, directional control valve, and a hydraulic actuator in both the front and rear stabilizer bars (Figure 8-57). The accelerometer and speed sensor may be common to systems other than the active roll control. The electrohydraulic pump may also be used as the power steering pump. The active roll control system may be called a roll stability control (RSC) system or a dynamic handling system (DHS). Some active roll control systems have a gyro sensor that provides a voltage signal to the control module in relation to the vehicle roll speed and angle.

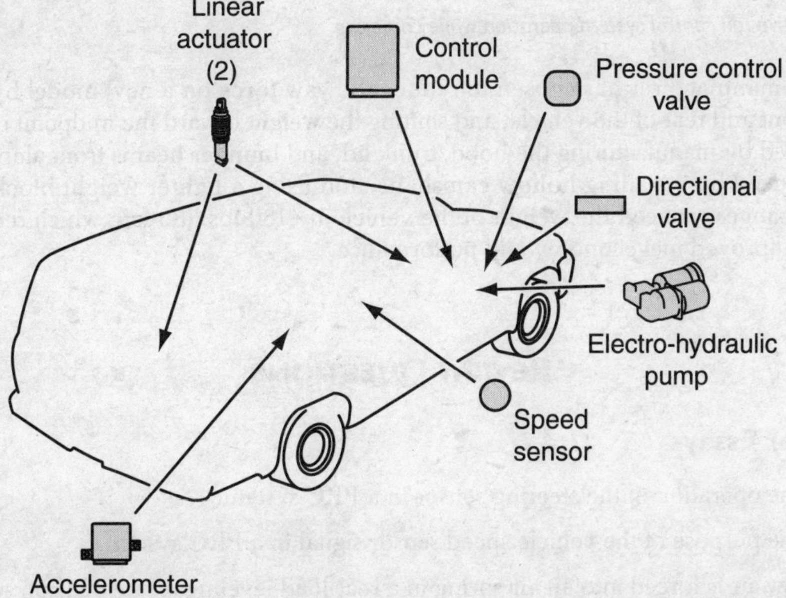

FIGURE 8-57 *Active roll control system components.*

When the vehicle is driven straight ahead, the active roll control system does not supply any hydraulic pressure to the linear actuators in the stabilizer bars. Under this condition, both stabilizer bars move freely until the linear actuators are fully compressed. This action provides improved individual wheel bump performance and better ride quality. If the chassis begins to lean while cornering, the module operates the directional valve so it supplies fluid pressure to the linear actuators in the stabilizer bars. This action stiffens the stabilizer bar and reduces body lean (Figure 8-58). The active roll control system increases safety by reducing body lean, which decreases the possibility of a vehicle rollover.

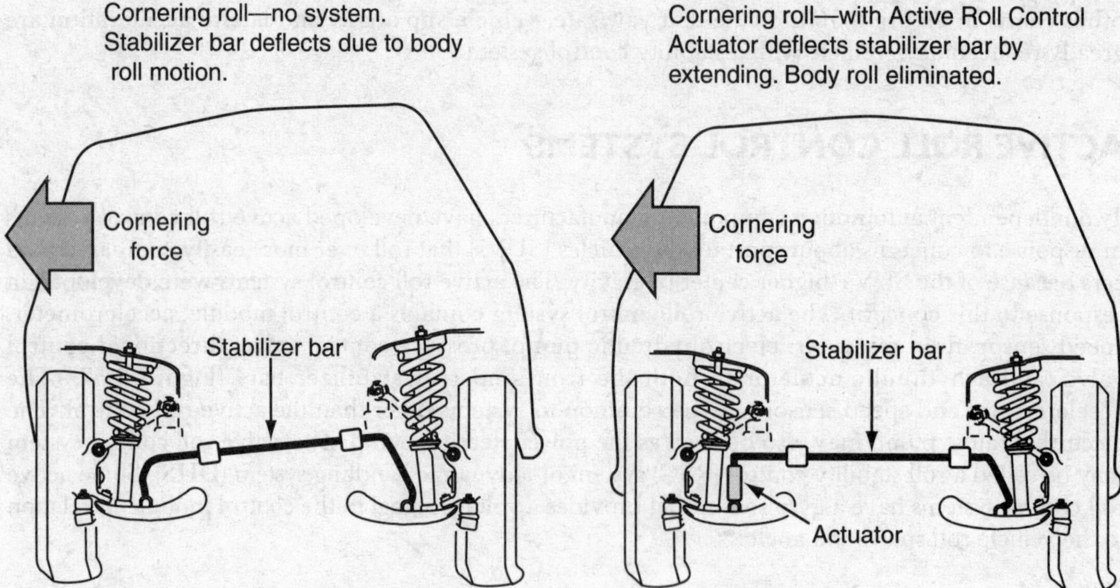

FIGURE 8-58 *Active roll control system operation while cornering.*

One vehicle manufacturer has chosen to reduce the yaw force on a new model by reducing the weight at the front and rear of the vehicle, and shifting the weight toward the midpoint on the car. This was accomplished by manufacturing the hood, trunk lid, and bumper beams from aluminum. Engine weight was reduced by installing hollow camshafts, and using a lighter weight block and cylinder heads. These changes reduced the weight of the vehicle by 180 lbs. (80 kg), which reduced the yaw force and also improved fuel economy and performance.

REVIEW QUESTIONS

Short Answer Essays

1. Describe the operation of the steering sensor in a PRC system.
2. Describe the purpose of the vehicle speed sensor signal in a PRC system.
3. Explain how air is forced into an air spring in a rear load-leveling air suspension system.
4. Describe the action taken by the control module if the control module in an electronic air suspension system receives a lower vehicle command from a rear suspension sensor with the doors closed, the brake pedal released, and the vehicle traveling at 60 mph (100 km/h).

5. Describe the action taken by the control module if the engine is running with a door open, and the control module receives a lower vehicle command from the height sensor in a rear load-leveling air suspension system.
6. List the conditions when the On/Off switch in an electronic air suspension system must be turned off.
7. Describe the conditions required for the control module to turn on the suspension warning lamp continually with the engine running in an electronic air suspension system.
8. Explain why the control module in an electronic air suspension system services all commands by a 45-second averaging method when the doors are closed and the brake pedal is released.
9. Explain why the suspension warning lamp in an electronic air suspension system may not indicate a defect immediately when the engine is started.
10. Explain how a vent solenoid is damaged by reversed battery polarity in a rear load-leveling air suspension system.

Fill-in-the-Blanks

1. The armature response time is ________________ milliseconds in a PRC system strut.
2. In a PRC system, if the car is accelerating with the throttle wide open, the PRC system is in the ________________ mode.
3. When the PRC mode switch is in the Auto position, the control module changes to the firm mode if lateral acceleration exceeds ________________.
4. In a PRC system, lateral vehicle acceleration is sensed from the ________________ sensor.
5. In a rear load-leveling air suspension system, the control module energizes the compressor relay when a ________________ ________________ command is received.
6. Two height sensors are mounted on the ________________ suspension in an electronic air suspension system.
7. In an electronic air suspension system two hours after the ignition switch is turned off, ________________ ________________ commands are completed, but ________________ ________________ commands are ignored.
8. In a rear load-leveling air suspension system, if the On/Off switch in the trunk is off, the system is ________________.
9. An electronic rotary height sensor contains a ________________.
10. In a continuously variable road sensing suspension system, the module senses vehicle lift and dive from some of the ________________ ________________ inputs.

Multiple Choice

1. While discussing a programmed ride control (PRC) system:
   A. The brake system pressure must be 300 psi (2,068 kPa) before this mode change occurs.
   B. A PRC system switches from the auto mode to firm mode if the vehicle accelerates with 90 percent throttle opening.
   C. The PRC system switches to the firm mode if lateral acceleration exceeds 0.25 g.
   D. The mode indicator light in the tachometer is illuminated in the plush ride mode.

2. To increase the rear trim height in an electronic air suspension system, the control module:
A. Starts the compressor and opens the vent valve.
B. Starts the compressor and closes the rear air spring valves.
C. Stops the compressor and opens the rear air spring valves.
D. Starts the compressor and opens the rear air spring valves.

3. All these statements about air springs, shock absorbers, and struts are true EXCEPT:
A. Air springs can be mounted separately from the shock absorbers.
B. Air springs can be mounted over the front and rear struts.
C. Some struts contain a solenoid actuator that controls strut firmness.
D. Some air suspension systems have seven driver selectable operating modes.

4. The magneto-rheological fluid in the shock absorbers or struts in an ESC system contains:
A. Automatic transmission fluid.
B. Suspended iron particles.
C. Power steering fluid.
D. 5W-30 engine oil.

5. A cross-axis ball joint contains:
A. A circular insulating bushing.
B. A ball and stud-type joint.
C. Spherical bearing.
D. A ball and socket.

6. In an ESC system with magneto-rheological fluid in the shock absorbers or struts, the control module can vary the shock absorber firmness in:
A. 1 millisecond.
B. 5 milliseconds.
C. 10 milliseconds.
D. 152 milliseconds.

7. All of these statements about data link systems are true EXCEPT:
A. A data link system can be a single-wire or dual-wire system.
B. Some data link systems operate between 0 V and 12 V.
C. Some vehicles have two data link systems.
D. A fiber-optic data link system has a very high data transmission rate.

8. In some traction control systems if the control module senses drive wheel spin, the first action taken by the control module is to:
A. Retard the spark advance and shut off the fuel injectors.
B. Apply the brakes on both non-drive wheels.
C. Apply the brake on the spinning drive wheel.
D. Apply the brake on the non-spinning drive wheel.

9. On a vehicle with a stability control system, if icy road conditions cause the vehicle to begin swerving sideways, the stability control module:
A. Applies the brakes on both rear wheels.
B. Applies the brakes on both front wheels.
C. Applies the brake on one front wheel.
D. Applies the brake on one front wheel and the opposite rear wheel.

10. All of these statements about a rear load-leveling suspension system are true EXCEPT:

A. The On/Off switch is mounted in the vehicle trunk.

B. The control module operates the compressor relay.

C. If a door is open, the control module completes the lower suspension height commands.

D. The rear suspension has one, nonserviceable suspension height sensor.

Steering Columns and Steering Linkage Mechanisms

9

Upon completion and review of this chapter, you should be able to:

- Explain how the steering column provides driver safety during a frontal collision.
- Describe two methods of steering column movement to protect the driver in a frontal collision.
- Define the purpose of a clock spring electrical connector.
- Explain the mechanism that locks the steering wheel and gear shift when the ignition switch is in the lock position.
- Describe a parallelogram steering linkage and explain the advantage of this type of linkage.
- List the components in a parallelogram steering linkage.
- Explain the purposes of the pitman arm and the idler arm.
- Describe two possible rack and pinion steering gear mountings.
- Describe the rack and pinion steering linkage, and explain the advantages of this type of linkage.

INTRODUCTION

Steering columns play a significant part in steering control, safety, and driver convenience. The steering column connects the steering wheel to the steering gear. The column components must be in satisfactory condition to minimize free play and to provide adequate steering control. If steering column components such as universal joints are worn, column free play is excessive and steering control is reduced.

Most steering columns provide some method of column collapse during a collision. Some vehicles have plastic pins that shear off in the column jacket, gearshift tube, and steering shaft if the driver hits the steering wheel in a frontal collision. This shearing action of the plastic pins allows the column to collapse away from the driver. In other vehicles, the column-to-instrument-panel mounting is designed to allow column movement if the driver hits the steering wheel in a collision. This action helps prevent driver injury.

All air-bag-equipped vehicles have a driver's side air bag located in the upper side of the steering wheel, and most vehicles also have a passenger's side air bag mounted in the instrument panel. Some vehicles now have seat belt pretensioners that tighten the seat belts and hold the driver or passengers back against the seat if the vehicle is involved in a collision. Many vehicles now have side air bags mounted in the outer edge of the seat back, or an air bag curtain mounted just above the front and rear door openings. The side air bags have a separate module and sensors, and deploy only when the vehicle is involved in a side collision.

A recent development on some vehicles is the installation of **pre-safe systems** that react during the few milliseconds before a collision occurs to increase driver and passenger safety. The input signals to the pre-safe system include vehicle speed, braking torque, brake pedal application speed, wheel slip, vehicle acceleration around the vertical axis, spring compression and rebound travel, steering wheel rotational speed, and tire pressure. The pre-safe system recognizes and acts in three crucial situations:

1. Sideways skidding
2. Avoidance maneuvers
3. Emergency braking beyond ABS operation

The pre-safe system can differentiate between a drama and a crisis. For example, if the vehicle is driven over a patch of ice and the brakes are applied lightly without any vehicle skidding, the ABS system can operate to prevent wheel lockup, but the pre-safe system recognizes this condition as a drama and remains inoperative. The pre-safe system also remains inoperative during mild avoidance maneuvers.

When the inputs indicate an impending crisis driving situation, the pre-safe system performs these functions:

1. Pretensions the driver and front passenger seat belts so the driver and front passenger are optimally restrained in their seats during emergency braking or a skid prior to a collision. When a collision occurs, pyrotechnic seat belt tensioners provide increased seat belt tension. If a collision does not occur, the seat belts return to normal tension.
2. If the front passenger seat is moved too far forward, the pre-safe system moves the seat rearward before a collision occurs. If appropriate, the front passenger seat cushion and backrest are moved to a position that provides increased passenger protection if a collision occurs. For example, a steeply inclined seat backrest or a flat seat cushion may impair passenger restraint during a collision.
3. The electronically adjustable, individual rear seat cushions are moved to the best possible angle to improve rear passenger restraint.
4. The sliding sunroof is closed to reduce the risk of occupant injury if a rollover occurs.

The brake assist system (BAS) also plays a crucial role in the pre-safe system operation. The BAS system operates beyond the ABS and electronic stability program (ESP) parameters. If the BAS detects an unstable driving condition such as severe vehicle skidding, it uses brake intervention and engine power reduction to correct the situation.

When the vehicle is involved in a frontal collision above a specific speed, the air bag sensor signals deploy the air bag or bags in a few milliseconds. As the driver is thrust forward during the frontal collision, the inflated air bag prevents the driver from striking the steering wheel, windshield, or instrument panel. The air bag deflates very quickly so it does not block the driver's vision in case the driver is still attempting to steer the vehicle. Since the driver's side air bag and some connecting components are mounted in the steering column, this column is a very important part of the vehicle safety equipment.

Steering columns may be classified as nontilting, tilting, and tilting/telescoping. Tilt steering columns facilitate driver entry to and exit from the front seat. These columns also allow the driver to position the steering wheel to suit individual comfort requirements (Figure 9-1). A tilting/telescoping steering column allows the driver to tilt and extend or retract the steering wheel. In this type of steering column, the driver has more steering wheel position choices.

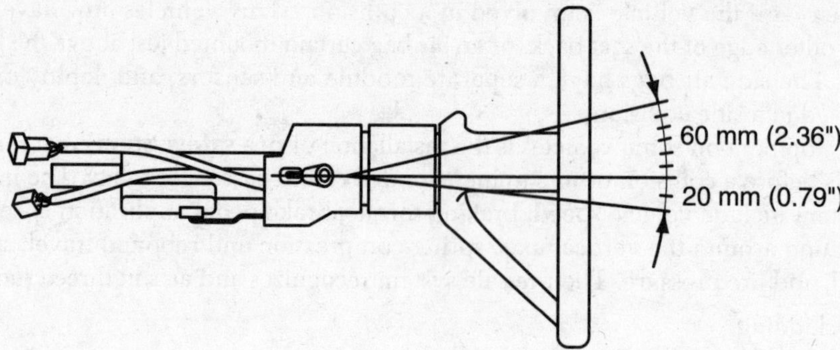

FIGURE 9-1 *Tilt steering column.*

CONVENTIONAL NONTILT STEERING COLUMN

Design

Many steering columns contain a two-piece steering shaft connected by two universal joints. A jacket and shroud surround the steering shaft. The upper shaft is supported by two bearings in the jacket. A **toe plate**, seal, and **silencer** surround the lower steering shaft and cover the opening where the shaft extends through the floor (Figure 9-2). The lower steering shaft is surrounded by a shield underneath the toe plate.

The lower universal joint couples the lower shaft to the stub shaft in the steering gear. In some steering columns, a flexible coupling is used in place of the lower universal joint (Figure 9-3).

Studs and nuts retain the steering column bracket to the instrument panel support bracket. The steering column is designed to protect the driver if the vehicle is involved in a frontal collision. An **energy-absorbing lower bracket** and lower plastic adapter are used to connect the steering column to the instrument panel mounting bracket. This bracket allows the column to slide down if the driver is thrown forward into the wheel in a frontal collision. The mounting bracket is also designed to prevent rearward movement toward the driver in a collision.

In some steering columns, the outer column jacket is a two-piece unit retained with plastic pins (Figure 9-4). In this type of column, the lower steering shaft is also a two-piece sliding unit retained

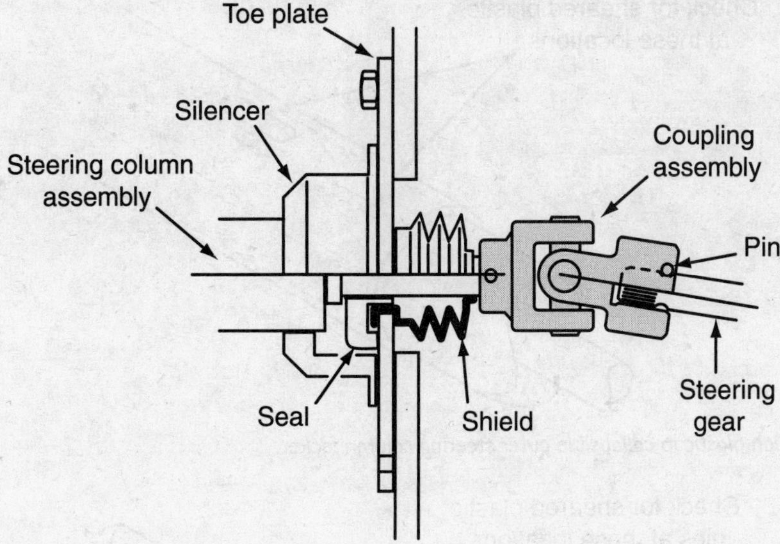

FIGURE 9-2 *Toe plate and silencer.*

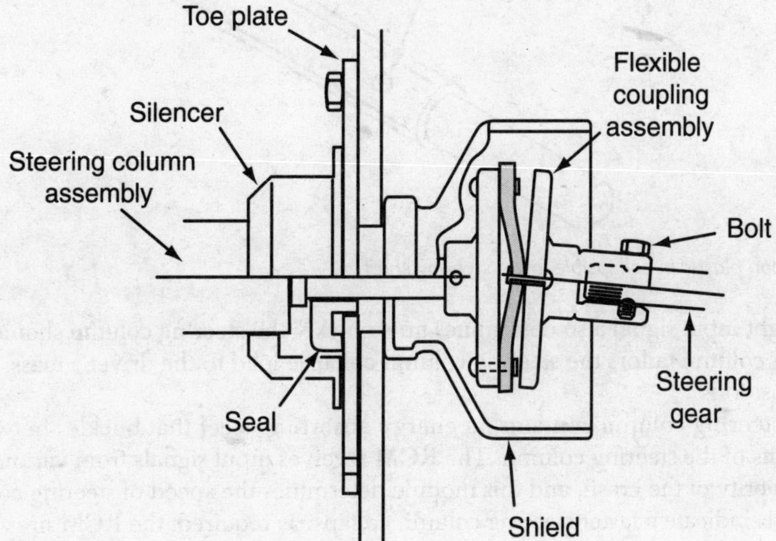

FIGURE 9-3 *Flexible coupling.*

with plastic pins (Figure 9-5). When the driver is thrown against the steering wheel in a frontal collision, the plastic pins shear off in the lower steering shaft and outer column jacket. The shearing action of the plastic pins allows the steering column to collapse away from the driver, which reduces the impact as the driver hits the steering wheel.

An adaptive steering column has recently been introduced to the automotive market on some new models. The adaptive steering column collapses at two different speeds based on information received about the driver. Many vehicles now have sensors in the lower part of a front seat to determine the weight of the driver and the weight and presence of a passenger. The driver's weight signal, and other input signals, are used by the restraints control module (RCM) to vary the air bag deployment force.

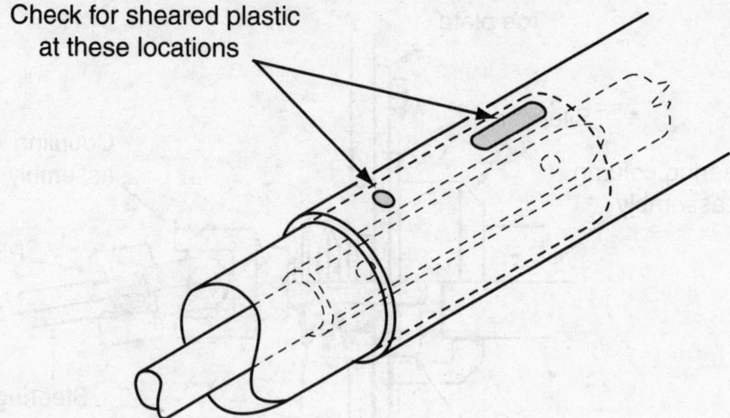

FIGURE 9-4 *Injection plastic in collapsible outer steering column jacket.*

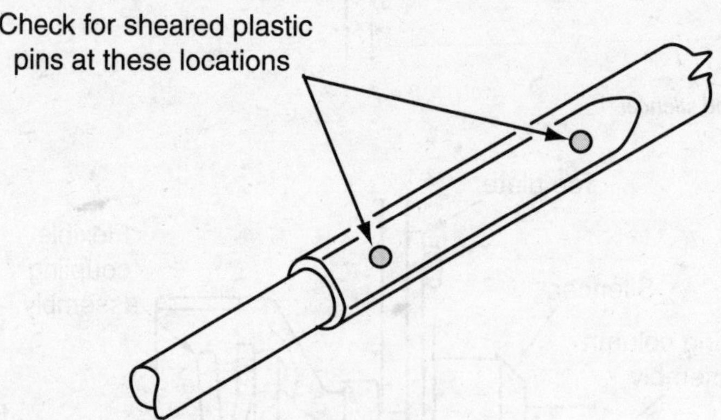

FIGURE 9-5 *Injection plastic in collapsible lower steering shaft.*

The driver's weight input signal also determines how quickly the steering column should collapse. The adaptive steering column tailors the steering column collapse load to the driver's mass, safety belt use, and seat track position.

An adaptive steering column contains an energy-absorbing steel that buckles between the upper and lower portions of the steering column. The RCM receives input signals from various crash sensors indicating the severity of the crash, and this module determines the speed of steering column collapse. If the input signals indicate a faster steering column collapse is required, the RCM fires a **pyrotechnic** device in the steering column that pulls a pin in the column and allows the energy-absorbing steel to buckle and provide faster column collapse. The result is a softer impact between the driver and the steering wheel. The adaptive steering column is designed to operate with the driver's air bag.

When the driver is thrown against the steering wheel during a collision, many steering wheels are designed to deform away from the driver to reduce the force on the driver's body.

CAUTION: When servicing a vehicle equipped with an air bag or bags, follow all service precautions in the vehicle manufacturer's service manual. Failure to follow these precautions may result in an expensive, accidental air bag deployment.

WARNING: Small amounts of sodium hydroxide are a by-product of an air bag deployment. Sodium hydroxide is a caustic chemical that causes skin irritation and eye damage. Always wear eye protection and gloves when servicing and handling a deployed air bag.

On many cars, the **air bag deployment module** is mounted in the top of the steering wheel (Figure 9-6). A **clock spring electrical connector**, or **spiral cable**, is mounted under the steering wheel. This component contains a ribbon-type conductor that maintains constant electrical contact between the air bag module and the air bag electrical system during steering wheel rotation.

The steering wheel splines fit on matching splines on the top of the upper steering shaft, and a nut retains the wheel on the shaft. Most steering wheels and shafts have matching alignment marks that must be aligned when the steering wheel is installed.

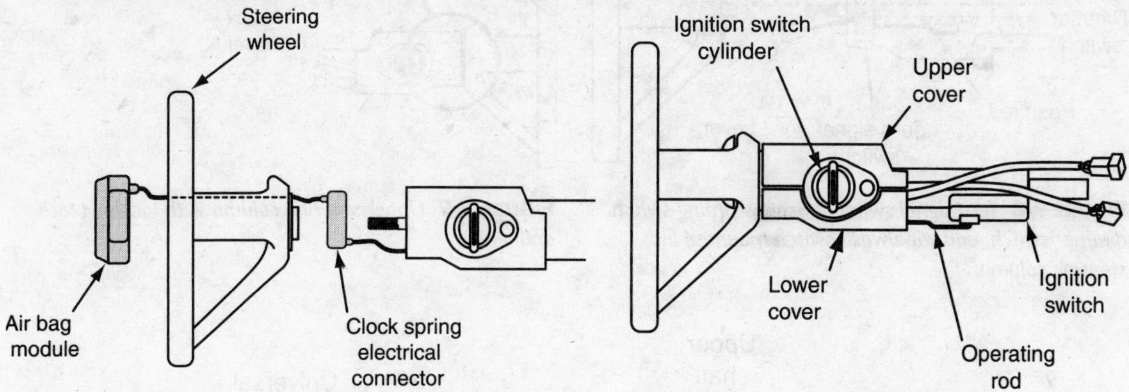

FIGURE 9-6 *Air bag inflator module mounted in the steering wheel and clock spring electrical connector located under the steering wheel.*

FIGURE 9-7 *Ignition switch and ignition switch cylinder mounted in steering column.*

An ignition switch cylinder is usually mounted in the upper right side of the column housing, and the ignition switch is bolted on the lower side of the housing (Figure 9-7). An operating rod connects the ignition switch cylinder to the ignition switch. Ignition switches are integral with the lock cylinder in some steering columns.

The turn signal switch and hazard warning switch are mounted on top of the steering column under the steering wheel. Lugs on the bottom of the steering wheel are used to cancel the signal lights after a turn is completed. On many vehicles, the signal light lever also operates the wipe/wash switch and the dimmer switch (Figure 9-8).

If the gear shift is mounted in the steering column, a tube extends from the gear shift housing to the shift lever at the lower end of the steering column. This shift lever is connected through a linkage to the transaxle or transmission shift lever. A lock plate is attached to the upper steering shaft, and a lever engages the slots in this plate to lock the steering wheel and gear shift when the gear shift is in Park and the ignition switch is in the Lock position (Figure 9-9).

TILT STEERING COLUMN

Design

Tilt steering columns have a short upper steering shaft connected to the steering wheel in the usual manner. This upper steering shaft is connected through a universal joint to the lower steering main shaft. An upper column tube surrounds the upper steering shaft, and the lower steering main shaft is supported on bushings in the lower column tube (Figure 9-10).

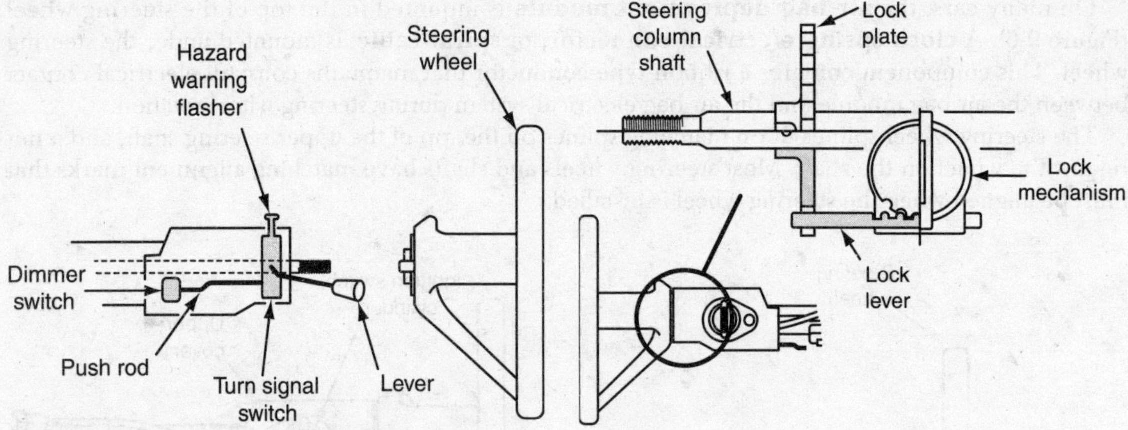

FIGURE 9-8 *Turn signal switch, hazard warning switch, dimmer switch, and wipe/wash switch mounted in steering column.*

FIGURE 9-9 *Upper steering column with locking plate and lever.*

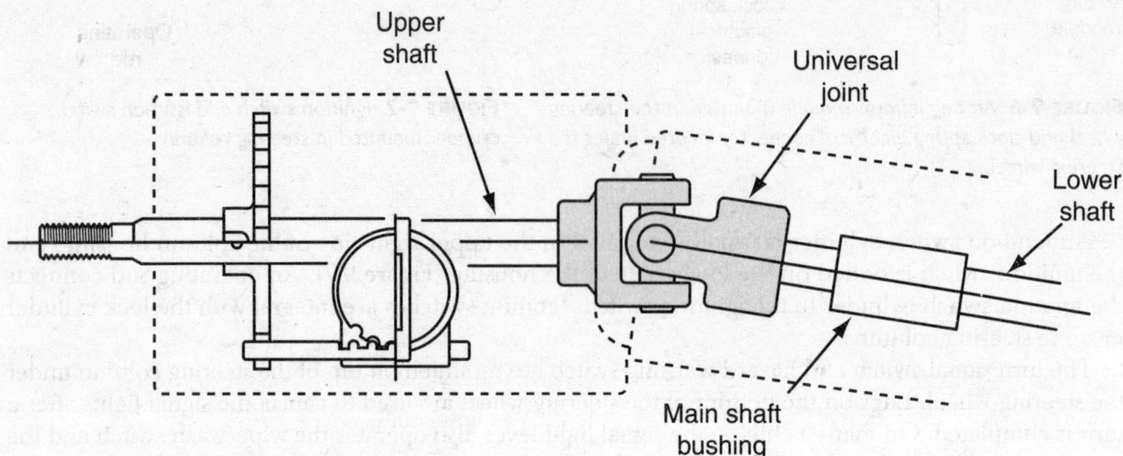

FIGURE 9-10 *Tilt steering column components.*

When the steering wheel is tilted, the wheel and upper steering column tube pivot on two bolts connected between the upper and lower column tubes. During the steering wheel tilting motion, the upper steering shaft pivots on the universal joint connected between the upper steering shaft and the lower steering main shaft. A release lever on the side of the steering column must be activated to allow the wheel and upper column to tilt. This steering wheel action allows the driver to position the steering wheel for greater comfort and easier movement in and out of the driver's seat.

In some steering columns, a **spherical bearing** acts as a pivot between the upper steering shaft and the lower steering main shaft (Figure 9-11).

Four bolts attach the lower column support tube to the instrument panel. The ignition lock cylinder and switch are mounted in an upper bracket that is clamped to the lower column tube. A universal joint is connected between the lower steering mainshaft and the intermediate shaft assembly, which is attached to the stub shaft on the steering gear (Figure 9-12).

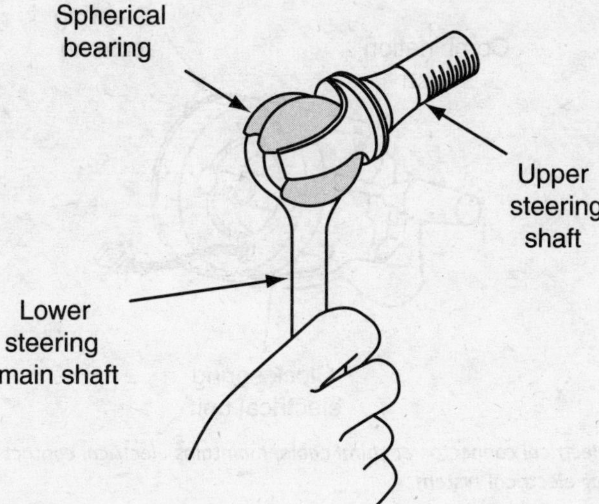

FIGURE 9-11 *Spherical bearing acts as a pivot between the upper steering shaft and the lower steering main shaft in some tilt steering columns.*

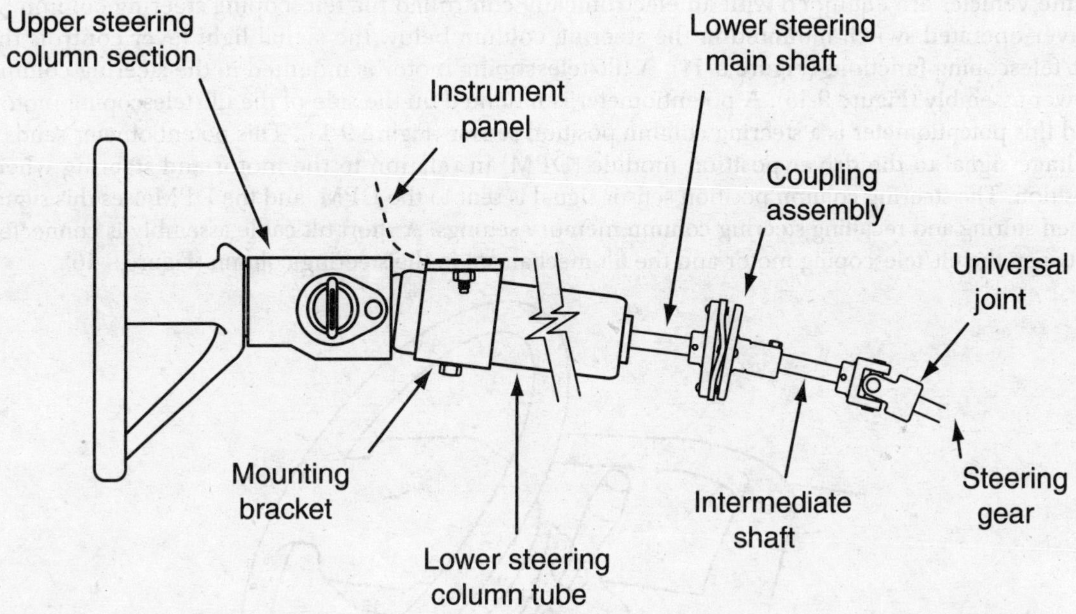

FIGURE 9-12 *Tilt steering column with universal joint, intermediate shaft, combination switch, and steering wheel.*

A steering wheel pad containing the air bag deployment module is mounted in the top of the steering wheel. Electrical contact between the air bag deployment module and the air bag electrical system is maintained by a clock spring electrical connector, or spiral cable, mounted directly under the steering wheel (Figure 9-13). A combination switch is mounted directly under the clock spring electrical connector. This switch contains the signal light switch, hazard light switch, dimmer switch, and wipe/wash switch. The upper side of the steering wheel also contains the horn switch contacts.

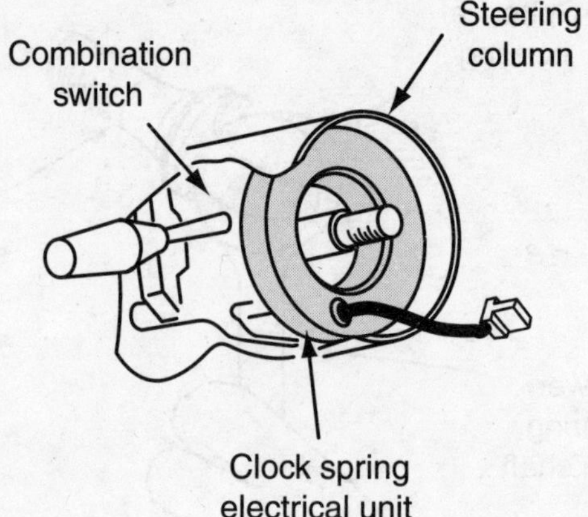

FIGURE 9-13 *Clock spring electrical connector, or spiral cable, maintains electrical contact between the air bag inflator module and the air bag electrical system.*

ELECTRONIC TILT/TELESCOPING STEERING COLUMN

Some vehicles are equipped with an electronically controlled tilt/telescoping steering column. A driver-operated switch mounted in the steering column below the signal light lever controls the tilt/telescoping functions (Figure 9-14). A tilt/telescoping motor is mounted in the steering column power assembly (Figure 9-15). A potentiometer is mounted on the side of the tilt/telescoping motor, and this potentiometer is a steering column position sensor (Figure 9-15). This potentiometer sends a voltage signal to the driver position module (DPM) in relation to the motor and steering wheel position. The steering column position sensor signal is sent to the DPM, and the DPM uses this signal when storing and recalling steering column memory settings. A short tilt cable assembly is connected between the tilt/telescoping motor and the tilt mechanism in the steering column (Figure 9-16).

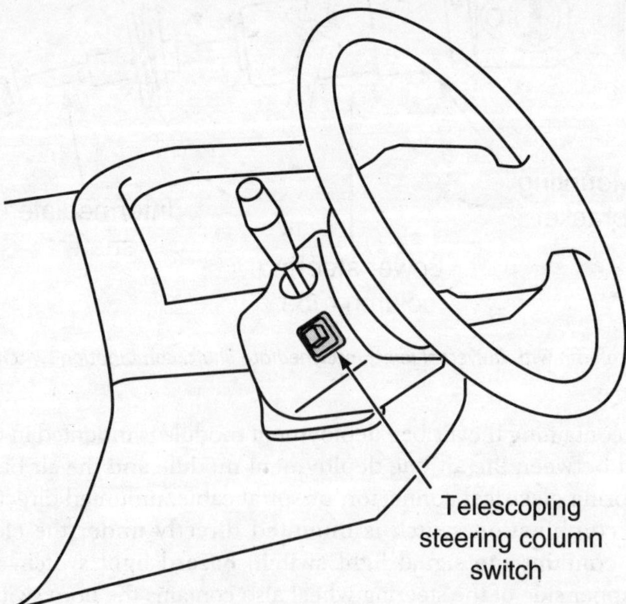

FIGURE 9-14 *Tilt/telescoping steering column switch.*

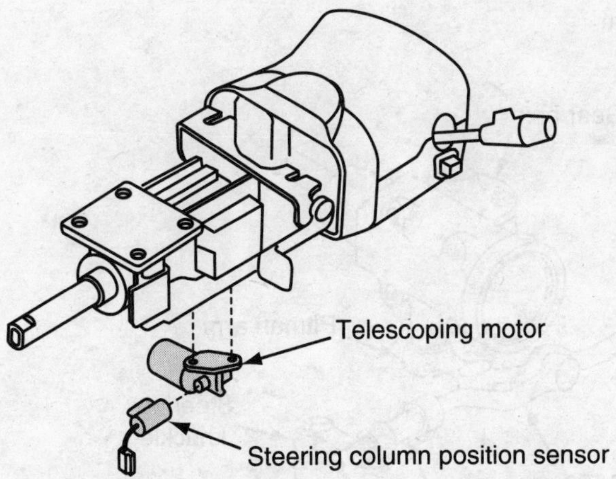

FIGURE 9-15 *Tilt/telescoping motor and steering column position sensor.*

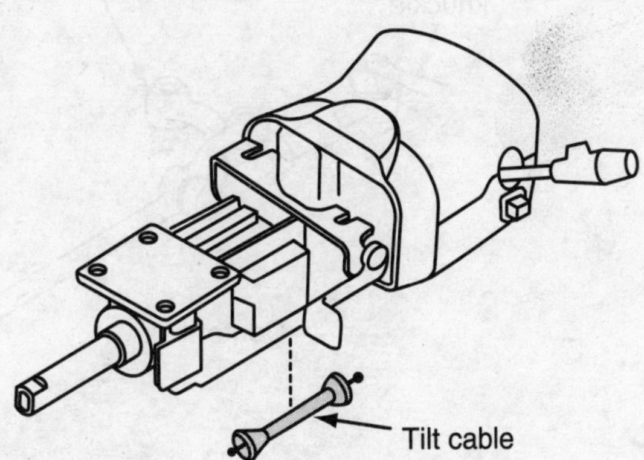

FIGURE 9-16 *Tilt cable for tilt/telescoping steering column.*

When the tilt/telescoping switch is operated by the driver, it sends voltage input signals to the DPM. If the driver operates the tilt/telescoping switch to request the telescoping function, the DPM operates the tilt/telescoping motor to move the steering wheel toward or away from the driver depending on the switch request. When the driver operates the tilt/telescoping switch to request the tilt function, the DPM operates the tilt/telescoping motor to tilt the wheel upward or downward depending on the switch request. The DPM is interconnected via data links to some of the other on-board computers. Therefore, the DPM can receive input signals from other computers such as the driver door switch (DDS) module via the data links. When the ignition switch is turned off and the driver pushes the unlock button on the driver's door, the DPM tilts the steering column to a position that allows easier exit from the driver's seat. When the driver enters the vehicle and turns on the ignition switch, the DPM moves the steering column back to the previous setting.

STEERING LINKAGE MECHANISMS

Parallelogram Steering Linkage

Steering linkage mechanisms are used to connect the steering gear to the front wheels. A **parallelogram steering linkage** may be mounted behind the front suspension (Figure 9-17) or in front of the front suspension (Figure 9-18). The parallelogram steering linkage must not interfere with the engine oil pan or chassis components.

WARNING: Always remember that a customer's life may depend on the condition of the steering linkages on his or her vehicle. State safety inspections play a very important role in maintaining suspension, steering, and other vehicle systems in safe driving condition and saving lives. During undercar service, always make a quick check of the steering linkage condition.

Regardless of the parallelogram steering linkage mounting position, this type of steering linkage contains the same components. The main components in this steering linkage mechanism are:

1. Pitman arm
2. Center link
3. Idler arm assembly
4. Tie-rods with sockets
5. Tie-rod ends

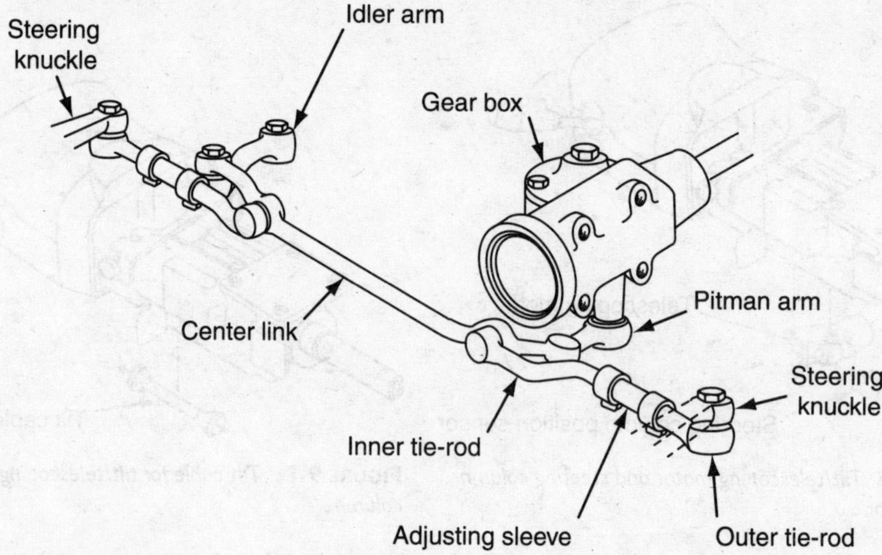

FIGURE 9-17 *Parallelogram steering linkage behind the front suspension.*

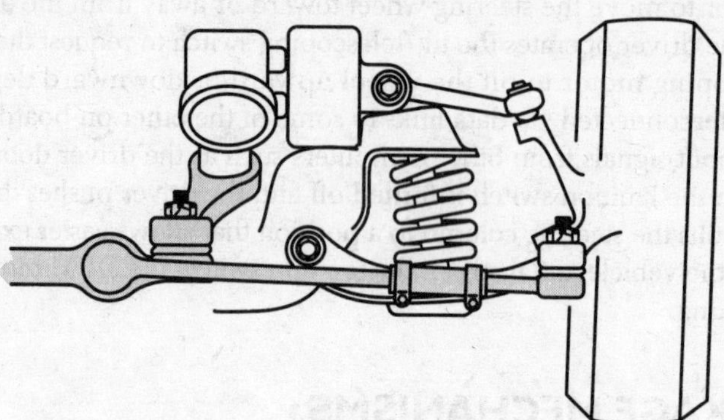

FIGURE 9-18 *Parallelogram steering linkage in front of the front suspension.*

Parallelogram steering linkages are found on independent front suspension systems. In a parallelogram steering linkage, the tie-rods are connected parallel to the lower control arms. Road vibration and shock are transmitted from the tires and wheels to the steering linkage, and these forces tend to wear the linkages and cause steering looseness. If the steering linkage components are worn, steering control is reduced. Since loose steering linkage components cause intermittent toe changes, this problem increases tire wear. The wear points in a parallelogram steering linkage are the tie-rod sockets and ends, idler arm, and center link end.

Tie-Rods

The **tie-rod** assemblies connect the center link to the steering arms, which are bolted to the front steering knuckles. In some front suspensions, the steering arms are part of the steering knuckle; in other front suspension systems, the steering arms are bolted to the knuckle. A ball socket is mounted on the inner end to each tie-rod, and a tapered stud on this socket is mounted in a center link opening. A castellated nut and cotter pin retain the tie-rods to the center link. A threaded sleeve is mounted on the outer end of each tie-rod, and a tie-rod end is threaded into the outer end of this sleeve (Figure 9-19).

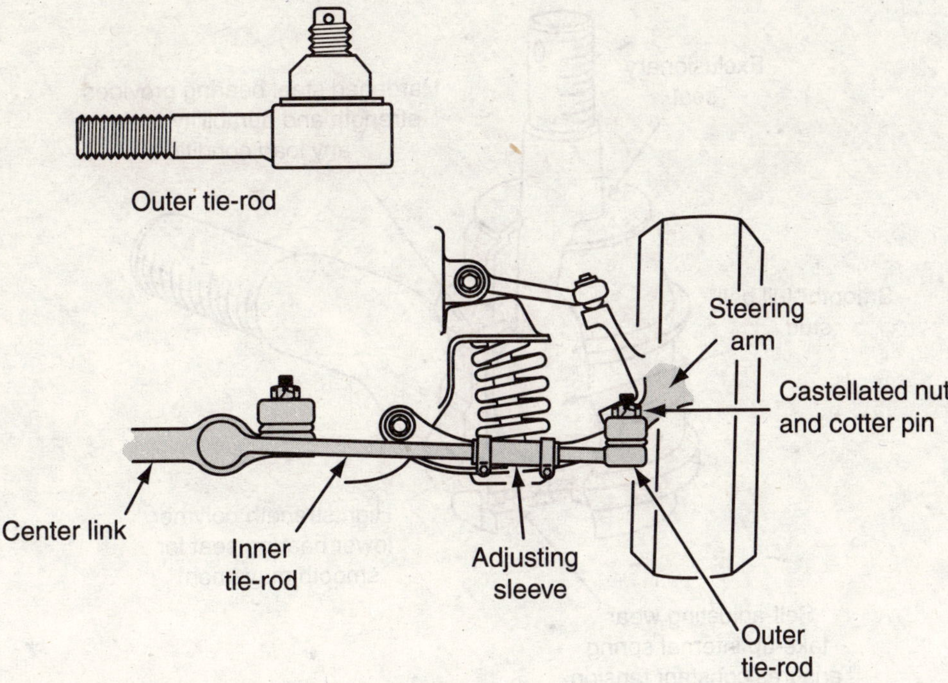

FIGURE 9-19 *Tie-rod design.*

Some outer tie-rod ends have a ball stud that is surrounded by an upper hardened steel bearing and a high-strength polymer lower bearing seat (Figure 9-20). The hardened steel upper bearing provides strength and durability, and the polymer lower bearing seat provides smooth rotation of the ball stud in the tie-rod end. An internal spring between the polymer lower bearing seat supplies self-adjusting action and constant tension on this seat. A seal in the upper part of the ball joint housing seals the ball stud to prevent contaminants from entering the tie-rod end. These tie-rod ends are installed on some original equipment manufacturer's vehicles, and they are available as replacement tie-rod ends on most vehicles.

Some Ford cars have rubber-encapsulated outer tie-rod ends in which a rubber bushing surrounds the lower end of the ball stud (Figure 9-21). Special service procedures required on these tie-rod ends are explained in the Shop Manual. Similar outer tie-rod ends are used on parallelogram steering linkages and rack and pinion steering linkages.

Each tie-rod sleeve contains a left-hand and a right-hand thread where it is threaded onto the tie-rod end and the tie-rod. Therefore, sleeve rotation changes the tie-rod length and provides a toe adjustment. Clamps are used to tighten the tie-rod sleeves. The clamp opening must be positioned away from the slot in the tie-rod sleeve. The design of the steering linkage mechanism allows multiaxial movement, since the front suspension moves vertically and horizontally. Ball-and-socket-type pivots are used on the tie-rod assemblies and center link.

If the front wheels hit a bump, the wheels move up and down and the control arms move through their respective arcs. Since the tie-rods are connected to the steering arms, these rods must move upward with the wheel. Under this condition, the inner end of the tie-rod acts as a pivot, and the tie-rod also moves through an arc. This arc is almost the same as the lower control arm arc because the tie-rod is parallel to the lower control arm. Maintaining the same arc between the lower control arm and the tie-rod minimizes toe change on the front wheels during upward and downward wheel movement. This action improves the directional stability of the vehicle and reduces tread wear on the front tires.

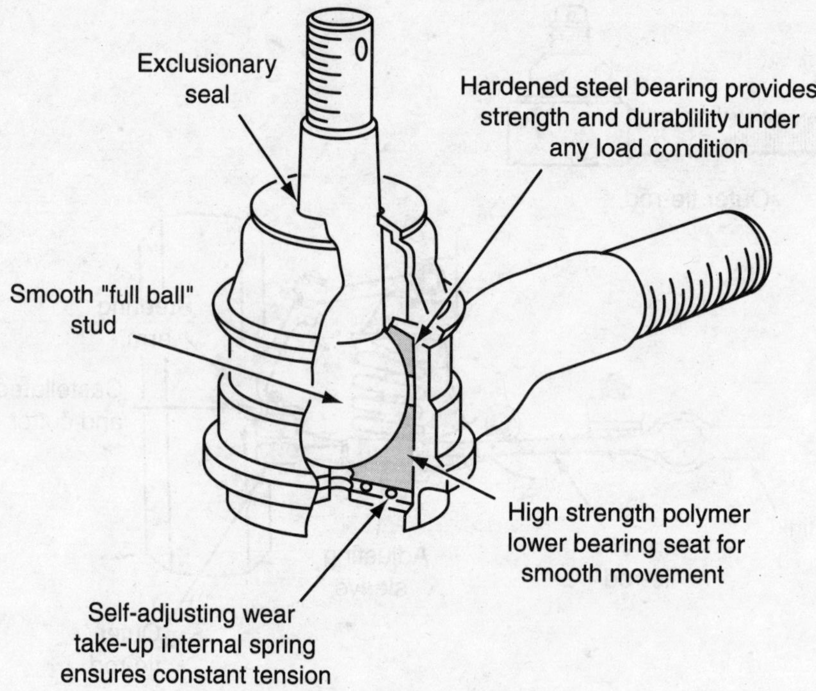

FIGURE 9-20 *Outer tie-rod end with hardened steel upper bearing and high-strength polymer lower bearing.*

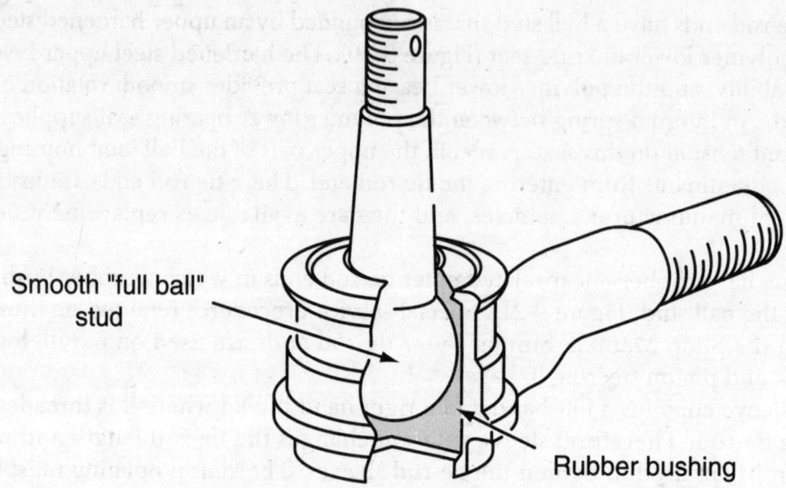

FIGURE 9-21 *Outer tie-rod end with rubber encapsulated ball stud.*

Pitman Arm

The **pitman arm** connects the steering gear to the center link. This arm also supports the left side of the center link. Motion from the steering wheel and steering gear is transmitted to the pitman arm, and this arm transfers the movement to the steering linkage. This pitman arm movement forces the steering linkage to move to the right or left, and the linkage moves the front wheels in the desired direction. The pitman arm also positions the center link at the proper height to maintain the parallel relationship between the tie-rods and the lower control arms.

Wear-type pitman arms have ball sockets and studs at the outer end, and this stud fits into the center link opening (Figure 9-22). The ball stud and socket are subject to wear, and pitman arm replacement is necessary if the ball stud is loose in the pitman arm. A nonwear pitman arm has a tapered opening in the outer end. A ball stud in the center link fits into this opening. The nonwear pitman arm only needs replacing if the arm is damaged or bent in a collision. The opening in the inner end of both types of pitman arms has serrations that fit over matching serrations on the steering gear shaft. A nut and lock washer retain the pitman arm to the steering gear shaft.

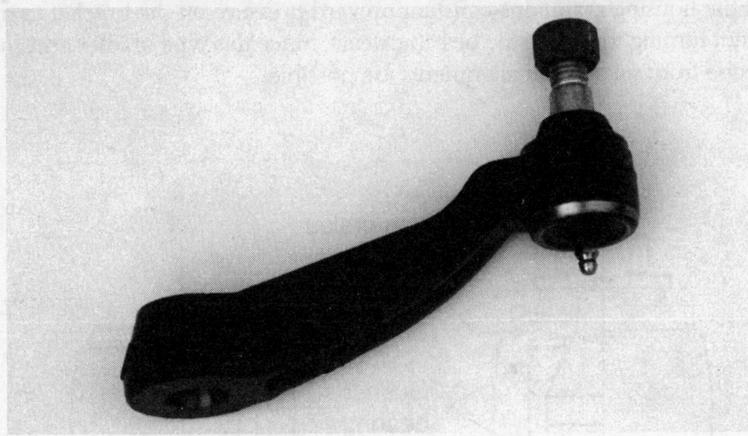

FIGURE 9-22 *Pitman arm design.*

Idler Arm

An idler arm support is bolted to the frame or chassis on the opposite end of the center link from the pitman arm. The **idler arm** is connected from the support bracket to the center link. Two bolts retain the idler arm bracket to the frame or chassis. In some idler arms, a ball stud on the outer end of the arm fits into a tapered opening in the center link (Figure 9-23), whereas in other idler arms, a ball stud in the center link fits into a tapered opening in the idler arm.

The idler arm supports the right side of the center link and helps maintain the parallel relationship between the tie-rods and the lower control arms. The outer end of the idler arm is designed to swivel on the idler arm bracket, and this swivel is subject to wear. A worn idler arm swivel causes excessive vertical steering linkage movement and erratic toe. This action results in excessive steering wheel free play with reduced steering control and front tire wear.

FIGURE 9-23 *Idler arm design.*

Some idler arms contain an upper and lower gusher bearing that surrounds the bearing surface on the lower end of the bracket. A newly designed idler arm has a one-piece powdered metal gusher bearing that extends the full length of the friction surface on the lower end of the bracket (Figure 9-24). Compared with previous designs, this new design has 50 percent more bearing surface, which provides extended service life. A Belleville washer installed below the gusher bearing maintains a precision preload on the thrust washer, bracket, and gusher bearing.

Other idler arms have a conical machined surface on the lower end of the bracket. This conical surface is seated on a matching conical surface on the bearing (Figure 9-25). A coil spring between the lower end of the bracket and the housing maintains constant upward pressure on the bracket to maintain minimal endplay and constant turning torque as the bearing wears. Since this type of idler arm maintains minimal endplay, more precise front suspension alignments are possible.

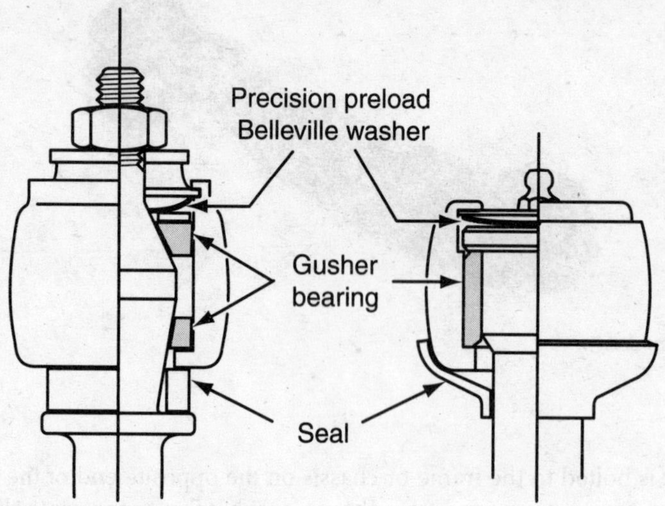

FIGURE 9-24 *Idler arm internal design.*

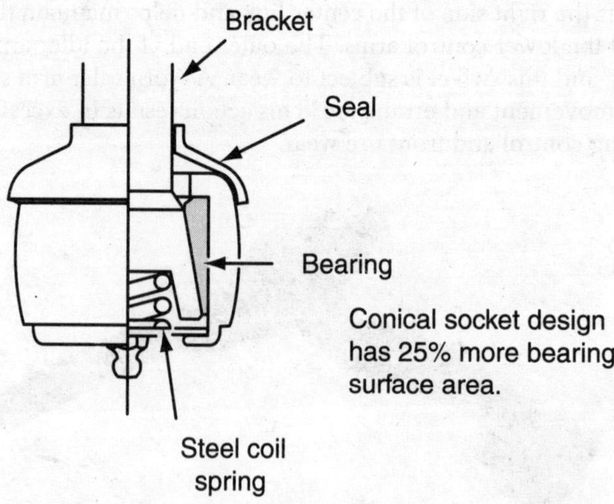

FIGURE 9-25 *Idler arm with conical bearing.*

Center Links

The **center link** controls the sideways steering linkage and wheel movement. The center link together with the pitman arm and idler arm provides the proper height for the tie-rods, which is very important to minimizing toe change on road irregularities. Some center links have tapered openings in each end, and the studs on the pitman arm and idler arm fit into these openings. This type of center link may be called a taper end, or nonwear, link. Other wear-type center links have ball sockets in each end with tapered studs extending from the sockets (Figure 9-26). These tapered studs fit into openings in the pitman arm and idler arm, and they are retained with castellated nuts and cotter pins.

FIGURE 9-26 *Center link design.*

Rack and Pinion Steering Linkage

The **rack and pinion steering linkage** is used with rack and pinion steering gears. In this type of steering gear, the rack is a rod with teeth on one side. This rack slides horizontally on bushings inside the gear housing. The rack teeth are meshed with teeth on a pinion gear, and this pinion gear is connected to the steering column. When the steering wheel is turned, the pinion rotation moves the rack sideways. Tie-rods are connected directly from the ends of the rack to the steering arms. The tie-rods are similar to those found on parallelogram steering systems. An inner tie-rod end connects each tie-rod to the rack, and bellows boots are clamped to the gear housing. The bellows boots keep dirt out of these joints (Figure 9-27). The inner tie-rod end contains a spring-loaded ball socket. The outer tie-rod ends connected to the steering arms are basically the same as those in parallelogram steering linkages (Figure 9-28). Some inner tie-rod ends contain a bolt and bushing. These tie-rod ends are threaded onto the rack. Since the rack is connected directly to the tie-rods, the rack replaces the center link in a parallelogram steering linkage.

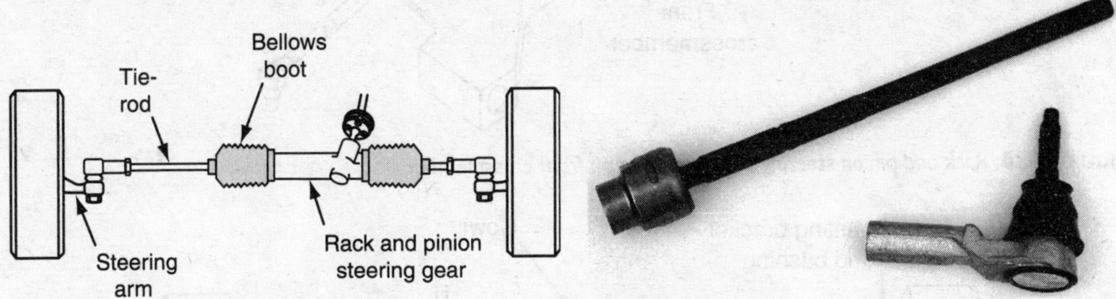

FIGURE 9-27 *Rack and pinion steering gear.*

FIGURE 9-28 *Inner tie-rod and outer tie-rod end, rack and pinion steering.*

Some inner tie-rod ends have a mirror-finished ball and a high-strength polymer bearing to ensure low torque, minimal friction, and extended life (Figure 9-29). A hardened alloy steel rod extends from the ball to the outer tie-rod end and provides maximum strength and durability.

The rack and pinion steering gear may be mounted on the front crossmember (Figure 9-30) or attached to the cowl behind the engine (Figure 9-31). Rubber insulating bushings surround the steering gear, and these bushings are clamped to the crossmember or cowl. The rack and pinion steering gear

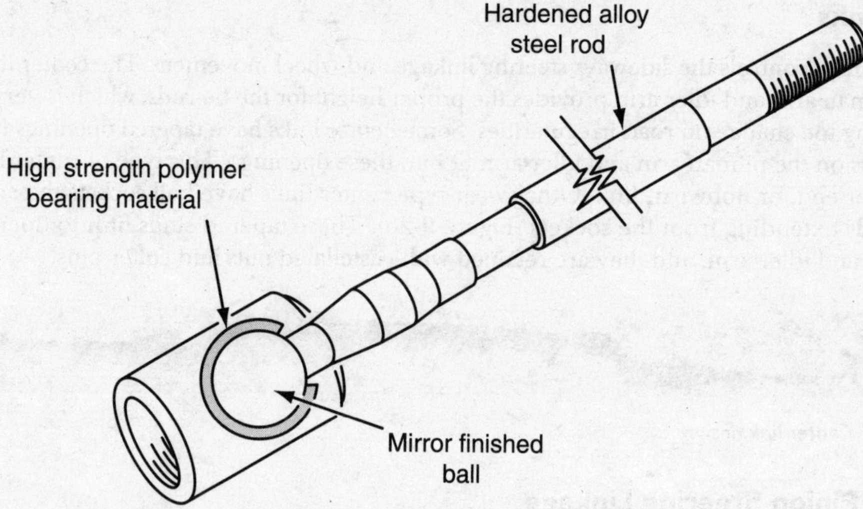

FIGURE 9-29 *Inner tie-rod design.*

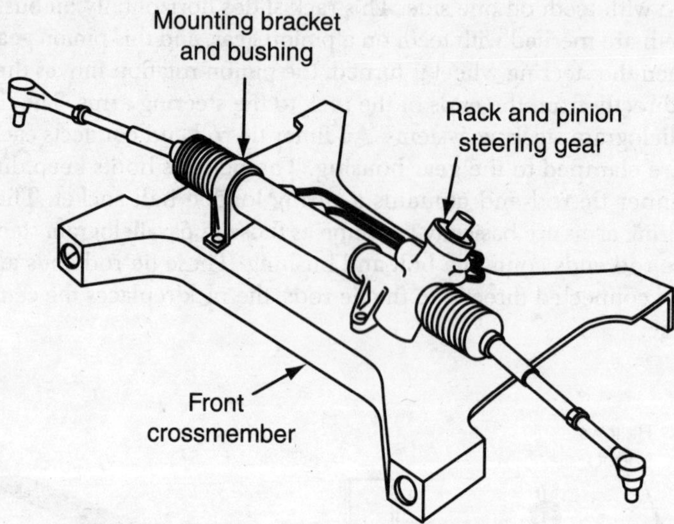

FIGURE 9-30 *Rack and pinion steering gear mounting on front crossmember.*

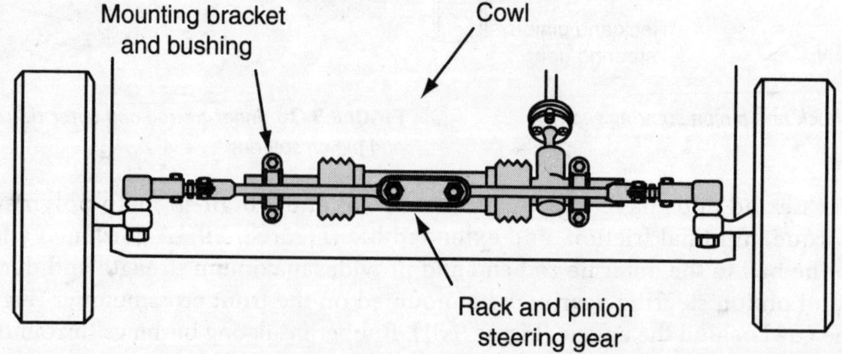

FIGURE 9-31 *Rack and pinion steering gear mounted on cowl.*

is mounted at the proper height to position the tie-rods and lower control arms parallel to each other. The number of friction points is reduced in a rack and pinion steering system, and this system is light and compact. Most front-wheel-drive unibody vehicles have rack and pinion steering. Since the rack is linked directly to the steering arms, this type of steering linkage provides good road feel.

STEERING DAMPER

A steering damper, or stabilizer, may be found on some parallelogram steering linkages. The steering damper is similar to a shock absorber. This component is connected from one of the steering links to the chassis or frame (Figure 9-32). When a front wheel strikes a road irregularity, a shock is transferred from the front wheel to the steering linkage, steering gear, and steering wheel. The steering damper helps absorb this road shock and prevent it from reaching the steering wheel. Heavy-duty steering dampers are available for severe road conditions such as those sometimes encountered by four-wheel-drive vehicles.

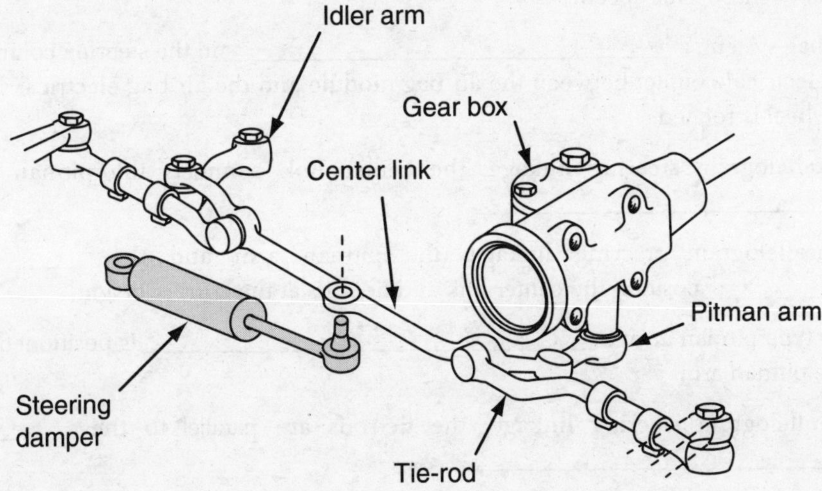

FIGURE 9-32 *Steering gear damper and linkage.*

REVIEW QUESTIONS

Short Answer Essays

1. Explain how a collapsible steering column protects the driver in a frontal collision.
2. Explain how the driver's side air bag protects the driver in a frontal collision.
3. Describe the purpose of a clock spring.
4. List the switches commonly found in a steering column.
5. Describe the type of mechanism used to lock the steering wheel and gear shift when the ignition is in the Lock position.
6. Describe the pivot points in the upper shaft and upper column tube in a tilt steering wheel.

7. List the wear points in a parallelogram steering linkage.
8. List the five main components in a parallelogram steering linkage, and explain the purpose of each component.
9. Describe the basic design of a rack and pinion steering linkage.
10. Explain the advantages of a rack and pinion steering linkage compared with a parallelogram steering linkage.

Fill-in-the-Blanks

1. In some collapsible steering columns, ______________ in the outer column jacket and steering shaft shear off if the driver is thrown against the steering wheel in a frontal collision.
2. The driver's side air bag protects the driver if the vehicle is involved in a ______________ collision above a specific speed.
3. In an air bag system, a ______________ ______________ in the steering column maintains positive electrical contact between the air bag module and the air bag electrical system as the steering wheel is rotated.
4. In a parallelogram steering linkage, the center link connects the pitman arm to the ______________ ______________.
5. In a parallelogram steering linkage, the pitman arm and the ______________ ______________ position the center link and tie-rods at the correct height.
6. In a wear-type pitman arm, a ______________ ______________ is positioned in the outer end of the pitman arm.
7. In a parallelogram steering linkage, the tie-rods are parallel to the ______________ ______________.
8. The clamp opening in a tie-rod sleeve must be positioned away from the ______________ in the tie-rod sleeve.
9. In a rack and pinion steering system, the rack is connected directly to the ______________ ______________.
10. Compared with a parallelogram steering linkage, a rack and pinion steering linkage has a reduced number of ______________ points.

Multiple Choice

1. A typical air bag deployment time is:
   A. 1.5 minutes.
   B. 1 minute.
   C. 30 seconds.
   D. 40 milliseconds.

2. Many collapsible steering columns have:
   A. Plastic pins in the two-piece outer jacket.
   B. A collapsible bellows in the two-piece outer jacket.
   C. Steel pins in the two-piece lower steering shaft.
   D. A rubber spacer in the two-piece lower steering shaft.

3. The clock spring electrical connector:
   A. Maintains electrical contact between the air bag inflator module and the air bag electrical system.
   B. Is mounted above the steering wheel.
   C. Contains three spring-loaded copper contacts.
   D. Provides electrical contact between the signal light switch and the signal lights.

4. In a parallelogram steering linkage:
   A. The outer tie-rod ends are parallel to the idler arm.
   B. The pitman arm is parallel to the center link.
   C. The center link is supported by the pitman arm and idler arm.
   D. The idler arm is parallel to the pitman arm.

5. All of these statements about rack and pinion steering linkages are true EXCEPT:
   A. The tie-rods are parallel to the lower control arms.
   B. The tie-rod position depends on the steering gear mounting.
   C. The tie-rods are connected to the pinion in the steering gear.
   D. The outer tie-rod ends connect the tie-rods to the steering arms.

6. All these statements about parallelogram steering linkages are true EXCEPT:
   A. Tie-rod sleeves have the same type of thread in both ends of the sleeve.
   B. Loose steering linkages may cause excessive tire tread wear.
   C. Loose steering linkage causes excessive steering wheel free play.
   D. The pitman arm helps maintain the proper center link and tie-rod height.

7. While discussing idler arms:
   A. Some idler arms contain a tapered roller bearing.
   B. The idler arm bracket is bolted to the upper control arm.
   C. A worn idler arm has no effect on front wheel toe.
   D. A partially seized idler arm bearing increases steering effort.

8. In a parallelogram steering linkage, the tie-rods are parallel to the lower control arms to:
   A. Improve ride quality.
   B. Provide longer steering linkage life.
   C. Extend shock absorber and spring life.
   D. Reduce toe change during upward and downward front wheel movement.

9. A rack and pinion steering gear:
   A. Has tie-rods that connect the rack directly to the steering arms.
   B. May be bolted to the vehicle frame.
   C. Has inner tie-rod ends that are pressed onto the rack.
   D. Has more friction points compared with a parallelogram steering linkage.

10. While discussing steering linkages and dampers:
    A. In a rack and pinion steering gear, the rack positions the tie-rods parallel to the lower control arms.
    B. A rack and pinion steering gear is used on most rear-wheel-drive cars.
    C. A steering damper is used on many front-wheel-drive vehicles.
    D. A defective steering damper may cause excessive steering effort.

POWER STEERING PUMPS 10

Upon completion and review of this chapter, you should be able to:

- Explain the difference between a conventional V-belt and a ribbed V-belt.
- Describe the advantages of a ribbed V-belt compared with a conventional V-belt.
- Describe the main components in a power-assisted rack and pinion steering system, and explain the steering gear mounting position.
- Explain two different types of power steering pump reservoirs.
- Describe the difference between a hydroboost power steering system and an integral power steering system.
- List three different types of power steering pump rotor designs.
- Describe the power steering pump operation while driving with the front wheels straight ahead.
- Describe the power steering pump operation while the vehicle is turning a corner.
- Describe the power steering pump pressure relief operation, and explain when this operation occurs.
- Describe the design and purpose of an electrohydraulic power steering module.

INTRODUCTION

Power steering systems have contributed to reduced driver fatigue and made driving a more pleasant experience. Nearly all power steering systems at the present time use fluid pressure to assist the driver in turning the front wheels. Since driver effort required to turn the front wheels is reduced, driver fatigue is decreased. The advantages of power steering have been made available on many vehicles, and safety has been maintained in these systems.

There are several different types of power steering systems, including integral, rack and pinion, hydroboost, and linkage type. In any of these systems, the power steering pump is the heart of the system because it supplies the necessary pressure to assist steering.

The power steering pump drive belt is a simple, but very important, component in the power steering system. A power steering pump in perfect condition will not produce the required pressure for steering assist if the drive belt is slipping. Various types of steering systems, drive belts, and pump designs are described in this chapter.

POWER STEERING PUMP DRIVE BELTS

Many power steering pumps are driven by a **V-belt** that surrounds the crankshaft pulley and the power steering pump pulley. The V-belt may also drive other components, such as the water pump. The sides of a V-belt are the friction surfaces that drive the power steering pump (Figure 10-1). If the sides of the

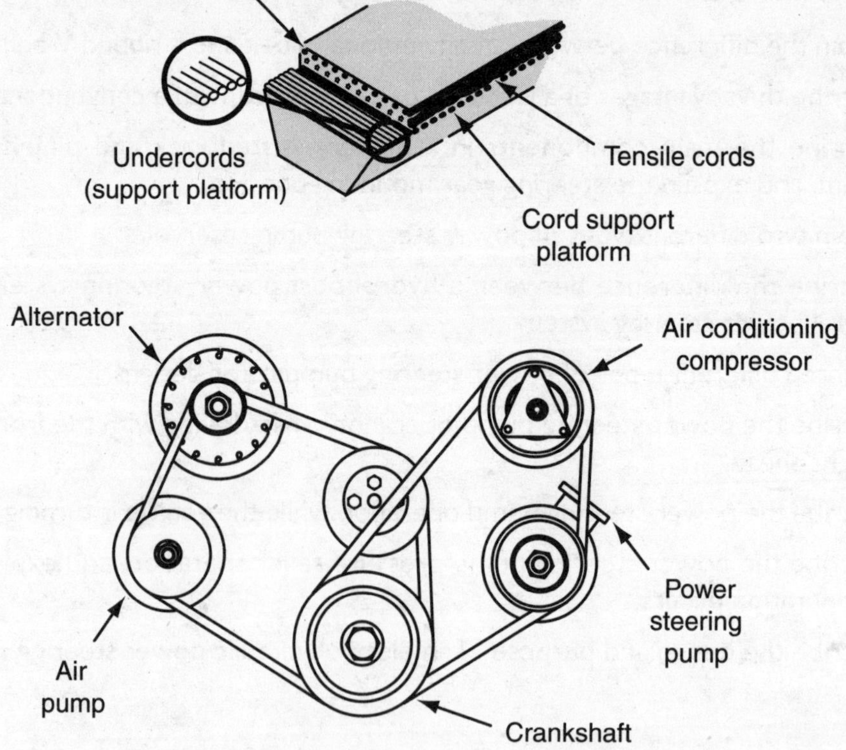

FIGURE 10-1 *Conventional V-belt.*

belt are worn and the lower edge of the belt is contacting the bottom of the pulley, the belt will slip. The power steering pump pulley, crankshaft pulley, and any other pulleys driven by the V-belt must be properly aligned. If these pulleys are misaligned, excessive belt wear occurs.

WARNING: Always keep hands, tools, and equipment away from rotating belts and pulleys. If any of these items become entangled in rotating belts, personal injury and equipment damage may result.

WARNING: Always keep long hair tied back while working in the automotive shop! If long hair is entangled in rotating belts and pulleys, personal injury will result.

A **ribbed V-belt** is used on many vehicles, and this belt may be used to drive all the belt-driven components. The ribbed V-belt is much wider than a conventional V-belt, and the underside of the belt has a number of small ribbed grooves. Most ribbed V-belts have spring-loaded automatic belt tensioners that eliminate periodic belt tension adjustments. Since the ribbed V-belt may be used to drive all the belt-driven components, these components are placed on the same vertical plane, which saves a considerable amount of underhood space (Figure 10-2). The smooth backside of the ribbed V-belt may also be used to drive one of the components. Regardless of the type of belt, the belt tension is critical. A power steering pump will never develop full pressure if the belt is slipping.

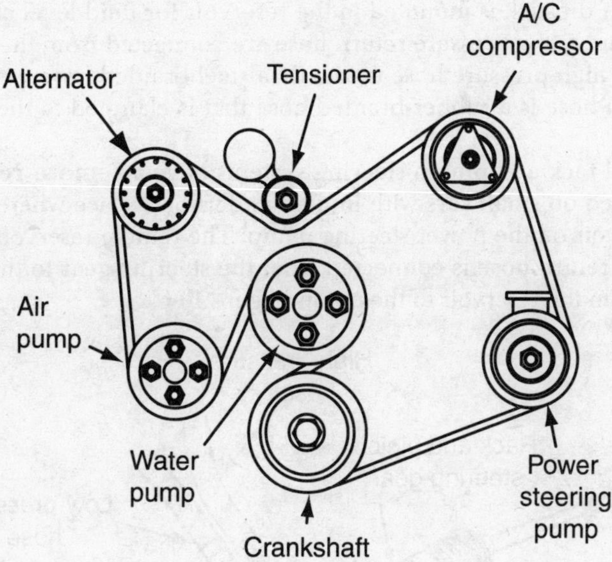

FIGURE 10-2 *Ribbed V-belt.*

TYPES OF POWER-ASSISTED STEERING SYSTEMS

Rack and Pinion Steering System

The **rack and pinion power steering system** is used on most front-wheel-drive cars. In this steering system, the power steering pump is bolted to a bracket on the engine, and the pump is driven by a belt from the crankshaft. In most front-wheel-drive cars, the engine is mounted transversely, and the steering gear is mounted on the cowl behind the engine or on the crossmember below the engine (Figure 10-3).

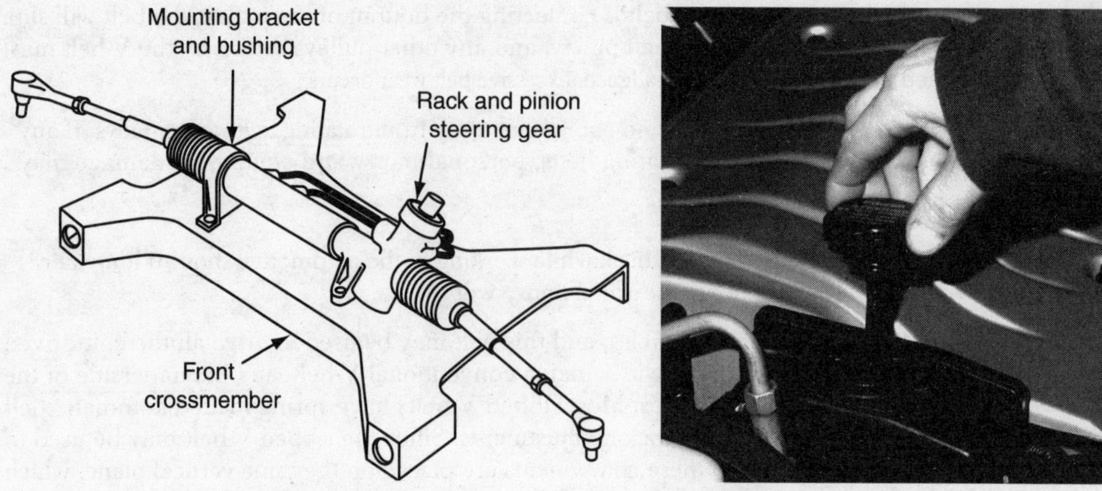

FIGURE 10-3 *Power steering gear mounting.*

FIGURE 10-4 *Power steering reservoir and dipstick.*

In many power-assisted rack and pinion steering systems, an **integral reservoir** is part of the power steering pump. A dipstick is mounted in the reservoir for fluid level checking (Figure 10-4). A high-pressure hose and a low-pressure return hose are connected from the pump to the steering gear (Figure 10-5). The high-pressure hose is usually a steel-braided hose with appropriate fittings in each end. The return hose is a rubber-braided hose that is clamped to the fittings on the pump and gear.

Some power-assisted rack and pinion steering systems have a **remote reservoir**. This type of system is commonly used on small cars with limited underhood space where it may be difficult to access an integral reservoir on the power steering pump. The remote reservoir is placed in a convenient position, and the return hose is connected from the steering gear to the reservoir. A second return hose is routed from the reservoir to the pump (Figure 10-6).

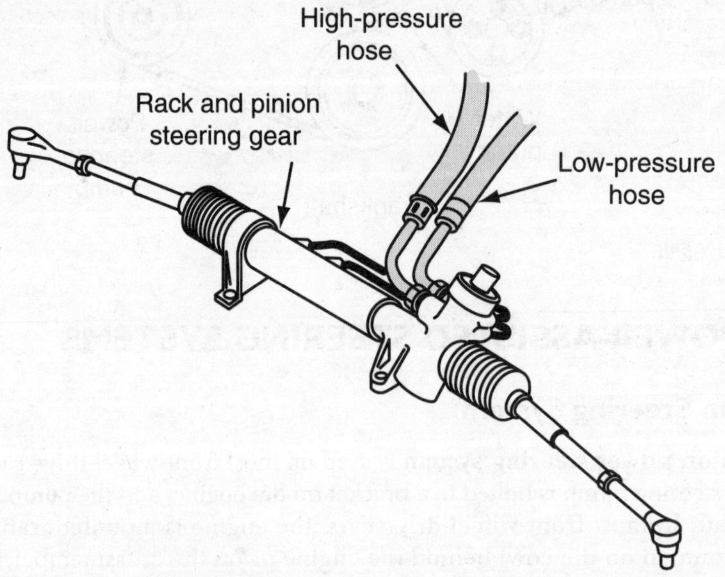

FIGURE 10-5 *Power steering pump to gear hoses.*

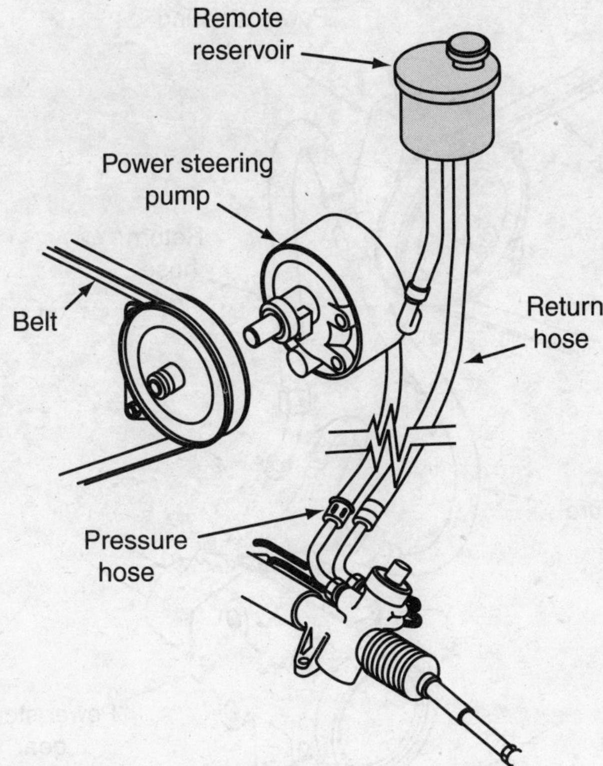

FIGURE 10-6 *Remote reservoir on power-assisted rack and pinion steering system.*

Integral Power-Assisted Steering System

In the **integral power-assisted steering system**, the pump is bolted to a bracket on the engine, and the recirculating ball steering gear is mounted on the frame beside the engine. This type of steering system is used on many rear-wheel-drive cars and light-duty trucks. The pump is driven by a belt from the crankshaft and an integral reservoir is mounted on the pump. A high-pressure hose and a return hose are connected from the pump to the steering gear (Figure 10-7).

Hydroboost Power-Assisted Steering System

The **hydroboost power-assisted steering system** is used on many light-duty trucks with diesel engines and on some cars. Since the hydroboost system does not use manifold vacuum for brake assist, this system is suitable for diesel engines, which have reduced intake manifold vacuum compared with gasoline engines. The power steering on these systems is similar to an integral unit, but the power steering pump pressure is also applied to the hydroboost unit in the brake master cylinder. Hydraulic lines are routed from the power steering pump to the steering gear, and another set of lines is connected from the pump to the master cylinder (Figure 10-8). In the hydroboost system, the power steering pump pressure applied to the master cylinder pistons acts as a brake booster to assist the driver in applying the brakes. The hydroboost system does not have a conventional vacuum booster on the master cylinder.

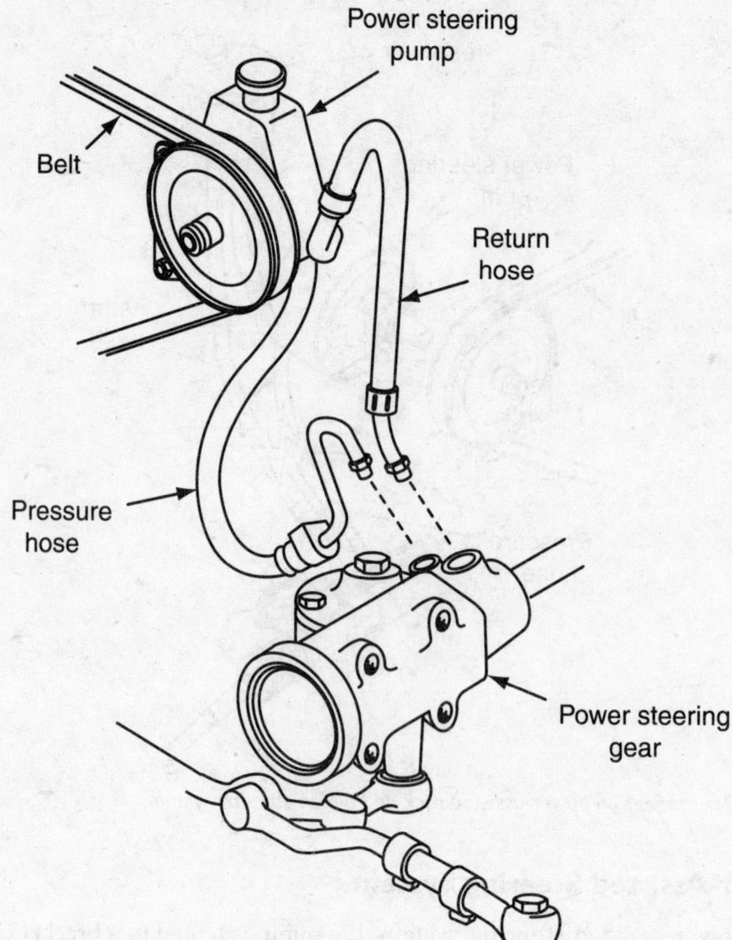

FIGURE 10-7 *Integral power-assisted steering system.*

POWER STEERING PUMP DESIGN

Various types of power steering pumps have been used by car manufacturers. Many **vane-type power steering pumps** have flat vanes that seal the pump rotor to the elliptical pump cam ring (Figure 10-9). Other vane-type power steering pumps have rollers to seal the rotor to the cam ring. In some pumps, inverted, U-shaped slippers are used for this purpose. The major differences in these pumps are in the rotor design and the method used to seal the pump rotor in the elliptical pump ring. The operating principles of all three types of pumps are similar.

A balanced pulley is pressed on the steering pump drive shaft. This pulley and shaft are belt-driven by the engine. The oblong pump reservoir is made from steel or plastic. A large O-ring seals the front of the reservoir to the pump housing (Figure 10-10).

Smaller O-rings seal the bolt fittings on the back of the reservoir. The combination cap and dipstick keeps the fluid reserve in the pump and vents the reservoir to the atmosphere.

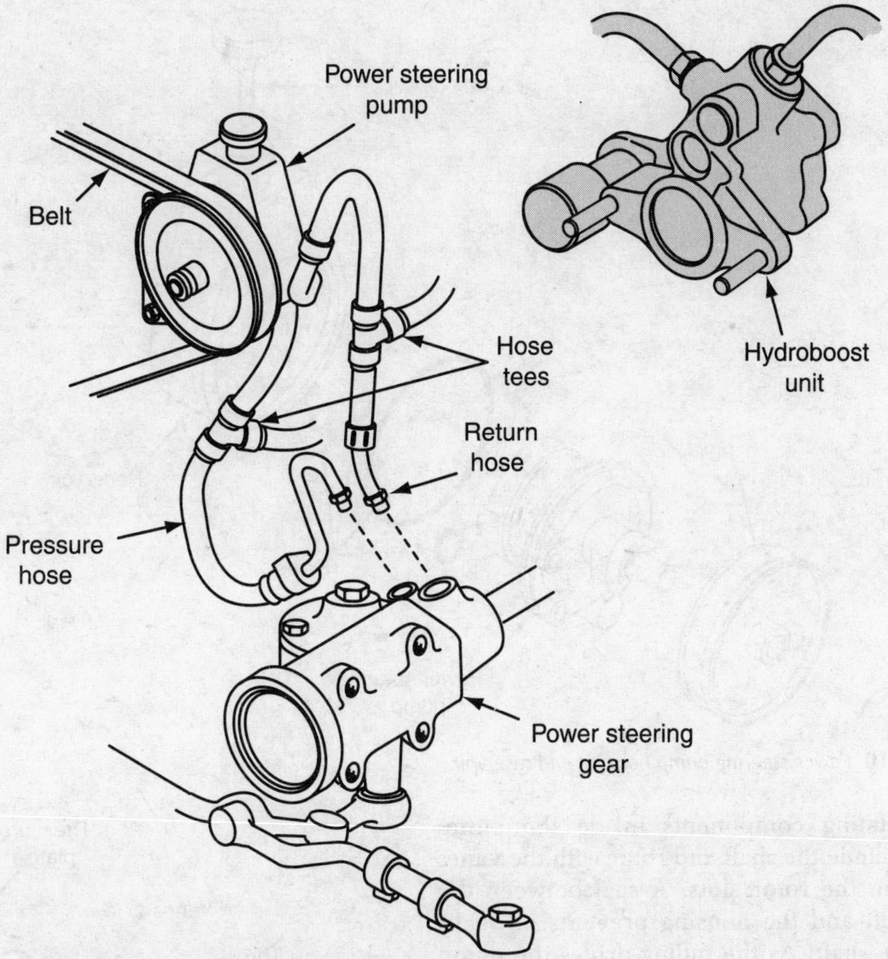

FIGURE 10-8 *Hydroboost power-assisted steering and brake system.*

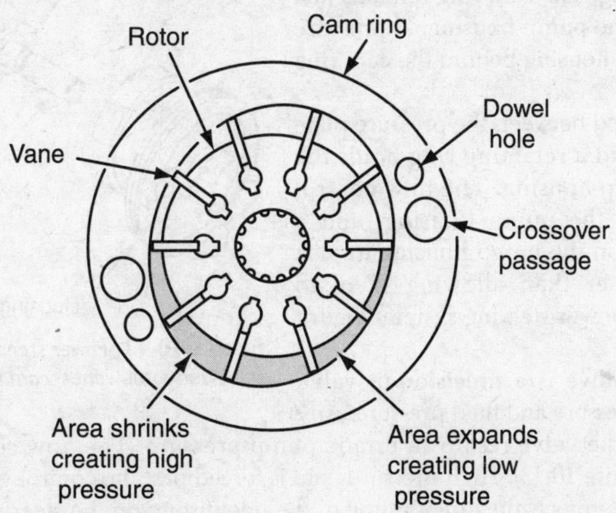

FIGURE 10-9 *Power steering pump rotor and vanes.*

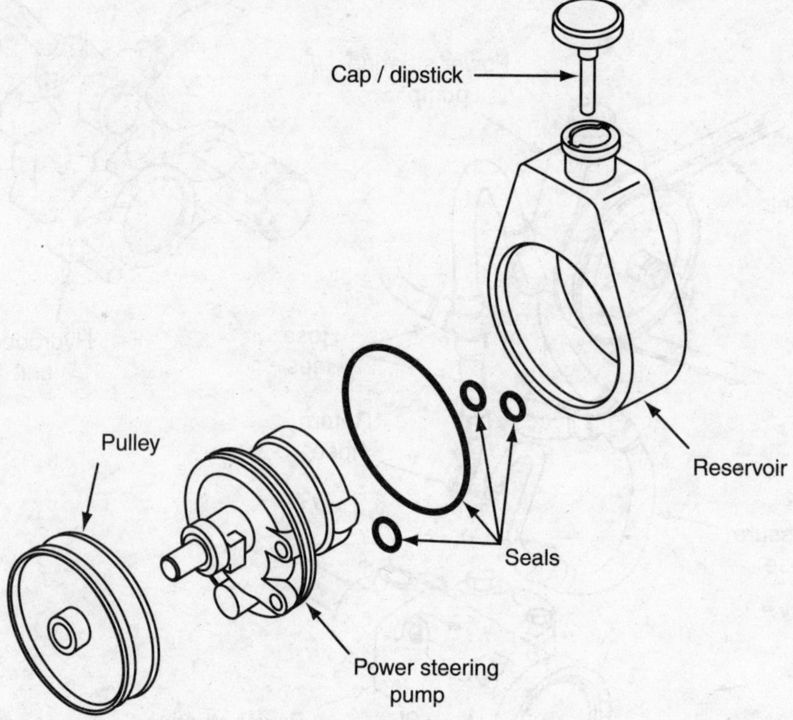

FIGURE 10-10 *Power steering pump housing and reservoir.*

The rotating components inside the pump housing include the shaft and rotor with the vanes mounted in the rotor slots. A seal between the output shaft and the housing prevents oil leaks around the shaft. As the pulley drives the pump shaft, the vanes rotate inside an elliptically shaped opening in the **cam ring**. The cam ring remains in a fixed position inside the pump housing. A pressure plate is installed in the housing behind the cam ring (Figure 10-11).

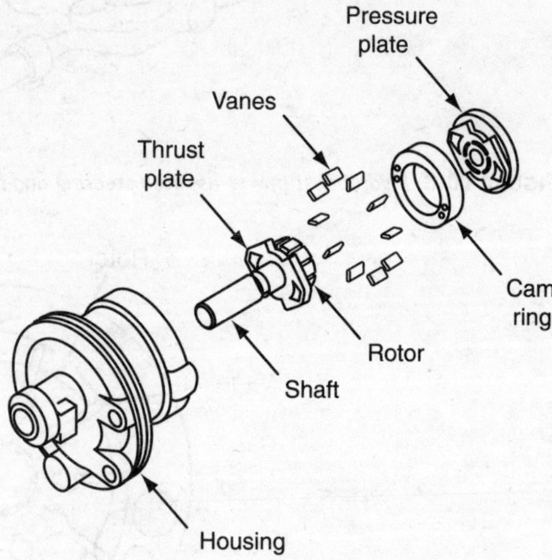

FIGURE 10-11 *Power steering pump housing with shaft and rotor, vanes, cam ring, and pressure plate.*

A spring is positioned between the pressure plate and the end cover, and a retaining ring holds the end cover in the pump housing. The flow control valve is mounted in the pump housing, and a magnet is positioned on the pump housing to pick up metal filings rather than allowing them to circulate through the power steering system (Figure 10-12).

The flow control valve is a precision-fit valve controlled by spring pressure and fluid pressure. Any dirt or roughness on the valve results in erratic pump pressure. The flow control valve contains a pressure relief ball (Figure 10-13). High-pressure fluid is forced past the control valve to the outlet fitting. A high-pressure hose connects the outlet fitting to the inlet fitting on the steering gear. A low-pressure hose returns the fluid from the steering gear to the inlet fitting in the pump reservoir.

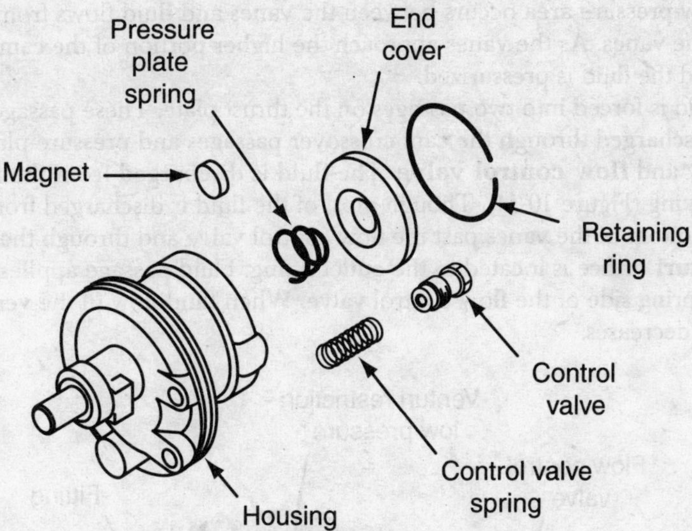

FIGURE 10-12 *Power steering pump housing assembly with end cover, flow control valve, and magnet.*

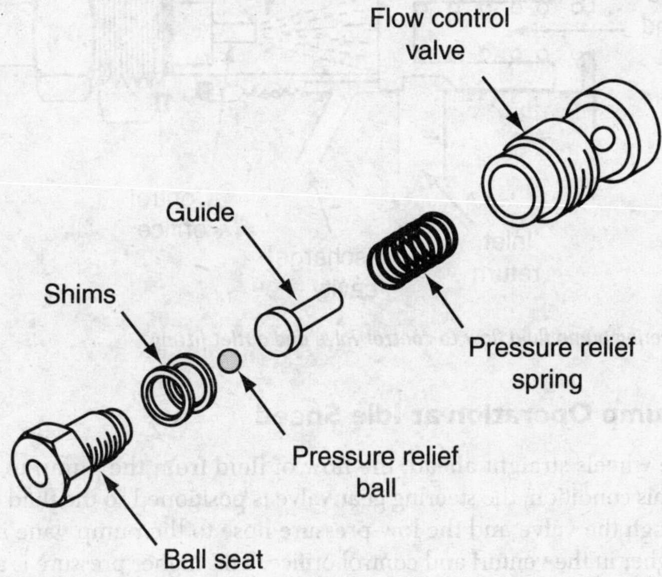

FIGURE 10-13 *Flow control valve.*

CAUTION: Avoid prying on the power steering pump reservoir, because this action can damage or puncture the reservoir.

POWER STEERING PUMP OPERATION

Vane and Cam Action

As the belt rotates the rotor and vanes inside the cam ring, centrifugal force causes the vanes to slide out of the rotor slots. The vanes follow the elliptical surface of the cam. When the area between the vanes expands, a low-pressure area occurs between the vanes and fluid flows from the reservoir into the space between the vanes. As the vanes approach the higher portion of the cam, the area between the vanes shrinks and the fluid is pressurized.

High-pressure fluid is forced into two passages on the thrust plate. These passages reverse the fluid direction. Fluid is discharged through the cam crossover passages and pressure plate openings to the high-pressure cavity and **flow control valve**. The fluid is discharged from the flow control valve through the outlet fitting (Figure 10-14). Though most of the fluid is discharged from the pump, some fluid returns to the bottom of the vanes past the flow control valve and through the bypass passage.

A machined **venturi** orifice is located in the outlet fitting. Fluid passage applies pressure from the venturi area to the spring side of the flow control valve. When fluid flow in the venturi increases, the pressure in this area decreases.

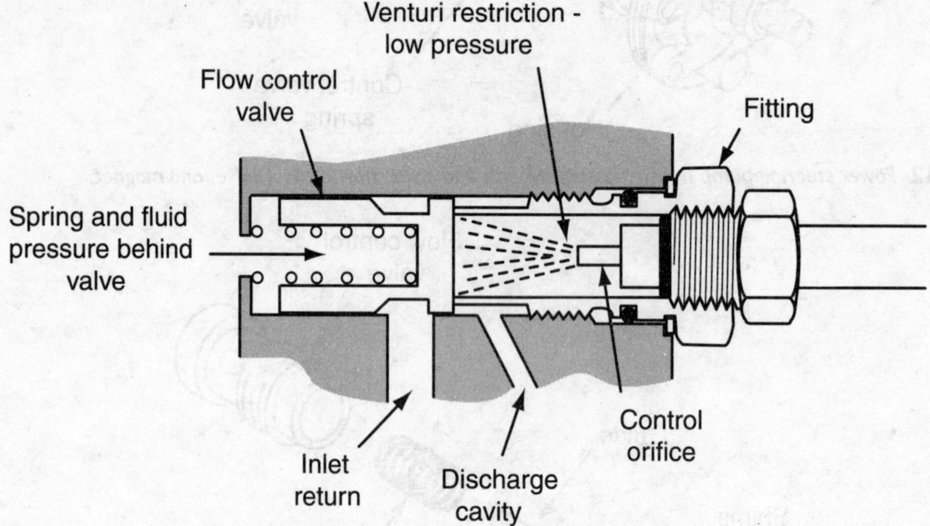

FIGURE 10-14 *Power steering pump fluid flow to control valve and outlet fitting.*

Power Steering Pump Operation at Idle Speed

At idle speed with the wheels straight ahead, the flow of fluid from the pump to the steering gear is relatively low. Under this condition, the steering gear valve is positioned so the fluid discharged from the pump is directed through the valve and the low-pressure hose to the pump vane inlet. With low fluid flow, the pressure is higher in the venturi and control orifice. This higher pressure is applied to the spring side of the flow control valve and helps the valve spring keep this flow control valve closed (Figure 10-15). Under this condition, pump pressure remains low, and all the fluid is discharged from the pump through the steering gear valve and back to the pump inlet.

Power Steering Pump Operation at Higher Engine Speeds

When engine speed is increased, the power steering pump delivers more fluid than the system requires. This increase in fluid flow creates a pressure decrease in the **outlet fitting venturi**. This pressure reduction is sensed at the spring side of the flow control valve, which allows the pump discharge pressure to force the flow control valve partially open. Under this condition, the excess fluid from the pump is routed past the flow control valve to the pump inlet. If the steering wheel is turned, the fluid discharged from the pump rushes into the pressure chamber in the steering gear.

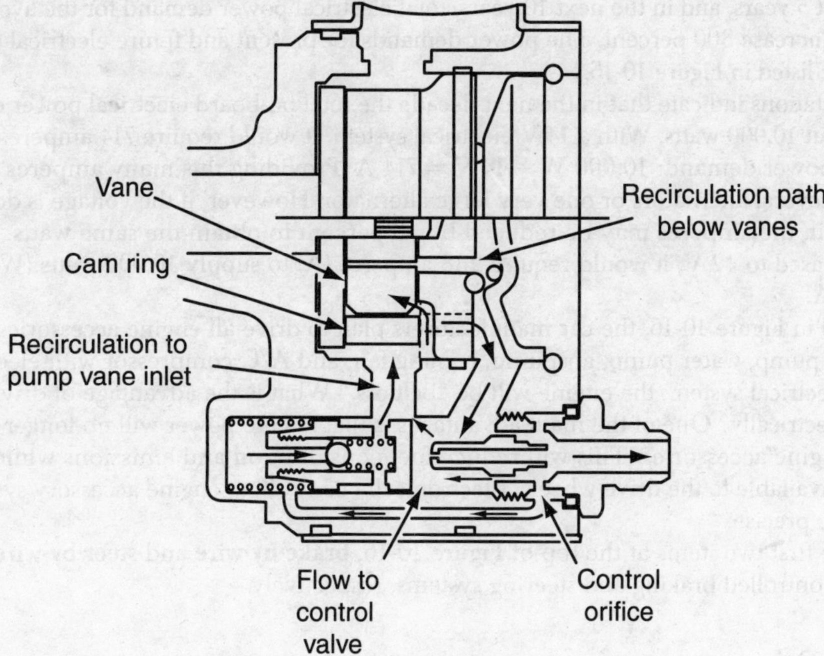

FIGURE 10-15 *Flow control valve operation under various conditions.*

Power Steering Pump Operation During Pressure Relief

If the steering wheel is turned fully in either direction until the steering linkage contacts the steering stops, the rack piston is stopped. Under this condition, pump pressure could become extremely high and damage hoses or other components. When the rack piston stops, the flow from the pump decreases, but the high pump pressure is still directed through the steering gear valve to the rack piston. Since the flow of fluid through the venturi and control orifice is reduced, a higher pressure is present in this area. This extremely high pressure is also supplied to the spring end of the flow control valve. At a predetermined pressure, the **pressure relief ball** in the center of the flow control valve is unseated and the flow control valve moves to the wide-open position. This action allows some of the high pressure in the steering system to return to the pump inlet, which limits pump pressure to a maximum safe value.

POWER STEERING PUMPS AND 42-VOLT ELECTRICAL SYSTEMS

Some vehicle manufacturers are considering the use of 42-V electrical systems to overcome problems associated with the increased use of vehicle electronics. There are a number of reasons for the change from 12-V to 42-V electrical systems. Electrical energy is measured in watts (W), and watts (W) are calculated by multiplying amperes (A) and volts (V). For example, if 3 amperes flow through a 12-V headlight, then 3 A x 12 V = 36 W.

The electronic content and electrical power demand on vehicles has increased steadily for the past 30 years. In the 1990s, the electronic content on vehicles increased at approximately 6 percent per year. The electrical content on the average high-end luxury car is now about $2,000. In 1970 the total electrical power demand on the average vehicle was 500 watts. In many current model vehicles, the total electrical power demand is 2,000 watts. Total electrical power demand has been growing at about 100 watts per year for the past 5 years, and in the next 10 years, total electrical power demand for the average vehicle is predicted to increase 300 percent. The power demands for present and future electrical components and systems are listed in Figure 10-16.

These expectations indicate that in the next decade the total on-board electrical power demand will increase to about 10,000 watts. With a 14-V electrical system, it would require 714 amperes (A) to meet a 10,000-watt power demand: 10,000 W ÷ 14 V = 714 A. Providing this many amperes to a vehicle would require several alternators or one very large alternator. However, if the voltage is doubled in an electrical circuit, the amperes may be reduced by 50 percent to obtain the same watts. Thus, if the voltage is increased to 42 V, it would require 238 amperes (A) to supply 10,000 watts (W): 10,000 W ÷ 42 V = 238 A.

As indicated in Figure 10-16, the car manufacturers plan to drive all engine accessories such as the power steering pump, water pump, air pump, cooling fan, and A/C compressor with electric motors. With a 42-V electrical system, the engine will be "beltless." What is the advantage of driving all these components electrically? One of the main advantages is that engine power will no longer be required to drive the engine accessories. This will reduce fuel consumption and emissions while increasing engine power available to the drive wheels. Electronically controlling engine accessory systems is also faster and more precise.

Observe the first two items at the top of Figure 10-16, **brake-by-wire** and **steer-by-wire**, which are electronically controlled braking and steering systems, respectively.

COMPONENT	PEAK WATTS
Brake by wire	2000
Steer by wire	1800
Rear defrost	1500
Electric fan	800
Heated front seats	2000
Active suspension	12000
Lights	600
Air pump	400
Wipers	300
Catalyst heating	3000
Electromechanical valve control	3200
Engine coolant pump	500
Infotronics	100
Electric A/C compressor	4000
Heated windshield	2500
Heated steering wheel	120
Rear wipers	90
ABS pump	600
Power door locks	400
Power windows	700
Power seats	1600
Power sunroof	200
Windshield pump	100
Trunk closer	200

FIGURE 10-16 *Watts required for present and future electrical systems and components.*

In a brake-by-wire system, one or more electronic sensors is connected to the brake pedal, but this pedal is not connected directly to the brake booster or master cylinder. An electric-drive pump supplies high-pressure brake fluid to a sealed chamber containing a flexible diaphragm. When the brake pedal is applied, the brake pedal sensor(s) send a voltage signal to the computer. When this signal is received, the computer operates actuators to apply the precise amount of fluid pressure from the high-pressure fluid chamber to the wheel calipers. The computer can perform this function faster than a conventional power-assisted antilock brake system. Applying the brakes a few milliseconds faster may prevent an accident in a panic situation. This very brief explanation provides the basic principles of a sophisticated brake-by-wire system. The 2002 Mercedes-Benz SL is equipped with an introductory brake-by-wire system, although it does not have a 42-V electrical system.

In a steer-by-wire system, the power steering pump is driven by an electric motor, and the steering wheel is connected only to the steering sensor(s). The steering sensor(s) send a voltage signal to the computer in relation to the amount and speed of steering wheel rotation. When the computer receives a voltage signal from the steering sensor(s), the computer energizes an actuator, which supplies fluid pressure from the power steering pump to the appropriate side of the steering gear piston and turns the front wheels.

Many 42-V systems will have an integral starter/generator (ISG) with a series of windings mounted in the flywheel housing surrounding the flywheel (Figure 10-17). A group of magnets is mounted around the circumference of the flywheel. A high current is supplied to the starter/generator windings to crank the engine. The starter/generator quickly cranks the engine up to 500 rpm, and then the powertrain control module (PCM) operates the injectors to start the engine, which reduces start-up exhaust emissions. (A conventional starting motor only cranks the engine at 100 to 200 rpm.) The starter/generator operation is very quiet because there is no starter engagement or disengagement. When the driver steps on the accelerator pedal, the engine will start quickly and quietly, and accelerate normally. This action is similar to a gasoline-powered golf cart, but the starter/generator operation is much quieter and smoother.

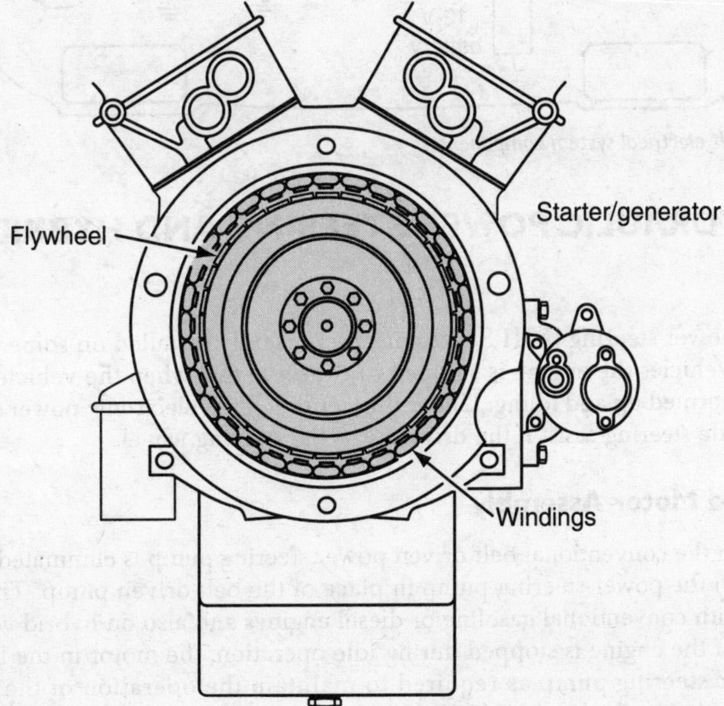

FIGURE 10-17 *Starter/generator.*

On many 42-V systems, the engine will stop running each time specific engine idling conditions occur. Stopping the engine during idle operation reduces fuel consumption and exhaust emissions. When the engine is running, the starter/generator supplies all the current demands of the electrical systems and components.

Introductory 42 V electrical systems will be a combination of 42 V and 14 V systems. The starter/generator will supply voltage to a computer that contains AC to DC and DC to DC converters. The AC to DC converter changes the AC from the starter/generator to DC voltage and supplies 36 V to 42 V to the 42 V loads and the 36 V battery(s) in the electrical system. The DC to DC converter changes 36 V to 12 V to 14 V and supplies this voltage to the 14 V loads and 12 V battery in the electrical system (Figure 10-18).

Although 42 V electrical systems have some advantages, they also present a number of challenges to automotive manufacturers. Perhaps the greatest challenge is the compatibility of some circuit components with the higher voltage. Compared to a 12 V system, a 42 V system has a greater tendency to cause arcing in relays and switches. Therefore, relays and switches must be redesigned to withstand this increased arcing. Some **hybrid vehicles** are presently equipped with a combination of 12 V and 42 V electrical systems.

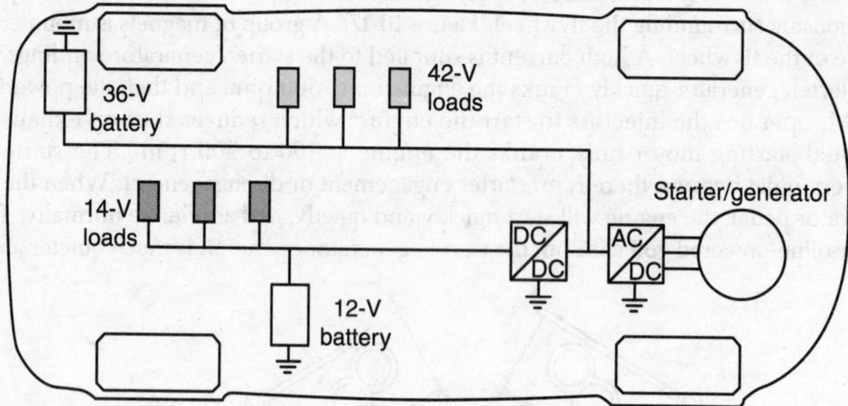

FIGURE 10-18 *42-volt electrical system components.*

ELECTROHYDRAULIC POWER STEERING AND HYBRID VEHICLES

Electrohydraulic power steering (EHPS) systems are presently installed on some hybrid vehicles. On most of these vehicles the engine is stopped to conserve fuel when the vehicle is standing still and the engine is warmed up and idling. Under this condition the electronic power steering is active and ready to provide steering assist if the driver turns the steering wheel.

EHPS Pump and Motor Assembly

In an EHPS system the conventional belt-driven power steering pump is eliminated, and an electric motor is coupled to the power steering pump in place of the belt-driven pump. The EHPS can be used on vehicles with conventional gasoline or diesel engines and also on hybrid vehicles with two sources of power. If the engine is stopped during idle operation, the motor in the EHPS continues to drive the power steering pump as required to maintain the operation of the power steering system. On some hybrid vehicles the EHPS motor is designed to operate on 36 V to 42 V. Other electrical systems on the vehicle such as the lights and accessories operate on 12 V.

The EHPS module assembly contains the power steering pump, electric pump drive motor, control module, and power steering fluid reservoir with filler cap (Figure 10-19). The usual high-pressure and low-pressure return hoses are connected from the pump to the steering gear. The EHPS module receives input signals directly from the digital steering wheel sensor in the steering column (Figure 10-20). Two wires are connected from the steering wheel position sensor to the EHPS module (Figure 10-21). These wires are referred to as steering wheel position signal A and signal B. The steering wheel position sensor signals inform the EHPS module regarding the amount and direction of the steering wheel rotation.

The EHPS module also receives input signals from the brake pedal position (BPP) sensor operated by the brake pedal linkage (Figure 10-22). The BPP sensor contains a potentiometer. A 5 V reference signal is sent from the EHPS module to the BPP sensor and a low reference or ground wire is also connected between these two components. As the brake pedal is depressed, an analog voltage signal is sent on the BPP sensor signal wire to the EHPS module in relation to the brake pedal movement.

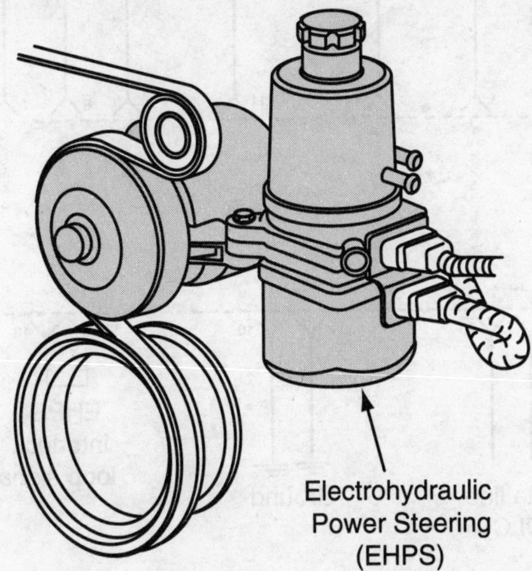

FIGURE 10-19 *Electrohydraulic power steering (EHPS) module.*

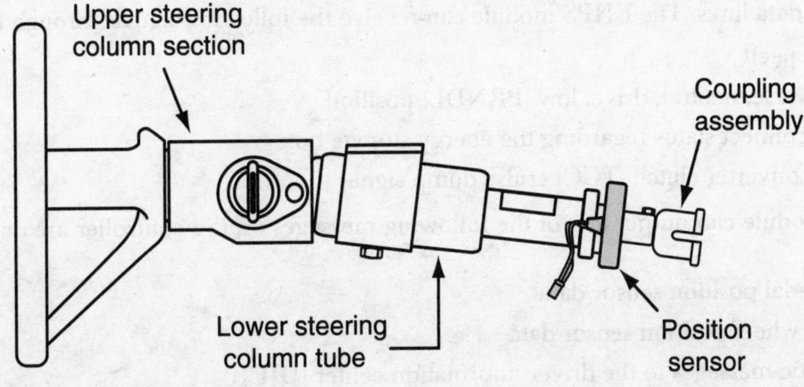

FIGURE 10-20 *Steering wheel position sensor.*

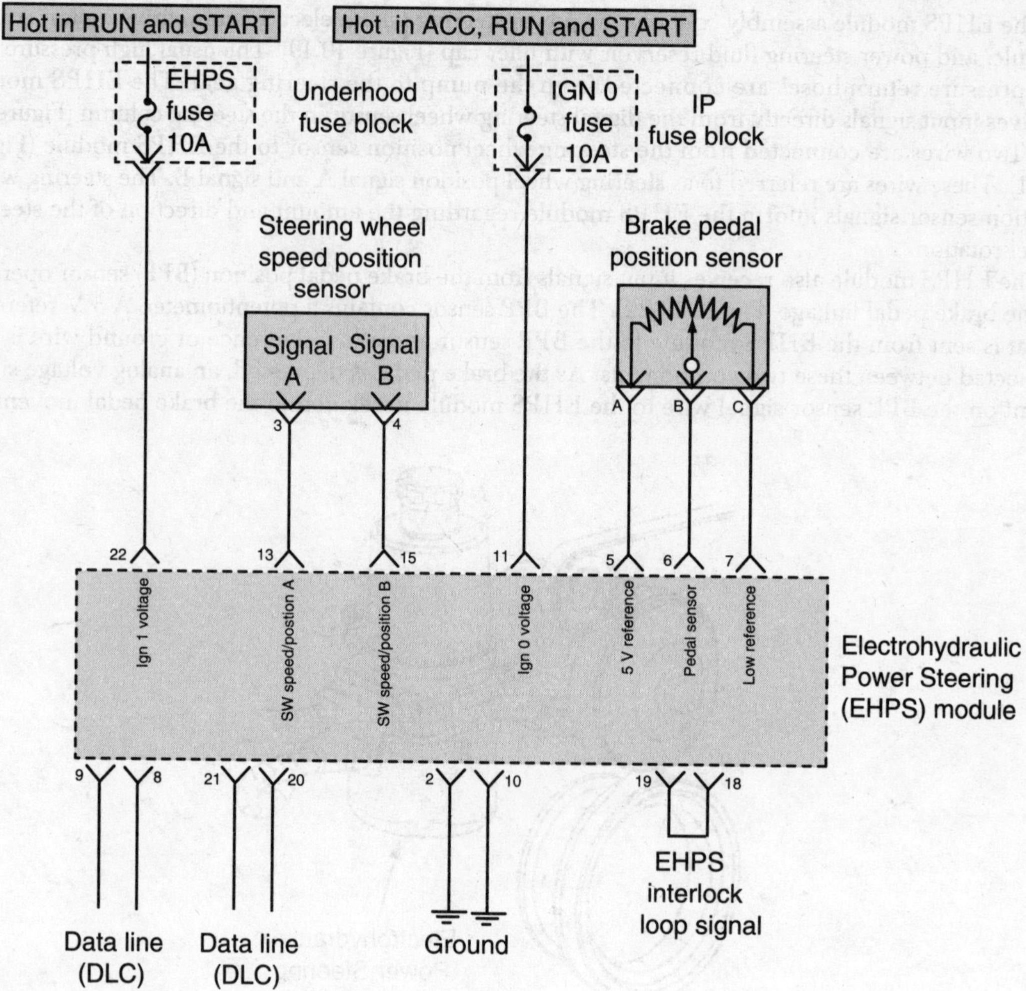

FIGURE 10-21 *EHPS inputs.*

The EHPS module also receives ignition RUN, START and ACCESSORY inputs. The EHPS module is interconnected to other computers on the vehicle and to the DLC via the local area network (LAN) bus or data links. The EHPS module can receive the following signals through the LAN bus:

1. Vehicle speed
2. Park, reverse, neutral, drive, low (PRNDL) position
3. Service connect status regarding the energy storage box
4. Torque converter clutch (TCC) cruise dump signal

The EHPS module can output any of the following messages on the controller area network (CAN) bus:

1. Brake pedal position sensor data
2. Steering wheel position sensor data
3. Diagnostic messages to the driver information center (DIC)
4. Diagnostic information requested by technicians via the scan tool
5. EHPS system status

Starter/Generator

A starter/generator is mounted in the flywheel housing and supplies high 3-phase AC voltage through the 3-phase cables to the starter generator control module (SGCM) mounted in the right side of the engine compartment (Figure 10-23). The starter/generator contains a rotor that is bolted to the engine crankshaft. A stator is mounted over the top of the rotor, and the stator is bolted to the rear of the engine block (Figure 10-24). When the engine is running, the rotor spins inside the stator. The stator contains high efficiency package-size coils formed by laser welding copper bars together rather than windings with copper wires. Current flow through the stator bars generates magnetic forces in the rotor that cause the rotor and the engine to turn. Conversely, when the engine is running the starter/generator is capable of producing a voltage to charge the batteries and supply current to the electrical system.

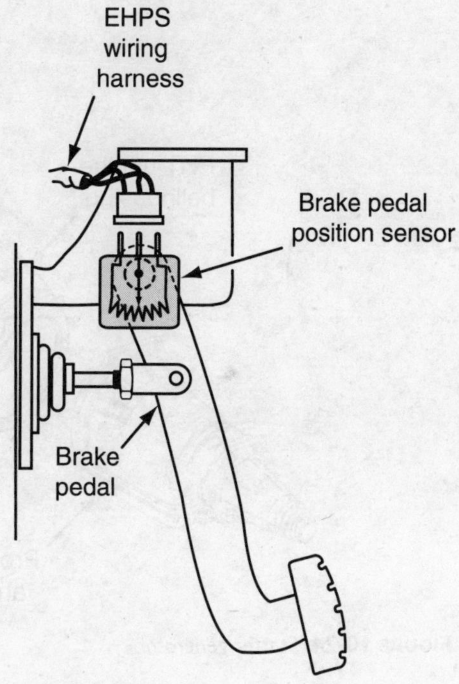

FIGURE 10-22 *Brake pedal position sensor.*

Starter/Generator Control Module

The starter/generator control module (SCGM) receives engine speed input signals directly from the powertrain control module (PCM) (Figure 10-25). Three terminals are connected from the stator in the starter/generator to the

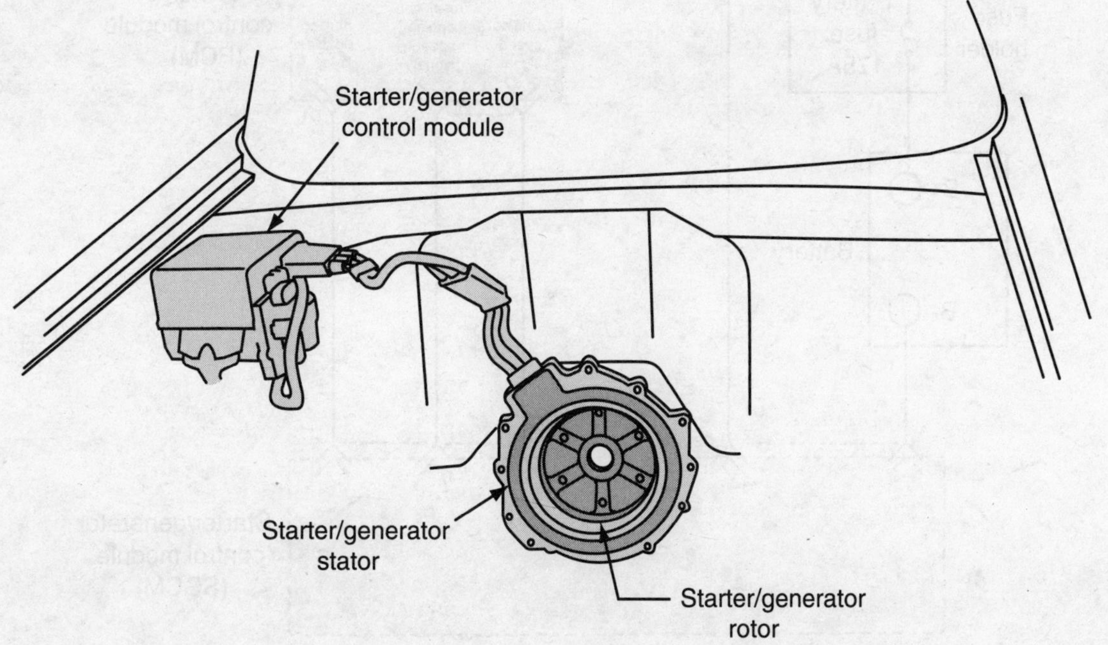

FIGURE 10-23 *Starter/generator and starter/generator control module (SGCM).*

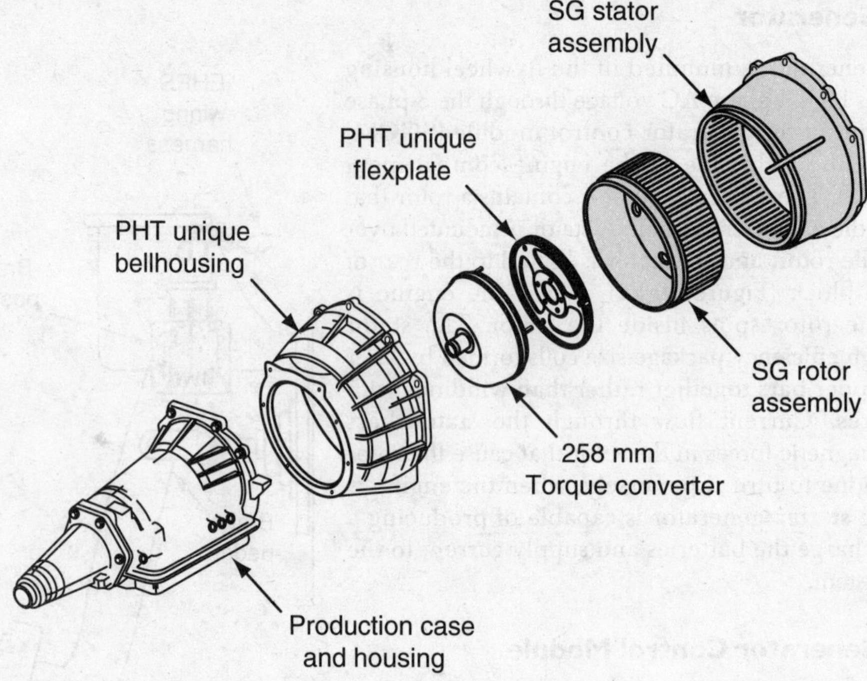

FIGURE 10-24 *Starter/generator.*

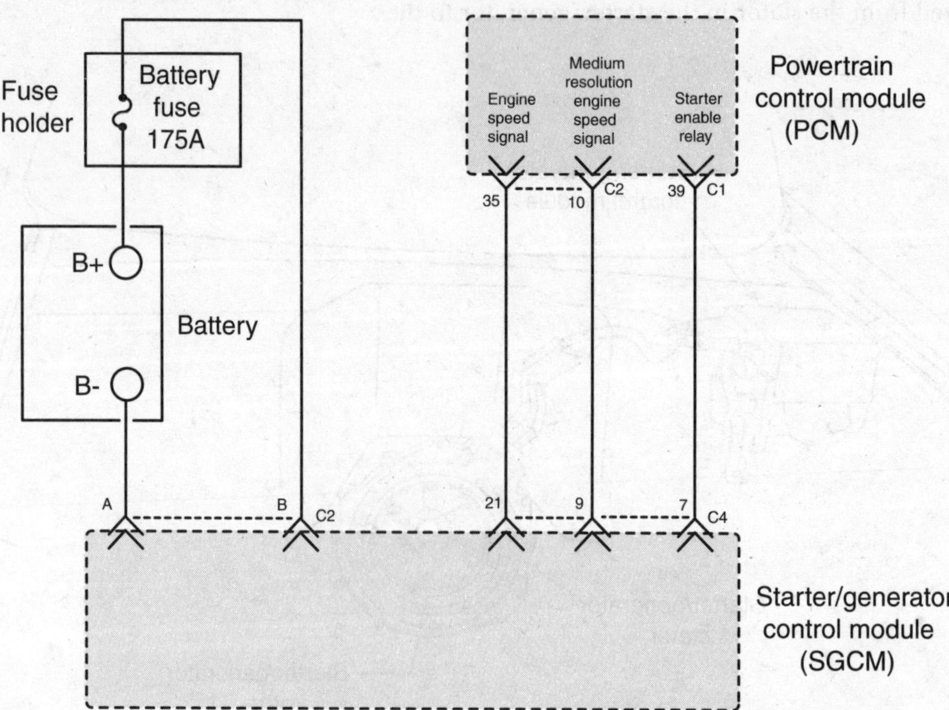

FIGURE 10-25 *Engine speed inputs from the PCM to the SGCM.*

SGCM mounted on the right side of the cowl. The SGCM uses the engine speed inputs and other input commands to perform these functions:

1. Performs bi-directional 36 V DC to 12 V DC electrical conversion between the 36 V DC system and the 12 V DC system for system energy management.
2. Performs bi-directional DC to AC electrical conversion between the 36 V electrical system and the 3-phase starter/generator. For example, if the engine is running, the SGCM converts the 3-phase voltage from the starter/generator to 42 V DC for the three batteries in the **energy storage box** mounted under the rear seat and 42 V components such as the EHPS pump motor (Figure 10-26 and Figure 10-27). When the engine is cranking, the SGCM converts 36 V DC from these three batteries to 3-phase AC voltage for the starter/generator so the starter/generator cranks the engine. Because of the starter/generator load on the batteries while cranking, the average DC voltage is 28 V during this function.
3. Supplies 120 V 60 Hz AC energy to the dual 120 V plugs in the energy storage box and truck box for operating 120 V electrical equipment when the engine is running. One plug is in the front of the energy storage box, and the other is in the right-rear corner of the truck box.

Hybrid Control Module

The hybrid control module (HCM) is mounted on the left side of the radiator shroud (Figure 10-28). The LAN bus interconnects the hybrid control module with the SGCM, PCM, EHPS module, energy storage box (ESB) module, and the DLC (Figure 10-29). The HCM receives inputs from 12 V battery positive voltage, and ignition ACC, RUN, and START voltage (Figure 10-30). The HCM also receives many inputs from other computers through the LAN bus. For example, the PCM receives a CRANK signal from the ignition switch and relays this signal through the LAN bus to the HCM (Figure 10-31). The HCM sends signals to the SGCM via the LAN bus to perform these functions:

1. Controls automatic engine starts and stops.
2. Controls the current flowing into the 14 V and 42 V batteries.
3. Enables and disables voltage to the 120 V outlets.
4. Enables and disables voltage to the starter/generator to provide engine damping under certain conditions.

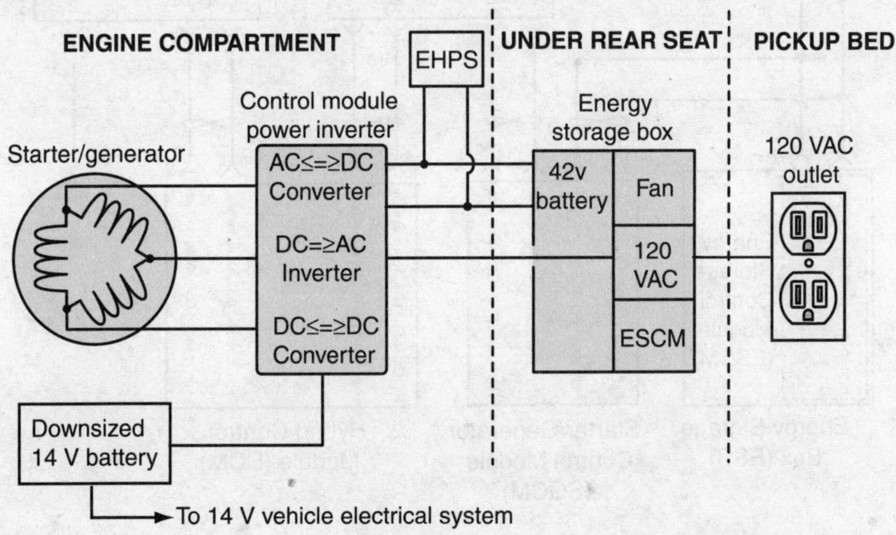

FIGURE 10-26 *SGCM internal voltage converters and external battery connections.*

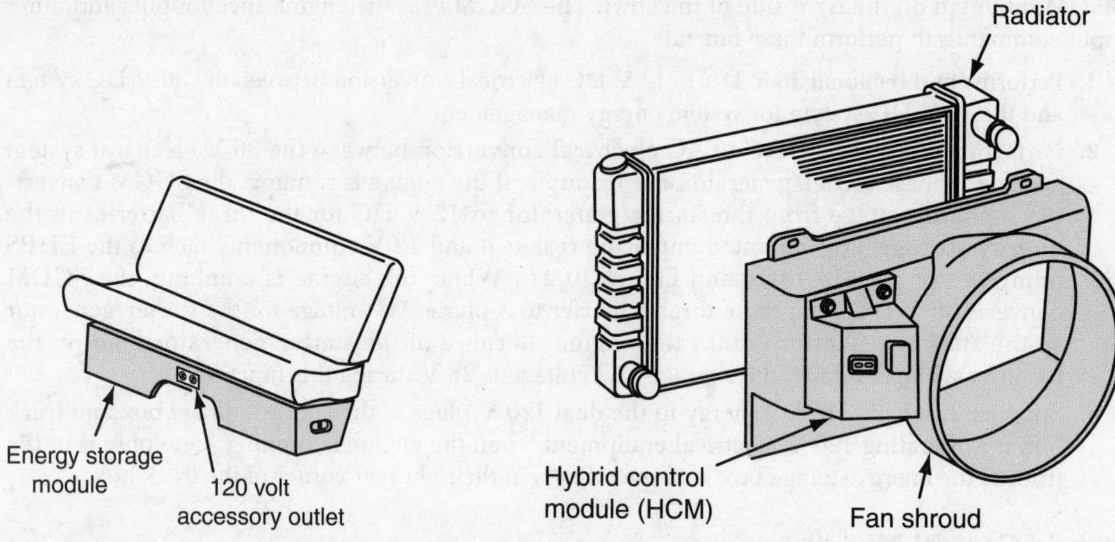

FIGURE 10-27 *Energy storage box with 120 V outlet.*

FIGURE 10-28 *Hybrid control module (HCM).*

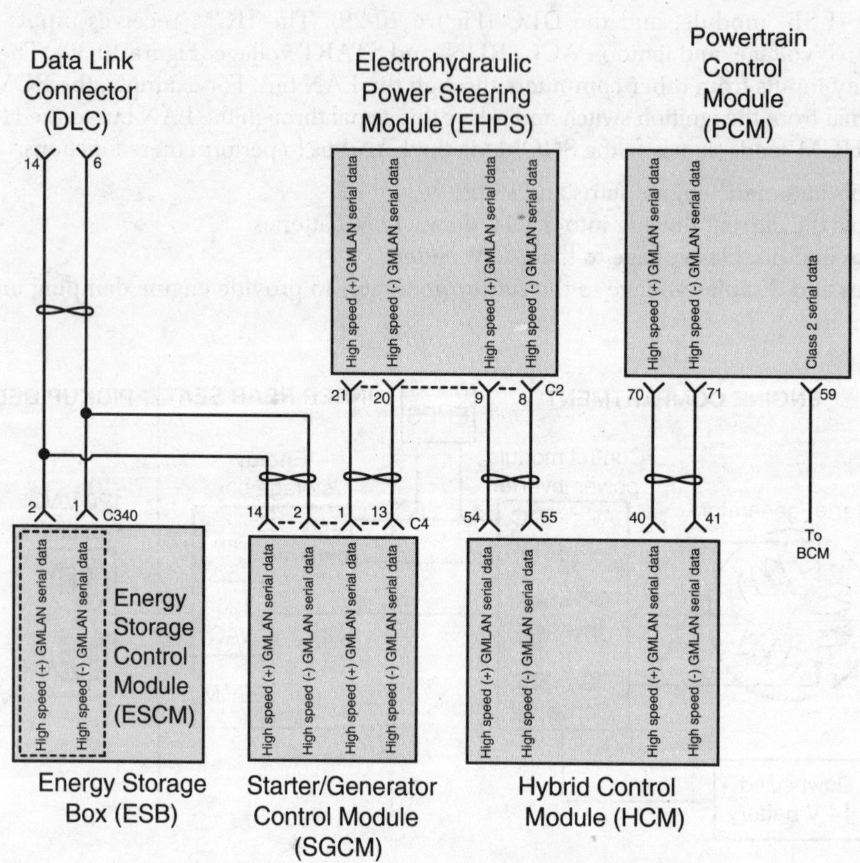

FIGURE 10-29 *The LAN bus interconnects the SGCM, PCM, EHPS module, ESB, and DLC.*

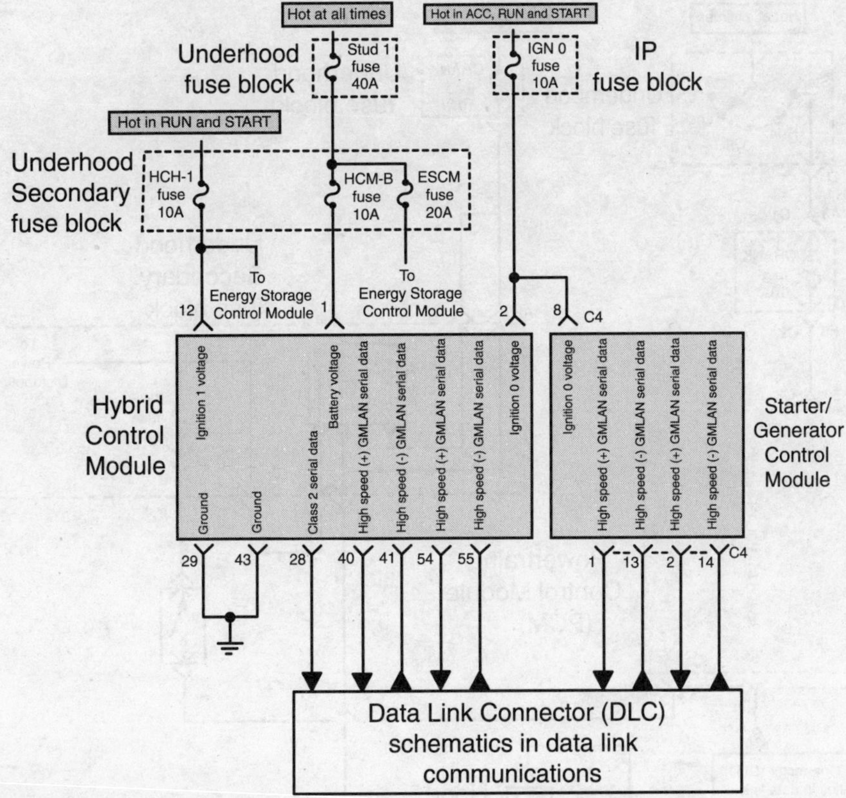

FIGURE 10-30 *Ignition inputs to the HCM.*

5. Supplies current to the starter/generator to control starter/generator and engine speed under certain conditions such as transmission downshifts.
6. Disables the starter/generator output voltage after air bag deployment.
7. Controls the auxiliary transmission pump, coolant pump, and power maintenance relay.

The HCM operates a transmission pump relay that supplies voltage to the auxiliary transmission pump mounted inside the transmission. When the HCM stops the engine with the vehicle stopped and the engine idling, the HCM starts the auxiliary transmission pump to maintain transmission pressures. This action provides very smooth engine and transmission operation when the accelerator pedal is depressed and the HCM restarts the engine.

The auxiliary coolant pump is located above the left side of the engine and is connected in the inlet heater hose. The HCM operates a relay that opens and closes the circuit to the auxiliary transmission pump. When the HCM commands the engine off during engine idle, the HCM closes the pump relay and operates the auxiliary coolant pump to supply coolant flow through the heater and maintain normal heater operation.

Energy Storage Box

The energy storage box contains these components:

1. Three 12 V Panasonic HV1255 V lead acid batteries
2. 2 – 120 V dual outlets in the ESB and truck box

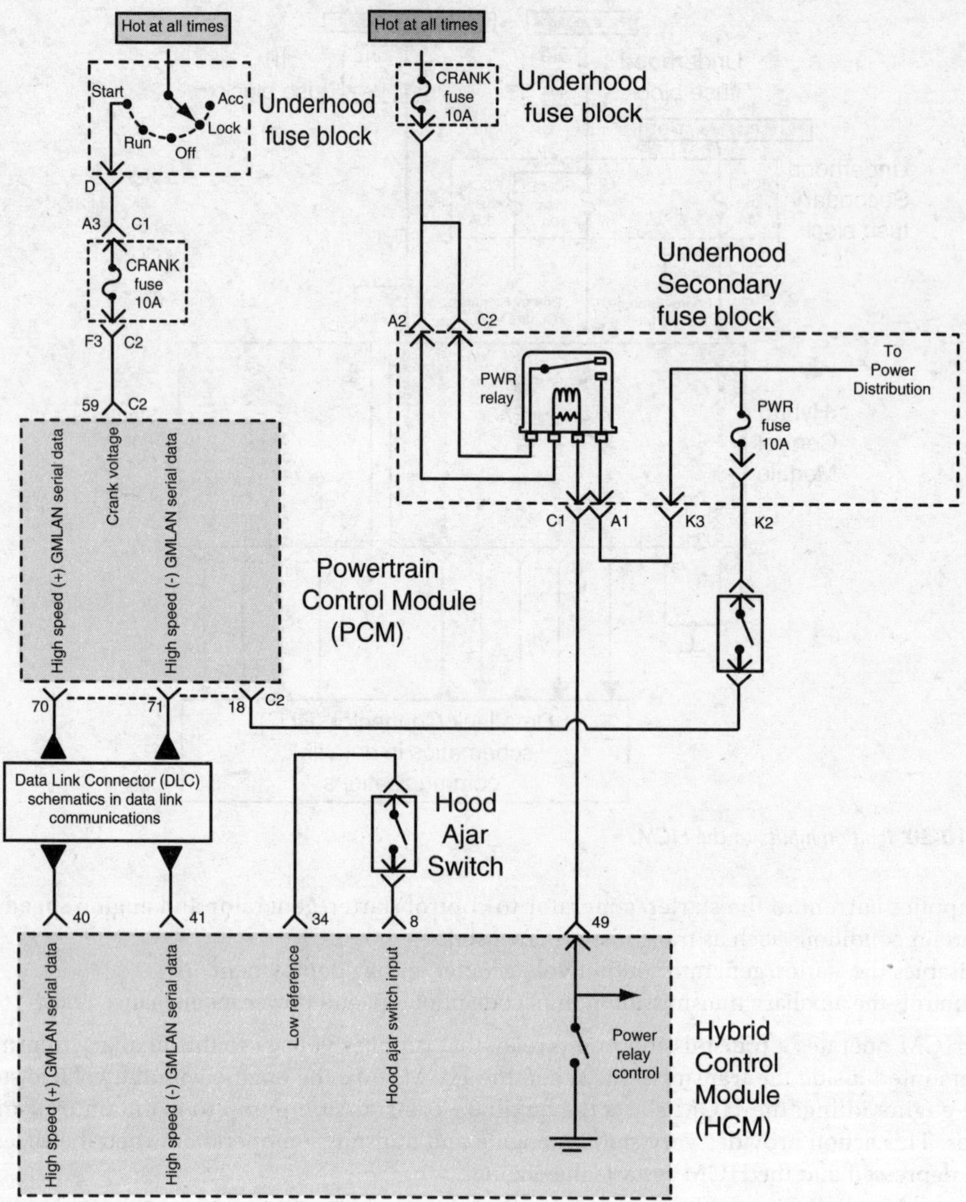

FIGURE 10-31 *The HCM receives inputs from the PCM through the LAN bus.*

3. Battery venting system
4. Energy storage control module (ESCM)
5. Service disconnect switch
6. 12 V ventilation fan and duct
7. Current sensor
8. 42 V wiring harness and connector
9. 12 V wiring harness and connector

The ESB performs the following functions:

1. Monitors battery temperature.
2. Stores electrical energy in the batteries.
3. Receives 42 V DC energy for battery charging.
4. Monitors and calculates energy transfer and status.
5. Determines the appropriate power mode.
6. Monitors and controls the ESB fan speed.
7. Provides venting of battery gases to the HVAC ventilation duct.
8. Monitors and controls the battery cut-off switch.
9. Provides a 42 V automatic disconnect in a side collision.
10. Sends information and fault data through the LAN network.

WARNING: When servicing the EHPS and hybrid electrical system, the higher voltages encountered in this system increase the risk of electrical shock. It is extremely important to follow the vehicle manufacturer's recommended service procedures when servicing any part of the hybrid electrical system. Severe electrical shock and system component damage can occur if this precaution is not observed.

The hybrid electrical system has a number of built-in safety features. When servicing the ESB, a panel must be removed from the end of the ESB to gain access to the battery disconnect key. This key must be turned to the horizontal position to disconnect the batteries prior to ESB service or diagnostic procedures (Figure 10-32).

When the vehicle hood is opened, a hood ajar switch sends a voltage signal to the HCM. This signal causes the HCM to cancel the starter/generator voltage output.

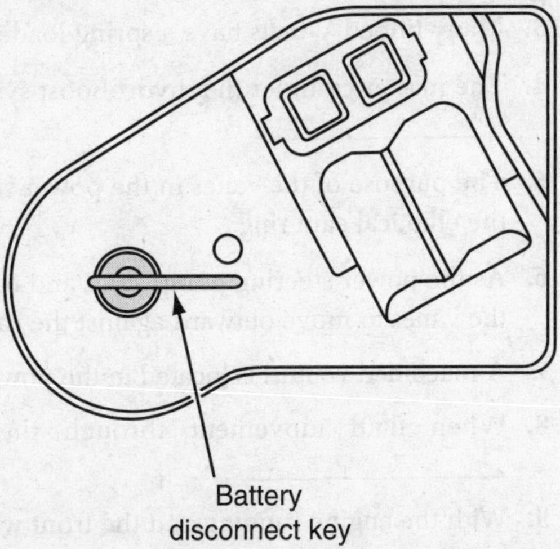

FIGURE 10-32 *Battery disconnect key in the ESB.*

REVIEW QUESTIONS

Short Answer Essays

1. Describe the proper position of a V-belt in a pulley.
2. Explain two advantages of a ribbed V-belt compared with a conventional V-belt.
3. List two possible locations for mounting a rack and pinion steering gear.
4. List the most common applications for rack and pinion and integral steering gears.
5. Describe how the brake boost pressure is obtained in a hydroboost power steering system.

6. Explain how the fluid pressure is produced in a vane-type power steering pump.
7. List the forces that move the flow control valve toward the closed position in a power steering pump.
8. Describe the operation of a venturi.
9. Explain the operation of the flow control valve when the steering wheel is turned.
10. Describe the operation of the power steering pump when the steering wheel is rotated all the way to the right or left until the front wheels contact the stops.

Fill-in-the-Blanks

1. The lower edge of a V-belt should never contact the ________________ ________________.
2. Excessive belt wear occurs if pulleys are ________________.
3. Many ribbed V-belts have a spring-loaded ________________.
4. The master cylinder in a hydroboost system does not have a conventional ________________ ________________.
5. The purpose of the vanes in the power steering pump rotor is to ________________ the rotor in the elliptical cam ring.
6. As the power steering pump shaft and rotor turn, ________________ ________________ causes the vanes to move outward against the cam ring.
7. A machined venturi is located in the power steering pump ________________ ________________.
8. When fluid movement through the venturi increases, the pressure in the venturi ________________.
9. With the engine running and the front wheels straight ahead, the power steering pump pressure is ________________.
10. The pressure relief ball in a power steering pump is forced open when the front wheels are turned against the ________________.

Multiple Choice

1. The most likely result of a ribbed power steering V-belt that is bottomed in the pulley is:
   A. Belt slipping.
   B. Belt breaking.
   C. Belt contamination.
   D. Wear on the power steering pump pulley.

2. All of these statements about a ribbed V-belt are true EXCEPT:
   A. A ribbed V-belt can be used to drive all the belt-driven components.
   B. The back side or a ribbed V-belt can drive one component.
   C. A ribbed V-belt is narrower than a conventional V-belt.
   D. A ribbed V-belt can have an automatic belt tensioner.

3. A hydroboost power steering system:
   A. Is used on many small front-wheel-drive vehicles.
   B. Uses pressure from the power steering pump to provide brake boost.
   C. Has a conventional vacuum brake booster.
   D. Has a very high capacity power steering pump.

4. In a conventional power steering pump:
   A. The cam ring rotates with the rotor and shaft.
   B. The inner cam ring surface is perfectly round.
   C. The rotor shaft and vanes rotate inside the cam ring.
   D. The pressure relief valve is opened by pressure at the pump inlet.

5. All of these statements about integral-type power steering pump sealing are true EXCEPT:
   A. A large O-ring seal is positioned between the reservoir and the pump housing.
   B. A lip seal on the pump drive shaft prevents oil leaks around the shaft.
   C. Lip seals are mounted on bolt fittings on the back of the reservoir.
   D. The cap and dipstick provide a seal on the top of the reservoir neck.

6. A power steering system experiences repeated belt failures with normal power steering system operation. The most likely cause of this problem is:
   A. A misaligned power steering pump pulley.
   B. A loose power steering pump belt.
   C. Low fluid level in the power steering reservoir.
   D. A worn cam ring in the power steering pump.

7. During normal power steering pump operation:
   A. The flow control valve spring moves this valve toward the open position.
   B. The fluid pressure from the outlet fitting venturi moves the flow control valve toward the open position.
   C. Pump flow increases as the engine speed increases.
   D. The pressure relief valve opens when the engine speed is increased with the front wheels straight ahead.

8. All of these statements about power steering pump design and operation are true EXCEPT:
   A. An increase in fluid movement through the outlet fitting venturi causes a pressure decrease in the venturi.
   B. An increase in the flow control valve opening allows more fluid to return to the pump inlet.
   C. The rotor is attached to the pump shaft and must rotate with this shaft.
   D. Fluid pressure from the pump vanes moves the flow control valve toward the closed position.

9. When discussing power steering pump operation:
   A. If the engine is idling and the front wheels are straight ahead, the flow control valve is near the closed position.
   B. When the engine is running at 2,000 rpm and the steering wheel is turned fully to the right, the pressure relief ball is closed.
   C. When the pressure relief ball is open, most of the pump flow is directed through the return hose to the pump inlet.
   D. If the pressure relief ball sticks closed, pump pressure becomes very low when the front wheels are turned fully to the right.

10. A vehicle experiences repeated ruptures of the high-pressure power steering hose. The most likely cause of this problem is:

A. A pressure relief ball sticking closed.
B. A flow control valve sticking open.
C. Worn pump vanes and cam ring.
D. A partially restricted power steering return hose.

RECIRCULATING BALL STEERING GEARS

11

Upon completion and review of this chapter, you should be able to:

- Define the purpose of a steering gear.
- Explain the advantage of a recirculating ball steering gear compared with earlier worm and roller or cam and lever steering gears.
- Describe the purpose of the worm shaft preload adjustment.
- Explain how the sector shaft is rotated in a manual recirculating ball steering gear.
- Describe the purpose of the interference fit between the sector shaft teeth and the recirculating ball teeth, and explain how this fit is obtained.
- Describe the difference between constant ratio sector teeth and variable ratio sector teeth in a recirculating ball steering gear, and explain the advantage of the variable ratio sector teeth.
- Define gear ratio.
- Explain the term "faster" steering as it relates to steering gears.
- Describe the power steering fluid movement in a power recirculating ball steering gear with the engine running and the front wheels straight ahead.
- Describe the power steering fluid movement in a power recirculating ball steering gear during a left turn.

- Describe the power steering fluid movement during a right turn.
- Explain how kickback action is prevented in a power recirculating ball steering gear.

INTRODUCTION

The purpose of the steering gear box is to provide a mechanical advantage that allows the driver to turn the front wheels with a reasonable amount of effort. In the early 1900s, steering gears were a **worm and gear** or **worm and sector design**. These steering gears gave the driver a mechanical advantage to turn the front wheels, but they created a lot of friction.

The **Ross cam and lever steering gear** was introduced in 1923. The cam in this gear was a spiral groove machined into the end of the steering shaft. A pin on the pitman shaft was mounted in the spiral groove in the steering shaft. When the steering wheel and shaft were turned, the pin was forced to move, and this action rotated the pitman shaft. When a front wheel struck a road irregularity, this steering gear design prevented serious **kickback** on the steering wheel. However, this steering gear design still created a considerable amount of friction and required higher steering effort.

In the mid-1920s, Saginaw Steering Division of General Motors Corporation developed the **worm and roller steering gear**. In this steering gear, the **sector** became a roller, which greatly reduced friction and steering effort. The Saginaw worm and roller steering gear was the forerunner of the recirculating ball steering gear that has been widely used on rear-wheel-drive cars for many years.

MANUAL RECIRCULATING BALL STEERING GEARS

Design and Operation

In a recirculating ball steering gear, the steering wheel and shaft are connected to the **worm shaft**. Ball bearings support both ends of the worm shaft in the steering gear housing. A seal above the upper worm shaft bearing prevents oil leaks, and an adjusting plug is provided on the upper worm shaft bearing to adjust **worm shaft bearing preload**. Proper preloading of the worm shaft bearing is necessary to eliminate **worm shaft endplay** and to prevent **steering gear free play** and **vehicle wander**. A ball nut is mounted over the worm shaft, and internal threads or grooves on the ball nut match the grooves on the worm shaft. Ball bearings run in ball nut and worm shaft grooves (Figure 11-1).

When the worm shaft is rotated by the steering wheel, the ball nut is moved up or down on the worm shaft. The gear teeth on the ball nut are meshed with matching gear teeth on the **pitman shaft sector**. Therefore, ball nut movement causes pitman shaft sector rotation. Since the pitman shaft sector is connected through the pitman arm and steering linkage to the front wheels, the front wheels are turned by the pitman shaft sector. The lower end of the pitman shaft sector is usually supported by a bushing or a needle bearing in the steering gear housing. A bushing in the side cover supports the upper end of this shaft.

When the front wheels are straight ahead, an **interference fit** exists between the sector shaft teeth and ball nut teeth. This interference fit eliminates **gear tooth backlash** when the front wheels are straight ahead and provides the driver with a positive feel of the road. Proper axial adjustment of the sector shaft is necessary to obtain the necessary interference fit between the sector shaft and worm shaft teeth. A sector shaft adjuster screw is threaded into the side cover to provide axial sector shaft adjustment (Figure 11-2).

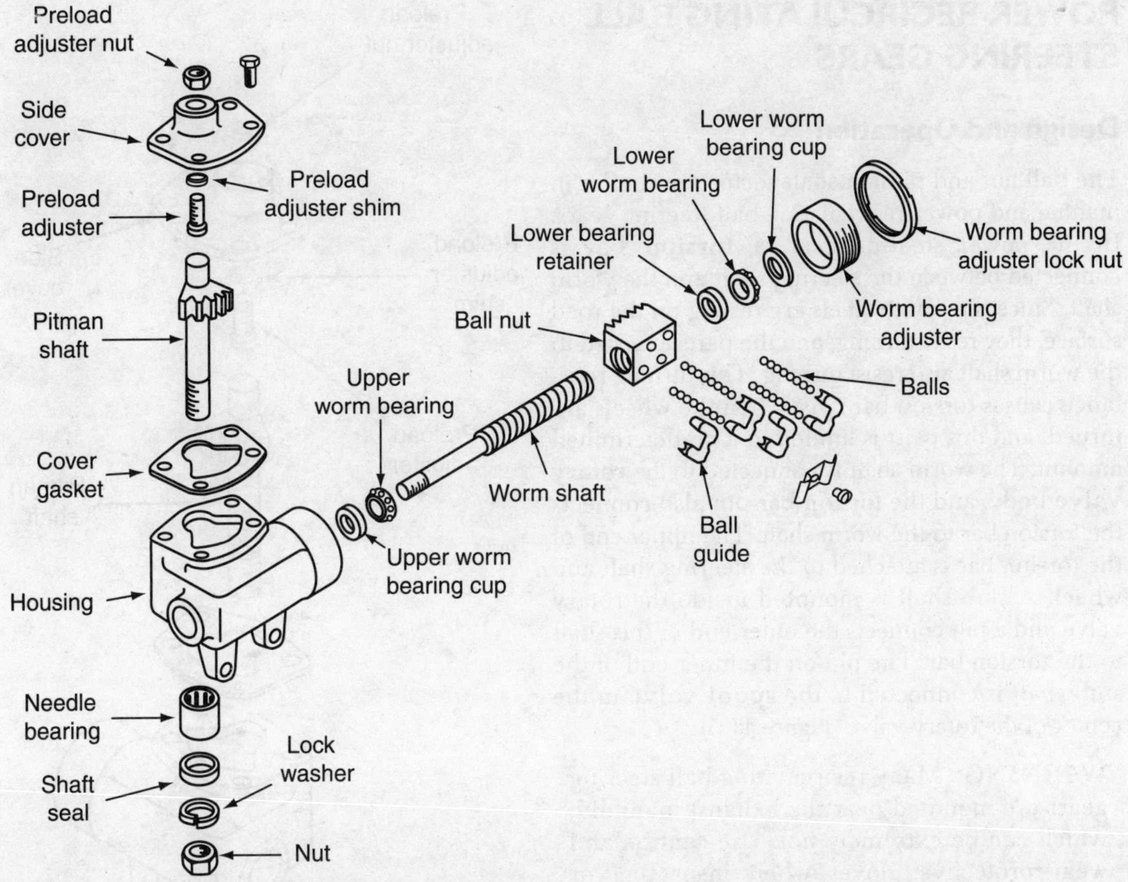

FIGURE 11-1 *Manual recirculating ball steering gear design.*

Manual recirculating ball steering gears have sector gear teeth designed to provide a constant ratio, whereas power recirculating ball steering gears usually have sector gear teeth with a variable ratio (Figure 11-3). The sector gear teeth have equal lengths in a constant ratio steering gear, but the center sector gear tooth is longer compared with the other teeth in a variable ratio gear. The variable ratio steering gear varies the amount of mechanical advantage provided by the steering gear in relation to steering wheel position. This variable ratio provides **faster steering**. The steering **gear ratio** in a constant ratio manual steering gear is usually 15:1 or 16:1, whereas the average variable ratio steering gear ratio may be 13:1. When the same types of steering gears are compared, a higher numerical ratio provides reduced steering effort and increased steering wheel movement in relation to the amount of front wheel movement.

Many recirculating ball steering gears are bolted to the frame with hard steel bolts (Figure 11-4). These bolts must be tightened to the vehicle manufacturer's specified torque.

CAUTION: Hard steel bolts can be used for steering gear mounting. Bolt hardness is indicated by the number of ribs on the bolt head. Harder bolts have five, six, or seven ribs on the bolt heads. Never substitute softer steel bolts in place of the original harder bolts, because these softer bolts may break, allowing the steering gear box to detach from the frame. This action results in a loss of steering control.

POWER RECIRCULATING BALL STEERING GEARS

Design and Operation

The ball nut and pitman shaft sector are similar in manual and power recirculating ball steering gears. In the power steering gear, a **torsion bar** is connected between the steering shaft and the worm shaft. Since the front wheels are resting on the road surface, they resist turning, and the parts attached to the worm shaft also resist turning. This turning resistance causes torsion bar twist when the wheels are turned, and this twist is limited to a predetermined amount. The worm shaft is connected to the **rotary valve** body, and the torsion bar pin also connects the torsion bar to the worm shaft. The upper end of the torsion bar is attached to the steering shaft and wheel. A stub shaft is mounted inside the rotary valve and a pin connects the outer end of this shaft to the torsion bar. The pin on the inner end of the stub shaft is connected to the **spool valve** in the center of the rotary valve (Figure 11-5).

WARNING: Many recirculating ball steering gears are mounted near the exhaust manifold, which can be extremely hot. Use caution and wear protective gloves when inspecting or servicing the steering gear to avoid burns to hands and arms.

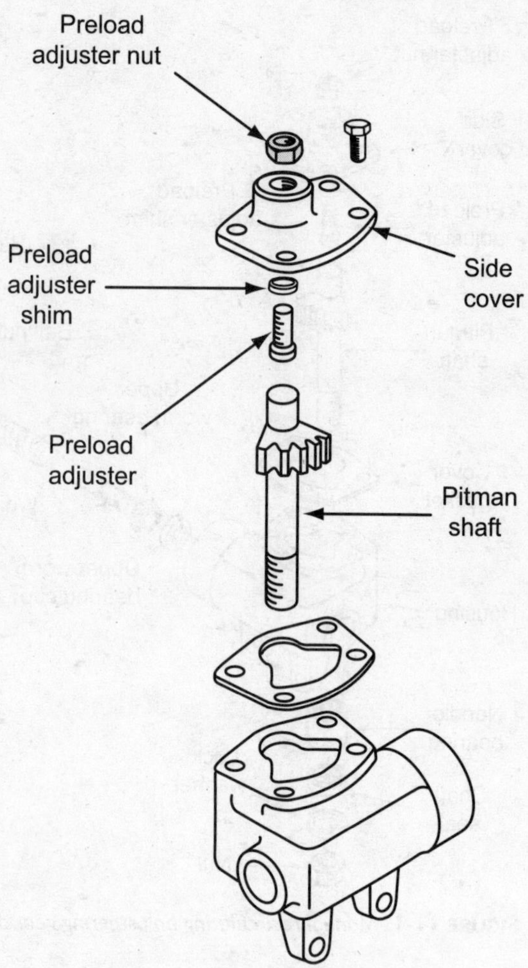

FIGURE 11-2 *Sector shaft adjusting nut.*

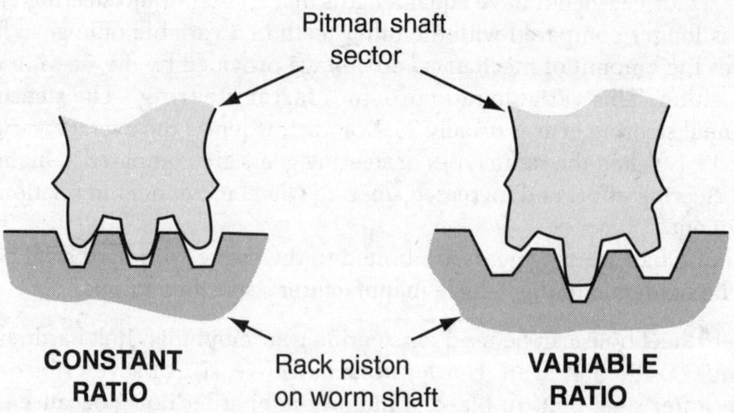

FIGURE 11-3 *Constant and variable ratio steering gears.*

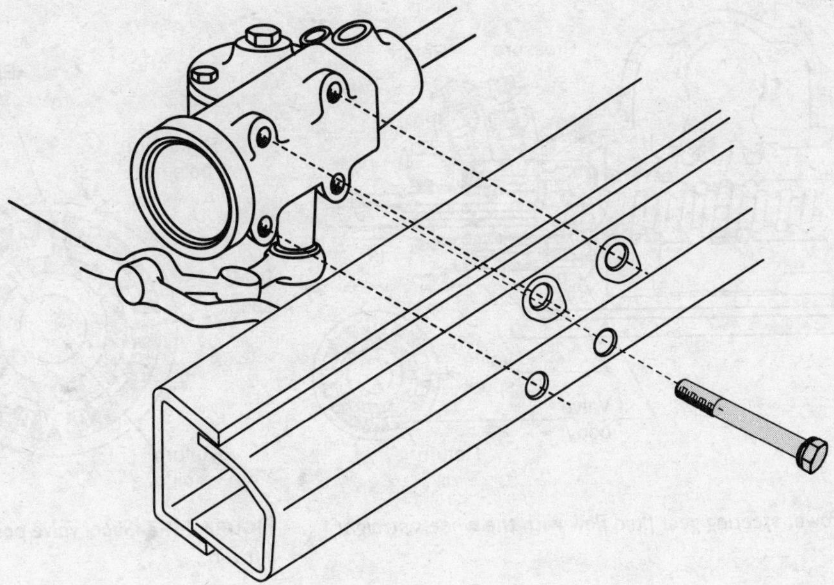

FIGURE 11-4 *Steering gear mounting on the vehicle frame.*

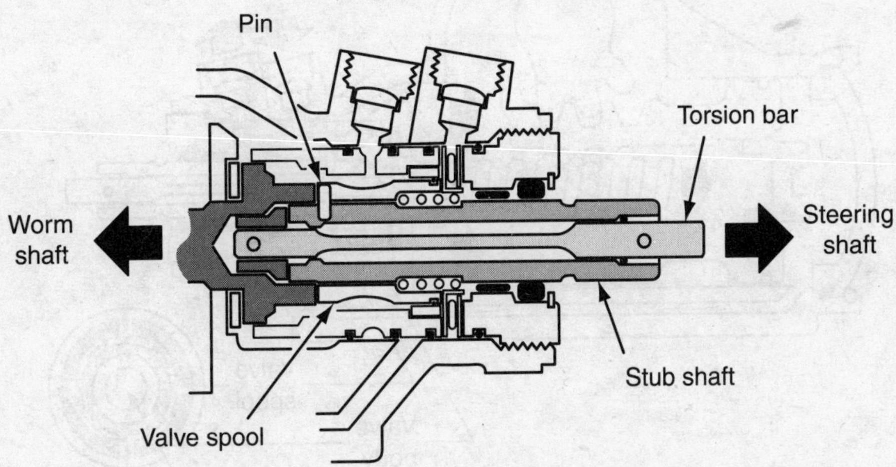

FIGURE 11-5 *Torsion bar and stub shaft.*

When the car is driven with the front wheels straight ahead, oil flows from the power steering pump through the spool valve, rotary valve, and low-pressure return line to the pump inlet (Figure 11-6). In the straight-ahead steering gear position, oil pressure is equal on both sides of the recirculating ball piston, and the oil acts as a cushion that prevents road shocks from reaching the steering wheel.

If the driver makes a left turn, torsion bar twist moves the valve spool inside the rotary valve body so that oil flow is directed through the rotary valve to the left-turn holes in the spool valve (Figure 11-7). Since power steering fluid is directed from these left-turn holes to the upper side of the recirculating ball piston (Figure 11-8), this hydraulic pressure on the piston assists the driver in turning the wheels to the left.

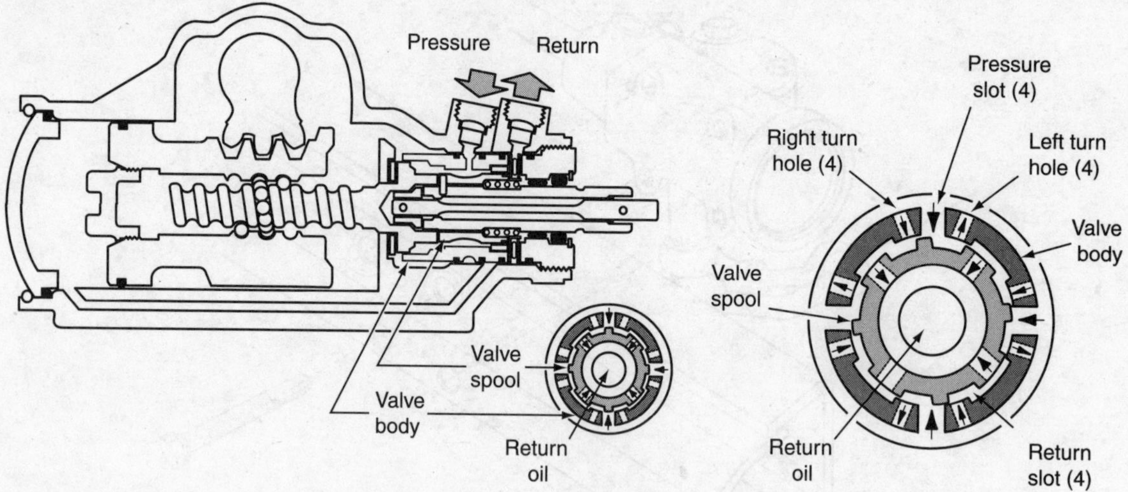

FIGURE 11-6 *Power steering gear fluid flow with the wheels straight ahead.*

FIGURE 11-7 *Spool valve position during a left turn.*

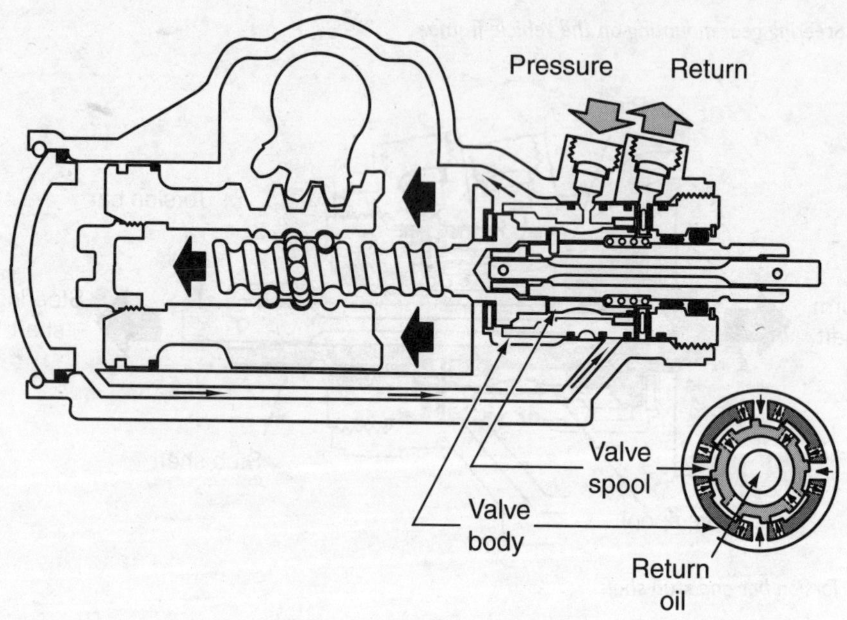

FIGURE 11-8 *Power steering gear fluid flow during a left turn.*

When the driver makes a right turn, torsion bar twist moves the spool valve so that oil flows through the spool valve, rotary valve, and a passage in the housing to the pressure chamber at the lower end of the ball nut piston (Figure 11-9). During a right turn, hydraulic pressure applied to the lower end of the recirculating ball piston helps the driver turn the wheels.

During a turn, if a front wheel strikes a bump and the front wheels are driven in the direction opposite the turning direction, the recirculating ball piston tends to move against the hydraulic pressure and force oil back out the pressure inlet port. This action would create a kickback on the steering wheel, but a poppet valve in the pressure inlet fitting closes and prevents kickback action.

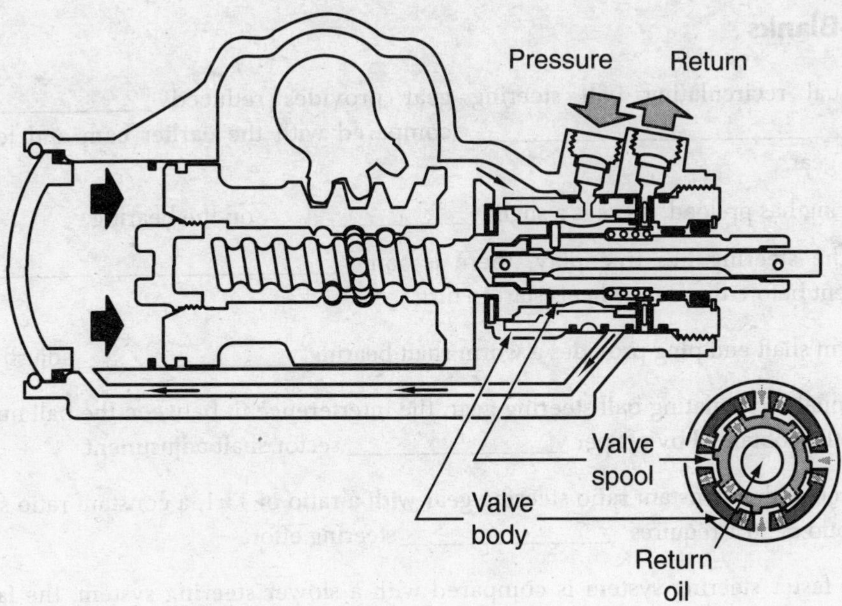

FIGURE 11-9 *Power steering gear fluid flow during a right turn.*

REVIEW QUESTIONS

Short Answer Essays

1. Describe the advantage of the manual recirculating ball steering gear compared with the previous cam and lever steering gear, and explain how this advantage is obtained.
2. Explain three purposes of the worm shaft preload adjustment.
3. Explain the purpose of the interference fit between the ball nut teeth and the sector shaft teeth in a manual recirculating ball steering gear, and describe how this interference fit is obtained.
4. Explain the difference in design between constant ratio and variable ratio sector shaft teeth.
5. Define the term faster steering.
6. Define steering gear ratio, and explain the effect of this ratio on steering effort with a manual recirculating ball steering gear.
7. Describe the flow of power steering fluid with the engine running and the front wheels straight ahead in a power recirculating ball steering gear.
8. Describe how torsion bar twist occurs in a recirculating ball steering gear.
9. Explain the purpose of torsion bar twist in a power recirculating ball steering gear.
10. Explain how kickbacks are prevented in a power recirculating ball steering gear.

Fill-in-the-Blanks

1. A manual recirculating ball steering gear provides reduced ________________ and ________________ ________________ compared with the earlier cam and lever manual steering gear.
2. If a bearing has preload, there is a slight ________________ on the bearing.
3. When the steering has free play, there is some ________________ ________________ movement before the front wheels start to turn.
4. The worm shaft end plug provides a worm shaft bearing ________________ adjustment.
5. In a manual recirculating ball steering gear, the interference fit between the ball nut and sector shaft teeth is obtained by proper ________________ sector shaft adjustment.
6. Compared with a constant ratio steering gear with a ratio of 13:1, a constant ratio steering gear with a ratio of 16:1 requires ________________ steering effort.
7. When a faster steering system is compared with a slower steering system, the faster system provides more front wheel movement with ________________ steering wheel rotation.
8. A variable ratio steering gear varies the amount of ________________ ________________ in relation to steering wheel position.
9. In a power recirculating ball steering gear with the front wheels straight ahead and the engine running, the fluid on each side of the recirculating ball piston helps prevent ________________ ________________ from reaching the steering wheel.
10. In a power recirculating ball steering gear during a turn, the ________________ ________________ movement directs the power steering fluid pressure to the appropriate side of the recirculating ball piston.

Multiple Choice

1. In a power recirculating ball steering gear, kickback is prevented by:
   A. The preload between the ball nut teeth and sector gear teeth.
   B. The bending of the torsion bar.
   C. A poppet valve in the pressure inlet fitting.
   D. The flexible coupling in the steering shaft.
2. When the worm shaft and bearings are properly installed and adjusted in a power recirculating ball steering gear:
   A. The worm shaft bearings should be preloaded.
   B. The worm shaft should have the specified end-play.
   C. The worm shaft endplay should be eliminated without any preload on the bearings.
   D. There must be an interference fit between the ball nut teeth and the worm shaft teeth.

3. All of these statements about recirculating ball steering gears are true EXCEPT:
   A. The steering gear provides a mechanical advantage.
   B. The steering gear reduces steering effort.
   C. Some early model steering gears had a worm and sector design.
   D. Ross cam and lever steering gears provided a very low internal friction.

4. A typical steering gear ratio in a manual steering gear is:
   A. 16:1.
   B. 18:1.
   C. 19:1.
   D. 22:1.

5. When comparing manual recirculating ball steering gears a higher numerical ratio provides:
   A. Increased steering effort.
   B. Increased steering wheel movement in relation to front wheel movement.
   C. Reduced kickback force on the steering wheel.
   D. Improved steering control.

6. In a manual recirculating ball steering gear:
   A. The interference fit between the sector shaft teeth and ball nut teeth is present when the front wheels are straight ahead.
   B. The proper interference fit between the sector shaft teeth and ball nut teeth is obtained by radial sector shaft movement.
   C. The interference fit between the sector shaft teeth and ball nut teeth becomes tighter when the front wheels are turned to the right or left.
   D. Tightening the worm shaft adjusting plug tightens the interference fit between the sector shaft teeth and ball nut teeth.

7. All of these statements about steering gear ratios are true EXCEPT:
   A. When a steering gear with a 15:1 ratio is compared with a steering gear with a 13:1 ratio, the gear with the 15:1 ratio requires more steering wheel rotation to turn the front wheels.
   B. When a steering gear with a 15:1 ratio is compared with a steering gear with a 13:1 ratio, the gear with the 15:1 ratio provides reduced steering effort.
   C. When a steering gear with a 15:1 ratio is compared with a steering gear with a 13:1 ratio, the gear with the 15:1 ratio may be called a faster steering gear.
   D. The 13:1 steering gear ratio may be used on a smaller, lighter car and the 15:1 steering gear ratio may be used on a larger, heavier vehicle.

8. In power recirculating ball steering gears:
   A. A variable ratio steering gear has sector shaft teeth with equal lengths.
   B. A variable ratio steering gear has a constant mechanical advantage regardless of steering wheel position.
   C. The torsion bar is connected between the steering shaft and the sector shaft.
   D. During a turn, power steering fluid is directed to the proper end of the ball nut piston by spool valve movement.

9. While driving with the front wheels straight ahead with a power recirculating ball steering gear:
   A. The torsion bar is twisted to move the spool valve inside the valve body.
   B. The fluid pressure is higher on the upper side of the ball nut piston compared with the lower side.
   C. The fluid pressure on each side of the ball nut piston cushions road shocks from reaching the steering wheel.
   D. The return passage from the steering gear valve body to the power steering pump is nearly closed.

10. When a vehicle with a power recirculating ball steering gear is making a right turn:
    A. Torsion bar twisting and spool valve movement has moved the spool valve and aligned the pressure ports with the right-turn ports.
    B. Fluid pressure is supplied to the upper side of the ball nut piston.
    C. Fluid pressure is exhausted from the lower side of the ball nut piston.
    D. Fluid pressure gradually leaks past the ball nut piston to reduce steering assist during long, gradual turns.

Rack and Pinion Steering Gears

12

Upon completion and review of this chapter, you should be able to:

- Explain the advantages of a rack and pinion steering system compared to a recirculating ball steering gear and parallelogram steering linkage.
- Describe how the tie-rods are connected to the rack.
- Explain the purpose of the rack bearing and adjuster plug.
- List two possible mounting positions for the rack and pinion steering gear.
- Describe the fluid movement in a rack and pinion steering gear during a right turn.
- Describe the fluid movement in a rack and pinion steering gear during a left turn.
- Explain the operation of the spool valve and rotary valve.
- Describe the operation of the power rack and pinion steering gear when hydraulic pressure is not available.
- Explain the purpose of the breather tube.
- List the main differences between a Saginaw and a TRW power rack and pinion steering gear.
- Explain the advantages of an electronic variable orifice (EVO) steering system.

- List the input sensors in an EVO steering system.
- Describe the driving conditions when an EVO steering system provides increased power steering assistance.
- Explain the operation of a rack-drive electronic power steering system during right and left turns.
- Explain the operation of the steering shaft torque sensor in a column-drive electronic power steering system.

INTRODUCTION

During the late 1970s and 1980s, the domestic automotive industry converted much of its production from larger rear-wheel-drive (RWD) cars to smaller, lightweight, and more fuel efficient front-wheel-drive (FWD) cars. These FWD cars required smaller, lighter components wherever possible. Manual and power rack and pinion steering gears are lighter and more compact than the recirculating ball steering gears and parallelogram steering linkages used on most RWD cars. Therefore, rack and pinion steering gears are ideally suited to these compact FWD cars.

Steering systems have not escaped the electronics revolution. Many cars are presently equipped with electronic variable orifice (EVO) steering, which provides greater power assistance during low-speed cornering and parking for increased driver convenience. Some cars are now equipped with electronic power steering. In these systems, an electric motor in the steering gear provides steering assist.

MANUAL RACK AND PINION STEERING GEAR MAIN COMPONENTS

Rack

The **rack** is a toothed bar that slides back and forth in a metal housing. The steering gear housing is mounted in a fixed position on the front crossmember or on the firewall. The rack takes the place of the idler and pitman arms in a parallelogram steering system and maintains the proper height of the tie-rods so they are parallel to the lower control arms. The rack may be compared to the center link in a parallelogram steering linkage. Bushings support the rack in the steering gear housing. Sideways movement of the rack pulls or pushes the tie-rods and steers the front wheels (Figure 12-1).

Pinion

The **pinion** is a toothed shaft mounted in the steering gear housing so the pinion teeth are meshed with the rack teeth. The pinion may contain **spur gear teeth** or **helical gear teeth**. The upper end of the pinion shaft is connected to the steering shaft from the steering column. Therefore, steering wheel rotation moves the rack sideways to steer the front wheels. The pinion is supported on a ball bearing in the steering gear housing.

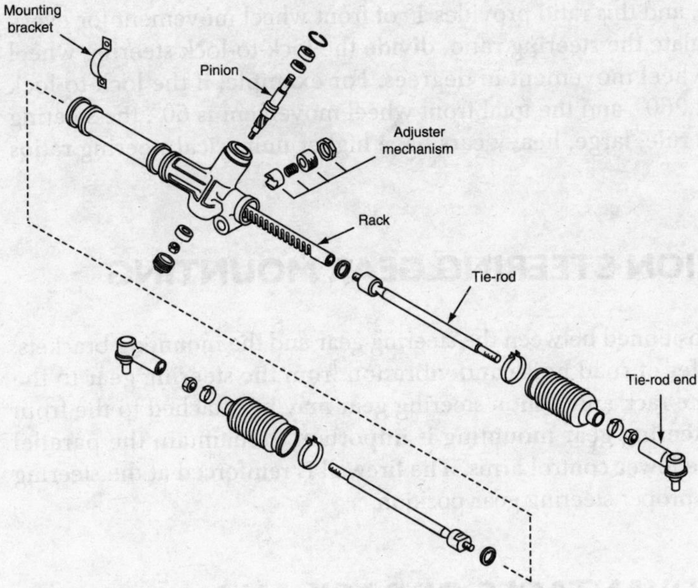

FIGURE 12-1 *Manual rack and pinion steering gear components.*

Tie-Rods and Tie-Rod Ends

The tie-rods are similar to those used on parallelogram steering linkages. A spring-loaded ball socket on the inner end of the tie-rod is threaded onto the rack. When these ball sockets are torqued to the vehicle manufacturer's specification, a preload is placed on the ball socket. A bellows boot is clamped to the housing and tie-rod on each side of the steering gear, and these boots keep contaminants out of the ball socket and rack.

A tie-rod end is threaded onto the outer end of each tie-rod. These tie-rod ends are similar to those used on parallelogram steering linkages. A jam nut locks the outer tie-rod end to the tie-rod.

Rack Adjustment

A rack bearing is positioned against the smooth side of the rack. A spring is located between the rack bearing and the rack adjuster plug that is threaded into the housing. This adjuster plug is retained with a locknut. The rack bearing adjustment sets the preload between the rack and pinion teeth, which affects **steering kickback**, harshness, and noise.

STEERING GEAR RATIO

When the steering wheel is rotated from **lock-to-lock** or **stop-to-stop**, the front wheels turn about 30° each in each direction from the straight-ahead position. Therefore, the total front wheel movement from left to right is approximately 60°. With a steering ratio of 1:1, 1° of steering wheel rotation would turn the front wheels 1°, and 30° of steering wheel rotation in either direction would result in lock-to-lock front wheel movement. This steering ratio is much too extreme because the slightest steering wheel movement would cause the vehicle to swerve. The steering gear must have a ratio that allows more steering wheel rotation in relation to front wheel movement.

A **steering ratio** of 15:1 is acceptable, and this ratio provides 1° of front wheel movement for every 15° of steering wheel rotation. To calculate the steering ratio, divide the lock-to-lock steering wheel rotation in degrees by the total front wheel movement in degrees. For example, if the lock-to-lock steering wheel rotation is 3.5 turns, or 1,260°, and the total front wheel movement is 60°, the steering ratio is $1{,}260 \div 60 = 21{:}1$. As a general rule, large, heavy cars have higher numerical steering ratios than small, lightweight cars.

MANUAL RACK AND PINION STEERING GEAR MOUNTING

Large rubber insulating grommets are positioned between the steering gear and the mounting brackets. These bushings help prevent the transfer of road noise and vibration from the steering gear to the chassis and passenger compartment. The rack and pinion steering gear may be attached to the front crossmember or to the cowl. Proper steering gear mounting is important to maintain the parallel relationship between the tie-rods and the lower control arms. The firewall is reinforced at the steering gear mounting locations to maintain the proper steering gear position.

ADVANTAGES AND DISADVANTAGES OF RACK AND PINION STEERING

As mentioned earlier, the rack and pinion steering gear is lighter and more compact than a recirculating ball steering gear and parallelogram steering linkage. Therefore, the rack and pinion steering gear is most suitable for FWD unibody vehicles.

Since there are fewer friction points in the rack and pinion steering than in the recirculating ball steering gear with a parallelogram steering linkage, the driver has a greater feeling of the road with rack and pinion steering gear. However, fewer friction points reduce the steering system's ability to isolate road noise and vibration. Therefore, drivers of a vehicle with a rack and pinion steering system may have more complaints of road noise and vibration transfer to the steering wheel and passenger compartment.

POWER RACK AND PINION STEERING GEARS

Design and Operation

A power-assisted rack and pinion steering gear uses the same basic operating principles as a manual rack and pinion steering gear, but in the power-assisted steering gear, hydraulic fluid pressure from the power steering pump is used to reduce steering effort. A **rack piston** is integral with the rack, and this piston is located in a sealed chamber in the steering gear housing. Hydraulic fluid lines are connected to each end of this chamber, and **rack seals** are positioned in the housing at ends of the chamber. A seal is also located on the rack piston (Figure 12-2).

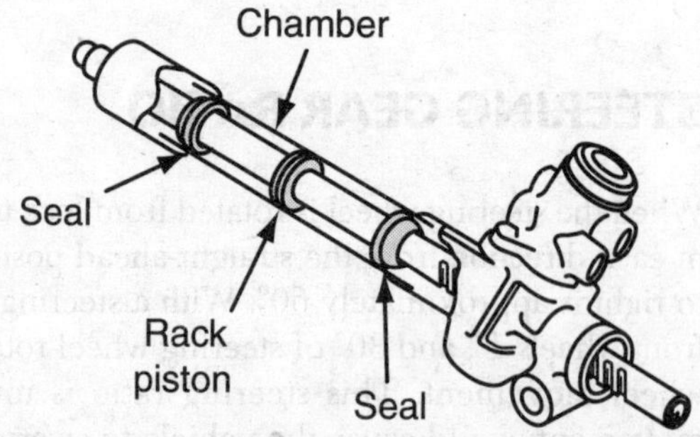

FIGURE 12-2 *Hydraulic chamber in a power rack and pinion steering gear.*

When a driver is completing a left turn, fluid is pumped into the left side of the fluid chamber and exhausted from the right chamber area. This hydraulic pressure on the left side of the rack piston helps the pinion move the rack to the right (Figure 12-3, view A).

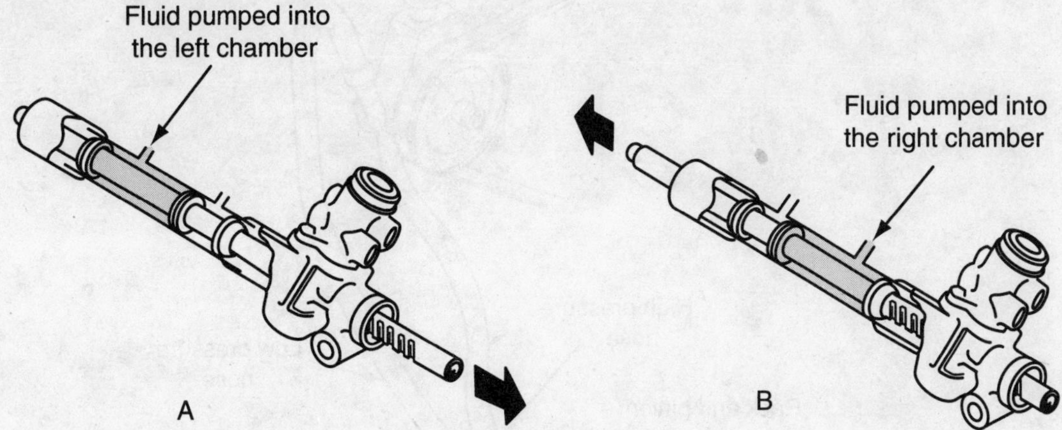

FIGURE 12-3 *Rack movement during left and right turns.*

When a right turn is made, fluid is pumped into the right side of the fluid chamber, and fluid flows out of the left end of the chamber. Thus, hydraulic pressure is exerted on the right side of the rack piston, which assists the pinion gear in moving the rack to the left (Figure 12-3, view B). Since the steering gear is mounted behind the front wheels, rack movement to the left is necessary for a right turn, whereas rack movement to the right causes a left turn.

Rotary Valve and Spool Valve Operation

Fluid direction in the steering gear is controlled by a rotary valve attached to the pinion assembly (Figure 12-4). A stub shaft on the pinion assembly is connected to the steering shaft and wheel. The pinion is connected to the stub shaft through a **torsion bar** that twists when the steering wheel is rotated and springs back to the center position when the wheel is released. A rotary valve body contains an inner **spool valve** that is mounted over the torsion bar on the pinion assembly.

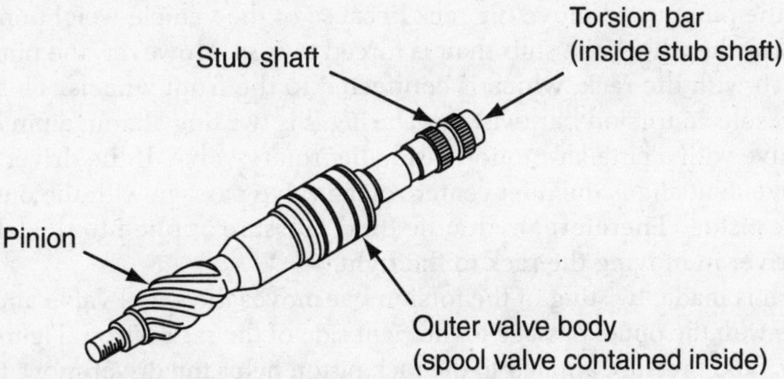

FIGURE 12-4 *Pinion assembly for a power rack and pinion steering gear.*

When the front wheels are in the straight-ahead position, fluid flows from the pump through the high-pressure hose to the center **rotary valve** body passage. Fluid is then routed through the valve body to the low-pressure return hose and the pump reservoir (Figure 12-5).

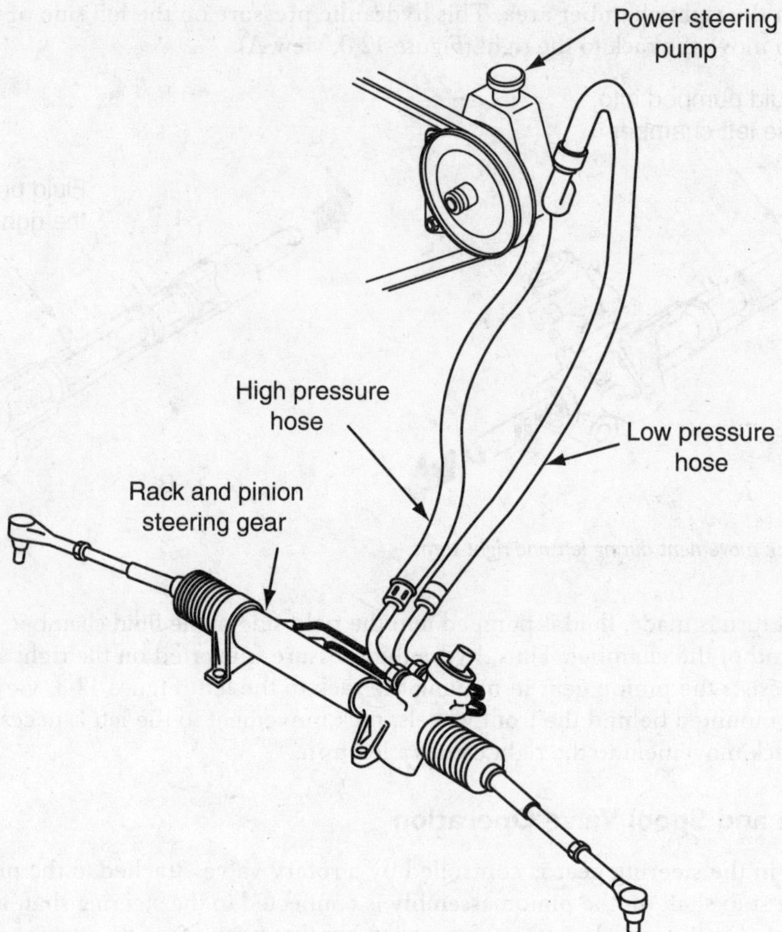

FIGURE 12-5 *Power rack and pinion steering gear with connecting hoses and lines.*

Teflon rings or O-rings seal the rotary valve ring lands to the steering gear housing. A lot of force is required to turn the pinion and move the rack because of the vehicle weight on the front wheels. When the driver turns the wheel, the stub shaft is forced to turn. However, the pinion resists turning because it is in mesh with the rack, which is connected to the front wheels. This resistance of the pinion to rotation results in torsion bar twisting. During this twisting action, a pin on the torsion bar moves the spool valve with a circular motion inside the rotary valve. If the driver makes a left turn, the spool valve movement aligns the inlet center rotary valve passage with the outlet passage to the left side of the rack piston. Therefore, hydraulic fluid pressure applied to the left side of the rack piston assists the driver in moving the rack to the right.

When a right turn is made, twisting of the torsion bar moves the spool valve and aligns the center rotary valve passage with the outlet passage to the right side of the rack piston (Figure 12-6). Under this condition, hydraulic fluid pressure applied to the rack piston helps the driver move the rack to the left. The torsion bar provides a **feel of the road** to the driver.

When the steering wheel is released after a turn, the torsion bar centers the spool valve and power assistance stops. If hydraulic fluid pressure is not available from the pump, the power steering system operates like a manual system, but steering effort is higher. When the torsion bar is twisted to a designed limit, tangs on the stub shaft engage with drive tabs on the pinion. This action

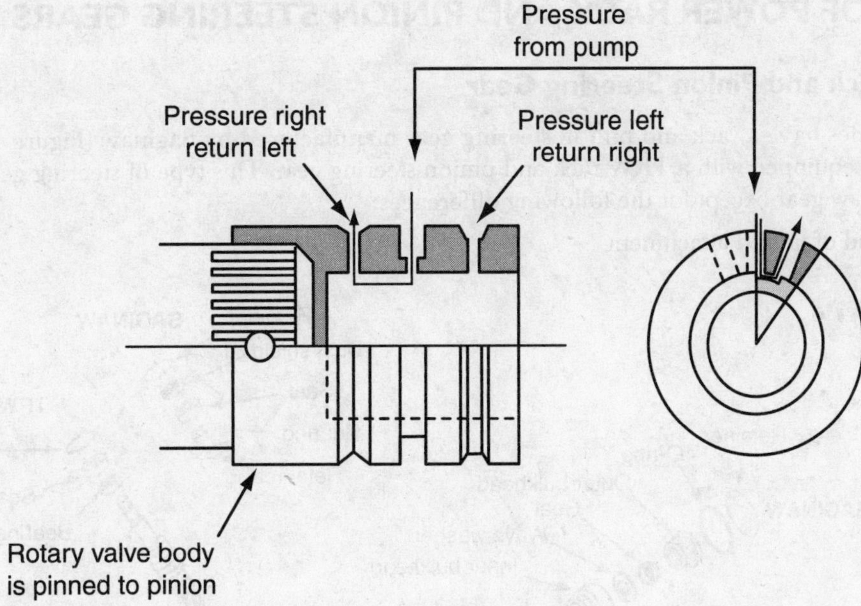

FIGURE 12-6 *Spool valve movement inside the rotary valve.*

mechanically transfers motion from the steering wheel to the rack and front wheels. Since hydraulic pressure is not available on the rack piston, greater steering effort is required. If a front wheel raises going over a bump or drops into a hole, the tie-rod pivots along with the wheel. However, the rack and tie-rod still maintain the left-to-right wheel direction.

The rack boots are clamped to the housing and the rack. Since the boots are sealed and air cannot be moved through the housing, a **breather tube** is necessary to move air from one boot to the other when the steering wheel is turned (Figure 12-7). This air movement through the vent tube prevents pressure changes in the bellows boots during a turn.

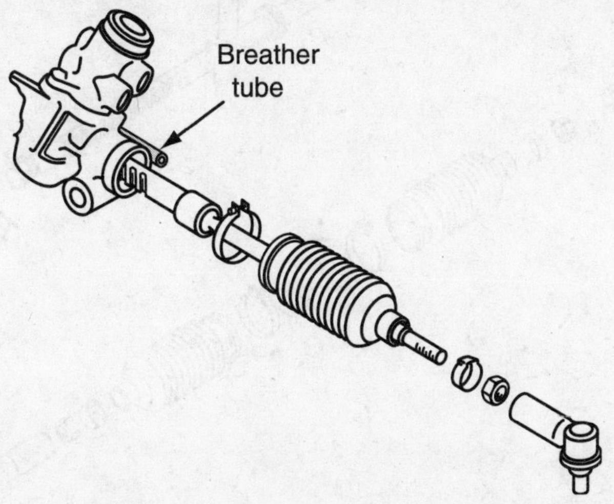

FIGURE 12-7 *Breather tube and boot.*

TYPES OF POWER RACK AND PINION STEERING GEARS

Power Rack and Pinion Steering Gear

Many vehicles have a rack and pinion steering gear manufactured by Saginaw (Figure 12-8). Some vehicles are equipped with a TRW rack and pinion steering gear. This type of steering gear is similar to the Saginaw gear except for the following differences:

1. Method of tie-rod attachment

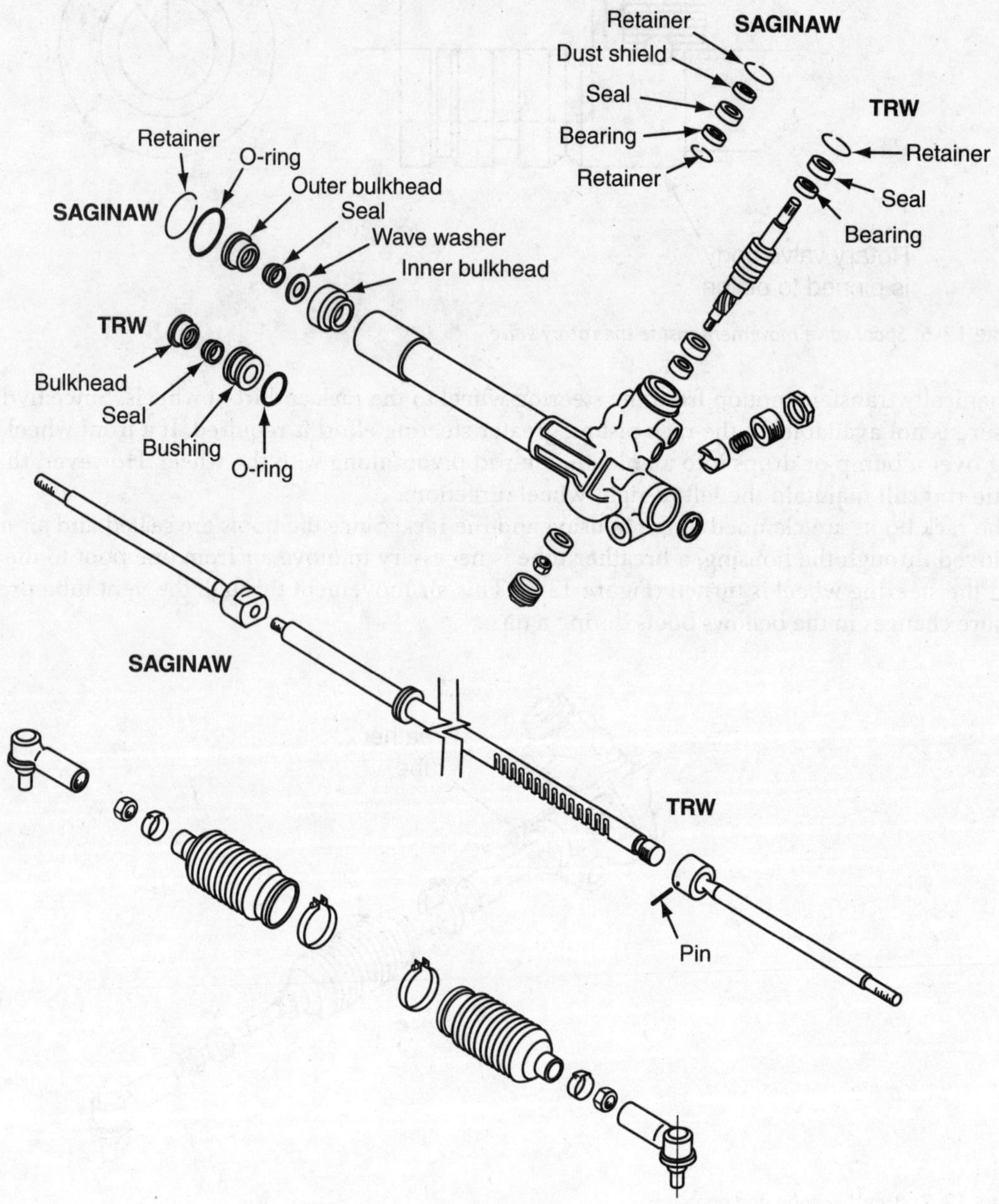

FIGURE 12-8 *Saginaw and TRW power rack and pinion steering gear.*

2. Bulkhead oil seal and retainer
3. Pinion upper and lower bearing hardware

On both the Saginaw and TRW power rack and pinion steering gears, the tie-rods are connected to the ends of the rack. This type of steering gear may be referred to as **end take-off (ETO)**. On other power rack and pinion steering gears, the rack piston and cylinder are positioned on the right end of the rack and the tie-rods are attached to a movable sleeve in the center of the gear (Figure 12-9). This type of steering gear may be called **center take-off (CTO)**.

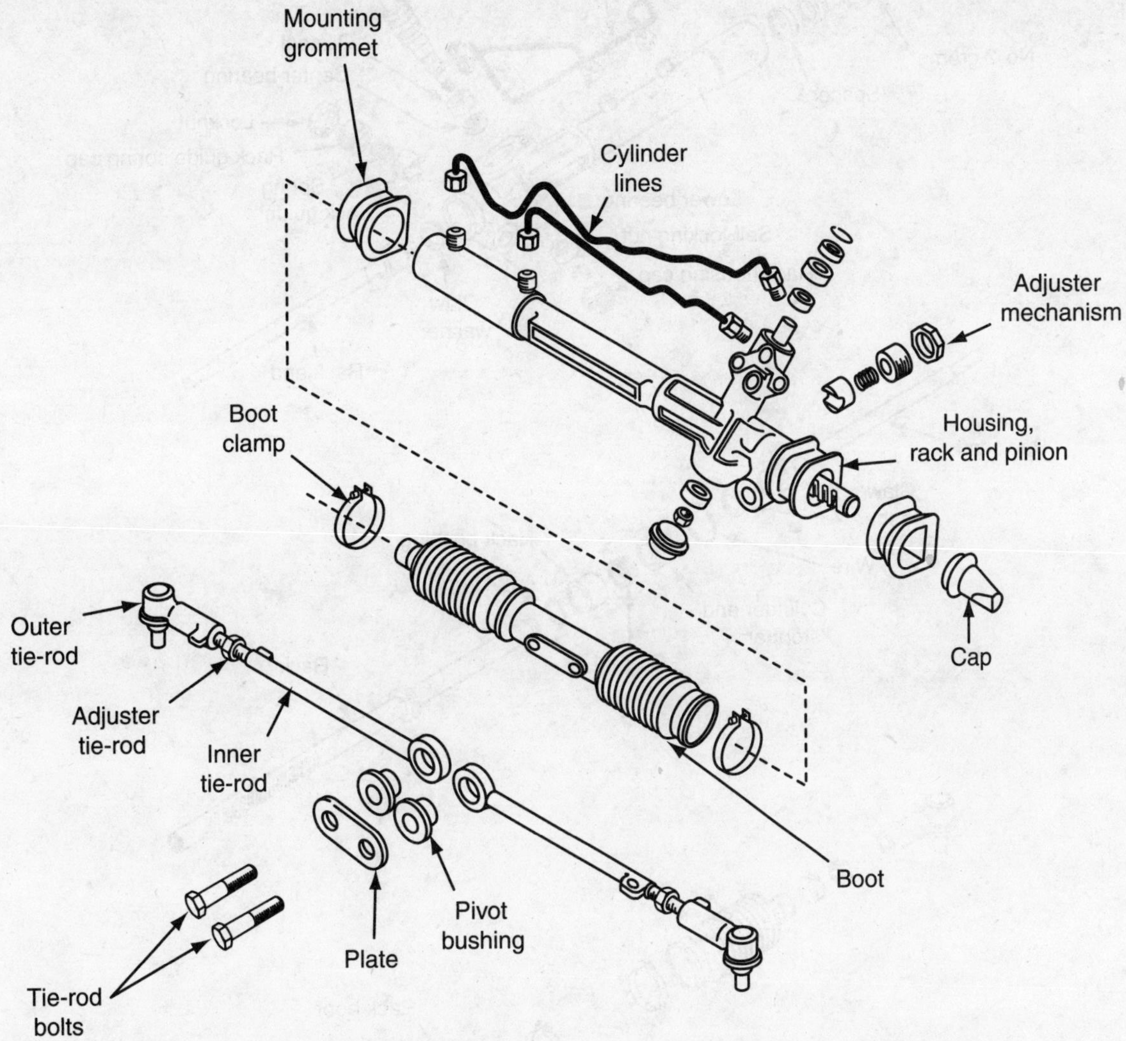

FIGURE 12-9 *Power rack and pinion steering gear with center take-off tie-rods.*

The Toyota power rack and pinion steering gear has a removable control valve housing surrounding the control valve and pinion shaft (Figure 12-10). In this steering gear, claw washers are used to lock the inner tie-rod ends to the rack. Apart from these minor differences, the Toyota power rack and pinion gear is similar to the Saginaw and TRW gears.

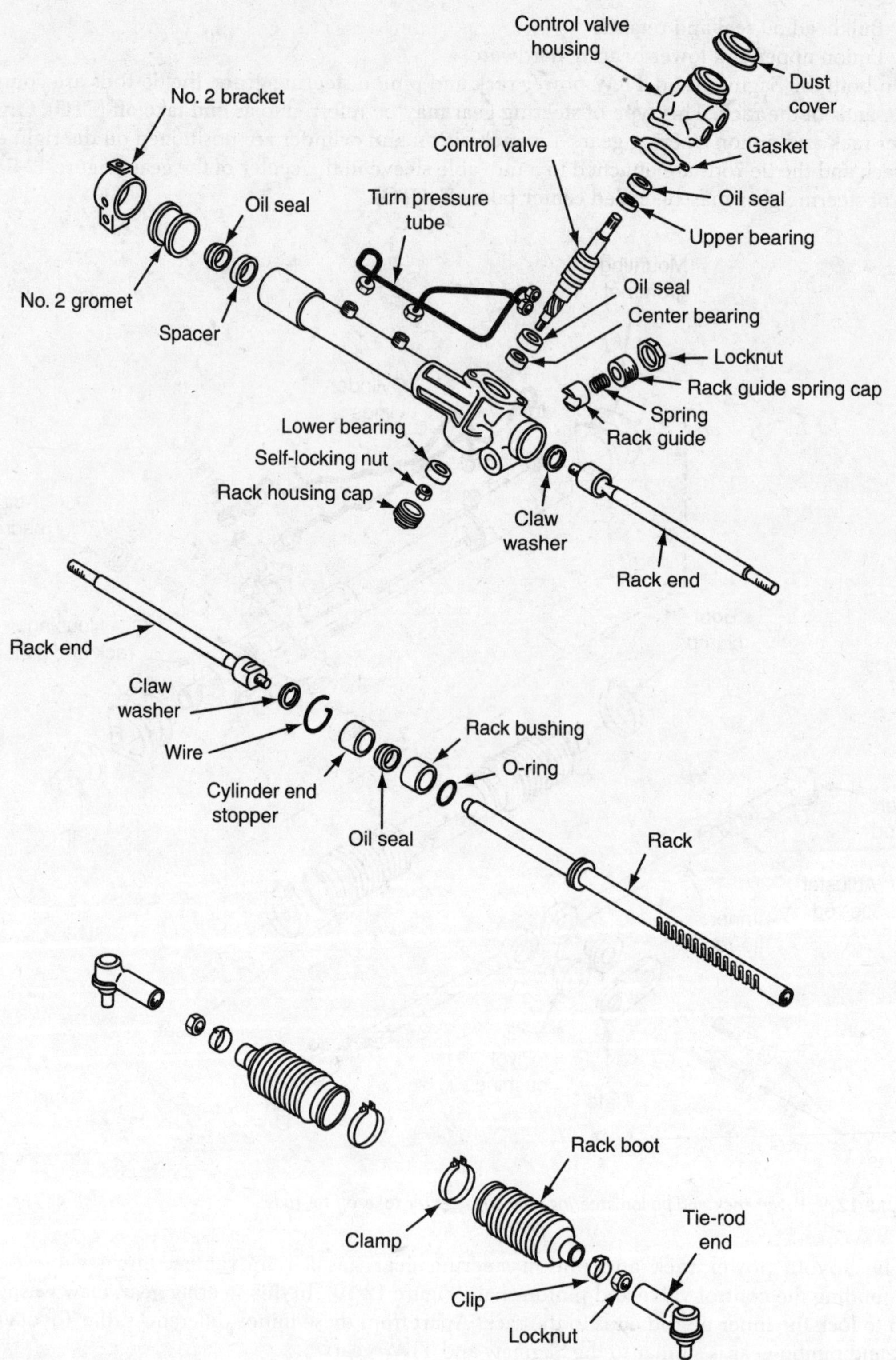

FIGURE 12-10 *Toyota power rack and pinion steering gear.*

WARNING: When working on any power steering system always wear protective gloves and use caution, because the system hoses, components, and fluid can be very hot if the system has been in operation for a period of time.

ELECTRONIC VARIABLE ORIFICE STEERING

Input Sensors

CAUTION: Never short across, or ground, any terminals in a computer-controlled system unless you are instructed to do so in the vehicle manufacturer's service manual. Such action may damage expensive electronic components.

The **electronic variable orifice** (EVO) steering system is standard on many late model vehicles. The EVO steering system provides high-power steering assistance during low-speed cornering and parking and normal power steering assistance at higher speeds for proper road feel. High-power steering assistance during low-speed cornering and parking increases driver convenience.

The **steering wheel rotation sensor** is mounted on the steering column, and a shutter disc attached to the steering shaft rotates through the sensor when the steering wheel is rotated. A row of slots is positioned near the outer edge of the shutter disc (Figure 12-11). When these slots rotate through the sensor, a steering wheel rotation speed signal is sent from the sensor to the control module.

FIGURE 12-11 *Steering wheel rotation sensor.*

The **vehicle speed sensor (VSS)** is mounted in the transaxle or transmission, and this sensor sends a signal to the control module in relation to vehicle speed (Figure 12-12). The VSS signal is also used for other purposes.

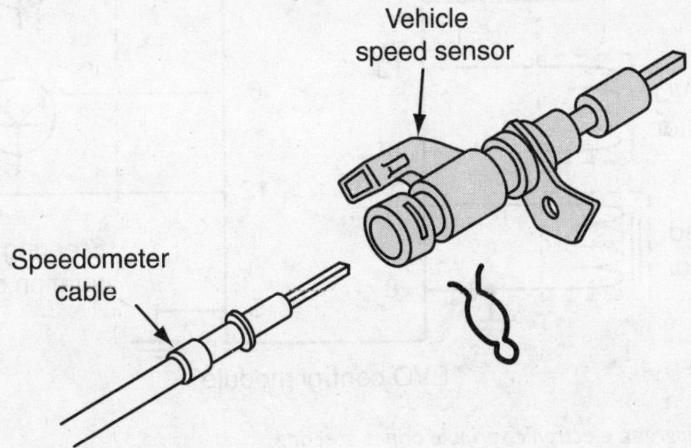

FIGURE 12-12 *Vehicle speed sensor (VSS).*

Control Module

On some vehicles, the control module is mounted in the trunk (Figure 12-13). This module continually monitors the input signals from the VSS and the steering wheel rotation sensor (Figure 12-14). Some models have a combined EVO steering system and rear air suspension system. On these models, the control module operates the EVO steering system and the rear air suspension system. In the combined EVO steering and rear air suspension system, the inputs and outputs from both of these systems are connected to the same control module. (The rear air suspension system is explained in Chapter 8.) If the EVO system is used alone without the air suspension system, a different control module is required.

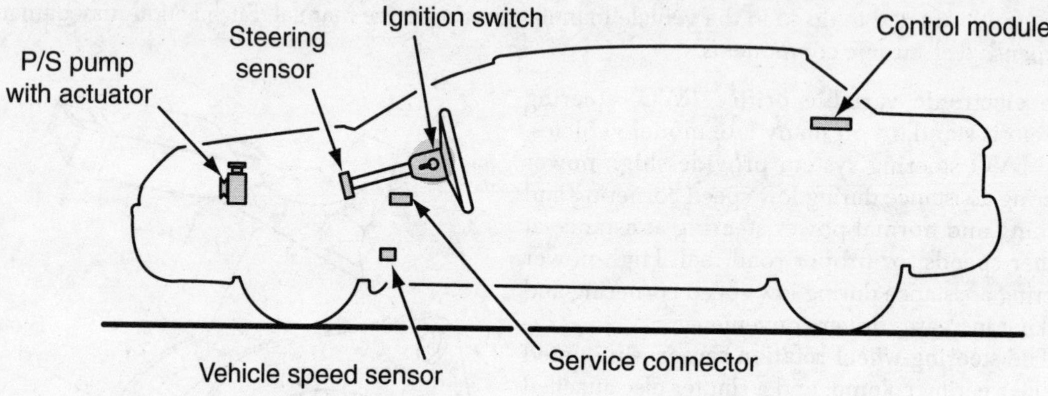

FIGURE 12-13 *Control module and main components, electronic variable orifice steering.*

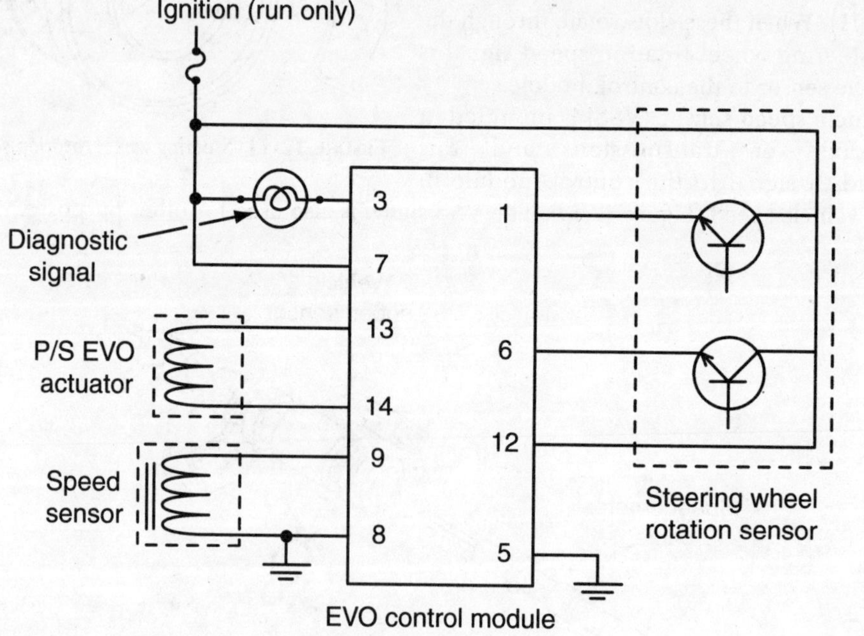

FIGURE 12-14 *Wiring diagram, electronic variable orifice steering.*

Output Control

A varying current flow is sent from the control module through the EVO actuator in the power steering pump (Figure 12-15). The actuator swivels freely when it is installed in the power steering pump. As the control module changes the current flow through the actuator, the actuator supplies a variable pressure to the spool valve in the power steering pump. Two wires are connected from the actuator to the control module. The power steering pump is mounted directly to the engine to reduce noise, vibration, and harshness (NVH).

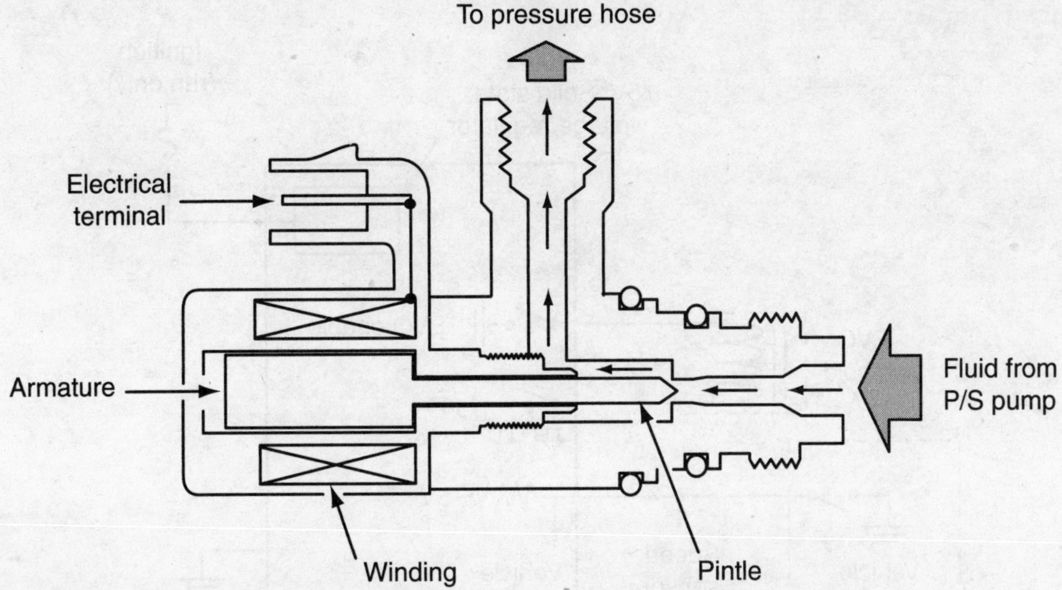

FIGURE 12-15 *Electronic variable orifice (EVO) actuator removed from the power steering pump.*

The control module positions the actuator and spool valve to provide full power steering assistance under these conditions:

1. Vehicle speed less than 10 mph (16 km/h)
2. Steering wheel rotation above 15 rpm

The full power-assist mode reduces driver effort required to turn the steering wheel during low-speed cornering and parking for increased convenience. In the full power-assist mode, the control module supplies 30 milliamps (ma) to the actuator.

The control module positions the actuator and spool valve to reduce power steering assistance under these conditions:

1. Vehicle speed above 25 mph (40 km/h)
2. Steering wheel rotation below 15 rpm

The reduced power-assist mode provides adequate road feel for the driver. In the reduced power-assist mode, the control module supplies 300 ma to the actuator. Above 88 mph (132 km/h), 590 ma is supplied from the control module to the actuator.

SAGINAW ELECTRONIC VARIABLE ORIFICE STEERING

Design and Operation

The term **variable effort steering** (VES) replaces the previous EVO terminology on some General Motors vehicles. In the EVO system, the vehicle speed sensor input is sent to the EVO controller. This controller supplies a pulse width modulated (PWM) voltage to the actuator solenoid in the power steering pump. The controller also provides a ground connection for the actuator solenoid (Figure 12-16).

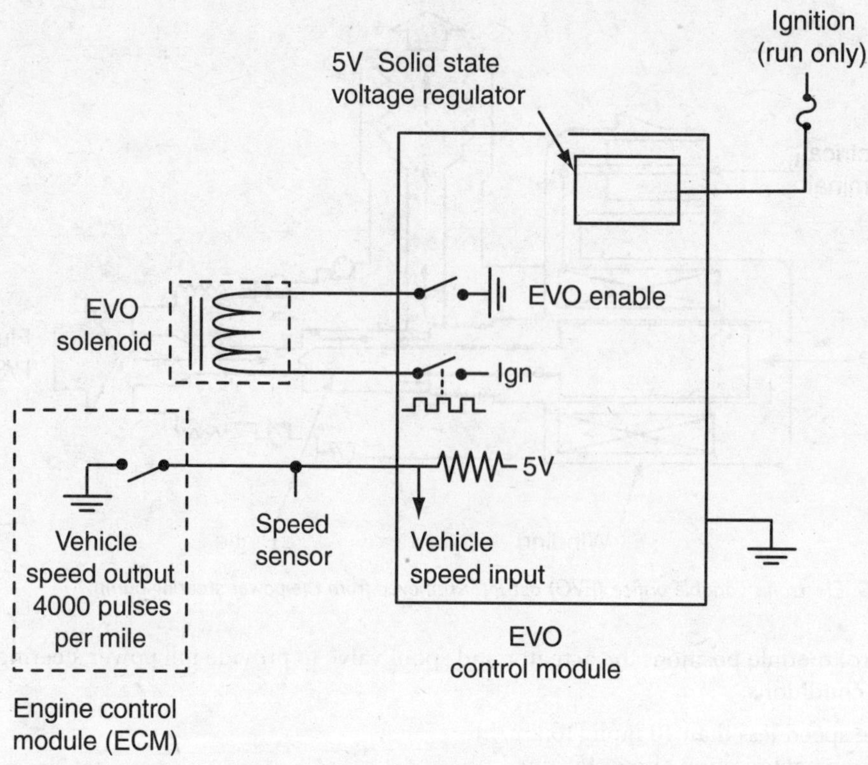

FIGURE 12-16 *Electronic variable orifice (EVO) steering system.*

When the vehicle is operating at low speeds, the controller supplies a **pulse width modulated (PWM) voltage signal** to position the actuator solenoid plunger so the power steering pump pressure is higher (Figure 12-17). Under this condition, greater power assistance is provided for cornering or parking. If the vehicle is operating at higher speed, the controller changes the PWM signal to the actuator solenoid, and the solenoid plunger is positioned to reduce power steering pump pressure. This action reduces power steering assistance to provide improved road feel for the driver.

In a **Magnasteer system**, a bi-directional steering actuator solenoid is mounted in the steering gear (Figure 12-18). The computer that operates the Magnasteer system is combined with the electronic brake and traction control module (EBTCM), and this module is usually mounted in the left-front corner of the engine compartment (Figure 12-19). Two wires are connected from the steering actuator to the EBTCM (Figure 12-20).

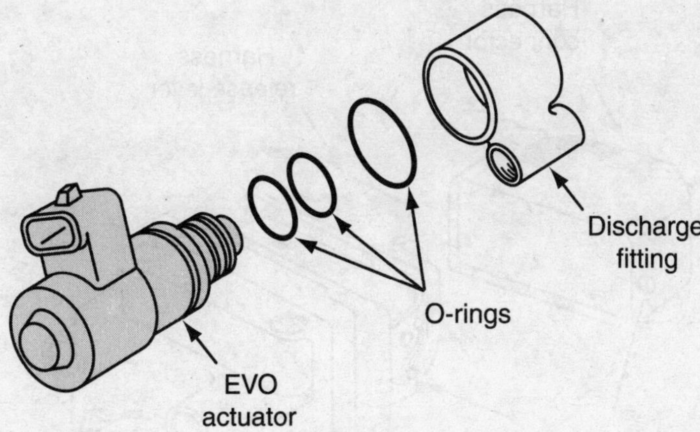

FIGURE 12-17 *Actuator solenoid.*

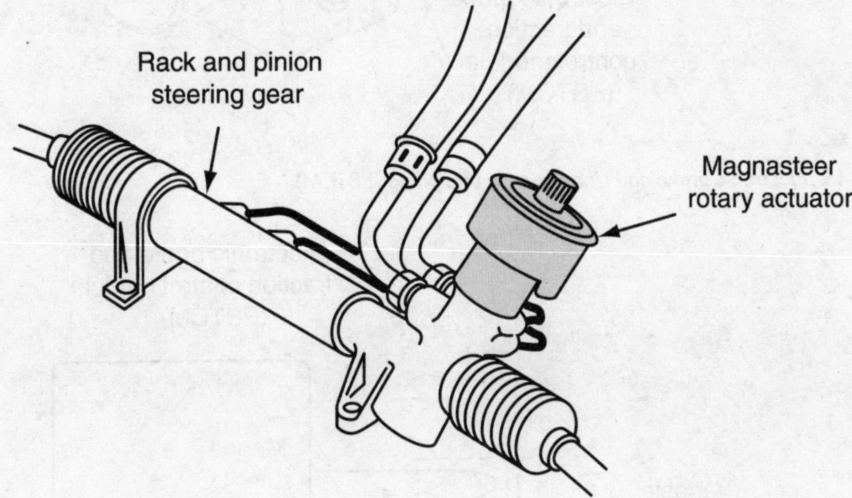

FIGURE 12-18 *Magnasteer, actuator solenoid.*

The steering actuator solenoid contains a pole piece with 16 magnetic segments and a coil. A matching 16-segment permanent magnet is attached to the spool valve. As the steering wheel and the spool valve rotate, the 16 segments on the spool valve move into and out of alignment with the segments on the actuator pole piece. The EBTCM can reverse the current flow through the steering actuator, and this action reverses the magnetic poles on the actuator segments. At low vehicle speeds, the EBTCM supplies current through the steering actuator so the magnetic poles on the actuator repel the permanent magnet segments on the spool valve. This repelling action assists the driver to turn the steering wheel and reduces steering effort. At higher speeds, the EBTCM reverses the current flow through the steering actuator, and this action reverses the poles on the actuator segments. Under this condition, the actuator segments are attracted to the permanent magnet segments on the spool valve. This action increases steering effort to improve driver road feel. The EBTCM also has the capability to vary the current flow through the steering actuator to provide variable steering effort in relation to vehicle speed.

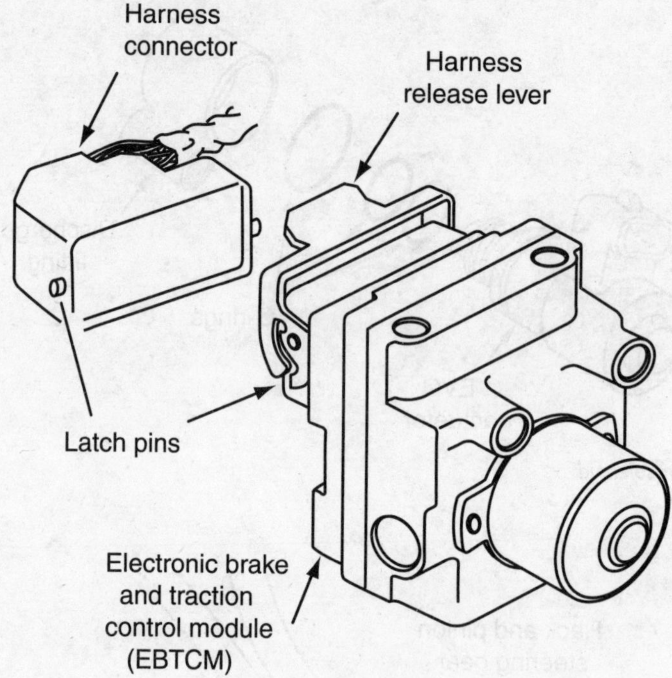

FIGURE 12-19 *Electronic brake and traction control module (EBTCM).*

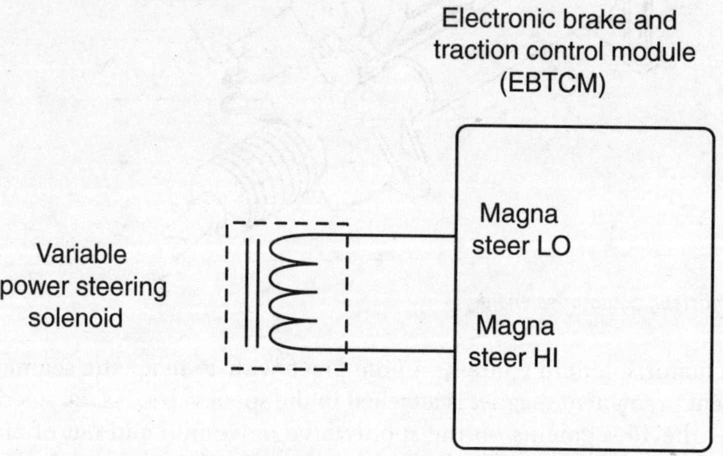

FIGURE 12-20 *Wiring connections between the Magnasteer actuator solenoid and the EBTCM.*

RACK-DRIVE ELECTRONIC POWER STEERING

Electronic power steering systems (EPS) may be classified as rack-drive, column-drive, or pinion-drive. All three types of EPS have a rack and pinion steering gear. In a **rack-drive EPS** the electric motor that provides steering assist is coupled to the rack in the steering gear. A **column-drive EPS** has an electric assist motor coupled to the steering shaft in the steering column, and in a **pinion-drive EPS** the electric motor is coupled to the steering gear pinion. The EPS system is light and compact compared to rack and pinion steering gear with hydraulic steering assist, because the power steering pump and hoses are not required on the EPS system. Since the EPS does not require a power steering pump driven by engine power, this system minimizes engine power loss and reduces fuel consumption. The EPS system reduces steering kickback while providing a linear steering feel.

System Components

The rack and pinion steering gear changes rotary steering wheel motion to transverse motion of the rack. The motor that provides electric steering assist is designed into the steering gear (Figure 12-21). The steering sensor is mounted in the pinion shaft. This sensor sends input voltage signals to the EPS control unit in relation to the direction, amount, and torque of the steering wheel rotation.

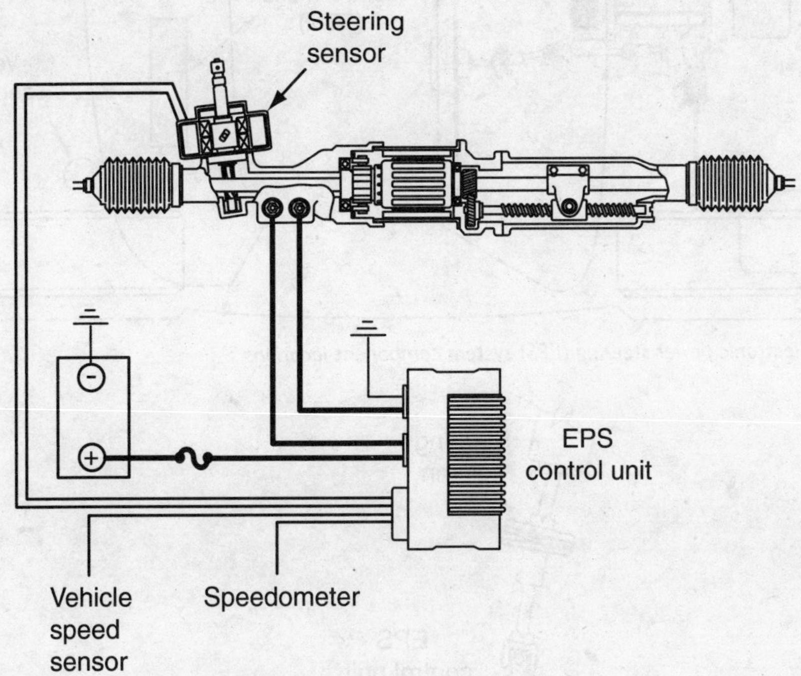

FIGURE 12-21 *Steering gear with electronic assist and related system components.*

If the vehicle has an automatic transaxle, a vehicle speed sensor (VSS) is mounted in the transaxle. This sensor sends voltage input signals to the transmission control module (TCM) in relation to transaxle output shaft rotational speed. These voltage signals are transmitted from the TCM to the EPS control unit. When the car is equipped with a manual transaxle, a differential speed sensor sends voltage signals to a pulse unit in relation to differential rotational speed. These voltage signals are transmitted from the pulse unit to the EPS control unit. The TCM and pulse unit is located in the rear of the vehicle (Figure 12-22). The speedometer also sends voltage signals to the EPS control unit. The voltage signals from the speedometer act as a double check and backup in a situation where the voltage signals from the VSS or differential speed sensor are inaccurate or nonexistent.

The EPS control unit is mounted above the steering gear (Figure 12-23). This control unit receives voltage input signals from the steering sensor, VSS, or differential speed sensor. When these signals are received, the EPS control unit calculates the proper amount and direction of steering assist. The

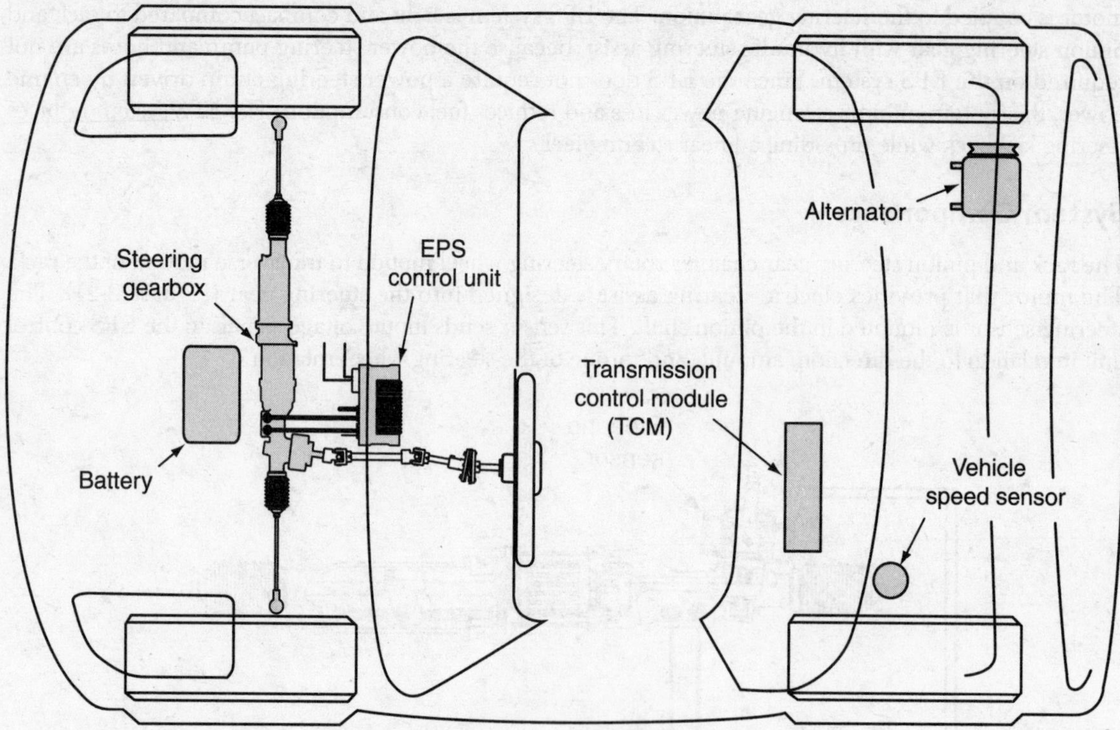

FIGURE 12-22 *Electronic power steering (EPS) system component locations.*

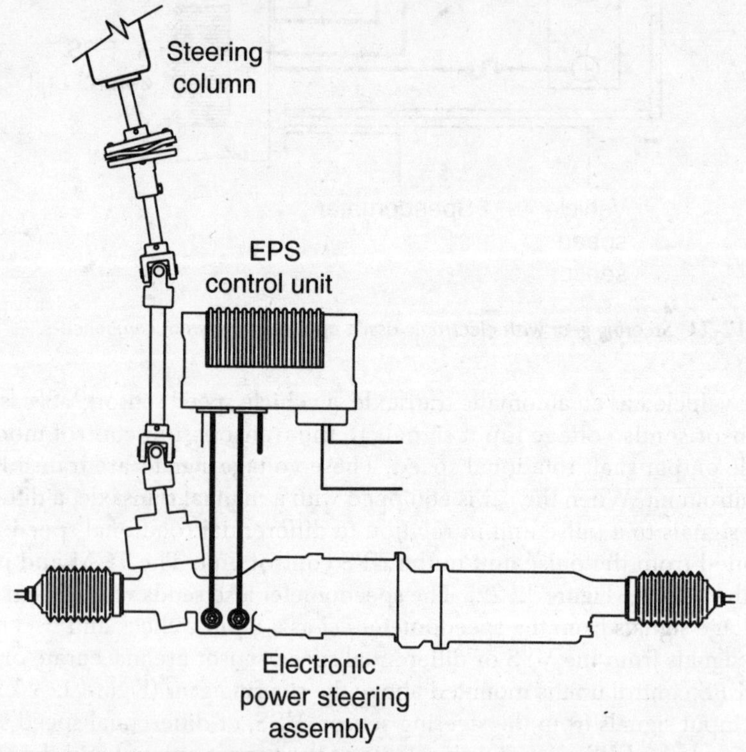

FIGURE 12-23 *Electronic power steering (EPS) control unit and steering gear.*

EPS control unit then commands a power module in the EPS control unit to drive the electric motor in the steering gear and provide the proper direction and amount of steering assist. The EPS control unit also contains self-diagnostic capabilities.

ELECTRONIC POWER STEERING SYSTEM OPERATION

Steering Sensor

The steering sensor contains a torque sensor and an interface. This sensor contains a slider core mounted on the pinion shaft. A spiral groove is located in each side of the slider, and two pins protruding from the pinion shaft are positioned in these grooves. The slider turns with the pinion shaft. When there is very little resistance to front wheel turning, the slider and pinion shaft rotate together and the pins remain centered in the spiral grooves in the slider. Very little resistance to front wheel turning occurs if the front tires are on a slippery road surface, or if the vehicle is raised so the front tires are off the floor. When there is resistance to front wheel turning, the torsion bar twists in the pinion shaft. This action causes the pins to move in the slider spiral grooves, and this movement causes upward or downward slider movement (Figure 12-24).

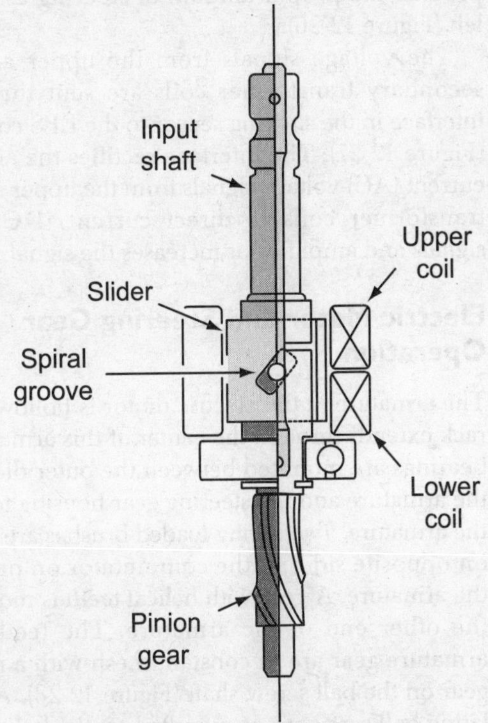

FIGURE 12-24 *Pinion shaft with slider and variable differential transformer.*

The slider core is surrounded by a variable differential transformer, and the slider moves upward or downward inside the transformer windings when the steering wheel is turned (Figure 12-25). The transformer has a primary coil and upper and lower secondary coils. When the ignition switch is turned on, an oscillation circuit in the steering sensor supplies an alternating current to the primary transformer coil. As the current alternates back and forth through the primary coil, the magnetic field is continually building up and collapsing around this coil. This rapidly expanding and collapsing magnetic field induces voltages in the upper and lower secondary coils. The position of the slider determines whether the voltage is induced in the upper or lower secondary coil.

While driving straight ahead, the slider is centered vertically between the upper and lower secondary coils. Under this condition, the voltage induced in these coils is equal. When voltages are equal in the upper and lower secondary coils, the voltage signals from these coils to the EPS control unit indicate the car is being driven straight ahead, or the steering wheel is being turned with no resistance and no electric power assist is required.

If the steering wheel is turned to the right, the slider moves upward. This slider position causes more induced voltage in the upper secondary coil and less induced voltage in the lower secondary coil. When these voltage signals from the upper secondary coil are sent to the EPS control unit, this control unit supplies current to the electric motor on the rack so the motor rotates in the appropriate direction to provide the proper amount of steering assist to the right (Figure 12-25).

When the steering wheel is turned to the left, the slider moves downward. This slider position causes more induced voltage in the lower secondary coil and less induced voltage in the upper secondary coil. When these voltage signals from the lower secondary coil are sent to the EPS control unit, the control unit supplies current to the electric motor on the rack so the motor rotates in the appropriate direction to provide the proper amount of steering assist to the left (Figure 12-26).

The voltage signals from the upper and lower secondary transformer coils are sent through the interface in the steering sensor to the EPS control unit (Figure 12-27). The interface rectifies the alternating current (AC) voltage signals from the upper and lower transformer coils to direct current (DC) voltage signals and amplifies or increases the signal strength.

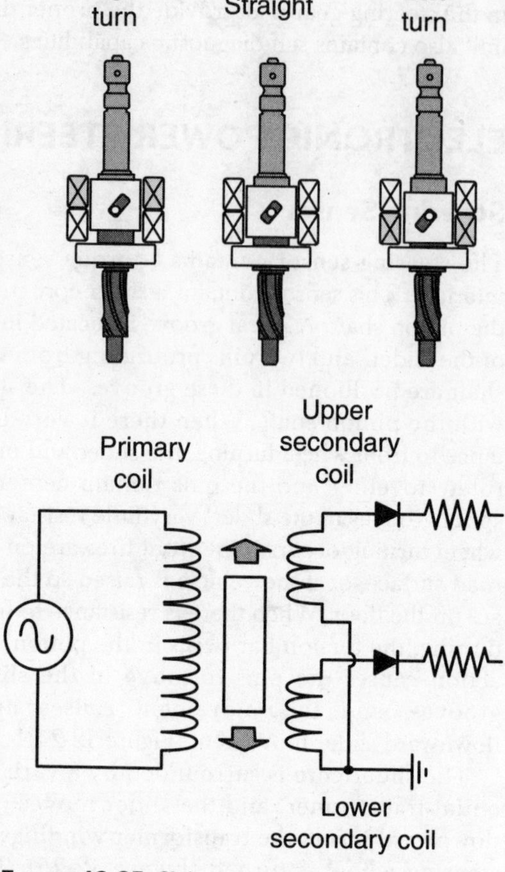

FIGURE 12-25 *Slider movement when turning the steering wheel.*

Electric Motor and Steering Gear Operation

The armature in the electric motor is hollow, and the rack extends through the center of this armature. Ball bearings are mounted between the outer diameter of the armature and the steering gear housing to support the armature. Two spring-loaded brushes are mounted on opposite sides of the commutator on one end of the armature. A gear with helical teeth is mounted on the other end of the armature. The teeth on the armature gear are in constant mesh with a matching gear on the ball screw shaft (Figure 12-28). A recirculating ball screw nut is mounted on the ball screw shaft. Ball bearings are mounted in grooves in the ball screw shaft and recirculating ball screw nut. The recirculating ball screw is bolted to the steering gear rack. The ball screw shaft and recirculating ball screw nut are similar in design to the worm shaft and ball nut in a recirculating ball steering gear. A permanent magnet is mounted in the steering gear

Steering condition	Slider movement	Induction voltage on secondary coil
Steering to right (load steering)	Upward shift	Voltage on upper coil increases, and voltage on the lower decreases
Advancing straight ahead (no load steering)	Neutral	Voltage on the upper and lower coils are equal
Steering to left (load steering)	Downward shift	Voltage on lower coil increases, and voltage on the upper increases

FIGURE 12-26 *Summary of steering sensor and transformer operation.*

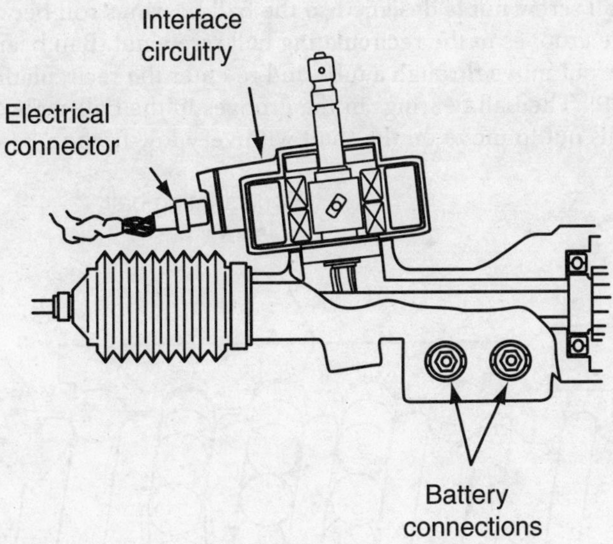

FIGURE 12-27 *Interface in the steering sensor.*

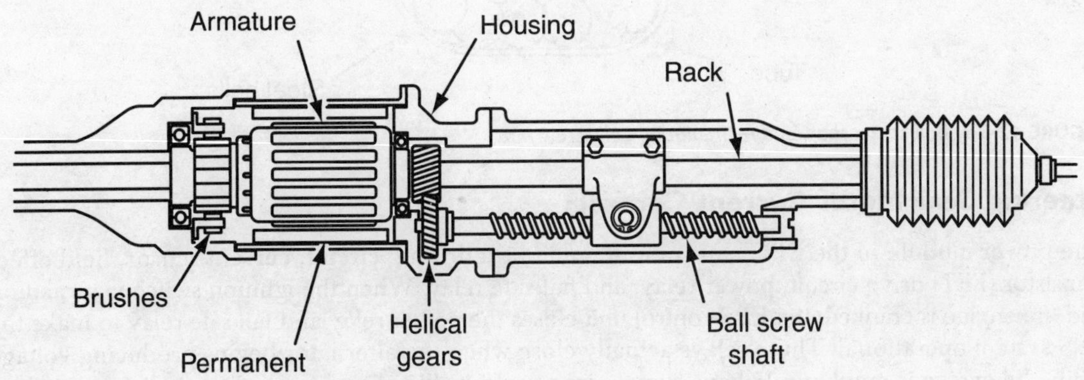

FIGURE 12-28 *Steering gear and electric motor.*

housing, and this magnet surrounds the armature core. There is a small clearance between the armature core and the permanent magnet.

When the steering wheel is turned, electric current is supplied from the power module in the EPS control unit through the brushes and armature windings to ground. This current flow creates strong magnetic fields around the armature windings. These magnetic fields around the armature windings react with the magnetic field of the permanent magnet and cause armature rotation in the proper direction to supply steering assist. When the armature rotates, the gear on the armature shaft drives the gear on the ball screw shaft. Ball screw shaft rotation moves the recirculating ball screw nut on the shaft. Since the recirculating ball screw nut is bolted to the steering gear rack, movement of this ball screw nut provides steering assist in the proper direction. The power module can reverse the armature rotation to provide steering assist in either direction by reversing the polarity of the brushes on the commutator. When the brush polarity is reversed, the current flow through the armature windings is reversed and this changes the direction of armature rotation.

The recirculating ball screw nut is designed so the ball bearings roll between the grooves in the ball screw shaft and the grooves in the recirculating ball screw nut. Ball bearings coming out of the recirculating ball screw nut move through a tube and re-enter the recirculating ball screw nut at the other end (Figure 12-29). The ball bearings in the grooves in the ball screw shaft and recirculating ball screw nut allow this nut to move on the shaft with very low friction.

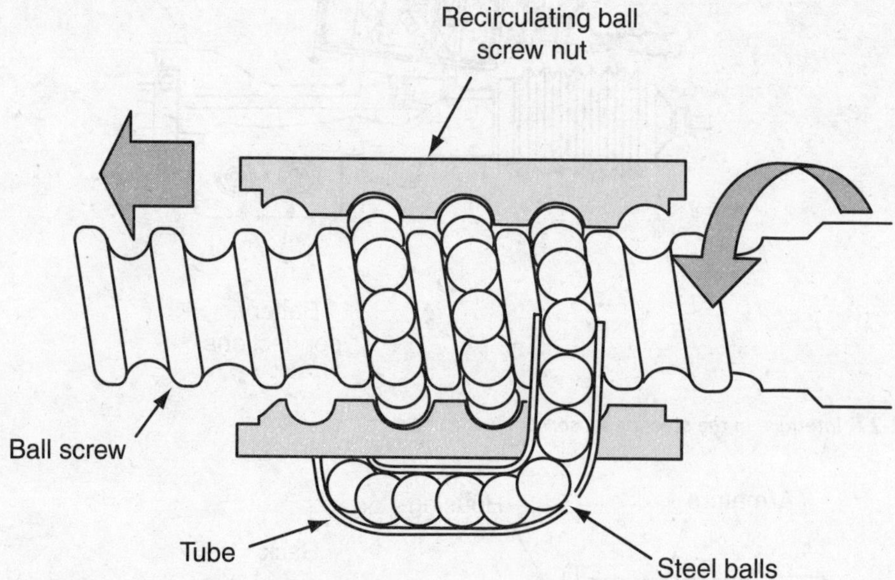

FIGURE 12-29 *Ball screw shaft and recirculating ball screw nut.*

Steering Gear Motor Current Control

The power module in the EPC control unit contains a driving circuit, current sensor, field effect transistor (FET) drive circuit, power relay, and fail safe relay. When the ignition switch is turned on and the engine is cranked, the EPS control unit closes the power relay and fail safe relay to make the EPS system operational. These relays actually close when the alternator begins producing voltage while the engine is cranking. Voltage signals are sent from the alternator and the ignition switch to the EPS control unit (Figure 12-30 and Figure 12-31). The EPS system remains operational if the engine stalls and the ignition switch is on. If the engine stalls on a hydraulically assisted power steering system, power steering assist is lost and the steering wheel becomes very hard to turn. This action may result in a collision if the engine stalls while turning a corner. Since the EPS system is still operational if the engine stalls and the ignition switch is on, the EPS system reduces the possibility of a collision resulting from loss of power steering assist during an engine stall.

When the driver turns the steering wheel, the steering sensor input voltage signals inform the EPS control unit that steering assist is necessary. The steering sensor input voltage signals also inform the EPS control unit regarding the direction and amount of steering assist required. If the driver supplies more torque to the steering wheel, the steering sensor input voltage signal indicates to the EPS control unit that more steering assist is necessary.

When the EPS control unit receives input voltage signals from the steering sensor indicating that steering assist is required, this control unit signals the FET drive circuit in the power module. This drive circuit supplies a pulse width modulated (PWM) voltage to the motor brushes with the proper polarity to provide the required direction and amount of steering assist. A PWM voltage signal is a pulsating voltage signal with a constant frequency but has a variable on time. One cycle of a PWM

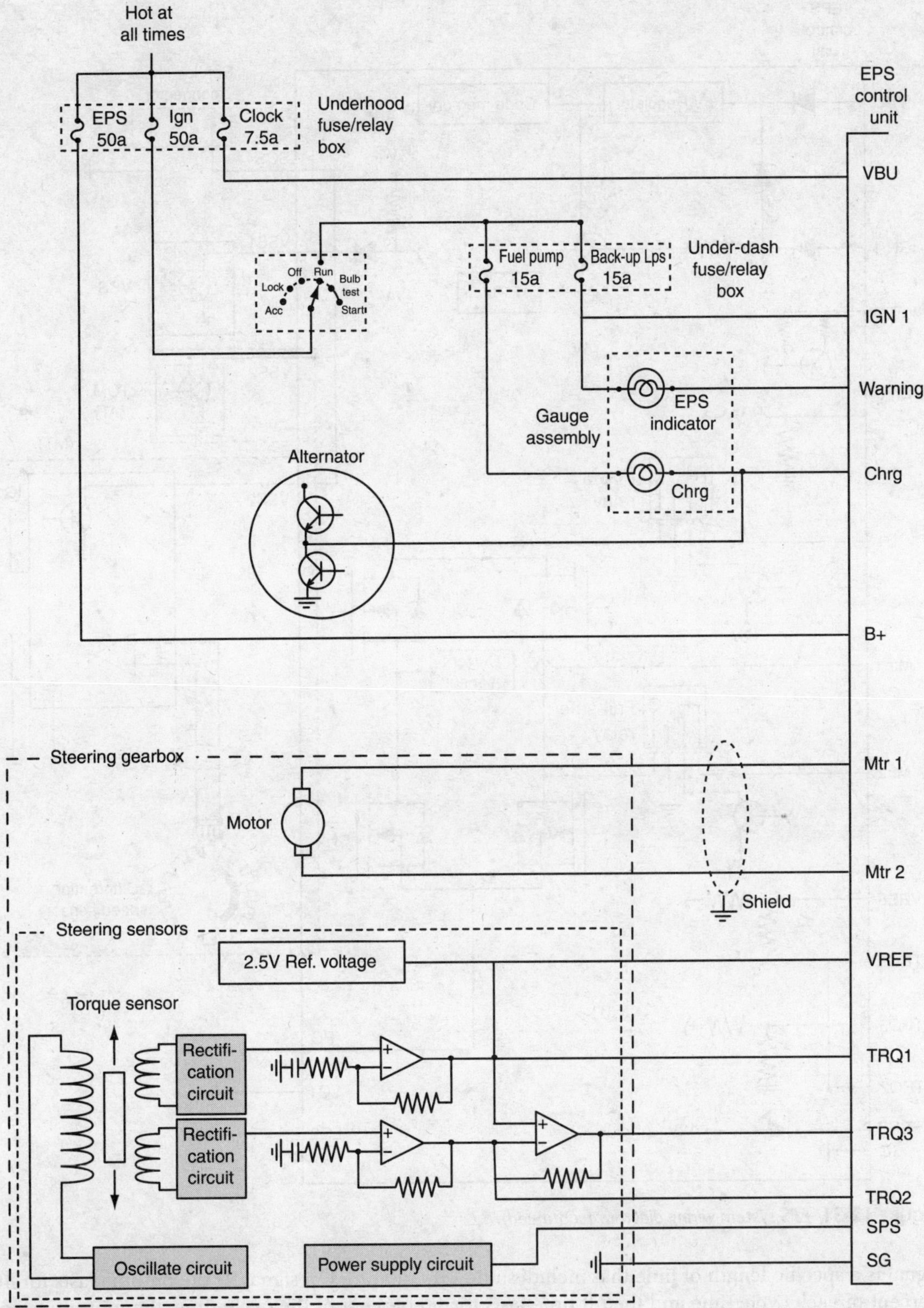

FIGURE 12-30 *EPS system wiring diagram.*

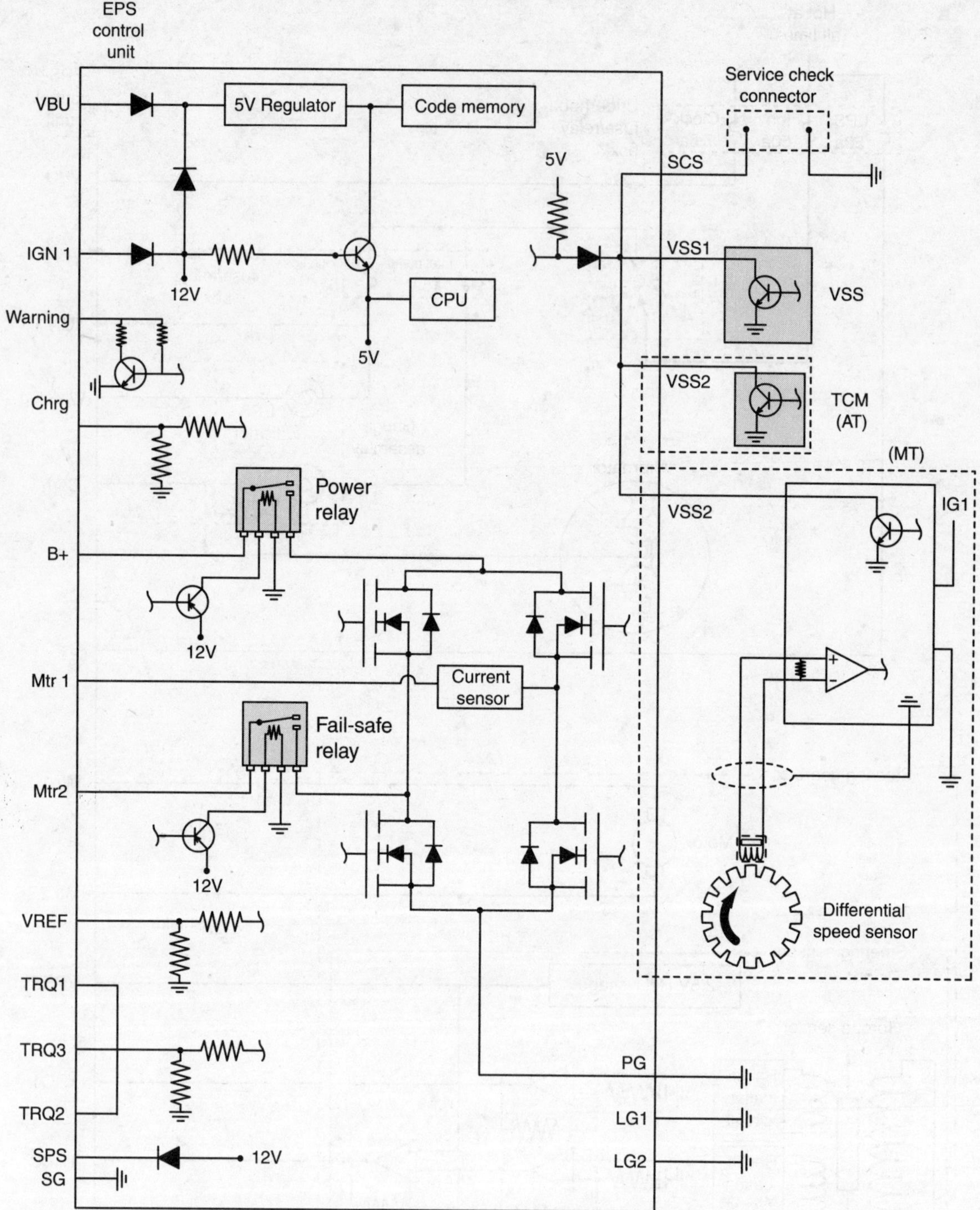

FIGURE 12-31 *EPS system wiring diagram (continued).*

signal is a specific length of time that includes one Off and one On signal. If the on time lasts for 40 percent of each cycle time and the off time lasts for 60 percent of the cycle time, the motor current remains lower and this reduces motor speed and steering assist. When the on time lasts for 60 percent of each cycle time, and the off time lasts for 40 percent of the cycle time, the motor current is higher and power steering assist is increased (Figure 12-32). The FET drive circuit operates the four FET transistors in the FET bridge to supply the proper direction and amount of voltage and current through the armature windings to provide the necessary direction and amount of steering assist (Figure 12-33).

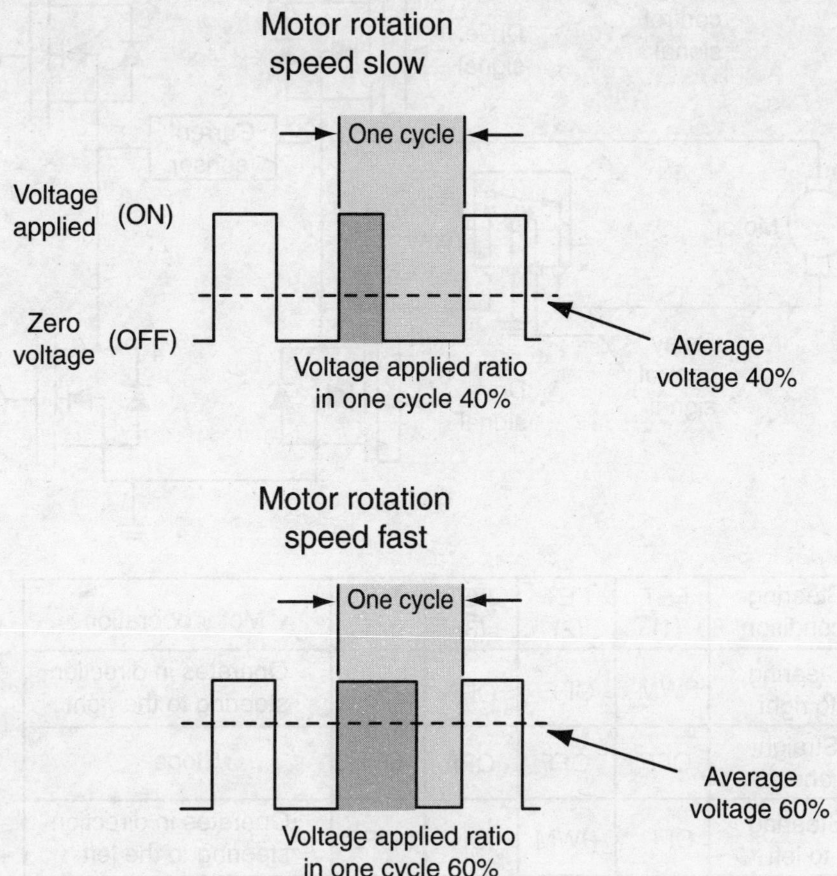

FIGURE 12-32 *Pulse width modulated (PWM) voltage signal.*

While the electric assist motor is operating, the motor current flows through a current sensor in the power module regardless of the direction of motor rotation. The current sensor sends a feedback voltage signal to the EPS control unit. If the motor current exceeds a predetermined average motor current for the current operating condition, the EPS control unit signals the drive circuit in the power module to reduce the motor current to prevent motor overheating. If the steering wheel is turned fully in one direction and held in this position, the motor current becomes much higher. Under this condition, the current sensor signals the EPS control unit, and this unit signals the drive circuit in the power module to reduce motor current to protect the motor.

If an electrical defect occurs in the EPS system, the EPS control unit illuminates an EPS indicator light in the instrument panel to inform the driver that a fault is present in the EPS system (Figure 12-34). Under this condition, the EPS unit opens the fail safe and power relays to make the EPS system inoperative. When this action occurs, manual steering without any power assist is available.

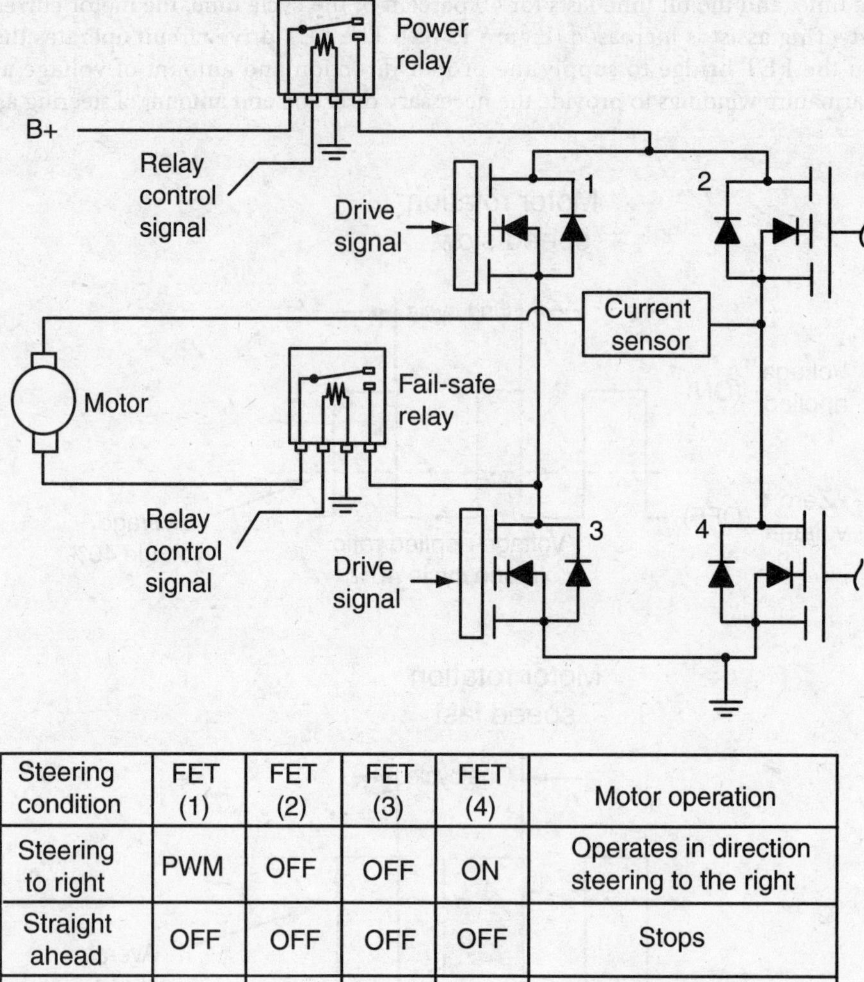

Steering condition	FET (1)	FET (2)	FET (3)	FET (4)	Motor operation
Steering to right	PWM	OFF	OFF	ON	Operates in direction steering to the right
Straight ahead	OFF	OFF	OFF	OFF	Stops
Steering to left	OFF	PWM	ON	OFF	Operates in direction steering to the left

FIGURE 12-33 *Drive circuit and field effect transistor (FET) bridge in the power module.*

If one of the front wheels strikes a large road irregularity, force from the front wheel is transferred to the steering gear rack. Rack movement attempts to move the ball screw nut on the ball screw shaft. This action tries to rotate the ball screw shaft and armature. A specific amount of force is required to move the ball screw nut and rotate the ball screw shaft and armature because the armature windings have to rotate through the magnetic field between the permanent magnets. This resistance to movement of the ball screw nut, ball screw shaft, and armature helps prevent road shock from being supplied through the steering gear to the steering wheel. When a very high road shock is transferred to the steering wheel, this road shock moves the pinion shaft and slider in the steering sensor. When this EPS control unit receives this steering sensor input signal, the EPS control unit immediately energizes the armature windings to oppose and cancel the road shock applied to the steering gear. Therefore, the EPS steering gear reduces road shock transferred from the front wheels to the steering wheel.

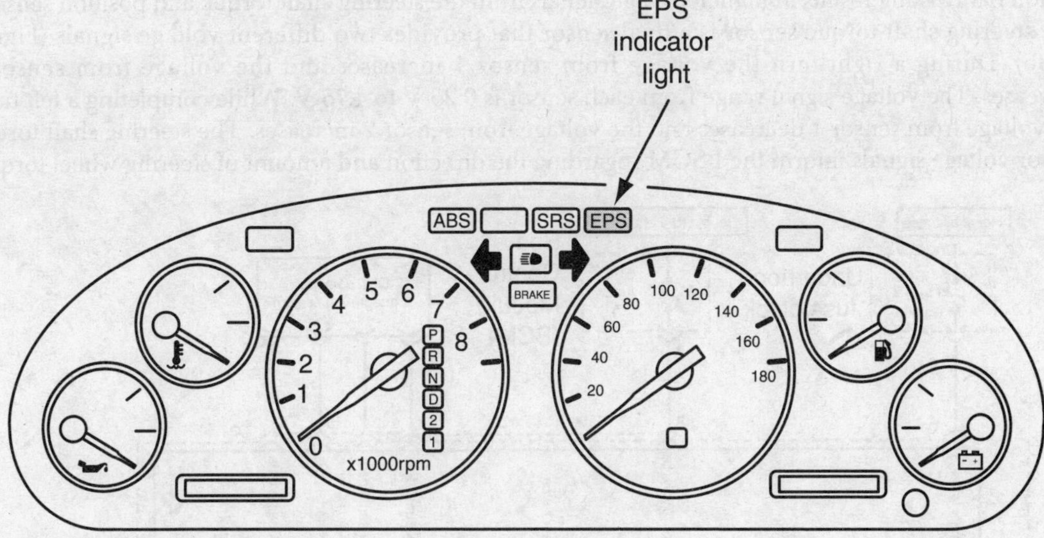

FIGURE 12-34 *EPS indicator light.*

COLUMN-DRIVE ELECTRONIC POWER STEERING

Some vehicles are presently equipped with a column-drive EPS. In this type of EPS, a motor/module assembly is bolted to the lower end of the steering column (Figure 12-35). A combined steering wheel position sensor and steering shaft torque sensor is mounted in the steering column at the motor/module attachment point. The module in the motor/module assembly is called the power steering control module (PSCM). Mounting the EPS motor/module assembly under the instrument panel provides underhood space for other components, subjects the assembly to less rigorous temperatures, and may provide better protection during a collision.

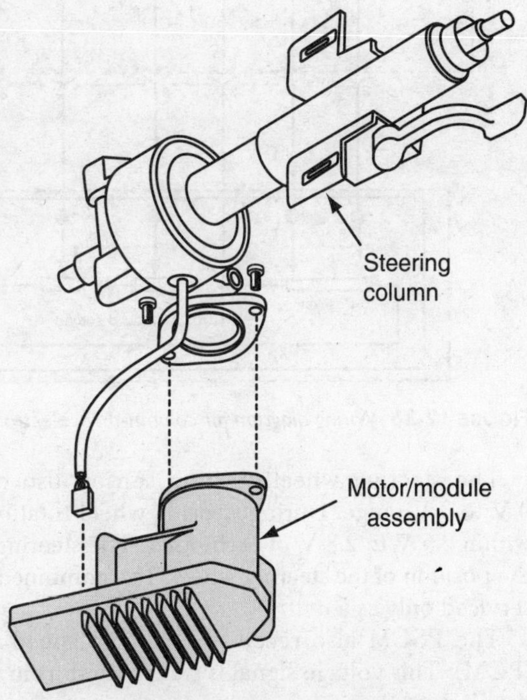

FIGURE 12-35 *Column-drive electronic power steering system.*

Input Sensors

The steering shaft torque sensor is the most important input used by the PSCM to supply the proper amount and direction of steering assist. The steering column contains a torque sensor input shaft connected from the steering wheel to the sensor, and an output shaft connected from the sensor to the steering shaft coupler. A torsion bar mounted inside the steering shaft torque sensor separates the input and output shafts. When the steering wheel is turned in either direction, the torque supplied from the steering wheel to the torsion bar causes this bar to twist. Increased torsion bar twisting results in higher voltage signals from the steering shaft torque and position sensors. The steering shaft torque sensor is a dual sensor that provides two different voltage signals (Figure 12-36). During a right turn the voltage from sensor 1 increases and the voltage from sensor 2 decreases. The voltage signal range from each sensor is 0.25 V to 4.75 V. While completing a left turn, the voltage from sensor 1 decreases and the voltage from sensor 2 increases. The steering shaft torque sensor voltage signals inform the PSCM regarding the direction and amount of steering wheel torque.

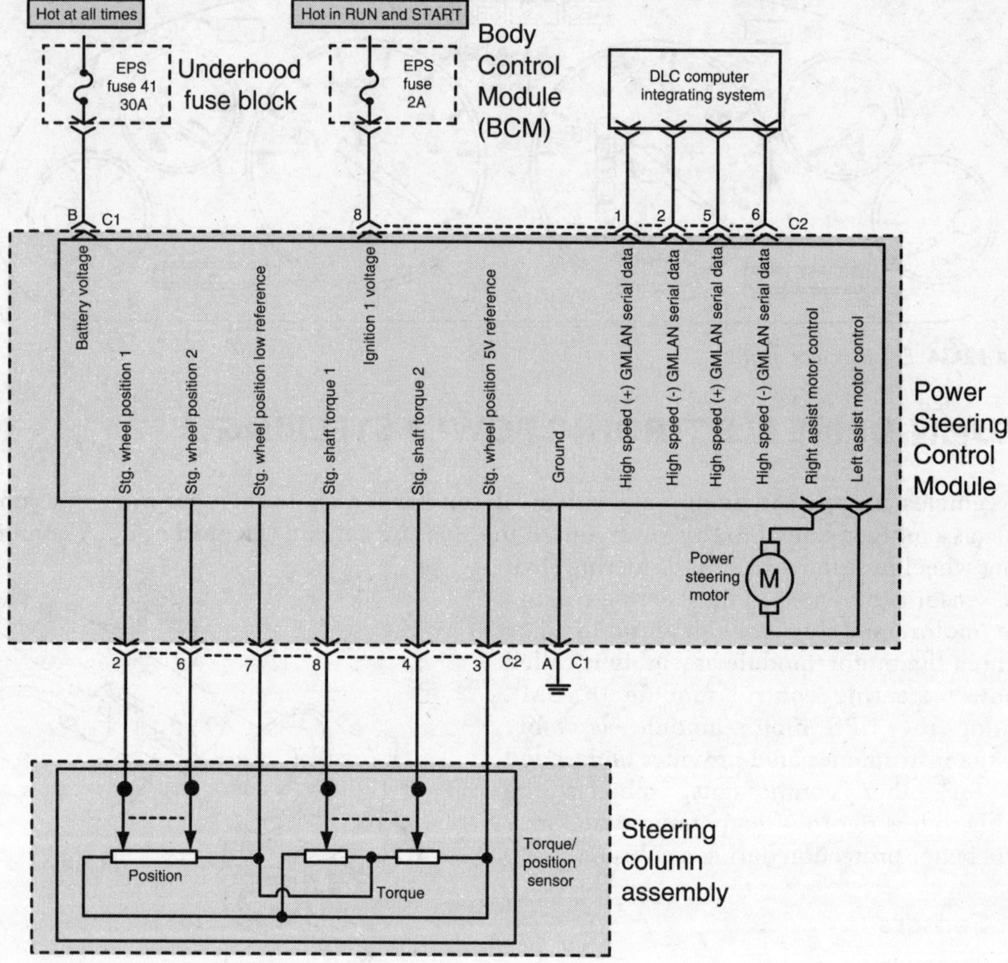

FIGURE 12-36 *Wiring diagram for column-drive electronic power steering.*

The steering wheel position sensor also contains dual voltage sensors that operate in the 0 V to 5 V range. During steering wheel rotation the voltage from these two sensors should remain within 2.5 V to 2.8 V of each other. The steering wheel position sensor informs the PSCM regarding the position of the steering wheel. The combined steering shaft torque and position sensor assembly is serviced only as a unit.

The PSCM also receives a vehicle speed input signal from the powertrain control module (PCM). This voltage signal is transmitted from the PCM to the PSCM through the interconnecting data links.

Power Steering Motor

The power steering motor is a 12 V brushless DC reversible motor rated at 65 amperes. This motor is coupled to the steering shaft through a worm gear and reduction gear located in the steering column housing.

COLUMN-DRIVE ELECTRONIC POWER STEERING OPERATION

When the input signals indicate the driver is beginning to turn the steering wheel, the PSCM supplies the proper amount of current to the power steering motor to provide the necessary power steering assist. At low vehicle speeds the PSCM provides more steering assist for easy steering wheel rotation during parking maneuvers. The PSCM reduces the motor current and provides reduced steering assist when the vehicle is driven at higher speeds to supply improved road feel and directional stability. If the EPS motor becomes overheated, the PSCM enters a protection mode that reduces motor current to avoid thermal damage to system components. The PSCM has the capability to detect electronic system defects in the EPS system. When a defect is detected, a POWER STEERING warning message is displayed in the driver information center (DIC) in the instrument panel and the malfunction light (MIL) may also illuminate. The PSCM must be programmed with the correct steering tuning in relation to the vehicle powertrain configuration.

PINION-DRIVE ELECTRONIC POWER STEERING

Some hybrid vehicles are equipped with a 12 V EPS, because on these vehicles the engine is automatically shut off during idle operation to conserve fuel and reduce emissions, and the power steering remains operational when the engine is stopped. The EPS also conserves fuel because it is used on demand only when the driver turns the steering wheel. On conventional hydraulic power steering systems the power steering pump operates all the time the engine is running. Some current hybrid vehicles have a pinion-drive EPS. The electric motor on the EPS is coupled to the pinion in the rack and pinion steering gear (Figure 12-37). Except for the drive motor and related drive gears, the other components in the EPS are conventional in design. The EPS is lubricated for life and has no reservoir, fluid, or hoses.

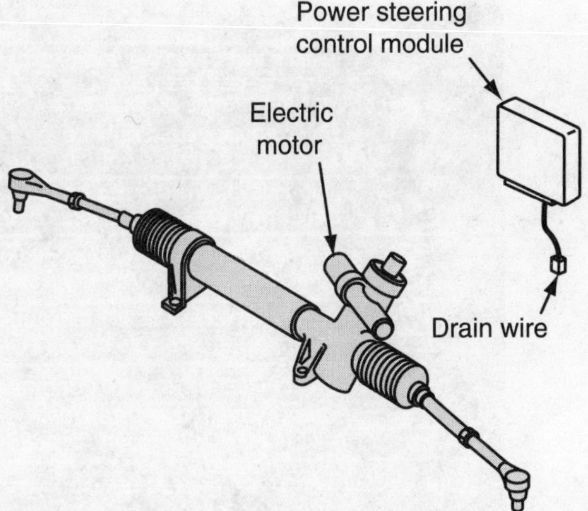

FIGURE 12-37 *Pinion-drive electronic power steering (EPS) steering gear.*

The EPS contains an electromagnetic-type rotational sensor mounted in the steering gear input shaft. This rotational sensor changes a rotational signal to a voltage signal representing the direction and amount of torque supplied from the steering wheel to the input shaft. The power steering control module (PSCM) is mounted on the cowl above the steering gear. The PSCM is interconnected to other on-board computers through the data link system. Additional inputs such as vehicle speed are transmitted from the PCM through the data links to the PSCM. When the PSCM receives input signals from the rotational sensor and the PCM, the PSCM supplies the proper amount and direction of current flow to the electric motor in the EPS to provide the required steering assist. A drain wire is connected from the PSCM to ground. This wire prevents the EPS from emitting electromagnetic interference that could affect other electrical/electronic systems in the vehicle. If a defect occurs in the EPS electrical system, a SERVICE PWR STEERING message illuminates in the instrument panel.

HYBRID VEHICLE SAFETY PRECAUTIONS

This section presents information only regarding EPS on some hybrid vehicles. However, most hybrid vehicles have high voltage systems and require special service precautions. For example, the Ford Escape Hybrid has a battery under the rear floor that contains 250 nickel metal hydride cells that are connected to produce 330 V. The hybrid vehicle also has a conventional 12 V battery mounted under the hood. The high voltage battery supplies high voltage and current to the electric motor in the continuously variable transmission (CVT) to drive the vehicle. An on-board computer determines whether power is supplied to the drive wheels from the electric motor, the gasoline engine, or both.

High voltage warning decals are located on all high voltage components and at other strategic locations on the vehicle (Figure 12-38). Before servicing any of the high voltage components on a hybrid vehicle, the high voltage service disconnect must be disconnected (Figure 12-39). Always wear high-voltage rubber safety gloves when working on hybrid vehicles. All the safety precautions in the hybrid vehicle manufacturer's service manual must be followed.

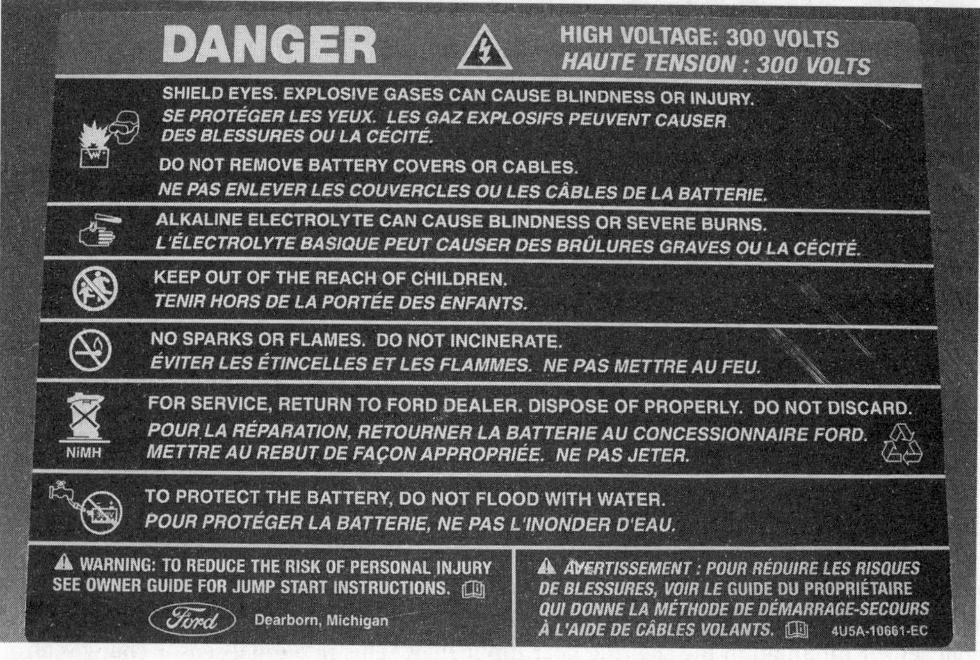

FIGURE 12-38 *High voltage warning labels on a hybrid vehicle.*

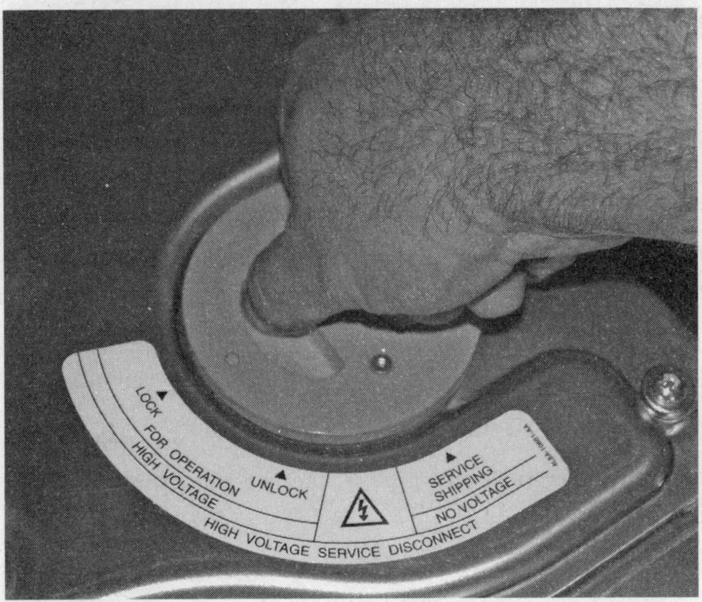

FIGURE 12-39 *High voltage service disconnect on a hybrid vehicle.*

REVIEW QUESTIONS

Short Answer Essays

1. Explain why the rack and pinion steering gear is ideally suited for unibody front-wheel-drive vehicles.
2. Identify the component in a parallelogram steering linkage that compares to the rack in a rack and pinion steering gear.
3. Describe the difference between spur and helical gear teeth, and explain the advantage of helical gear teeth.
4. Explain the purpose of the bellows boots in a rack and pinion steering gear.
5. Describe two possible mounting positions for rack and pinion steering gears.
6. Explain why a rack and pinion steering gear provides improved feel of the road compared with a recirculating ball steering gear and parallelogram steering linkage.
7. Describe the fluid movement in the rack piston chamber during a right turn.
8. Explain how the spool valve is moved inside the rotary valve in a power rack and pinion steering gear.
9. Explain the operation of each input sensor in a Ford electronic variable orifice (EVO) steering system.
10. Describe the driving conditions required for an electronic variable orifice (EVO) steering system to provide high-power steering assistance.

Fill-in-the-Blanks

1. The preload on the rack and pinion teeth affects steering harshness, noise, and ____________.
2. Compared to a recirculating ball steering gear and parallelogram steering linkage, a rack and pinion steering system has a reduced ability to isolate road noise and vibration because the rack and pinion system has fewer ____________ ____________.
3. During a left turn, the power steering pump forces fluid into the ____________ side of the rack chamber, and fluid is removed from the ____________ side of this chamber.
4. During a turn, fluid is directed to the appropriate side of the rack piston chamber by the ____________ valve and ____________ valve position.
5. When the torsion bar twists, it changes the position of the ____________ valve.
6. In an end take-off power rack and pinion steering gear, the tie-rods are connected to the ____________.
7. In a center take-off power rack and pinion steering gear, the tie-rods are attached to a ____________ ____________.
8. In an EVO steering system, the power steering assistance is decreased at higher speeds to provide improved ____________ ____________.
9. The input sensors in an EVO steering system are the vehicle speed sensor and the ____________ ____________ ____________ ____________.
10. In an EVO steering system, the actuator solenoid is mounted in the ____________ ____________ ____________.

Multiple Choice

1. Compared to a recirculating ball steering gear, a rack and pinion steering gear provides:
   A. Improved capability to isolate road noise.
   B. Better capability to reduce steering harshness on road irregularities.
   C. Increased capability to absorb steering kickback.
   D. Increased road feel.
2. If the lock-to-lock steering wheel rotation is 4 turns and the total front wheel movement is 75 degrees, the steering ratio is:
   A. 15.6:1. **C.** 18.4:1.
   B. 16.1:1. **D.** 19.2:1.
3. All of these statements about a power rack and pinion steering gear are true EXCEPT:
   A. During a left turn fluid pressure is directed to the left side of the rack piston.
   B. During a right turn fluid pressure is directed to the right side of the rack piston.
   C. Fluid is directed to the appropriate side of the rack piston by the position of the rotary valve inside the spool valve.
   D. The spool valve is moved by torsion bar twisting during a turn.

4. In a power rack and pinion steering gear, feel of the road is provided by:
A. Torsion bar twisting.
B. Rack bearing adjusting nut torque.
C. The rack piston.
D. The spool valve and rotary valve.

5. In a power rack and pinion steering gear the breather tube:
A. Vents the right rack piston chamber during a left turn.
B. Moves air from one boot to the other during a turn.
C. Allows air into the rotary valve area while driving straight ahead.
D. Prevents pressure buildup in both rack piston chambers when driving straight ahead.

6. The power steering pump belt breaks on a rack and pinion power steering system. Under this condition:
A. The torsion bar may be broken when the front wheels are turned to the right or left.
B. The steering operates like a manual steering system, and steering effort is higher.
C. The spool valve no longer moves inside the rotary valve when the steering wheel is turned.
D. Power steering fluid may be forced from the rack seals when the steering wheel is turned.

7. In electronic variable orifice (EVO) steering systems:
A. Steering assistance is increased if vehicle speed is above 25 mph (40 km/h).
B. The control unit operates a relay in the steering gear to control steering assist.
C. Steering assistance is increased if the vehicle speed is below 10 mph (16 km/h) and steering wheel rotation is above 15 rpm.
D. The control unit increases steering assistance at higher speed to provide improved road feel.

8. All of these statements about electronic power steering are true EXCEPT:
A. The system remains operational if the engine stalls and the ignition switch is on.
B. The power module is a separate unit from the electronic power steering control unit.
C. The power module controls current flow through the steering gear motor with a pulse width modulated (PWM) voltage signal.
D. The interface in the steering sensor rectifies AC current to DC current and amplifies the steering sensor voltage signals.

9. If an electrical defect occurs in the electronic power steering (EPS) system:
A. The system continues to operate normally, but the EPS warning light is illuminated.
B. The system continues to operate with a slightly reduced power steering assist.
C. The EPS control unit shuts the system down by opening the fail safe and power relays.
D. The EPS control unit locks the armature in the steering gear to prevent armature and screw shaft damage.

10. In an electronic power steering (EPS) system:
A. The EPS control unit determines the direction of steering wheel rotation from the steering sensor signals.
B. The variable differential transformer in the steering sensor contains one primary and one secondary winding.
C. When driving straight ahead, the slider in the steering sensor is at the lower end of its travel.
D. The vehicle speed sensor (VSS) voltage signal is sent directly to the EPS control unit.

FOUR-WHEEL STEERING SYSTEMS

13

Upon completion and review of this chapter, you should be able to:

- Explain the advantages of four-wheel steering (4WS).
- Explain how the rear steering rack is driven in a Quadrasteer system.
- Describe the two inputs used by the control unit to operate the rear steering in a Quadrasteer system.
- Explain why a higher output alternator is required on a vehicle equipped with Quadrasteer.
- Describe negative-phase and positive-phase steering in a Quadrasteer system.
- Explain the advantages of a Quadrasteer system when towing a trailer.
- Describe the input sensors in an electronically controlled four-wheel steering system and give the location of each sensor.
- Describe the type of signal produced by a wheel speed sensor.
- Explain the steering action of the rear wheels in relation to vehicle speed in an electronically controlled four-wheel steering system.

INTRODUCTION

If a car with conventional front wheel steering is parallel parked at a curb between two vehicles, this car may be driven from the parking space without hitting the car in front if the front wheels are turned all the way to the left (Figure 13-1, view A). When the same car is equipped with 4WS and the rear wheels steer in the same direction as the front wheels at low speed, the car will not steer out of the parking space without striking the vehicle in front (Figure 13-1, view B).

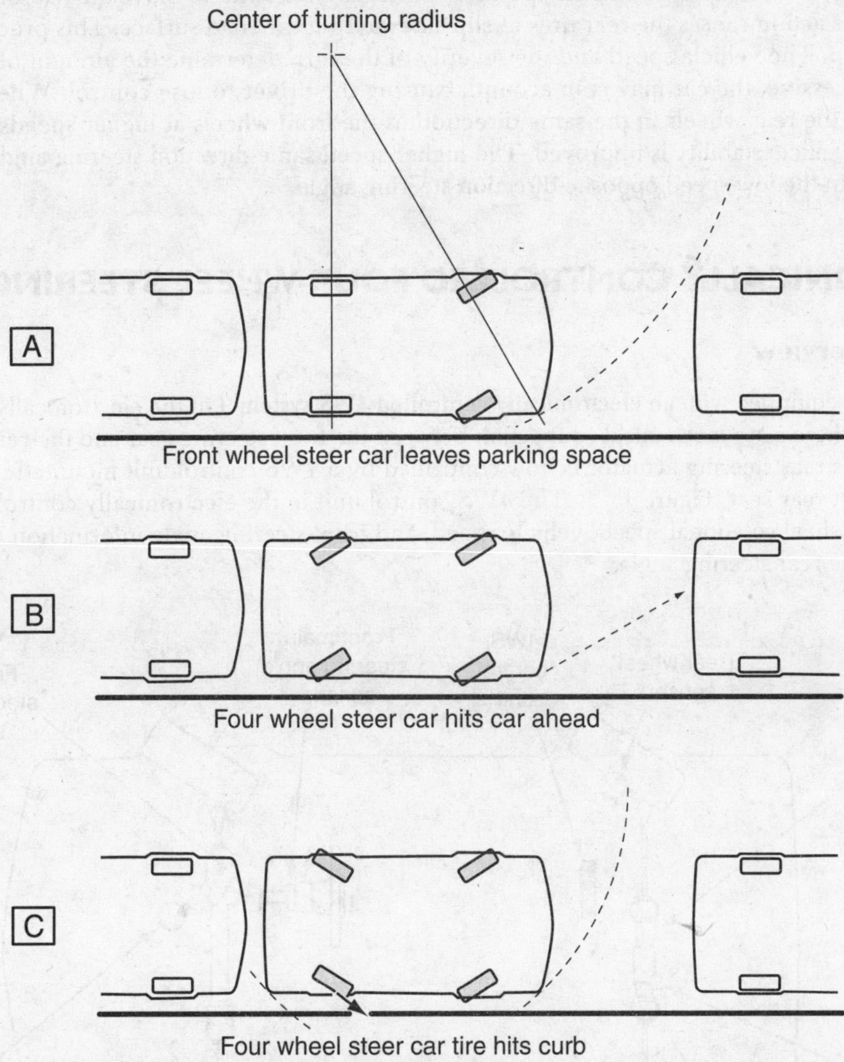

FIGURE 13-1 *Parallel parking with conventional front wheel steering and four-wheel steering.*

When the car in the same parking space has a 4WS system that steers the rear wheels in the opposite direction to the front wheels at low speed, the car steers out of the parking space with plenty of distance between the vehicle parked in front (Figure 13-1, view C). When the rear wheels steer in the opposite direction to the front wheels, the rear wheels steer toward the curb. This action causes the right rear tire to strike the curb if the car is parked close to the curb. Therefore, the maximum rear

steering angle must be considerably less than the maximum front wheel steering angle to help prevent this problem. A car with 4WS has a smaller **turning circle**, or turning radius, compared to a vehicle with conventional front wheel steering. This improves maneuverability while parking.

The rear wheel steering in a 4WS system may be controlled in relation to vehicle speed or the amount of steering wheel rotation. At low vehicle speeds or with a considerable amount of steering wheel rotation, the rear wheels are steered in the opposite direction to the front wheels. When the vehicle is operating at higher speeds or with a small amount of steering wheel rotation, the rear wheels are steered in the same direction as the front wheels.

When a vehicle is cornering at higher speeds, centrifugal force tends to move the rear of the vehicle sideways. This action causes the rear tires to slip sideways on the road surface. This process may be called **sideslip.** The vehicle speed and the severity of the turn determine the amount of sideslip. If sideslip is excessive, the car may spin around, causing the driver to lose control. When the 4WS system steers the rear wheels in the same direction as the front wheels at higher speeds, sideslip is reduced and vehicle stability is improved. The higher speed same-direction steering angle is considerably less than the low-speed opposite-direction steering angle.

ELECTRONICALLY CONTROLLED FOUR-WHEEL STEERING

System Overview

Some cars are equipped with an **electronically controlled 4WS system**. On the electronically controlled 4WS system, there is no mechanical connection between the front steering gear and the **rear steering actuator**. This rear steering actuator is now controlled by a 4WS control unit mounted in the trunk behind the left rear seat (Figure 13-2). The 4WS control unit in the electronically controlled system uses steering wheel rotational speed, vehicle speed, and front steering angle information to calculate and control the rear steering angle.

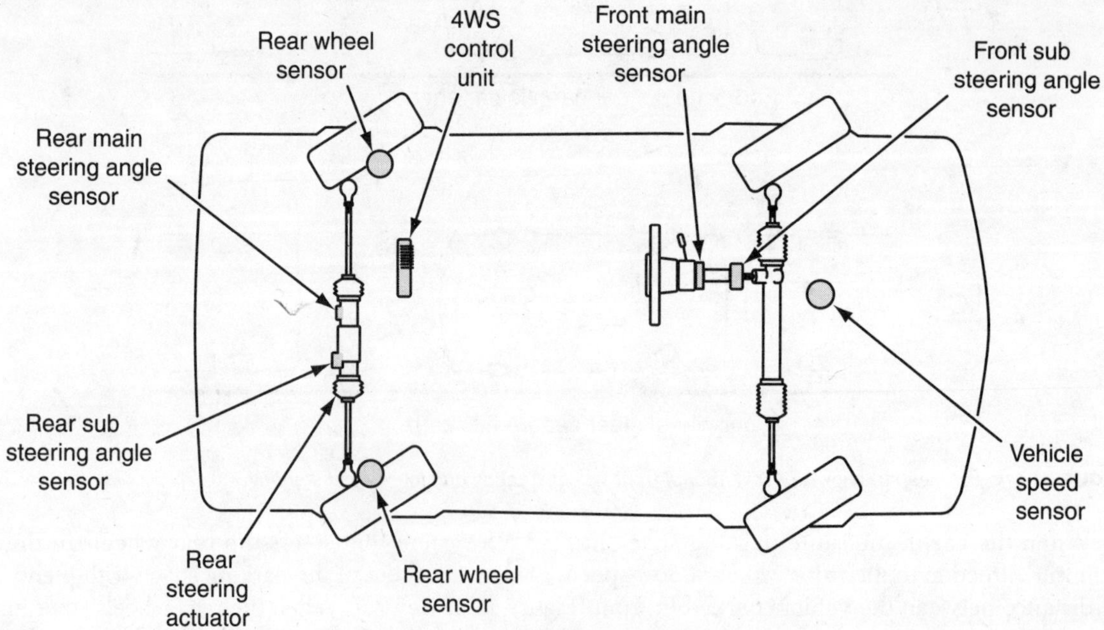

FIGURE 13-2 *Electronically controlled 4WS with control unit mounted in the trunk.*

Rear Steering Actuator

The rear steering actuator may be compared to an electric steering gear. This actuator contains an electric motor that drives a steering rack through a ball screw mechanism (Figure 13-3). Conventional tie-rods are connected from the steering actuator to the rear steering arms and spindles. A return spring inside the actuator moves the rear wheels to the straight-ahead position when the ignition switch is turned off or when a defect occurs in the 4WS system. A main rear wheel angle sensor and a sub rear wheel angle sensor are mounted on top of the rear steering actuator.

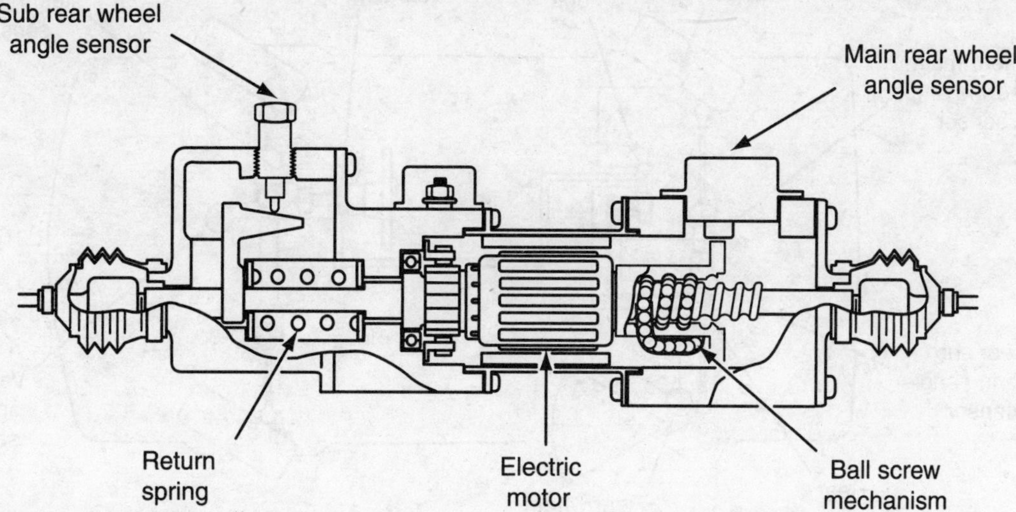

FIGURE 13-3 *Rear steering actuator, electronically controlled 4WS system.*

INPUT SENSORS

Input sensors in the electronically controlled 4WS include the following:

1. Main rear wheel angle sensor in the rear steering actuator.
2. Sub rear wheel angle sensor in the rear steering actuator.
3. Main **steering wheel angle sensor** in the steering column under the combination switch.
4. Sub front wheel steering angle sensor in the front rack and pinion steering gear.
5. Conventional rear ABS wheel speed sensors.
6. Conventional vehicle speed sensor (VSS).

CAUTION: Some electronic sensor wires have a special shield surrounding them to prevent electromagnetic interference (EMI) from other voltage sources. If this shield is damaged or removed, computer system operation may be adversely affected. Do not reroute sensor wires close to other voltage sources such as spark plug wires.

FOUR-WHEEL STEERING SYSTEM OPERATION

4WS Control Unit Operation

When the engine is running, the 4WS control unit continually receives information from all the input sensors. If the steering wheel is turned, the 4WS control unit analyzes information from the vehicle speed sensor, main steering wheel angle sensor, sub front wheel angle sensor, main rear wheel angle sensor, sub rear wheel angle sensor, and the rear wheel speed sensors. The 4WS control unit calculates the proper rear wheel steering angle and then sends battery voltage to the rear steering actuator motor to provide this rear steering angle (Figure 13-4).

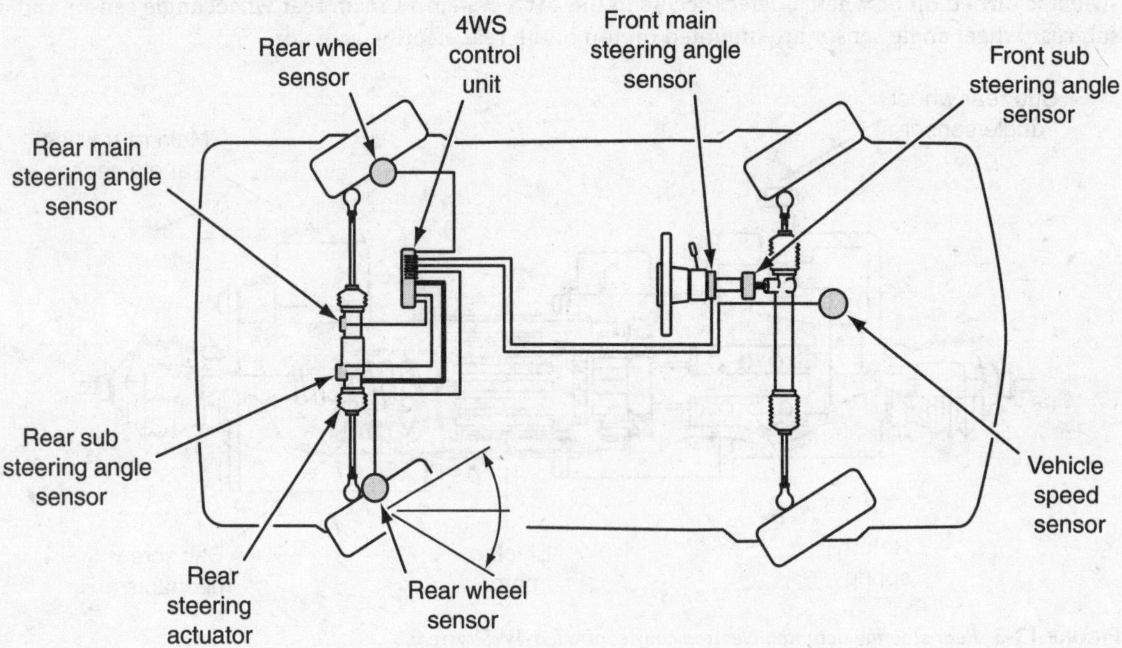

FIGURE 13-4 *The 4WS control unit analyzes input sensor information, calculates the required rear steering angle, and operates the rear steering actuator motor to provide the proper rear steering angle.*

Battery voltage is sent to the rear steering actuator motor through two heavy-duty output **transistors**. One of these transistors conducts current during a right turn, whereas the other transistor is activated during a left turn. The main rear wheel angle sensor and the sub rear wheel angle sensor send feedback signals to the 4WS control unit, indicating the proper rear steering angle has been supplied.

4WS Operating Characteristics

When the vehicle speed is less than 18 mph (29 km/h), the rear wheels immediately begin to steer in the opposite direction to the front wheels if the steering wheel is turned (Figure 13-5). Maximum rear steering angle is 6° at 0 mph. The rate of rear steering angle decreases in relation to vehicle speed, and at 18 mph (29 km/h) the amount of rear steering angle is almost zero.

When the vehicle speed increases above 18 mph (29 km/h), the rear wheels steer in the same direction as the front wheels through the first 200° of steering wheel rotation. The rear steering angle reverts to the opposite phase if the steering wheel is rotated more than 200° in this vehicle speed range. When the vehicle speed is 60 mph (96 km/h) and the steering wheel rotation is 100°, the rear wheels steer about 1° in the same direction as the front wheels. If the steering wheel is rotated 500° at this speed, the rear wheels are steered about 1° in the opposite direction to the front wheels.

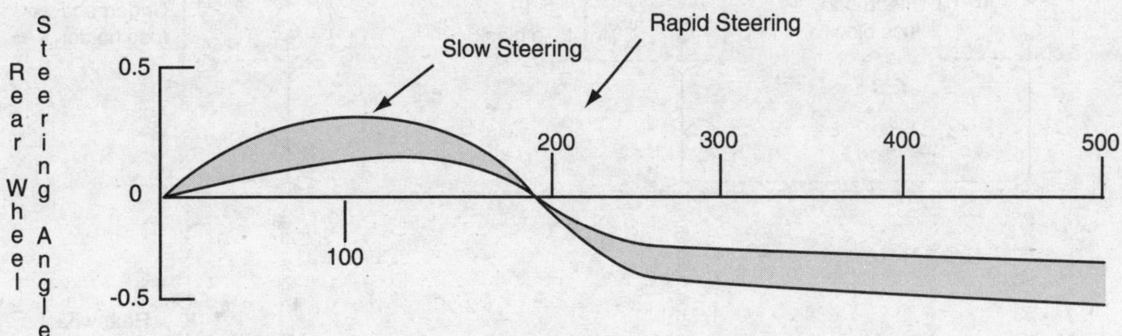

FIGURE 13-5 *Rear steering angle in relation to vehicle speed and steering wheel rotation.*

QUADRASTEER FOUR-WHEEL STEERING SYSTEMS

A **Quadrasteer** system is available on some light-duty trucks and SUVs. The Quadrasteer system is a 4-wheel steering (4WS) system that improves low speed maneuverability, high speed stability, and towing capability. The Quadrasteer system has an electronically powered rear steering system. Vehicles with a Quadrasteer system require a higher output alternator because of the additional electrical load of the rear wheel steering actuator motor.

Rear Wheel Steering Control Module and Driver Select Switch

The rear wheel steering control module is mounted on the frame under the rear of the vehicle (Figure 13-6). This module controls all the rear wheel steering functions. A 125A mega fuse in an underhood fuse holder supplies voltage to the control module at all times (Figure 13-7). Battery voltage is also

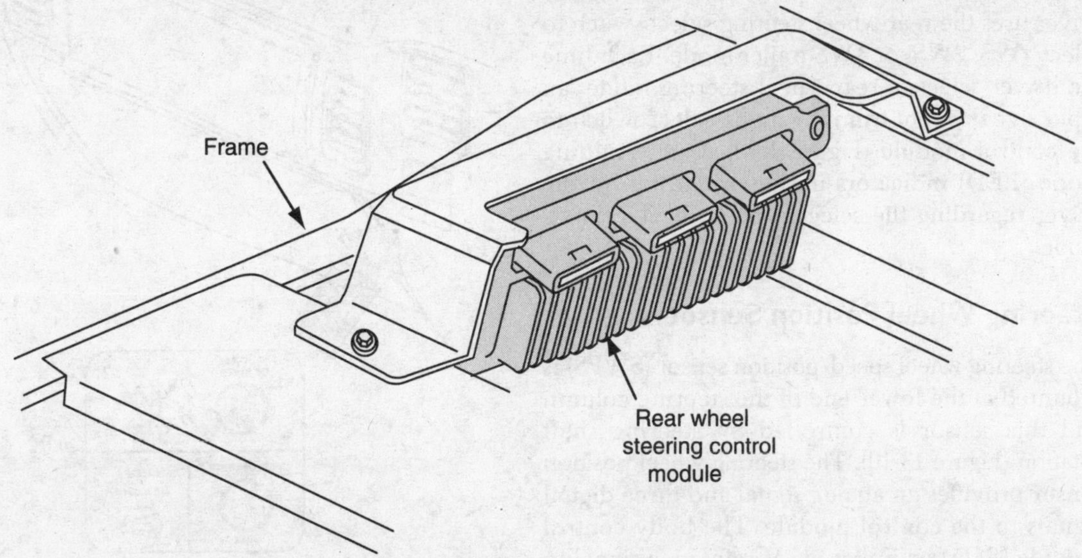

FIGURE 13-6 *Rear wheel steering control module.*

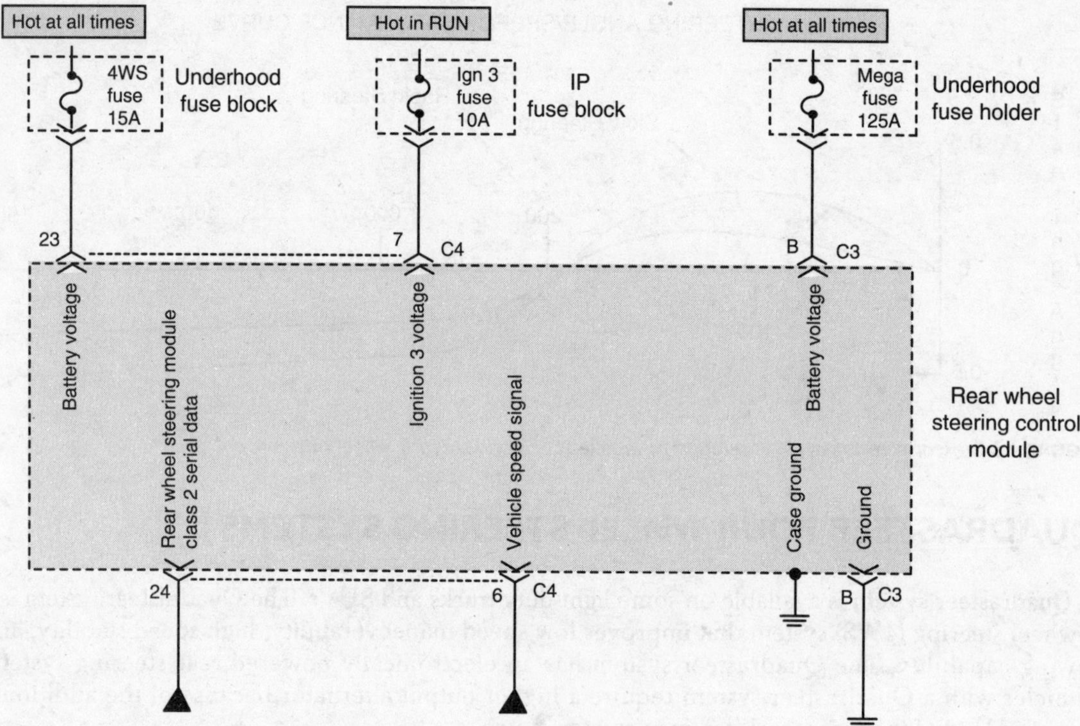

FIGURE 13-7 *Battery and ignition voltage inputs to the rear wheel steering control module.*

supplied to the control module from the 4WS fuse, and the control module receives ignition voltage through the 10A ignition fuse.

The rear wheel steering mode select switch is mounted in the instrument panel (Figure 13-8). The driver uses the rear wheel steering select switch to select 4WS, 2WS, or 4WS trailer mode. Each time the driver selects a rear wheel steering mode, an input signal is sent from the mode select switch to the control module (Figure 13-9). Light emitting diode (LED) indicators in the switch inform the driver regarding the selected rear wheel steering mode.

Steering Wheel Position Sensor

The steering wheel speed/position sensor (SWPS) is mounted at the lower end of the steering column and this sensor is controlled by steering shaft rotation (Figure 13-10). The steering wheel position sensor provides an analog signal and three digital signals to the control module. The body control module (BCM) supplies a 5 V reference signal to the SWPS, and a low reference or ground wire is

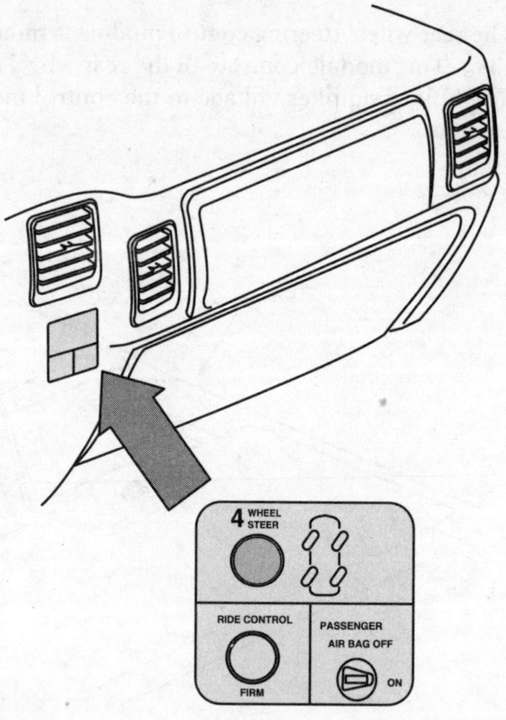

FIGURE 13-8 *Rear wheel steering mode select switch.*

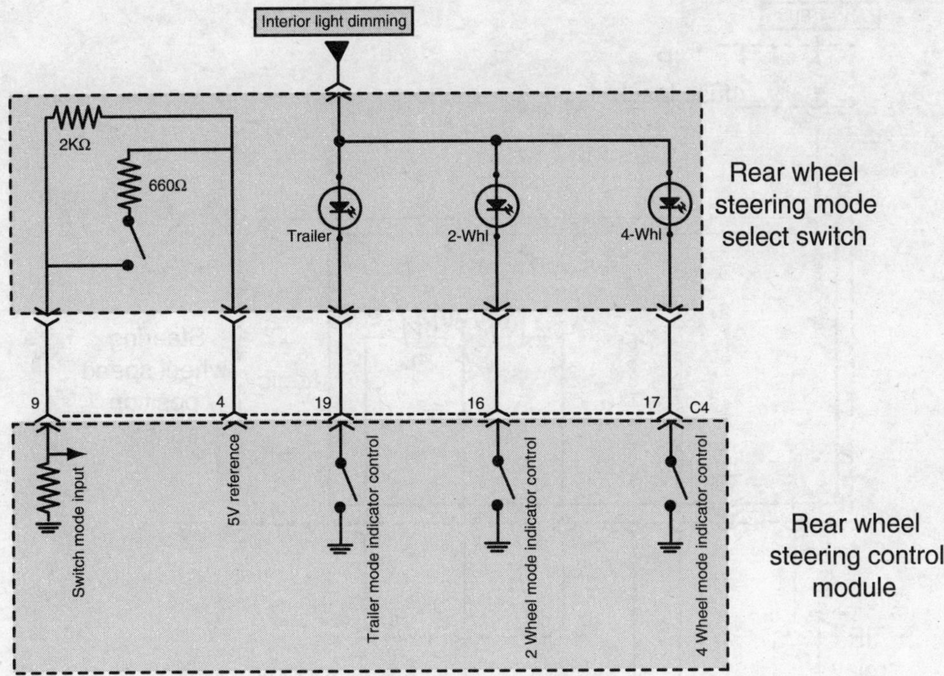

FIGURE 13-9 *Rear wheel steering mode select switch inputs to the control module.*

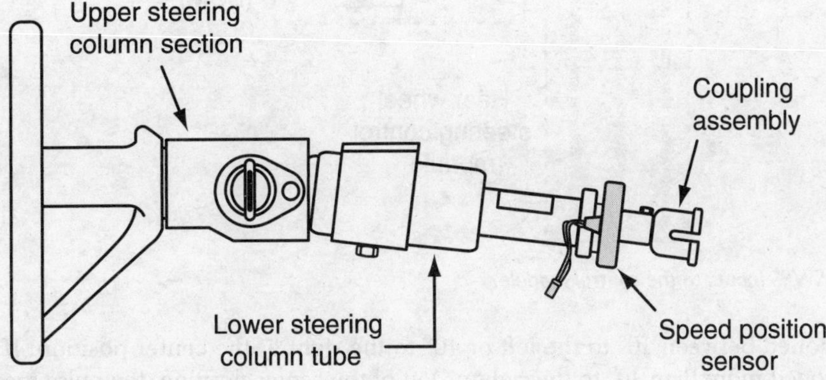

FIGURE 13-10 *Steering wheel speed/position sensor.*

also connected from the SWPS to the BCM. The SWPS contains a potentiometer, which sends an **analog voltage signal** to the BCM in relation to steering wheel rotation (Figure 13-11). The analog voltage signal from the SWPS to the BCM ranges from 0.25 V with the steering wheel positioned one turn to the left of the center position to 4.75 V when the steering wheel is positioned one turn to the right of the center position. With the steering wheel in the center position, the SWPS analog voltage signal is 2.5 V. When the steering wheel is turned more than one turn to the right of left of the center position, the SWPS signal does not change. The BCM relays the SWPS analog voltage signal through class 2 data links to the rear wheel steering control module.

The SWPS sends digital signals through the phase A, phase B, and marker pulse circuits directly to the control module. The marker pulse digital signal is displayed on a scan tool as High if the steering

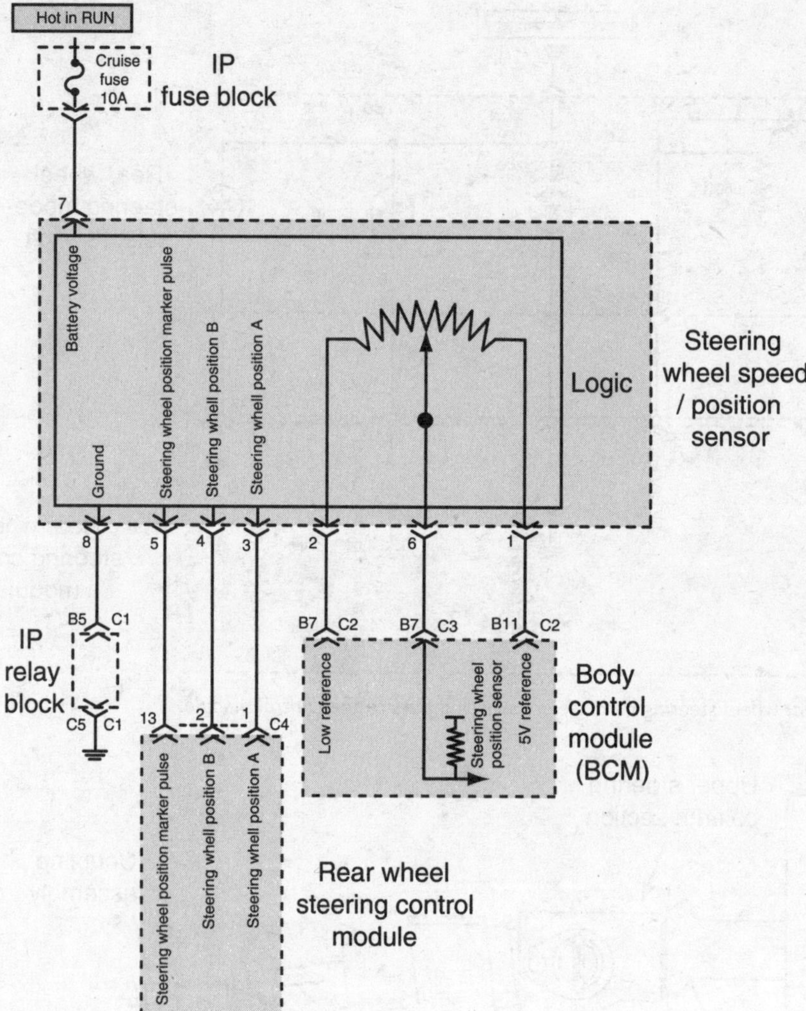

FIGURE 13-11 *SWPS inputs to the control module.*

wheel is positioned between 10° to the left or 10° to the right of the center position. If the steering wheel is positioned more than 10° to the right or left of the center position, the pulse marker signal is displayed as Low. The phase A and phase B signals are displayed on a scan tool as High or Low as the steering wheel is rotated. These signals change from High to Low every one degree of steering wheel rotation.

Rear Wheel Position Sensor

The rear wheel position sensor is mounted on the lower side of the rear wheel steering gear (Figure 13-12). The rear wheel position sensor has two signal circuits connected to the rear wheel steering control module (Figure 13-13). The position 1 signal is a linear measurement of voltage per degree of rear steering position sensor rotation. For the position 1 input the measurement in degrees is from –620° to the left to +620° to the right. The voltage signal from the position 1 input is 0.25 V to 4.75 V. If the signal voltage from position 1 is 0.25 V, the steering wheel has been rotated –600° past center. When the signal voltage from position 1 is 4.75 V, the steering wheel has been rotated +600° past center. The voltage signal from position 2 increases or decreases from 0.25 V to 4.75 V every 180° of steering wheel rotation.

Rear Steering Gear

The rear steering gear is a rack and pinion–type gear mounted on the differential cover. The rack is connected through tie-rods and outer tie-rod ends to the steering knuckles. The outer tie-rod ends are threaded onto the tie-rods and retained with a jam nut. The inner ends of the tie-rods are clamped to the ends of the steering gear rack. Special tools are required to remove and install the inner ends of the tie-rods on the rack. The steering knuckles pivot on upper and lower ball joints that are bolted into extensions on the differential housing (Figure 13-14). Constant velocity (CV) joints are mounted near the outer end of each rear axle shaft. Splined shafts extend from the outer side of the CV joints into the rear hub and bearing assemblies that are bolted to the

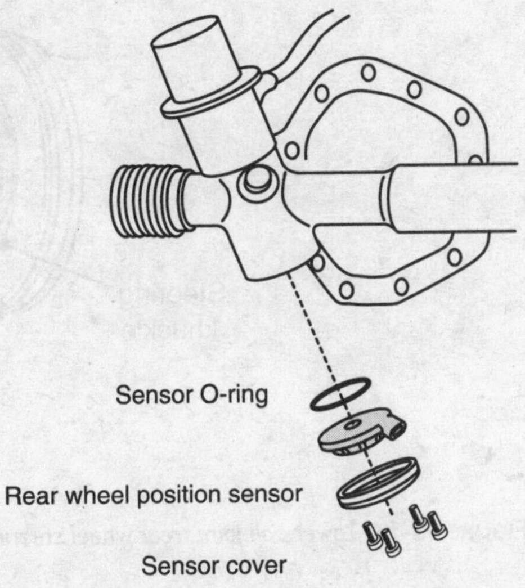

FIGURE 13-12 *Rear wheel position sensor.*

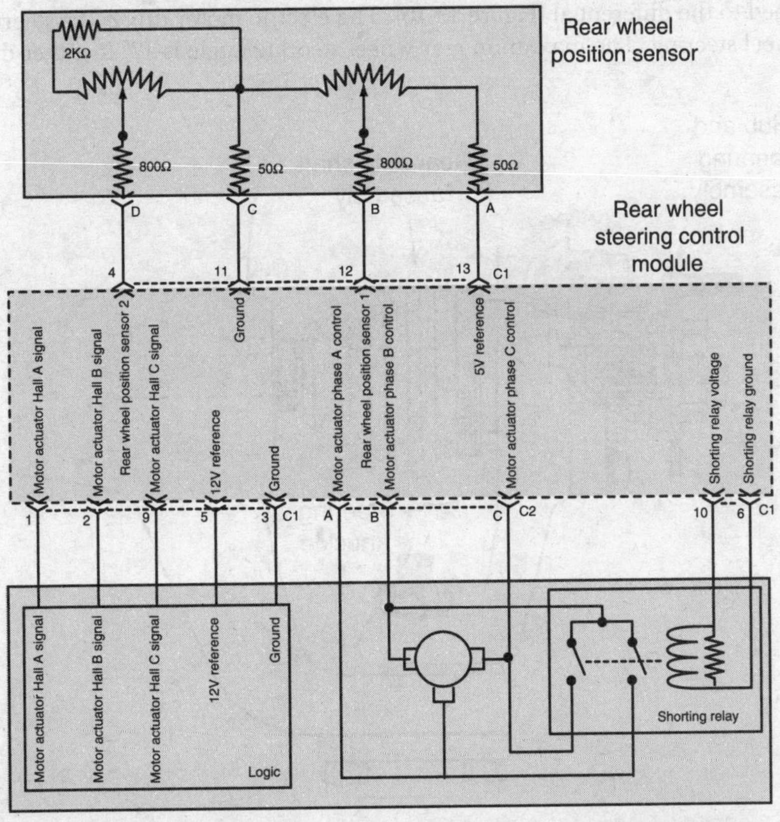

FIGURE 13-13 *Rear wheel position sensor inputs to the rear wheel steering control module.*

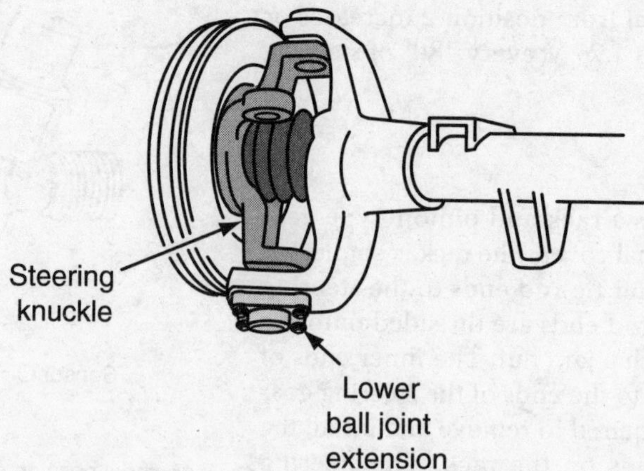

FIGURE 13-14 *Lower ball joint, rear wheel steering.*

steering knuckles (Figure 13-15). A nut, lock, and cotter pin retain the outer ends of the splined shafts in the hub and bearing assemblies. The brake rotors are retained on the studs in the hub and bearing assemblies. The hub and bearing assemblies are not serviceable. The electric drive motor for the rear steering gear is mounted on the top of the steering gear, and this motor is protected by a shield and skid plate attached to the differential (Figure 13-16). The electric motor drives the steering gear rack to provide rear wheel steering. The maximum rear wheel steering angle is 12° in either direction.

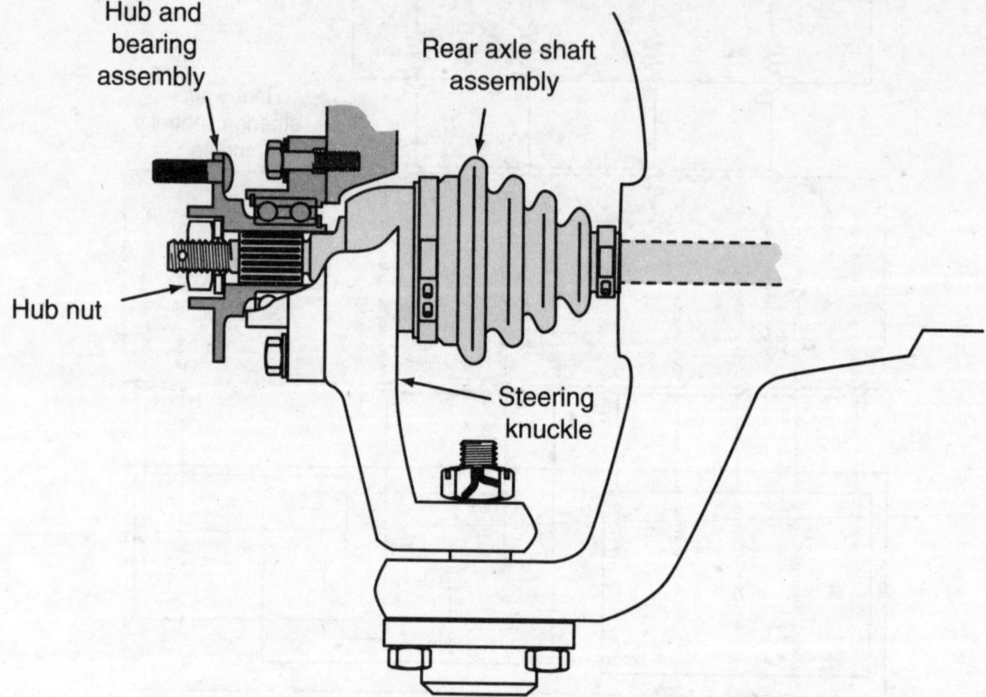

FIGURE 13-15 *Rear axle shaft, hub and bearing assembly, and knuckle, rear wheel steering.*

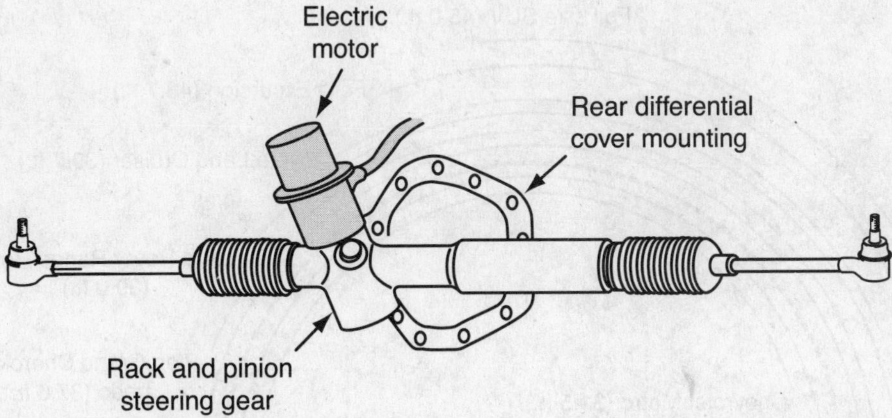

FIGURE 13-16 *Four-wheel steering gear and motor.*

QUADRASTEER FOUR-WHEEL STEERING SYSTEM OPERATION

The rear wheel steering module receives inputs from these sources:

1. Battery voltage
2. Ignition voltage
3. Class 2 serial data links
4. Steering wheel position sensor analog, marker pulse, and phase signals
5. Rear wheel position sensor signals
6. Vehicle speed sensor signal from the instrument panel cluster (IPC)
7. Rear wheel steering mode switch

In response to these input signals, the module commands the rear wheel steering motor to operate the rear wheel steering gear and provide the proper rear wheel steering angle.

In the 2-wheel steer mode the rear wheels are held in a centered position, and the rear wheel steering is disabled.

In the 4-wheel steer mode the rear wheel steering can provide negative phase steering, **neutral phase steering,** or **positive phase steering.** In the negative phase the rear wheels are steered in the opposite direction to the front wheels, and this phase occurs at low vehicle speeds. When the rear wheels are steered in the opposite direction to the front wheels, the vehicle turning radius is reduced and parking maneuverability is improved (Figure 13-17). In the neutral phase the rear wheels remain centered. If an electronic defect occurs in the rear wheel steering system, the rear wheels remain in the neutral phase. When the rear wheel steering control module commands positive phase steering, the module drives the electric motor and steers the rear wheels in the same direction as the front wheels. This action reduces **yaw forces** on the rear of the vehicle and improves steering control at higher speeds. The transition from negative phase to positive phase steering occurs at 40 mph (65 km/h).

In the 4-wheel steer tow mode, the degrees of positive phase steering is increased compared to the 4-wheel steer mode, and the transition speed from negative phase steering to positive phase steering occurs at 25 mph (40 km/h). Below this speed the negative phase steering is similar to the negative phase steering in the 4-wheel steer mode.

WARNING: When diagnosing, servicing, or adjusting a 4WS system, it is very important to follow the diagnostic, service, and adjustment procedures in the vehicle manufacturer's service manual. Failure to follow these procedures may cause improper rear wheel steering operation and reduced vehicle stability that could result in a vehicle collision.

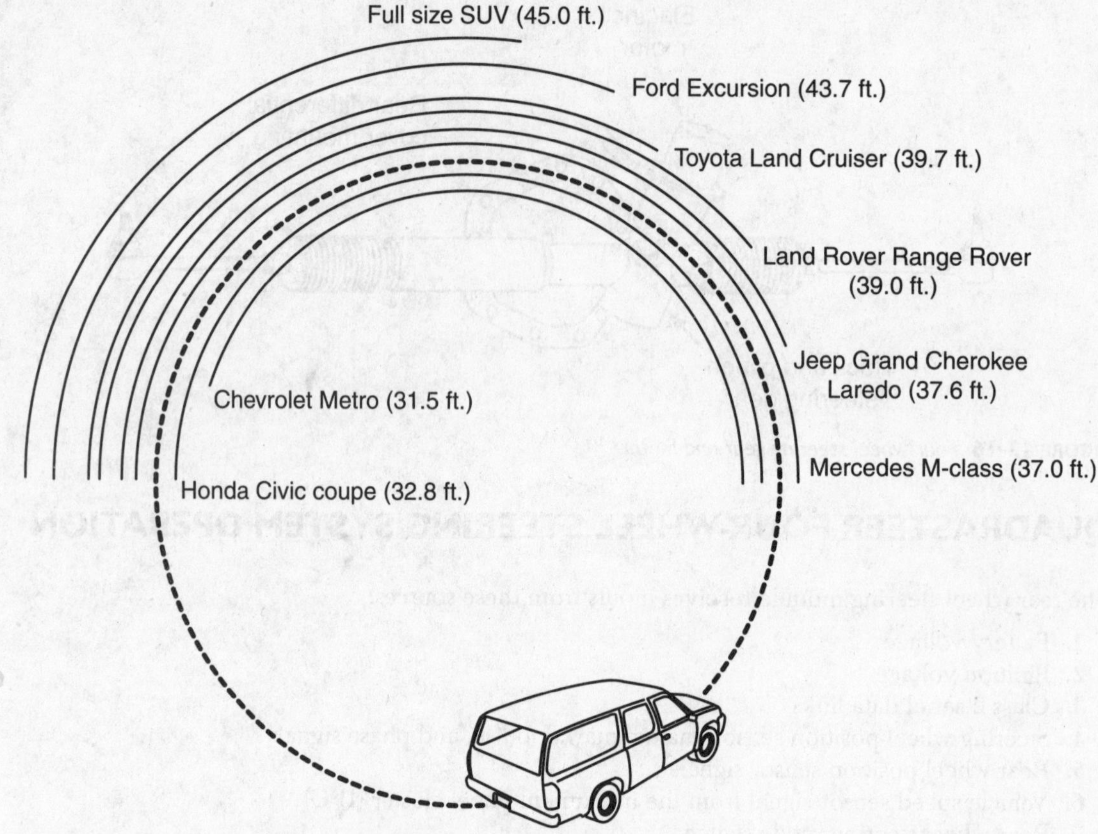

FIGURE 13-17 *Turning circle diameter, four-wheel steering system.*

General Motors engineers decided to install the Quadrasteer system on an SUV because of the advantages of this system when hauling a trailer. When the rear vehicle wheels are steered in the opposite direction to the front wheels during low-speed turning, the trailer follows the true vehicle path more closely than it does with a two-wheel steering system. When backing up a trailer, steering the rear wheels in the opposite direction to the front wheels provides better trailer response to vehicle steering inputs, and this action makes it easier to back the trailer into the desired position. When steering the vehicle at higher speeds such as lane changing, the positive steering action of the rear wheels reduces the articulation angle between the tow vehicle and the trailer. This action reduces the lateral forces applied to the rear of the tow vehicle by the trailer, which in turn reduces yaw velocity gain and improves trailer stability. On a full-size SUV, the Quadrasteer system reduces turning circle diameter from 45 ft. to 33.9 ft. (Figure 13-17).

REAR ACTIVE STEERING SYSTEM

Rear active steering (RAS) has recently been introduced as standard equipment on the 2006 Infinity M series luxury car. The manufacturer claims this car is the most technologically advanced Infinity model ever developed, and also claims the RAS is probably the most significant new technology on the vehicle. This technology is new to the luxury car segment. The RAS makes the steering and handling characteristics on this long-wheelbase car more nimble and agile compared to models without this technology.

The RAS improves steering and handling by adjusting the geometry of the rear suspension in relation to steering input and vehicle speed. The RAS control unit calculates the ultimate vehicle dynamics from the input signals from a group of sensors. In response to these inputs the control unit operates the electric actuator to lengthen or shorten each lower rear suspension link (Figure 13-18). This action provides a possible 1° turn on each rear wheel.

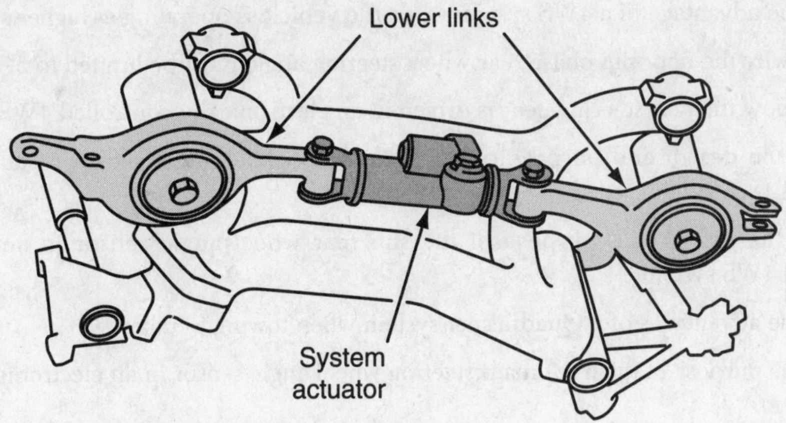

FIGURE 13-18 *Rear steering actuator and adjustable lower links.*

When the vehicle begins turning a corner, driving around a curve, or making a lane change at midspeed, the control unit operates the RAS actuator to initially turn the rear wheels in the negative phase mode in relation to the front wheels (Figure 13-19). This action provides improved turn-in response.

When the steering wheel rotation indicates the vehicle is exiting a corner or making a lane change at mid-speed, the control unit operates the RAS actuator to turn the rear wheels in the positive phase mode in relation to the front wheels (Figure 13-20). Under this condition yaw forces are reduced on the rear of the vehicle to provide improved vehicle stability.

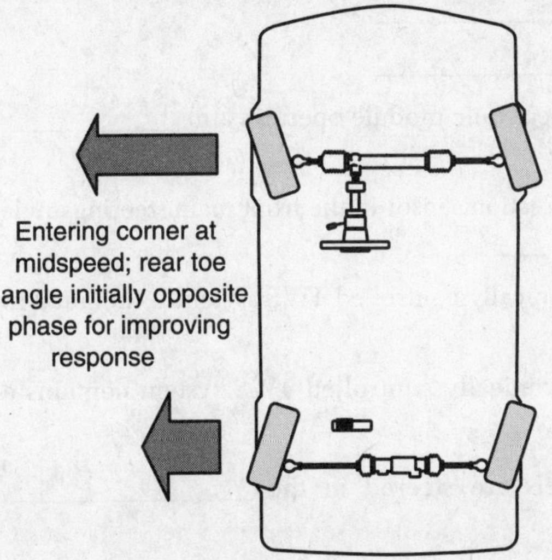

FIGURE 13-19 *Rear wheel steering during negative phase operation.*

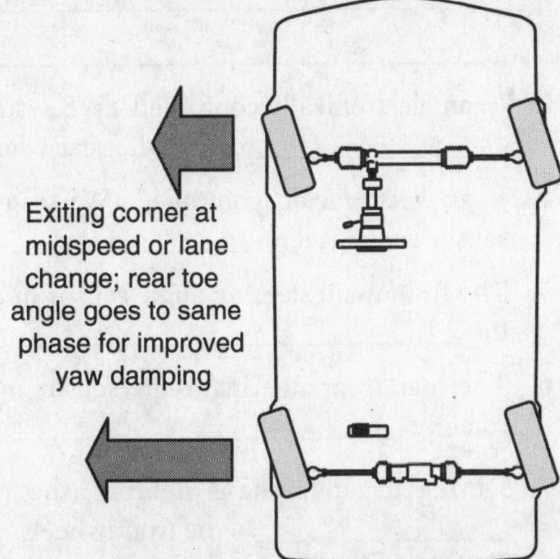

FIGURE 13-20 *Rear wheel steering during positive phase operation.*

REVIEW QUESTIONS

Short Answer Essays

1. Explain the advantage of a 4WS system while parking a vehicle.
2. Explain the advantage of a 4WS system while the vehicle is operating at higher speed.
3. Describe why the opposite phase rear wheel steering angle must be limited to 5° or 6°.
4. Describe how the rear steering gear is driven in an electronically controlled 4WS system.
5. Describe the design and purpose of the main rear wheel angle sensor in an electronically controlled 4WS system.
6. Describe the design and purpose of the sub rear wheel angle sensor in an electronically controlled 4WS system.
7. Explain the advantages of a Quadrasteer system when towing a trailer.
8. Explain the purpose of the front main steering wheel angle sensor in an electronically controlled 4WS system.
9. Explain the advantages of a Quadrasteer system when backing up a trailer.
10. Describe the effect of a 4WS system on turning circle diameter.

Fill-in-the-Blanks

1. When a vehicle with 4WS is parked near the curb, the rear wheels may strike the ______________ while driving out of the parking space.
2. In an electronically controlled 4WS system, the electronic module receives input signals from these sensors:

   ______________ ______________ ______________

   ______________ ______________ ______________

3. In an electronically controlled 4WS system, the electronic module operates a(n) ______________ ______________ to steer the rear wheels.
4. In an electronically controlled 4WS system, the direction sensor in the front main steering angle sensor contains a(n) ______________ ______________.
5. The front main steering angle sensor in an electronically controlled 4WS system is mounted in the ______________ ______________.
6. The main rear steering angle sensor in an electronically controlled 4WS system contains a rotating ______________ ______________.
7. During negative-phase steering, the rear wheels are steered in the ______________ ______________ to the front wheels.
8. When towing a trailer and changing lanes at higher speeds, the Quadrasteer system reduces ______________ ______________ on the rear of the vehicle.

9. A 4WS switch on the dash allows the driver to select ______________ or ______________.

10. In a Quadrasteer system, the rear steering arms are integral with the spindles, and these arms face ______________.

Multiple Choice

1. When a typical Quadrasteer system is operating in the 4-wheel steer mode, the rear wheels are steered in the opposite direction to the front wheels if the vehicle is operating at:
   A. 30 mph (48 km/h).
   B. 45 mph (72 km/h).
   C. 55 mph (88 km/h).
   D. 65 mph (104 km/h).

2. All of these statements about a 4WS system are true EXCEPT:
   A. A 4WS system reduces yaw forces on the vehicle at higher speeds.
   B. A 4WS system provides a smaller turning circle.
   C. A 4WS system reduces tire wear.
   D. A 4WS system improves vehicle maneuverability at low speeds.

3. When a Quadrasteer system is switched from the 4WS mode to the 4WS tow mode, the positive steering angle:
   A. Decreases.
   B. Remains the same.
   C. Increases.
   D. Is reversed.

4. If an electrical defect occurs in a 4WS system the:
   A. The rear wheels remain in the centered position.
   B. Positive phase rear wheel steering is cancelled.
   C. Negative phase rear wheel steering is increased.
   D. Positive phase rear wheel steering angle is increased, and negative phase rear wheel steering is decreased.

5. In a typical Quadrasteer system the rear wheel bearings:
   A. Must be repacked with grease every 60,000 mi. (96,000 km/h).
   B. Must be adjusted each time they are serviced.
   C. Are nonserviceable and must be replaced as a unit.
   D. Must be serviced when the rear axle joints are replaced.

6. In an electronically controlled 4WS system:
   A. The rear steering gear pinion is driven by an electric motor.
   B. There is a mechanical connection between the front steering gear and the rear steering actuator.
   C. The rear wheel speed sensor voltage frequency is constant regardless of wheel speed.
   D. The voltage signal from the vehicle speed sensor is only used by the 4WS control unit.

7. All of these statements about electronically controlled 4WS systems are true EXCEPT:
   A. The rear wheel steering angle is greater in the opposite phase compared to the same phase.
   B. The rear wheel steering angle decreases when the vehicle speed is increased from 0 mph to 18 mph (29 km/h).
   C. When the rear wheels are steered, voltage is sent directly to the armature in the rear steering actuator.
   D. When the ignition switch is turned off, a spring in the rear steering actuator centers the rear wheels.

8. In a Quadrasteer system, the rear steering actuator is operated by:
   A. Linkage to the front steering gear.
   B. An electric motor.
   C. Hydraulic pressure from the power steering system.
   D. Transmission fluid pressure.

9. All of these statements about a Quadrasteer system are true EXCEPT:
   A. It is equipped with an independent rear suspension system.
   B. It requires a higher output alternator.
   C. It is equipped with upper and lower rear ball joints.
   D. The rear axles contain CV joints.

10. In an electronically controlled 4WS system the control module uses all of these inputs EXCEPT:
    A. Steering wheel rotational speed.
    B. Vehicle speed.
    C. Front steering angle.
    D. Brake pedal movement.

FRAMES AND FRAME DAMAGE

14

Upon completion and review of this chapter, you should be able to:

- Explain the purposes of a vehicle frame.
- Define different types of frame construction.
- Describe different types of frame designs.
- Describe unitized body construction, and explain how this body design obtains its strength.
- Define directional stability.
- Define vehicle tracking, and explain how the four wheels on a vehicle must be positioned to obtain proper tracking.
- Define wheelbase, and explain how the wheels on a vehicle must be positioned to provide correct wheelbase.
- Describe setback on a front wheel, and explain the effect that setback has on vehicle steering.
- Explain rear axle offset, and describe the effect of this problem on steering control.
- Define rear axle sideset and explain the effect of rear axle sideset on steering control.

- Explain side sway frame damage.
- Describe frame sag.
- Explain frame buckle.
- Describe a diamond-frame condition.
- Explain frame twist.

INTRODUCTION

The frame in a vehicle may be compared to the skeleton in the human body. Without the skeleton, a human body would not be able to stand erect. Likewise, if a vehicle did not have a frame, it could not support its own weight or the weight of its passenger or cargo load. The vehicle frame:

1. Enables the vehicle to support its total weight.
2. Enables the vehicle to absorb stress from road irregularities.
3. Enables the vehicle to absorb torque from the engine and drive wheels.
4. Provides a main member for attachment of body and other components.

The frame, together with the front and rear suspension systems, must position the wheels properly to minimize tire tread wear and provide accurate steering control.

TYPES OF FRAMES AND FRAME CONSTRUCTION

Frame Construction

Vehicle frame construction may contain three types of steel members: **channel** (partial box) **frame**, **complete box frame**, or **tubular frame** (Figure 14-1). On modern vehicles, most frames include all three types.

Compared to a channel frame or tubular frame, the complete box frame has increased torsional rigidity and improved crash performance. Therefore, in many frames the front section is a complete box design and the other part of the frame is a channel design. Some frames have X-shaped bracing at the rear of the frame for increased strength. Many vehicles now have frames or partial frames that are manufactured by a **hydro-forming** process. Hydro-formed frames are considerably more rigid than frames manufactured by heat-treating. Therefore, hydro-formed frames reduce the flexing of the frame and body components, which reduces squeaks and rattles to decrease noise, vibration, and harshness (NVH). Hydro-formed frames also provide more stable wheel position, which improves steering quality and reduces tire tread wear.

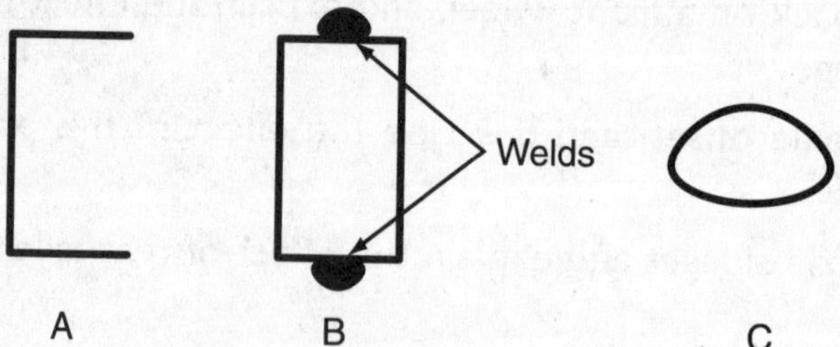

FIGURE 14-1 *Types of frame construction: (A) channel or partial box, (B) complete box, (C) tubular cross member.*

Ladder-Type Frames

The **ladder frame design** is used on trucks and full-size vans. In this type of frame, the side rails have very little offset and are in a straight line between the front and rear wheels. The ladder-type frame has more cross members for increased load-carrying capacity and rigidity (Figure 14-2).

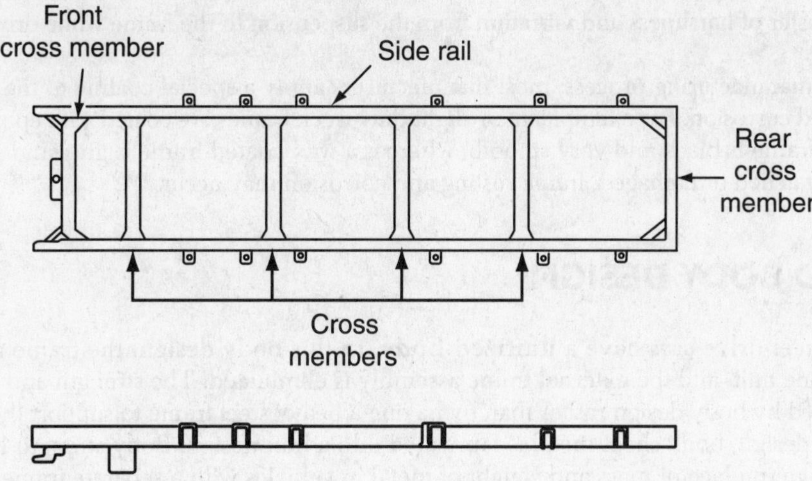

FIGURE 14-2 *Ladder-type frame.*

Perimeter-Type Frames

The **perimeter-type frame** is used in some rear-wheel-drive cars. This type of frame forms a border around the passenger compartment. The frame rails are stepped inward at the cowl area to provide increased strength, which supports the engine mounts and front suspension. This inward step at the cowl area also provides room for movement of the front wheels. Lateral support is provided by cross members welded between the frame rails near the front and rear of the frame. A transmission support member is welded or bolted between the frame rails at the back of the transmission. The rear frame kickup side rails support the rear suspension and the rear portion of the body weight. A front torque box is positioned just ahead of the transmission support member, and a rear torque box is located in front of the rear frame kickup side rails (Figure 14-3). These torque boxes are designed to absorb most of the impact during a side collision and thus reduce damage to other body components. The torque boxes also provide some protection for the vehicle occupants during a side collision.

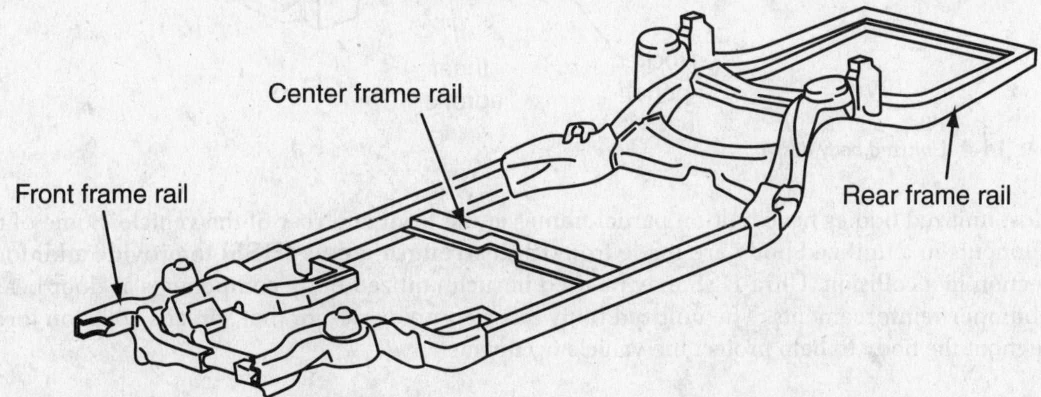

FIGURE 14-3 *Perimeter-type frame components.*

The body components are bolted to the frame, but rubber insulating bushings are positioned between the body and frame mounting locations. These bushings help prevent the transfer of road noise and vibration from the suspension and frame to the body and vehicle interior. Rubber insulating mounts are positioned between the engine and transmission and the frame mounting positions. These engine and transmission mounts reduce the transfer of engine vibration to the frame, body, and vehicle interior. Many suspension components are also connected to the frame through rubber insulating bushings to reduce the transfer of harshness and vibration from the suspension to the frame while driving over road irregularities.

During the manufacturing process, most manufacturers apply a special coating to the frame to help prevent rust and corrosion. For example, many light-duty truck frames are coated with epoxy or wax. An epoxy-coated frame is black and very smooth, whereas a wax-coated frame is gray and sticky. If these coatings are scratched or damaged, frame rusting and corrosion may occur.

UNITIZED BODY DESIGN

Most front-wheel-drive cars have a **unitized body.** In this body design, the frame and body are combined as one unit, and the external frame assembly is eliminated. The strength and rigidity of the body is achieved by body design rather than by having a heavy steel frame to support the body. In the unitized body design, body sheet metal is fabricated into a box design. Body strength is obtained by shape and design in place of mass and weight of metal in vehicles with a separate frame.

All the members of a unitized body are load-carrying components. The floor pan, roof, inner aprons, quarter panels, pillars, and rocker panels are integrally joined to form a unitized body (Figure 14-4).

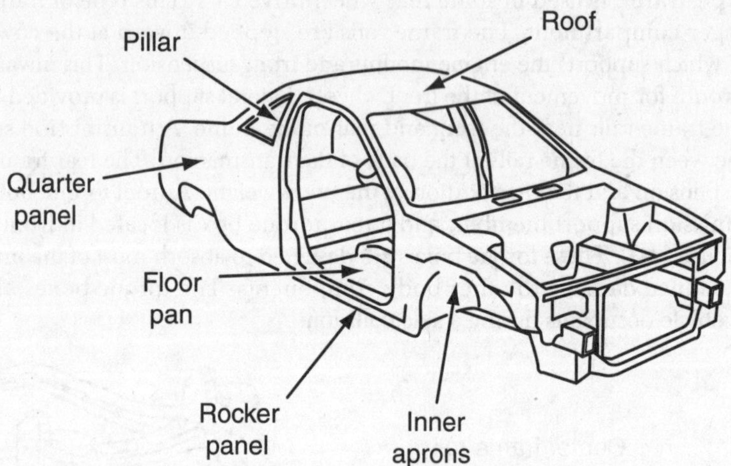

FIGURE 14-4 *Unitized body design.*

Most unitized bodies have bolt-on partial frames at the front and rear of the vehicle. Some of the components in a unitized body are made from **high-strength steels (HSS)** to provide additional protection in a collision. Ultra-HSS may be used in such unitized body components as door beams and bumper reinforcements. The unitized body has a complex design that spreads collision forces throughout the body to help protect the vehicle occupants.

VEHICLE DIRECTIONAL STABILITY

The front and rear suspension systems are attached to the frame, partial frame, or unitized body. Therefore, the frame or unitized body must support the suspension systems properly to provide directional stability. Vehicle **tracking** is the parallel relationship between the front and rear wheels during forward vehicle motion. To provide proper tracking, each front wheel must be the same distance from the vehicle centerline, and each rear wheel must be an equal distance from the same centerline. The distance between the front wheels and the distance between the rear wheels does not necessarily have to be the same, but all four wheels must have a parallel relationship to provide proper tracking (Figure 14-5).

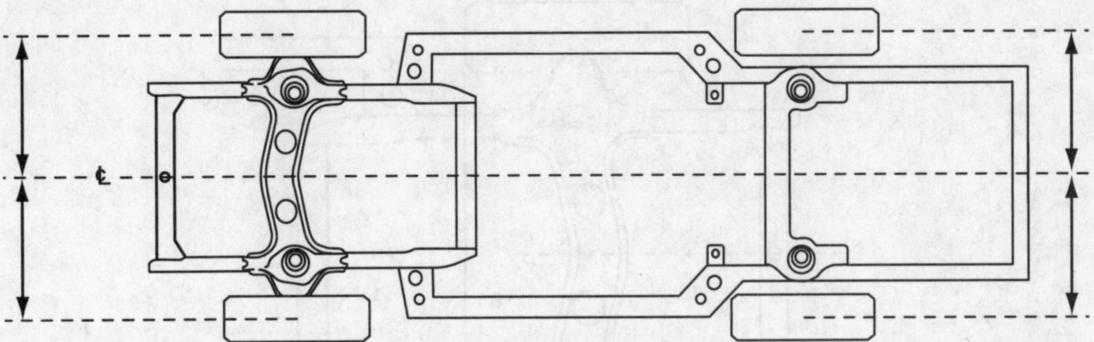

FIGURE 14-5 *Front and rear wheels must be the same distance from the vehicle centerline to provide proper tracking.*

The vehicle **wheelbase** is the distance between the centers of the front and rear wheels. To provide an accurate wheelbase measurement, the centers of the front spindles and the centers of the rear axles must be square with the centerline of the vehicle (Figure 14-6). For this condition to exist, the front and rear axle centers must be at a 90° angle in relation to the vehicle centerline, and the wheelbase measurements must be equal on each side of the vehicle. Equal wheelbase measurements on each side of the vehicle and proper tracking are absolutely essential to providing **directional stability.**

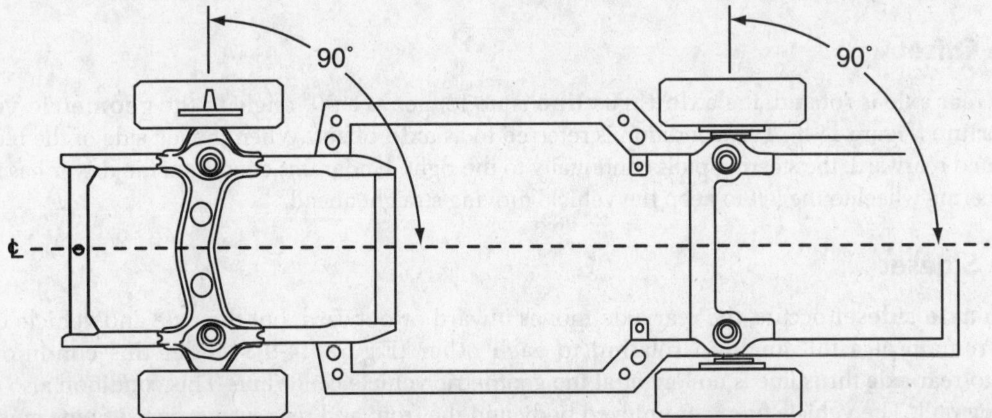

FIGURE 14-6 *To provide accurate wheelbase measurement, the front spindle centerlines and the rear axle centers must be at a 90° angle to the vehicle centerline.*

VEHICLE TRACKING

Wheel Setback

Front **wheel setback** occurs when the spindle on one front wheel is rearward in relation to the other front wheel. The centerline of each front wheel is still at a 90° angle to the vehicle centerline, but the front wheels no longer share the same centerline (Figure 14-7).

When left front wheel setback occurs, the vehicle has a tendency to steer to the left as it is driven straight ahead. Under this condition, the driver has to continually turn the steering wheel to the right to keep the vehicle moving straight ahead.

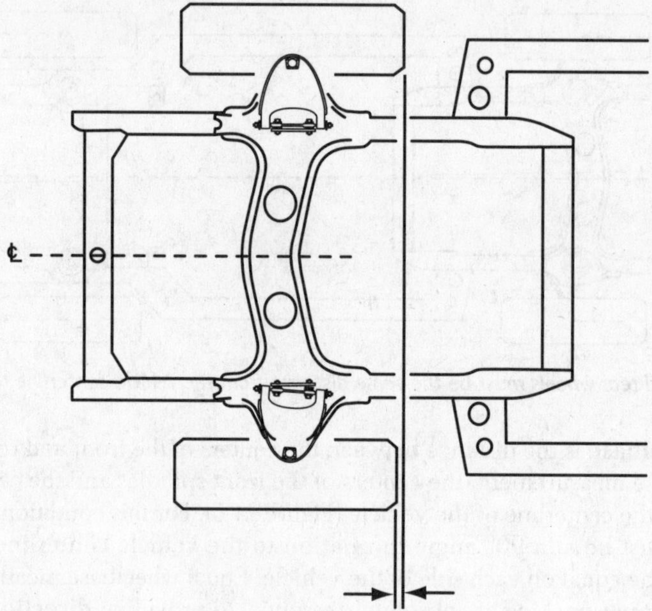

FIGURE 14-7 *Setback occurs when one front wheel is positioned rearward in relation to the other front wheel.*

Axle Offset

If the rear axle is rotated, the **axle thrustline** is no longer at a 90° angle to the **geometric vehicle centerline** (Figure 14-8). This condition is referred to as **axle offset.** When the left side of the rear axle is rotated rearward, the steering pulls continually to the right. Under this condition, the driver has to turn the steering wheel to the left to keep the vehicle moving straight ahead.

Axle Sideset

When **axle sideset** occurs, the rear axle moves inward or outward, but the axle and vehicle centerlines remain at a 90° angle in relation to each other (Figure 14-9). Under this condition, the front-to-rear axle thrustline is no longer at the geometric vehicle centerline. This condition also causes steering pull. The vehicle frame or unitized body and the front and rear suspension systems must have proper tracking and equal wheelbase measurements on each side of the vehicle to provide directional stability and steering control.

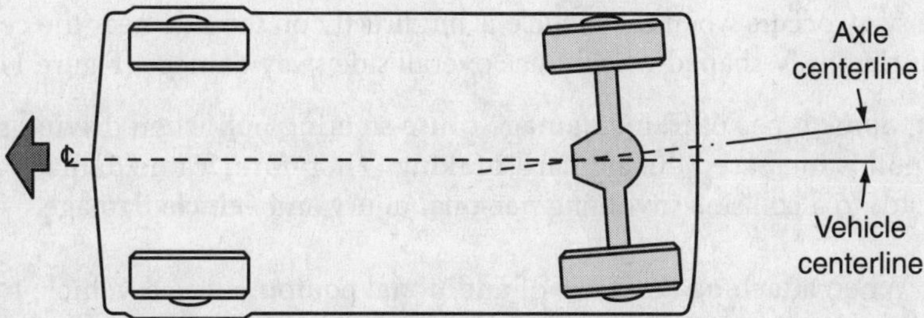

FIGURE 14-8 *Rear axle offset occurs when the rear axle is rotated so the axle centerline and the vehicle centerline are no longer at a 90° angle.*

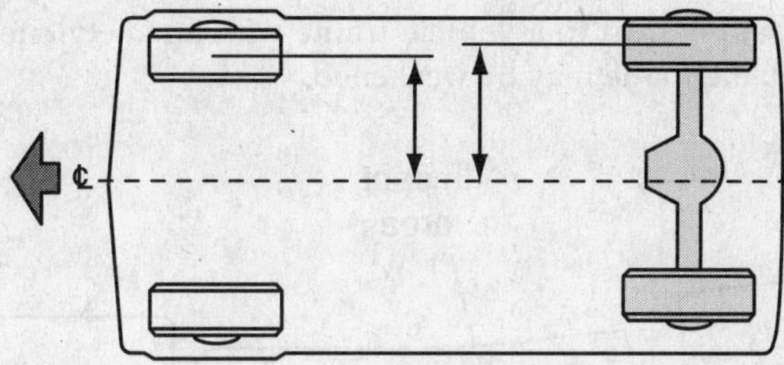

FIGURE 14-9 *Axle sideset occurs when the rear axle moves inward or outward and the axle centerline remains at a 90° angle in relation to the vehicle centerline.*

TYPES OF FRAME DAMAGE

Side Sway

Side sway on the front or rear of a vehicle is usually the result of the vehicle being involved in a collision that pushes the front or rear frame sideways (Figure 14-10). Under this condition, the wheelbase on one side of the vehicle is longer than the opposite side. This side sway condition causes the steering to pull to the side with the shorter wheelbase.

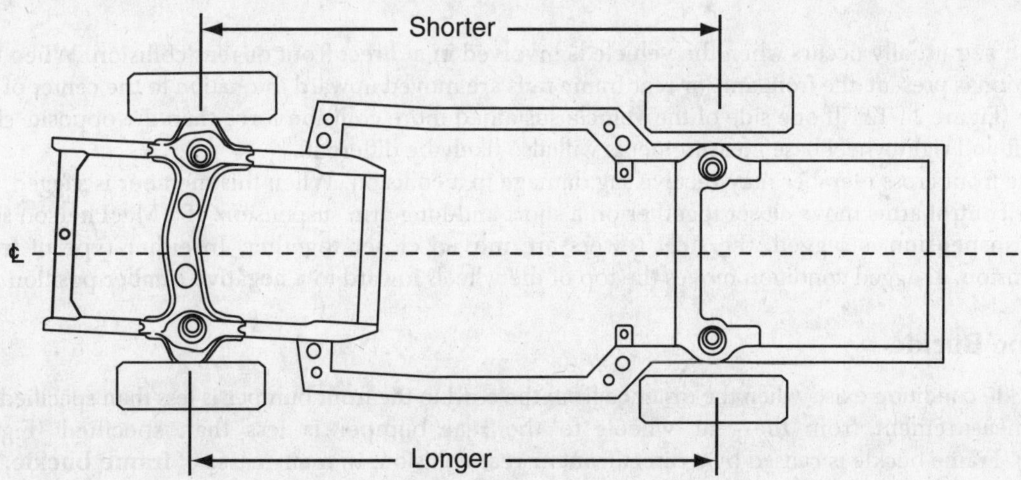

FIGURE 14-10 *Side sway frame condition caused by collision damage.*

Overall side sway occurs when the vehicle is hit directly on the side near the center in a collision. A vehicle frame is slightly V-shaped when it has overall side sway damage (Figure 14-11).

WARNING: Some types of frame damage cause steering pull when driving straight ahead, and this steering pull is increased during hard braking. Therefore, frame damage can create a safety hazard that leads to a collision involving personal injury and vehicle damage.

CAUTION: When attaching any type of additional equipment to a vehicle frame, always try to use the holes that already exist in the frame. Do not drill holes in a vehicle frame except at locations specified by the vehicle manufacturer, and do not attach additional equipment to a vehicle frame unless this procedure is approved by the vehicle manufacturer.

CAUTION: Do not apply heat to a vehicle frame with an acetylene torch. When the metal is heated to a cherry red, the frame may be weakened.

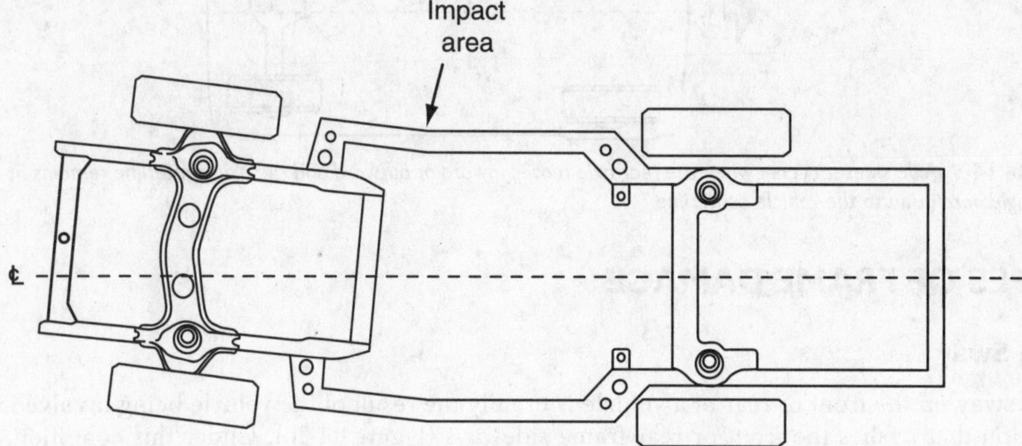

FIGURE 14-11 *When a frame has overall side sway damage, it is slightly V-shaped.*

Sag

Frame sag usually occurs when the vehicle is involved in a direct front or rear collision. When this condition is present, the front and/or rear frame rails are moved upward in relation to the center of the frame (Figure 14-12). If one side of the vehicle sustained more collision force than the opposite side, the left and right wheel base measurements will also likely be different.

The front cross member may receive sag damage in a collision. When this member is sagged, the upper control arms move closer together on a short-and-long arm suspension. If a MacPherson strut front suspension is sagged, the strut towers are moved closer together. In either type of front suspension, a sagged condition moves the top of the wheels inward to a **negative camber** position.

Frame Buckle

A buckle condition exists when the distance from the cowl to the front bumper is less than specified, or the measurement from the rear wheels to the rear bumper is less than specified (Figure 14-13). Frame buckle is caused by a direct front or rear collision. In many cases of **frame buckle,** the wheelbase is reduced on one or both sides of the vehicle. This type of collision damage may cause the sides of the vehicle to bulge outward, especially on unibody cars. Under this condition, the side rails and door openings are distorted.

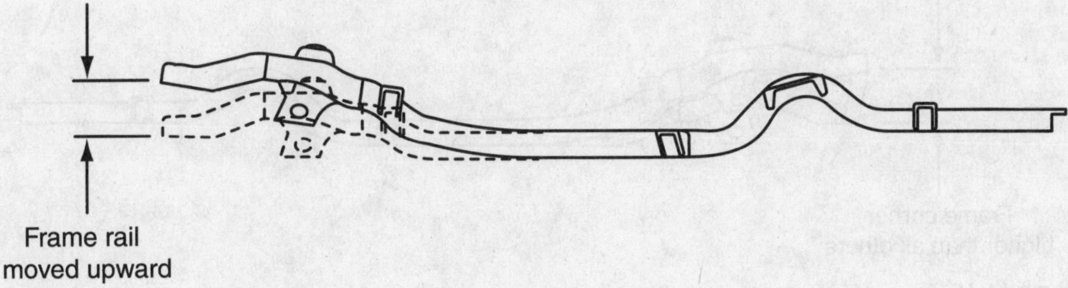

FIGURE 14-12 *Frame sag caused by direct front or rear collision damage.*

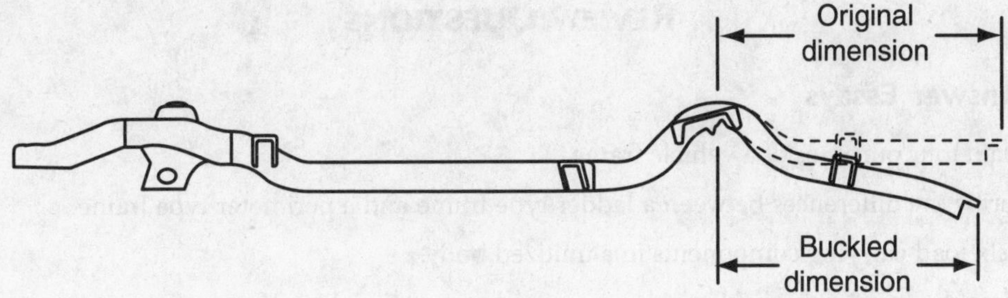

FIGURE 14-13 *Rear frame buckle.*

Diamond-Frame Condition

A **diamond-frame condition** is present when collision damage causes a frame to be out of square. Under this condition, the frame is shaped like a parallelogram (Figure 14-14). If the right rear wheel is driven rearward in relation to the left rear wheel, the rear suspension steers the vehicle to the right, and this forces the front end of the vehicle to the left. Under this condition, the steering wheel must be held continually to the right to overcome the steering pull to the left. A diamond condition usually occurs on vehicles with frames. Vehicles with unitized bodies seldom have this type of condition.

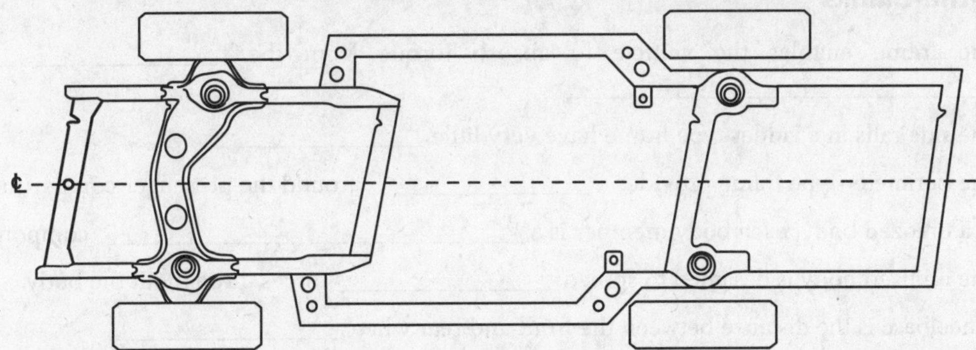

FIGURE 14-14 *Diamond-frame condition.*

Frame Twist

A **frame twist** condition exists when one corner of the frame is higher than the other corners. When frame twist is present, the front or rear chassis does not sit level in relation to the road surface (Figure 14-15). Frame twist is usually caused by vehicle rollover.

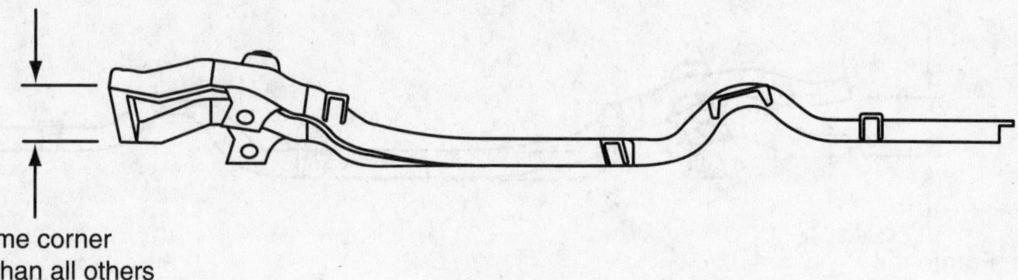

FIGURE 14-15 *Frame twist.*

REVIEW QUESTIONS

Short Answer Essays

1. Explain four purposes of a vehicle frame.
2. Describe the differences between a ladder-type frame and a perimeter-type frame.
3. List six load-carrying components in a unitized body.
4. Explain the necessary wheel position to provide proper tracking.
5. Describe the necessary axle position to provide correct wheelbase.
6. Explain the effects of front wheel setback.
7. Describe the effects of rear axle offset.
8. Describe two areas in the frame where sag may occur.
9. Explain the type of collision that causes frame buckle.
10. Explain frame twist, including the type of collision that causes this problem.

Fill-in-the-Blanks

1. The frame enables the vehicle to absorb torque from the ________________ and ________________ ________________.
2. The side rails in a ladder-type frame have very little ________________.
3. The perimeter-type frame provides a ________________ around the passenger compartment.
4. In a unitized body, each body member is a ________________ ________________ component.
5. The unitized body is designed to spread ________________ forces throughout the body.
6. Wheelbase is the distance between the front and rear wheel ________________.
7. Directional stability is the tendency of a vehicle to remain in the ________________ ________________ position when driven straight ahead on a level road.
8. Tracking refers to the ________________ relationship between the front and rear wheels.
9. When the front of the frame is buckled, the distance is reduced between the front ________________ and the ________________.
10. Frame buckle may be called frame ________________ or ________________.

Multiple Choice

1. A ladder-type frame is most commonly used on a:
   A. Rear-wheel-drive car.
   B. Front-wheel-drive car.
   C. Light-duty truck.
   D. Compact car.

2. A perimeter-type frame:
   A. Forms a border around the passenger compartment.
   B. Has frame rails that are stepped outward at the cowl area.
   C. Has a front torque box mounted behind the transmission support member.
   D. Does not have cross members welded between the frame rails.

3. All of these statements about unitized body design are true EXCEPT:
   A. The frame and body are combined as one unit.
   B. The external frame assembly is eliminated.
   C. Some body members such as quarter panels do not contribute to body strength and rigidity.
   D. Body strength is obtained by body shape and design.

4. All of these statements about vehicle tracking are true EXCEPT:
   A. The distance between the front wheels and the distance between the rear wheels must be equal.
   B. Each front wheel must be the same distance from the vehicle centerline.
   C. Each rear wheel must be the same distance from the vehicle centerline.
   D. Each front and rear wheel must be parallel to the vehicle centerline.

5. Front wheel setback occurs when one front wheel is:
   A. Tilted inward from the true vertical position.
   B. Moved rearward in relation to the opposite front wheel.
   C. Tilted rearward from the true vertical position.
   D. Inward from its original position.

6. While diagnosing rear axle offset and sideset:
   A. If the left rear wheel is moved rearward in relation to the right rear wheel, the steering pulls to the left.
   B. If the vehicle has rear leaf springs, rear axle offset may be caused by a broken spring center bolt.
   C. If rear axle sideset is present, one side of the rear axle is moved forward in relation to the opposite side or the rear axle.
   D. Rear axle sideset causes harsh ride quality and excessive vertical rear wheel oscillations.

7. All these statements about frame side sway and buckle are true EXCEPT:
   A. Frame side sway causes unequal wheelbase on the two sides of the vehicle.
   B. When a vehicle frame has a severe side sway condition, the frame is V-shaped.
   C. Frame buckle reduces the distance between the front and rear suspension systems.
   D. Frame side sway causes one corner of the vehicle to be higher compared to the other corners.

8. While diagnosing a diamond-frame condition and frame twist:
   A. A diamond-frame condition causes the wheelbase to be unequal on the two sides of the vehicle.
   B. A diamond-frame condition does not affect steering pull and directional stability.
   C. Frame twist is usually caused when a vehicle is involved in a side collision.
   D. When frame twist occurs, the front or rear chassis does not sit level in relation to the road surface.

9. On various types of vehicle frames:
   A. The load-carrying capacity is greater on a perimeter frame than on a ladder-type frame.
   B. A torque box on a perimeter-type frame absorbs most of the impact during a side collision.
   C. The frame rails are stepped inward in the cowl area to protect the engine and transmission on a perimeter-type frame.
   D. Rubber frame insulating bushings provide improved directional stability and steering characteristics.

10. In a unitized body:
    A. The partial bolt-on frames may be located at the front or rear of a vehicle with a unitized body.
    B. The rocker panels and the roof are the main load-carrying components in a unitized body.
    C. Ultra-high-strength steels are used in most unitized body components.
    D. The floor plan and the inner fender aprons do not carry any load in a unitized body.

Four Wheel Alignment 15

Upon completion and review of this chapter, you should be able to:

- Describe the variables that affect wheel alignment.
- Define wheel alignment, and explain five reasons for performing a wheel alignment.
- Explain why four wheel alignment is essential on front-wheel-drive unitized body cars.
- Define thrust line and geometric centerline and describe the effect of an improper thrust line on vehicle steering.
- Explain the result of improper rear wheel toe and its effect on the thrust line.
- Explain the causes of improper rear wheel toe.
- List the causes of rear axle offset.
- Define rear axle sideset, setback, and dogtracking.
- Diagnose front and rear tire tread wear caused by inaccurate rear wheel toe and thrust line settings.

- Define geometric centerline alignment and explain the problem with this type of alignment.
- Define thrust line alignment and describe the shortcoming of this type of alignment.
- Define total four wheel alignment and explain the advantage of this type of alignment.
- Describe the safety hazards created by incorrect wheel alignment or worn suspension and steering components.
- Explain the effect of excessive positive camber on front suspension systems.
- Describe camber changes during front wheel jounce and rebound travel.
- Describe the relationship between camber and vehicle directional stability.
- Explain how front suspension camber and caster may be adjusted to compensate for road crown.
- Describe the effects of positive and negative caster on directional control and steering effort.
- Describe positive and negative caster as they relate to ride quality.
- Describe how higher or lower than specified front or rear suspension height affects front suspension caster.
- Explain the steering axis inclination (SAI) angle and the included angle.
- Describe how SAI helps return the front wheels to the straight-ahead position.
- Explain how SAI eliminates the need for excessive positive camber and caster.
- Describe the effect that front suspension defects such as dislocated upper strut towers and bent struts or spindles have on SAI.
- Explain negative and positive scrub radius and the effect of each on steering quality.
- Describe setback on front suspension systems.
- Describe toe-in and toe-out on front suspension systems.
- Compare the toe-in settings required on front-wheel-drive and rear-wheel-drive vehicles.
- Describe tire tread wear caused by excessive toe-in.
- Explain how the front suspension system is designed to provide toe-out on turns.
- Describe the customer complaints that may arise from incorrect rear wheel toe and thrust line adjustments.
- Explain suspension and chassis defects that may cause improper rear wheel toe, thrust line, or camber.

INTRODUCTION

Automotive engineers design suspension and steering systems that provide satisfactory vehicle control with acceptable driver effort and road feel. The vehicle should have a tendency to go straight ahead without being steered. This tendency is called **directional stability**. A vehicle must have predictable directional control, which means the steering must provide a feeling that the vehicle will turn in the direction steered. The wheels must be reasonably easy to turn and tire wear should be minimized. These steering qualities and tire conditions are achieved when front and rear **wheel alignment** angles are within the vehicle manufacturer's specifications.

The condition of suspension system components and wheel alignment are extremely important to maintaining driving safety and normal tire wear. Worn suspension components such as tie-rod ends, ball joints, and control arms can suddenly fall apart and cause complete loss of steering. This disastrous event may result in not only some very expensive property damage but also the loss of human life. When alignment angles are incorrect, an uncontrolled vehicle swerve or skid may occur during hard braking, resulting in a serious accident. Severe misalignment may reduce tire life to one-third of the normal expected tire life with correct alignment. After suspension components such as ball joints or control arms are replaced, wheel alignment is essential.

Improper steering axis inclination (SAI) angles on either side of the front suspension may cause hazardous steering conditions while braking or accelerating. Therefore, technicians must be familiar with SAI and other related steering geometry.

When the front wheel toe is not adjusted to the manufacturer's specifications, front tire tread wear is excessive. If one of the tie-rods is not parallel to the lower control arms, toe change on the front wheels is not equal during front wheel jounce and rebound. This action may result in bump steer when a front wheel strikes a road irregularity. While checking front wheel toe, improper toe change during suspension jounce and rebound should be checked to be sure the tie-rods are parallel to the lower control arms. Technicians must understand front wheel toe and improper toe changes.

Technicians must be familiar with the symptoms that indicate incorrect rear wheel alignment. The rear wheel alignment procedures required to correct improper rear wheel alignment must be understood.

WHEEL ALIGNMENT THEORY

Road Variables

Vehicles are subjected to many **road variables** that affect wheel alignment. These variables must be counteracted by the suspension design and alignment, or steering would be very difficult. Some of the variables that affect wheel alignment and suspension design follow:

1. **Road crown** (the curvature of the road surface)
2. Bumps and holes
3. Natural crosswinds or crosswinds created by other vehicles
4. Heavy loads or unequal weight distribution
5. Road surface friction and conditions such as ice, snow, and water
6. Tire traction and pressure

7. Side forces while cornering
8. Drive axle forces in front-wheel-drive vehicles
9. Relationship between suspension parts as the front wheels turn and move vertically when road bumps and holes are encountered

A desirable plan to reduce tire wear would be to place the front wheels and tires so they are perfectly vertical. The tires would then be flat on the road. However, if the wheels and tires are perfectly vertical, such variables as the driver entering the car, turning a corner, or adding weight to the luggage compartment would move the tire from its true vertical position. Therefore, tire wear and steering operation would be adversely affected.

Rather than allowing the variables to adversely affect tire wear and steering operation, the suspension and steering are designed with characteristics to provide directional stability, predictable directional control, and minimum tire wear. Wheel alignment angles are designed to provide these desired requirements despite road variables. Wheel alignment angles also control the **tracking** of the rear wheels in relation to the front wheels.

IMPORTANCE OF FOUR WHEEL ALIGNMENT

Until the late 1970s, most vehicles in the United States were rear-wheel drive. The majority of these vehicles had one-piece rear axle housings and frames. This type of vehicle design did not experience many rear wheel alignment problems and rear wheel alignment was usually not a concern in these years.

Beginning in the late 1970s, many domestic car makers began manufacturing front-wheel-drive cars with unitized bodies. The gasoline shortages in the 1970s and the introduction of federal corporate average fuel economy (CAFE) laws brought about a massive change to lighter weight, more fuel efficient front-wheel-drive cars. A significant number of these cars had four-wheel independent suspension systems.

Cars with unitized bodies and independent or semi-independent rear suspension systems are more likely to experience rear wheel alignment problems compared with rear-wheel-drive vehicles with frames and one-piece rear axle housings. This is especially true after collision damage. Therefore, with the introduction of unitized bodies in massive numbers, four wheel alignment became a necessity.

REAR WHEEL ALIGNMENT AND VEHICLE TRACKING PROBLEMS

Result of Proper Rear Wheel Alignment

The driver uses the steering wheel to turn the front wheels and steer the vehicle in the desired direction. However, the rear wheels determine the direction of the vehicle to a large extent. When the **thrust line** is positioned at the **geometric centerline** and the front and rear wheels are parallel to the vehicle geometric centerline, the vehicle moves straight ahead with minimum guidance from the steering wheel (Figure 15-1).

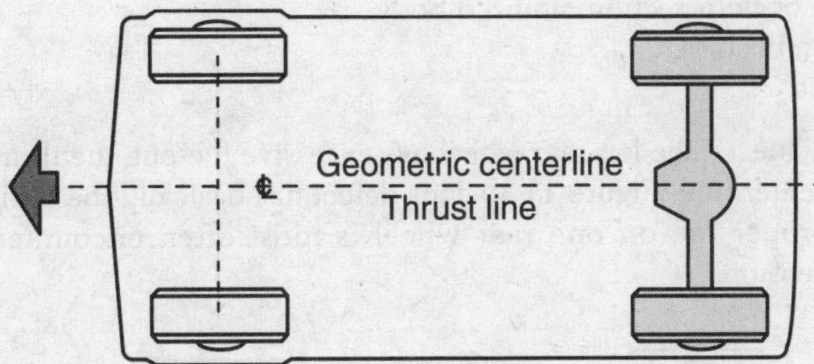

FIGURE 15-1 *Front and rear wheels parallel to the vehicle centerline.*

Result of Improper Rear Wheel Alignment

Rear Axle Offset. A **rear axle offset** may occur on a rear-wheel-drive vehicle with a one-piece rear axle housing or on a front-wheel-drive car with a trailing arm rear suspension. If the rear axle is offset, the thrust line is no longer at the vehicle centerline (Figure 15-2). The **thrust angle** is the angle between the geometric centerline and the thrust line.

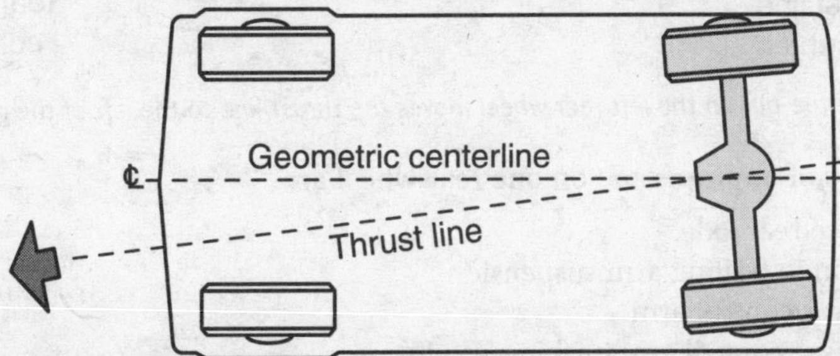

FIGURE 15-2 *Rear axle offset and improperly positioned thrust line.*

With the rear axle offset problem shown in Figure 15-2, the thrust line is positioned to the left of the geometric centerline. Under this condition, the rear wheels steer the vehicle in a large clockwise circle. If the driver's hands are removed from the steering wheel, the steering pulls to the right. This steering action is similar to the rear wheels on a forklift. The rear wheels are used to steer the forklift because of the heavy load on the front wheels. If the rear wheels are pointed toward the left, the forklift turns to the right.

On a vehicle with this problem, the left front wheel toes out and the right front wheel toes in when the vehicle is driven straight ahead. This front wheel situation occurs because the front wheels try to compensate for the rear suspension defect. The front wheels are turned slightly to the left to compensate for the drift to the right caused by the rear suspension problem. Under this condition, both the front and rear tires may have feathered tire wear.

The ideal correction for this rear suspension problem is to reposition the rear suspension so the thrust line is at the vehicle centerline, then set the front wheel toe-in to the thrust line. The rear suspension problem that we have described also causes the steering wheel to be off-center when the vehicle is driven straight ahead.

Some of the causes of rear axle offset are:

1. A broken center bolt in rear leaf spring.
2. Worn shackles in rear leaf springs.
3. A bent frame.

4. A bent subframe or floor section, unitized body.
5. Worn trailing arm bushings.
6. Bent trailing arms.

Improper Rear Wheel Toe. If the left rear wheel has excessive toe-out, the thrust line is moved to the left of the geometric center line (Figure 15-3). This defect has basically the same effect on steering as rear axle offset. Improper toe on one rear wheel is most often encountered on vehicles with independent rear suspension.

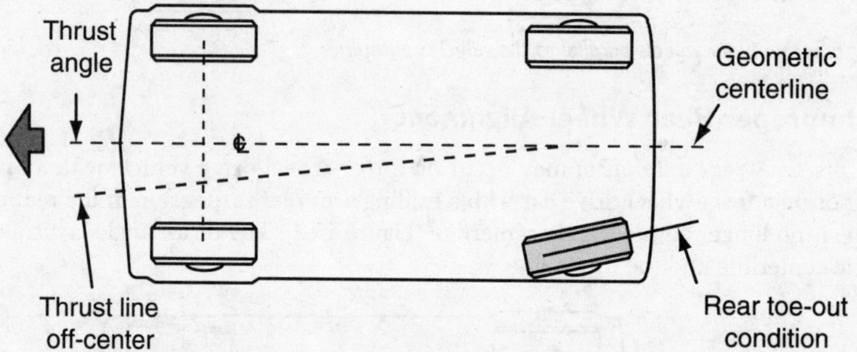

FIGURE 15-3 *Excessive toe-out on the left rear wheel moves the thrust line to the left of the geometric centerline.*

Some of the causes of improper toe on one rear wheel are:

1. A bent one-piece rear axle.
2. A bent U section in trailing arm suspension.
3. A bent rear lower control arm.
4. A worn rear lower control arm bushing.
5. A bent rear spindle.
6. An improper rear toe adjustment.

The necessary correction for this defect is to adjust the left rear wheel toe to the manufacturer's specifications. This adjustment moves the thrust line to the geometric centerline of the vehicle (Figure 15-4).

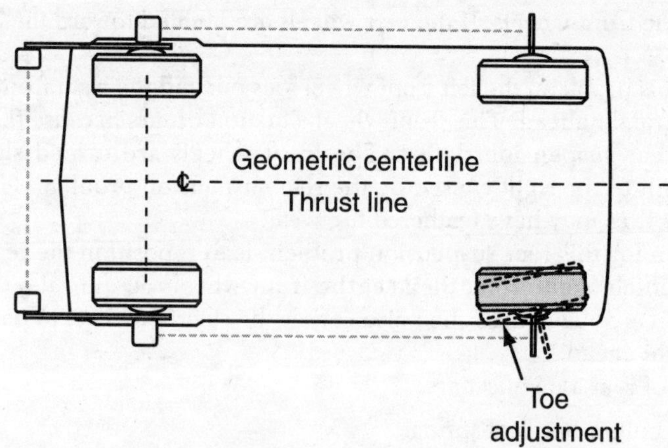

FIGURE 15-4 *Adjusting toe to specifications on the left rear wheel moves the thrust line to the geometric centerline.*

Rear Axle Sideset. When rear axle sideset occurs, the rear wheels are parallel to each other but the rear axle assembly has moved straight sideways so the geometric centerline is no longer at the proper vehicle centerline position (Figure 15-5). Since the rear wheels do not follow directly behind the front wheels when the vehicle is driven straight ahead, the vehicle dogtracks. Rear axle sideset does not affect steering pull as much as rear axle offset, but sideset will cause steering pull if it is severe.

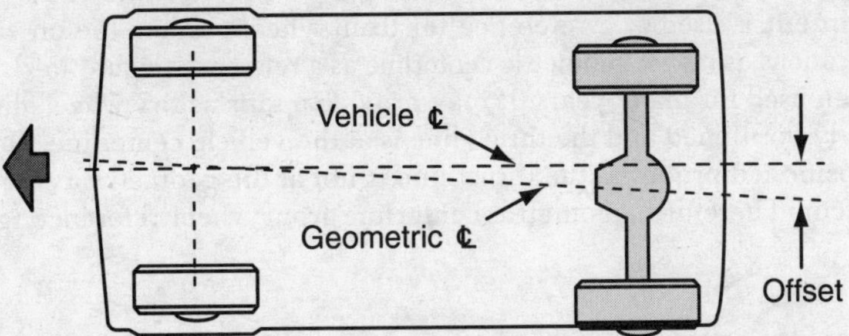

FIGURE 15-5 *Rear axle offset occurs when the rear axle assembly has moved straight sideways and the geometric centerline is shifted away from the proper vehicle centerline position.*

Wheel Setback. Wheel setback is a condition where one front or rear wheel is moved rearward in relation to the opposite wheel (Figure 15-6). This condition is usually caused by front-end collision damage, and thus it is most likely to be a front suspension problem. However, setback may occur on independent rear suspension systems. A severe setback condition causes steering pull.

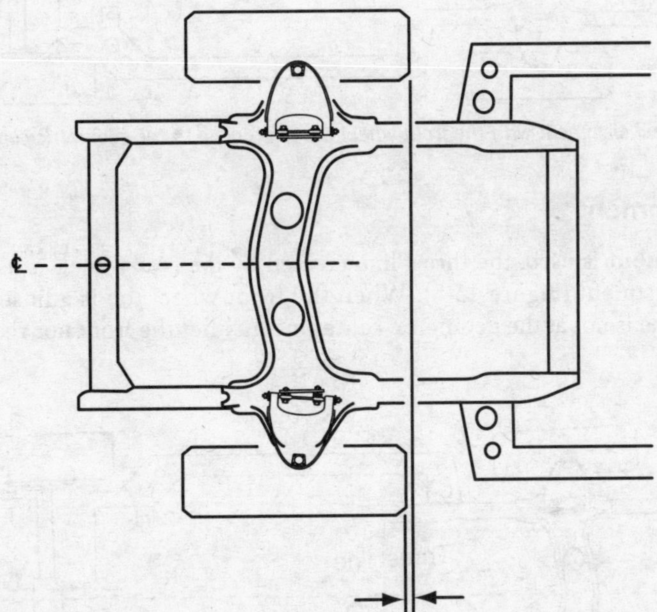

FIGURE 15-6 *Front wheel setback occurs when one front wheel is moved rearward in relation to the opposite front wheel.*

TYPES OF WHEEL ALIGNMENT

Geometric Centerline Alignment

Toe refers to the angle between the plane of a front or rear wheel and a reference line. Either the geometric centerline or the thrust line may be used as a toe reference line. When **geometric centerline alignment** is used as a reference for front wheel toe, the toe on each front wheel is adjusted to specifications using the geometric centerline as a reference (Figure 15-7). This type of wheel alignment has been used for many years. It may provide a satisfactory wheel alignment if the rear wheels are properly positioned and the thrust line is at the vehicle centerline. However, if the rear wheels are not positioned properly, the thrust line is not at the geometric centerline and steering problems will occur. Therefore, geometric centerline front wheel reference ignores rear wheel misalignment.

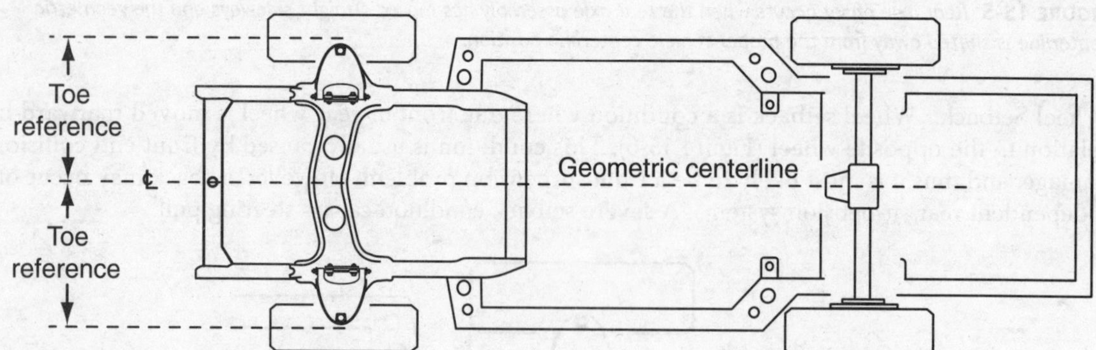

FIGURE 15-7 *Front wheel alignment with the front wheel toe referenced to the geometric centerline.*

Thrust Line Alignment

If **thrust line alignment** is used, the thrust line created by the rear wheels is used as a reference for front wheel toe adjustment (Figure 15-8). When the front wheel toe is adjusted with a thrust line reference, and this line is not at the geometric centerline, neither the front nor rear wheels are parallel

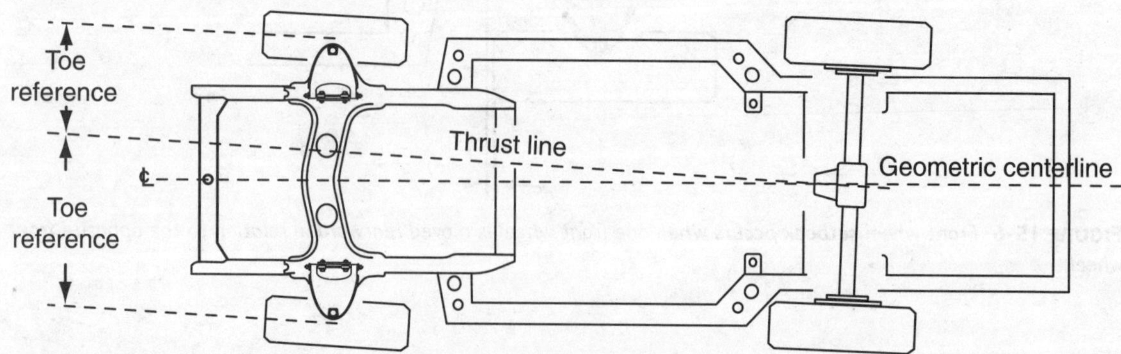

FIGURE 15-8 *Thrust line alignment with the front wheel toe referenced to the thrust line.*

to the geometric centerline. Under this condition, none of the four wheels is facing straight ahead when the vehicle is driven straight ahead. This action results in excessive feathered wear on all four tire treads. This type of alignment ensures a centered steering wheel when the vehicle is driven straight ahead.

Four Wheel Alignment

When a **four wheel alignment** is completed, the thrust line position is measured in relation to the geometric centerline. Individual rear wheel toe-in is measured and adjusted to manufacturer's specifications. This adjustment moves the thrust line to the geometric centerline. Thrust angle is measured to be sure the thrust line is positioned at the geometric centerline. Front wheel toe is measured using the common geometric centerline and thrust line as a reference (Figure 15-9). When a four wheel alignment is completed, all four wheels are parallel to the geometric centerline and the steering wheel is centered as the vehicle is driven straight ahead. Wheel aligners have different alignment capabilities. Modern computer wheel alignment systems have four-wheel alignment capabilities, and this type of wheel alignment must be performed on today's vehicles to ensure proper steering control and vehicle safety.

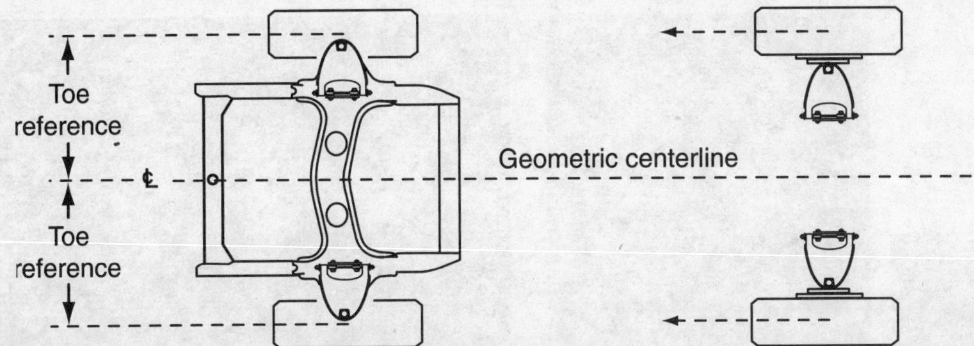

FIGURE 15-9 *Four wheel alignment with the thrust line adjusted so it is at the geometric centerline and the front wheel toe is referenced to the geometric centerline.*

COMPUTER ALIGNMENT SYSTEMS

Computer Wheel Aligner Features

Some computer wheel aligners have four high-resolution digital cameras that measure wheel target position and orientation. The front and rear wheel alignment angles are sensed by the digital cameras and wheel targets and then displayed on the wheel alignment monitor. The vehicle is raised to a comfortable working height on the aligner lift, and two digital cameras are mounted in each end of a crossbar on a post in front of the vehicle (Figure 15-10). The post and crossbar height may be adjusted to match the vehicle height.

One digital camera is aimed at each wheel target (Figure 15-11). A target is mounted on each wheel with a self-centering adapter. The adapters are adjustable to fit rims up to 24 in. (60 cm) in diameter. The targets contain a polished aluminum faceplate that acts as a mirror (Figure 15-12). The targets do not contain any electronics, glass, or cables, and they do not require calibration. The targets are also lightweight and do not require any maintenance.

This type of computer aligner is very simple to use. After the pre-alignment procedures and checks have been performed on the vehicle, and the vehicle is positioned at the desired height and position

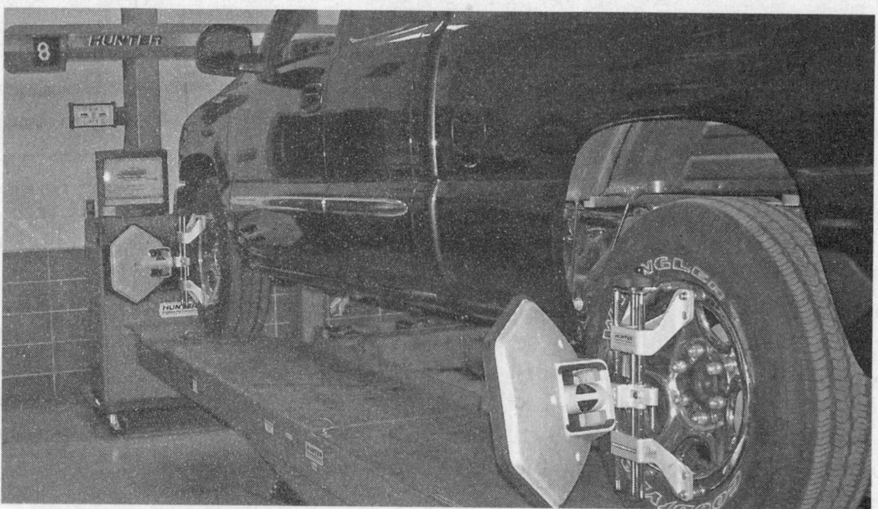

FIGURE 15-10 *Computer wheel aligner with digital cameras and wheel targets.*

FIGURE 15-11 *One digital camera is aimed at each wheel target.*

FIGURE 15-12 *Each target contains a polished aluminum face plate with no electronics, glass, or cables.*

on the lift and turntables, the first step is to mount the wheel targets on the wheels. The second step is to roll the vehicle back a short distance until the on-screen indicators on the monitor turn green. The third step is to roll the vehicle forward and stop the vehicle so the front wheels are centered on the turntables. The fourth step is to observe all the front and rear camber and toe angles displayed on the monitor.

A remote control is wired into the monitor so the technician can perform the same functions when the monitor is not in the technician's view. A handheld remote control is used to measure the vehicle ride height (Figure 15-13). This remote is held against the lower edge of the fender well to measure the ride height, and the remote transmits the ride height measurement electronically to the console and monitor.

On some computer wheel aligners the **wheel sensors** contain a microprocessor and a **high-frequency transmitter** that acquire measurements and process data and then send these data to a **receiver** mounted

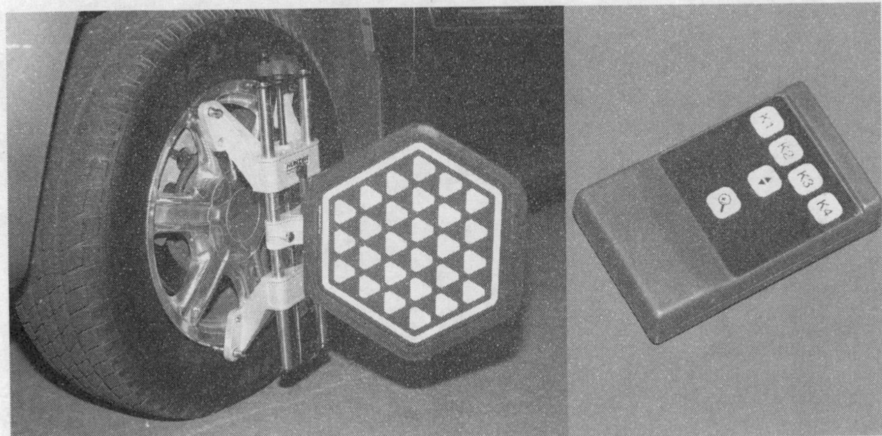

FIGURE 15-13 *A handheld remote control transmits ride height measurements electronically to the console and monitor.*

on top of the wheel alignment monitor (Figure 15-14 and Figure 15-15). This type of wheel sensor does not require any cables connected between the sensors and the computer wheel aligner. The data from this type of wheel sensor are virtually uninterruptible, even by solid objects. When these wheel sensors are stored on the computer wheel aligner, a "docking station" feature charges the batteries in the wheel sensors. The front wheel sensors have optical arms that project ahead of the tires to provide front toe readings. Some rear wheel sensors also have optical arms that project behind the rear tires (Figure 15-16). This type of rear wheel sensor measures rear wheel setback.

FIGURE 15-14 *Cordless wheel sensor containing a high-frequency transmitter.*

FIGURE 15-15 *Computer wheel aligner with data receiver on top of the monitor.*

CAUTION: When using a computer wheel aligner, the equipment manufacturer's recommended alignment procedures must be followed to provide accurate readings and adjustments.

CAUTION: Because wheel units contain sensitive electronic circuits, excessive shock such as dropping them on the floor can damage them.

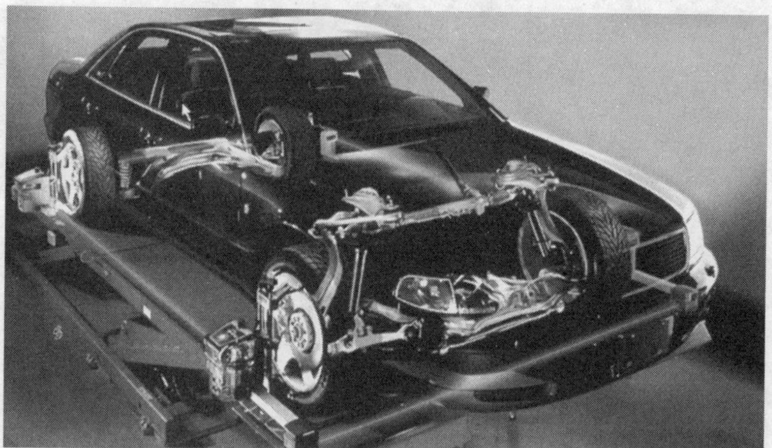

FIGURE 15-16 *Front and rear wheel sensors with optical arms.*

On some computer alignment systems, the reference signals between the wheel sensors are provided by light-emitting diodes (LEDs) or electronic signals. Cables are connected from the wheel units to the computer aligner. Reference signals between the wheel units are provided by strings on some older model computer alignment systems (Figure 15-17). Most wheel sensors provide wheel runout compensation. Since the wheel unit is clamped to the rim, a bent rim will affect the alignment readings. On older computer wheel aligners, the technician had to perform a wheel runout check at each wheel. Newer wheel units use audible and visual prompts on the monitor screen to inform the technician if the wheel sensors require leveling or calibration. Wheel runout compensation may be completed by pressing a button on the wheel sensor. Wheel sensor leveling is done by adjusting the sensor level control.

FIGURE 15-17 *Front wheel sensor with optical arm and string connected to the rear wheel sensor.*

Computer alignment systems have the capability to measure thrust angle and setback as well as other front and rear alignment angles. A typical computer wheel aligner has the following features:

1. Color monitor and computer (Figure 15-18).
2. Computer software program stored on a hard disc drive. This program contains vehicle four-wheel alignment procedures and diagnostic drawings.
3. Compact disc (CD) or digital video disk (DVD) drive. The vehicle specifications and alignment program may be contained on CDs or DVDs, and updates are possible by replacing the CDs or DVDs (Figure 15-19). Wheel alignment specifications include domestic and imported vehicles for the current year and a minimum of 10 previous years.
4. The software in some computer wheel aligners includes a CD or DVD image database containing 2,100 digital photos of the adjustment and inspection points. In some computer aligners, a list of inspection points appears on the left of the screen. When the operator clicks on a listed inspection

FIGURE 15-18 *Computer wheel aligner.*

FIGURE 15-19 *CDs for wheel alignment program and specifications.*

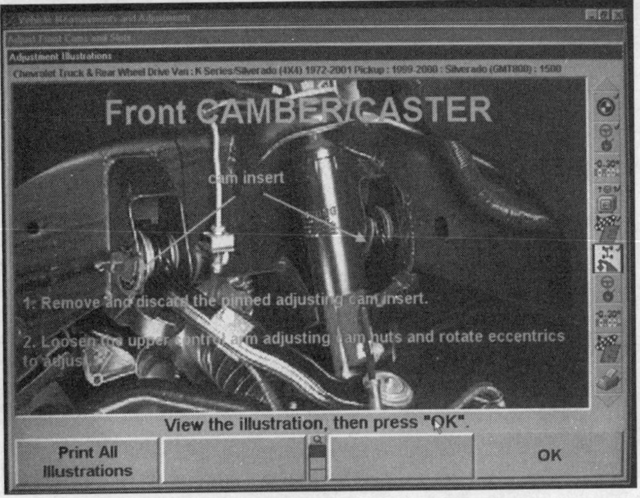

FIGURE 15-20 *Point and click suspension inspection screen.*

point, the matching photo appears, illustrating the selected inspection point (Figure 15-20). Special digital photos are available for inspection of the cradle and cradle-to-body alignment.

5. Live action inspection videos may be accessed instantly from the inspection screen. These inspection videos are part of the 142-video training library.
6. A tire inspection screen illustrates various types of tire tread wear and the related causes (Figure 15-21). This screen may be printed out and shown to the customer.
7. Measurement and adjustment screens illustrate suspension measurements. If a measurement is within specifications, the measurement is illustrated with a green bar and an arrow indicates the measurement. A red measurement bar indicates the adjustment is not within specifications (Figure 15-22). In the adjustment mode, the measurement remains on the screen, and as the necessary suspension adjustment is performed, the adjustment bar turns green when the arrow moves within specifications.

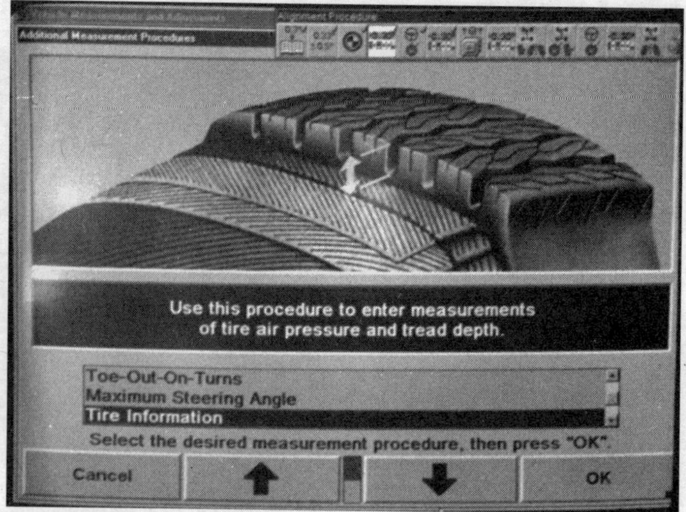

FIGURE 15-21 *Tire inspection screen.*

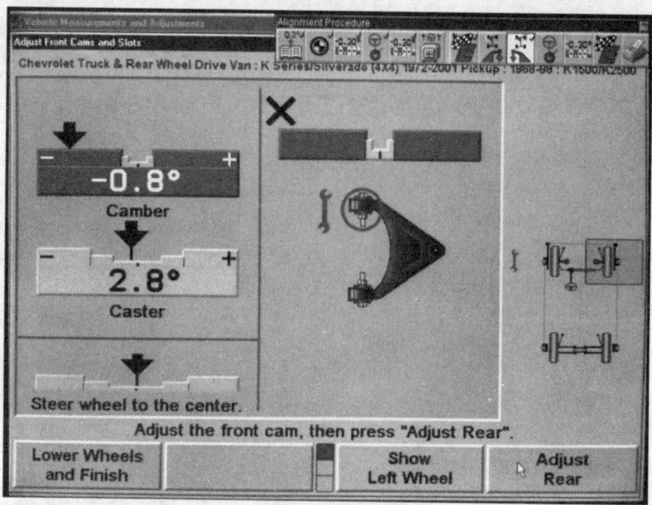

FIGURE 15-22 *Wheel alignment adjustment screen.*

8. An alignment procedure bar is available in some computer aligners. This vertical bar contains an icon for each step in an alignment procedure (Figure 15-23). These steps are arranged in the proper sequence. A check mark appears when a step has been completed, and the technician may select and click any step to move to that adjustment.
9. Correction kit videos may be accessed to illustrate the installation of aftermarket wheel alignment correction kits. Special tools videos are available in the computer wheel aligner software. These videos indicate the special wheel alignment adjustment tools required for the vehicle being aligned. Operation videos may be accessed to show the technician how to operate the computer wheel aligner.
10. Some computer wheel aligners have multilingual capabilities. These capabilities usually include three languages; however, up to twenty languages may be available from the equipment manufacturer.

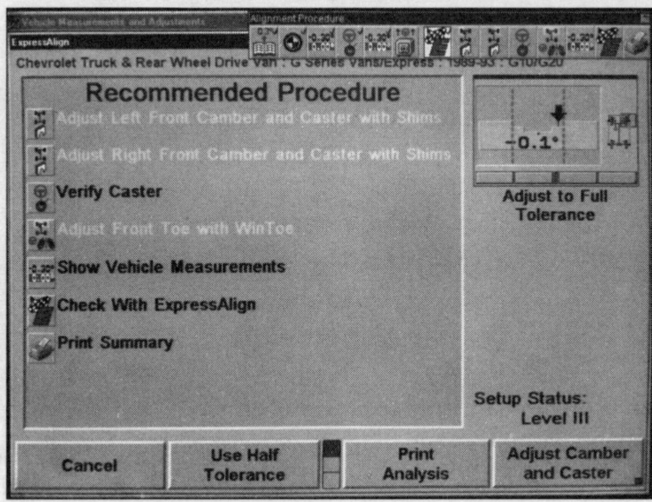

FIGURE 15-23 *Wheel alignment procedure screen.*

11. Full-function keyboard allows the technician to enter such information as the customer's name and address and the make and year of the vehicle.
12. Set of four self-centering adjustable rim clamps and four wheel sensors.
13. Full-function remote control that allows the technician to control the alignment program and see the results of suspension adjustments while working under the vehicle.
14. Color or laser printer provides detailed wheel alignment reports for the customer and specific alignment messages and diagrams for the technician.
15. In some computer wheel aligners, the **Motorist Assurance Program** (MAP) uniform inspection guidelines may be accessed for many steering, suspension, and brake components (Figure 15-24).

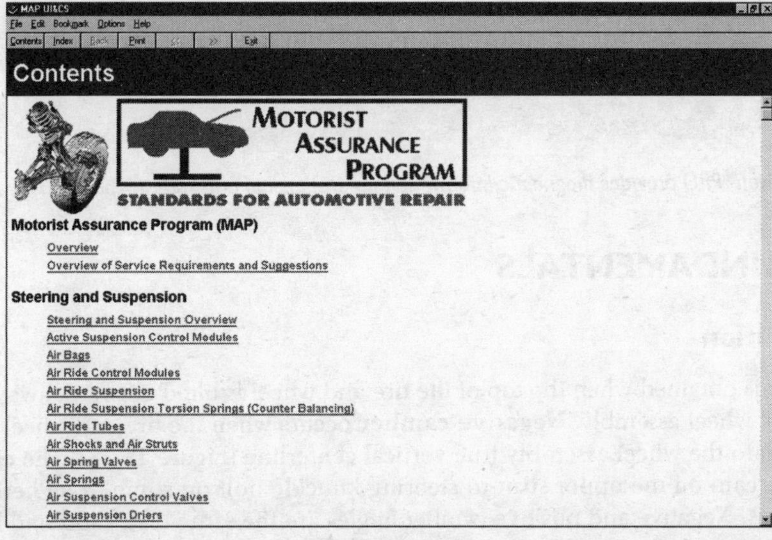

FIGURE 15-24 *The Motorist Assurance Program (MAP) parts inspection guidelines may be accessed in computer wheel aligners.*

The MAP program establishes uniform parts inspection guidelines to improve customer satisfaction with the automotive industry.

16. A variety of software programs are available with some computer wheel aligners. Much of the software may be extra-cost options. This software may include:
    - Hunter WinAlign®: This software provides the technician with a very extensive vehicle information database as well as many patented adjustment and productivity features (Figure 15-25).
    - Chilton®PRO provides service bulletins and other information on domestic and import vehicles (Figures 15-26 and 15-27). Chilton®PRO also provides labor estimates for automotive repairs.

FIGURE 15-25 *Hunter WinAlign® software for computer wheel aligners. (Courtesy of Hunter Engineering.)*

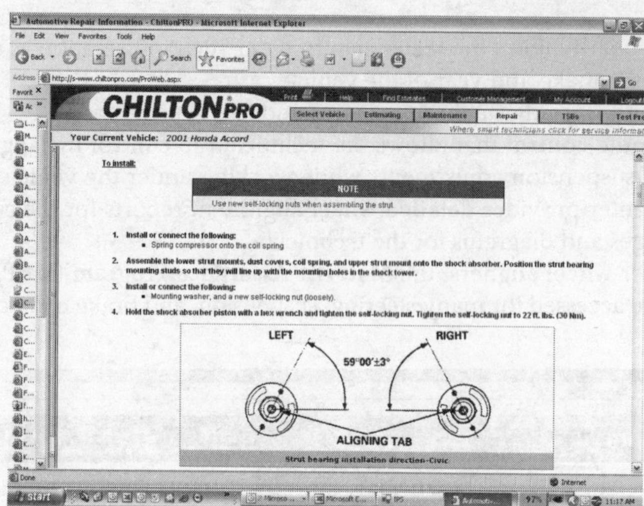

FIGURE 15-26 *Chilton®PRO provides diagnostic information for suspension and steering problems.*

CAMBER FUNDAMENTALS

Camber Definition

Positive camber is obtained when the top of the tire and wheel is tilted outward, away from the true vertical line of the wheel assembly. **Negative camber** occurs when the tire and wheel centerline tilts inward in relation to the wheel assembly true vertical centerline (Figure 15-28). The camber may be adjusted with the cam on the upper strut-to-steering knuckle bolt on some MacPherson strut front suspension systems. Negative and positive camber angles are the same on a short-and-long arm front suspension system as they are on a MacPherson strut suspension system (Figure 15-29).

Front cradle position is extremely important to provide proper front wheel camber on a front-wheel-drive vehicle. For example, if the vehicle is involved in a side collision and most of the collision force is supplied to the front wheel and chassis, the cradle may be pushed sideways. On the side of the

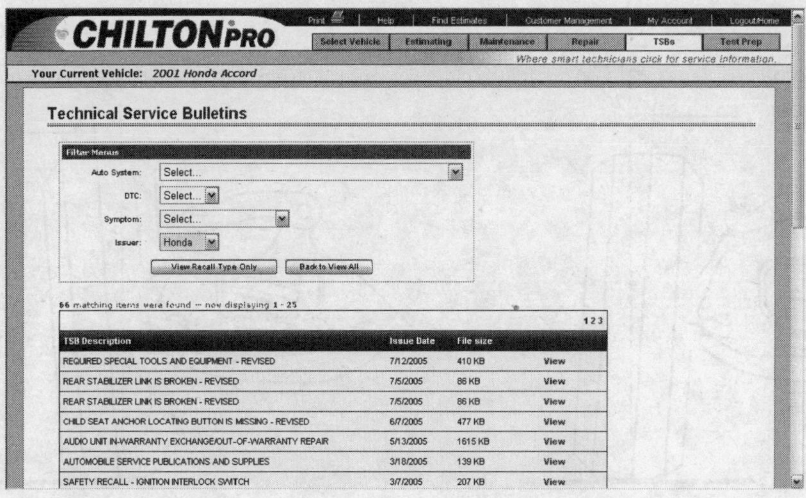

FIGURE 15-27 *Chilton®PRO may be used in some computer wheel aligners.*

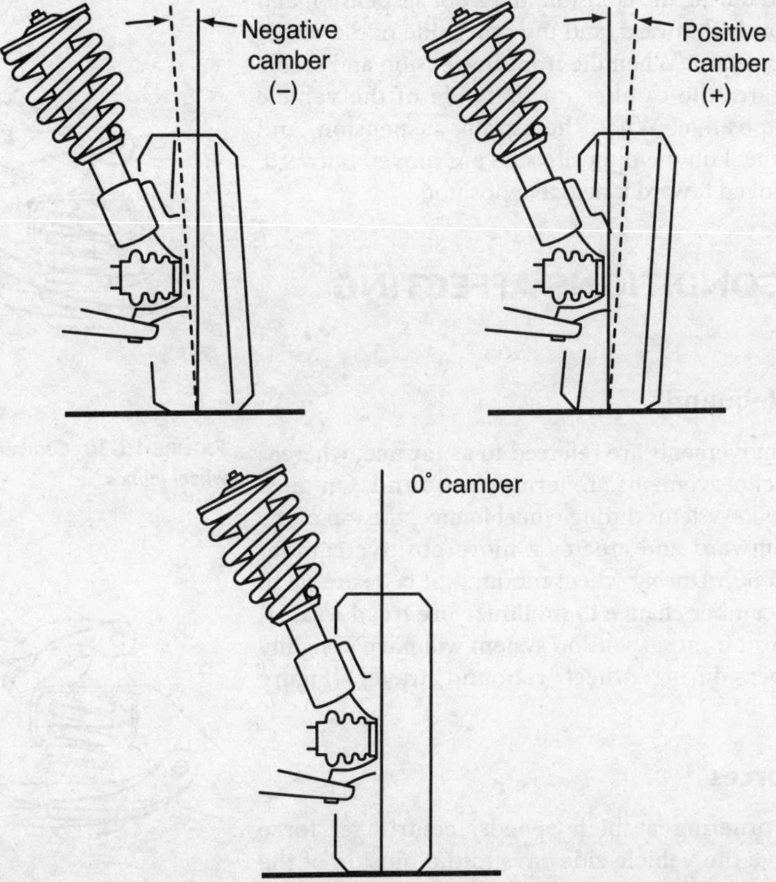

FIGURE 15-28 *Negative and Positive camber angles on a MacPherson strut front suspension system.*

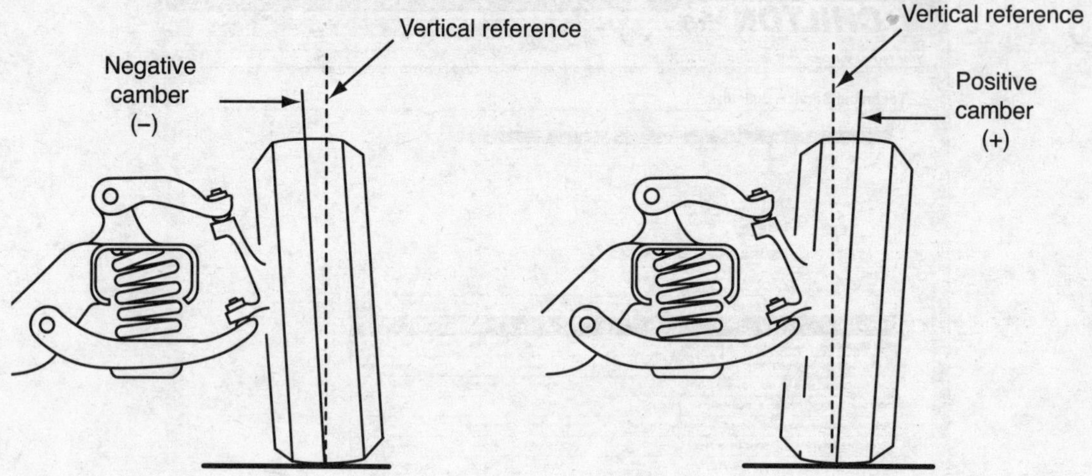

FIGURE 15-29 *Negative and positive camber angles on a short-and-long arm front suspension system.*

vehicle impacted during the collision, the front suspension and cradle may be pushed inward, and the other side of the cradle may be forced outward. When the front suspension and cradle are moved inward, the camber on that side of the vehicle becomes more positive. When the cradle, suspension, and bottom of the wheel on the opposite side are moved outward, the camber is moved toward a negative position.

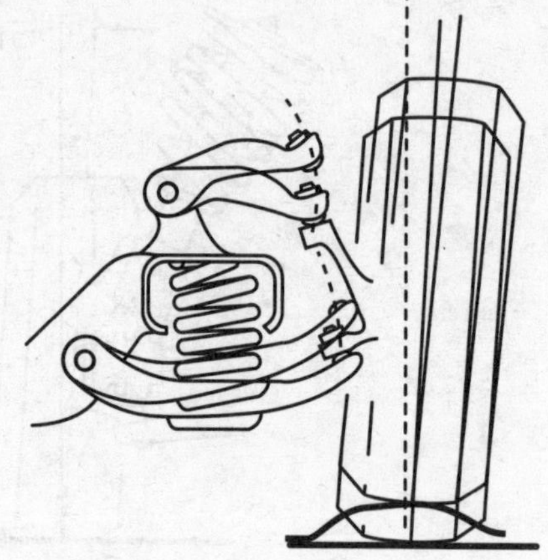

FIGURE 15-30 *Camber change during wheel jounce.*

DRIVING CONDITIONS AFFECTING CAMBER

Jounce and Rebound

Upward wheel movements are referred to as **jounce,** whereas downward wheel movements are termed **rebound.** On most modern suspension systems during wheel jounce, the top of the wheel moves outward and creates a more positive camber angle (Figure 15-30). During wheel rebound, it is desirable to have very little camber change to minimize tire tread wear. A short-and-long arm front suspension system will have a slightly negative camber during wheel rebound travel (Figure 15-31).

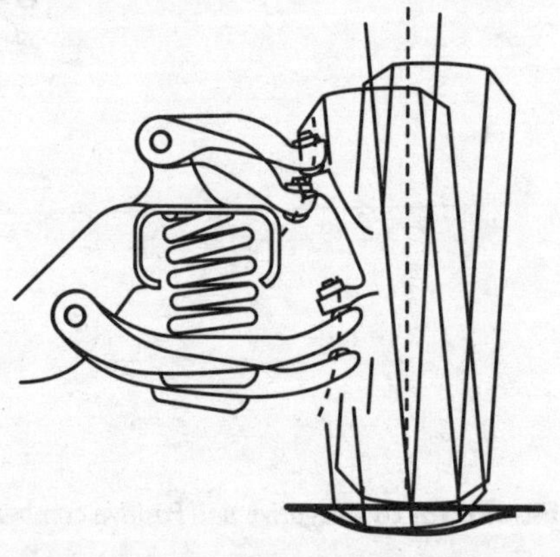

FIGURE 15-31 *Camber change during wheel rebound.*

Cornering Forces

During hard cornering at high speeds, centrifugal force attempts to move the vehicle sideways to the outside of the turn. Under this condition, more vehicle weight is transferred to the side of the vehicle on the outside of the curve. Therefore, the front suspension on the outside of the curve is forced downward, whereas the front suspension on the inside of the curve is lifted upward. When this action occurs, the camber on the inside wheel becomes less positive and the inside edge of the tire grips the road surface to help prevent sideways skidding (Figure 15-32).

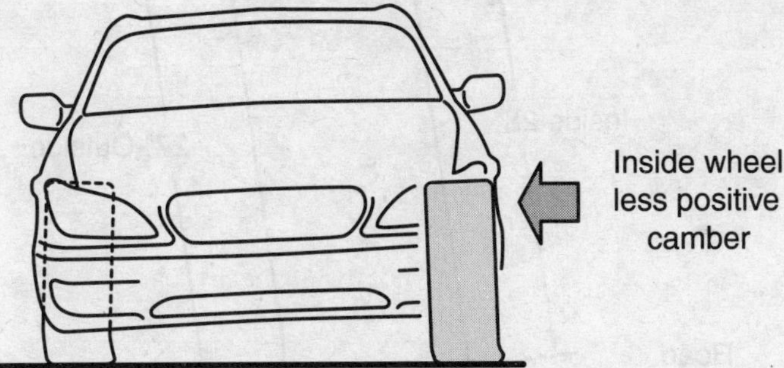

FIGURE 15-32 *While cornering at high speed, the camber on the inside front wheel becomes less positive and the inside edge of the tire grips the road surface to resist lateral skidding.*

Simultaneously, the camber on the outside wheel moves to a slightly more positive position. This action on the outside wheel causes the outside edge of the tire to grip the road surface, which helps prevent sideways skidding (Figure 15-33). Frequent, hard, high-speed cornering causes wear on the edges of the tire treads.

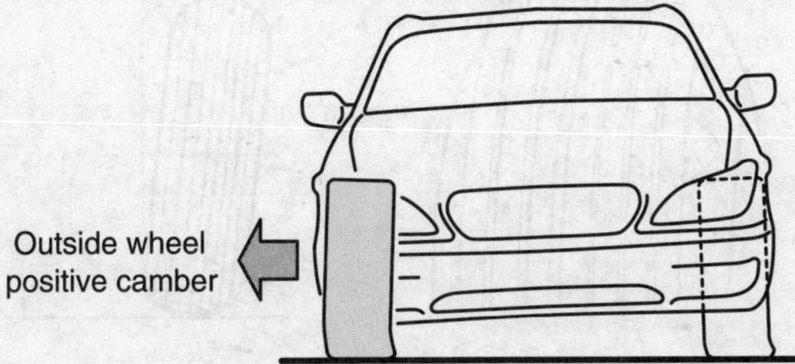

FIGURE 15-33 *While cornering at high speed, the camber on the outside front wheel moves to a slightly more positive position and the outside edge of the tire grips the road surface to resist lateral skidding.*

Tire Tread Wear

The camber angle may be referred to as one of the tire wear alignment angles. When the front wheels are adjusted to the manufacturer's specified camber setting, the front wheels will remain at, or very close to, the 0° camber position during average driving conditions. Therefore, maximum tire tread life and directional stability are maintained.

If a front wheel has excessive positive camber, the wheel is tilted outward and the vehicle weight is concentrated on the outside edge of the tire. Under this condition, the outside edge of the tire has a smaller diameter than the inside tire edge. Therefore, the outside tire edge has to complete more revolutions to travel the same distance as the inside tire edge. Since both edges are on the same tire, the outside edge must slip and scuff on the road surface as the tire and wheel revolve (Figure 15-34).

Excessive negative camber tilts the wheel inward and concentrates the vehicle weight on the inside edge of the tire. This condition causes wear and scuffing on the inside edge of the tire tread (Figure 15-35). Therefore, correct camber adjustment is extremely important to providing normal tire tread life.

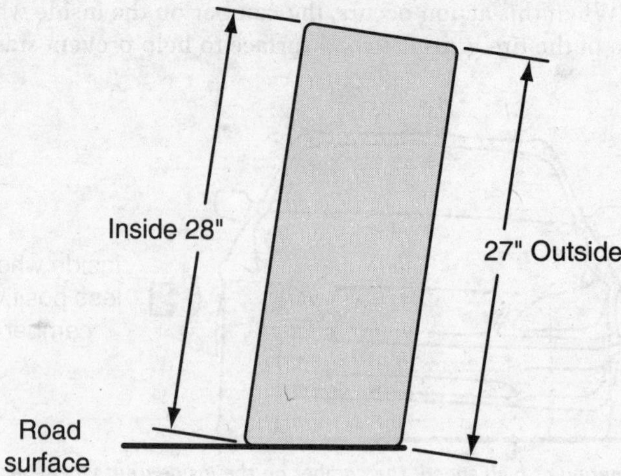

FIGURE 15-34 *Excessive positive camber causes a smaller diameter on the outside edge of the tire compared to the inside edge of the tire.*

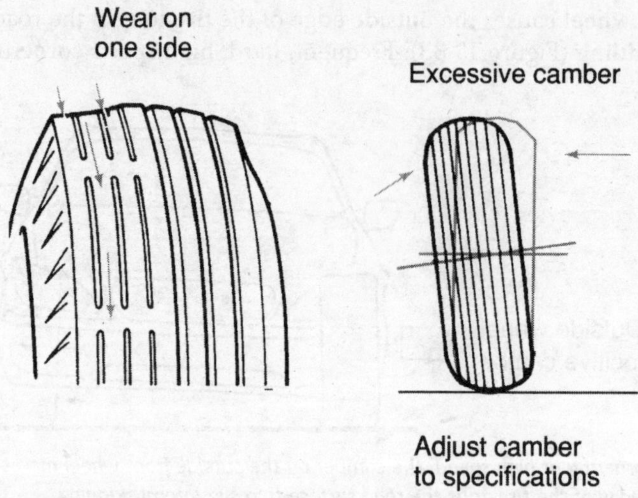

FIGURE 15-35 *Tire tread wear caused by incorrect camber adjustment.*

WARNING: Improper camber adjustment may result in rapid tire tread wear and steering pull, which is a vehicle safety hazard.

Road Crown

A wheel that is tilted tends to steer in the direction it is tilted (Figure 15-36). For example, a bicycle rider tilts the bicycle in the direction he or she wishes to turn, making the turning process easier.

When camber angles are equal on both front wheels, the camber steering forces are equal, and the vehicle tends to maintain a straight-line position. If the camber on the front wheels is significantly unequal, the vehicle will drift to the side with the greatest degree of positive camber.

Crowned highway design prevents water buildup on the driving surface. When a vehicle is driven on a crowned road, it is actually driven on a slight slope, which causes the vehicle steering to pull toward the right (Figure 15-37). Some car manufacturers use the pulling effect of camber to offset this

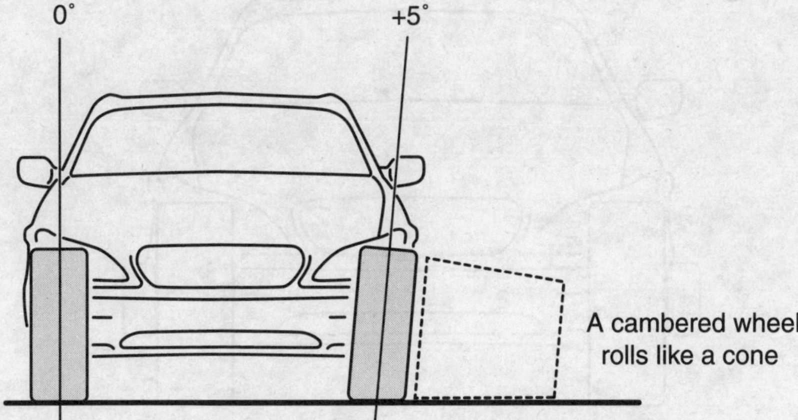

FIGURE 15-36 *A wheel turns in the direction of the tilt.*

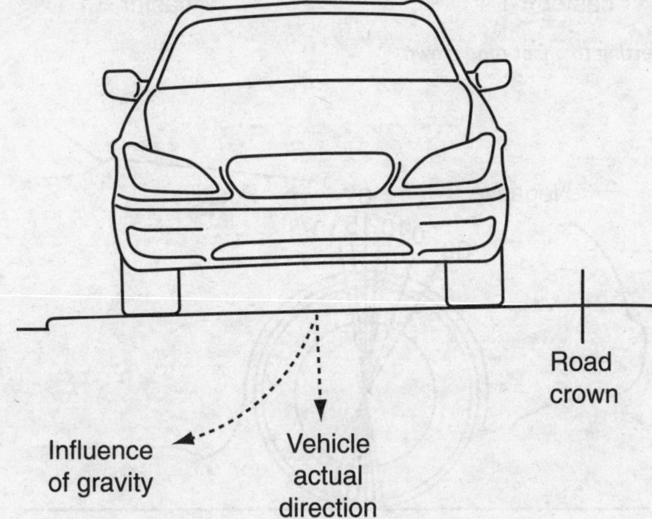

FIGURE 15-37 *A crowned road surface causes the vehicle steering to pull to the right.*

pull to the right caused by road crown. In these vehicles, the left front wheel may have 1/4° to 1/2° more positive camber than the right front wheel.

When the camber on the front wheels is adjusted to the manufacturer's specifications, vehicle directional stability is maintained. If the camber adjustment on the left front wheel is used to offset road crown, the caster on both front wheels must be the same (Figure 15-38).

CASTER FUNDAMENTALS

Caster Definition

On a short-and-long arm suspension system, the caster line intersects the center of the upper and lower ball joints. **Positive caster** occurs when the caster line is tilted backward toward the rear of the vehicle in relation to the vertical centerline of the spindle and wheel viewed from the side (Figure 15-39).

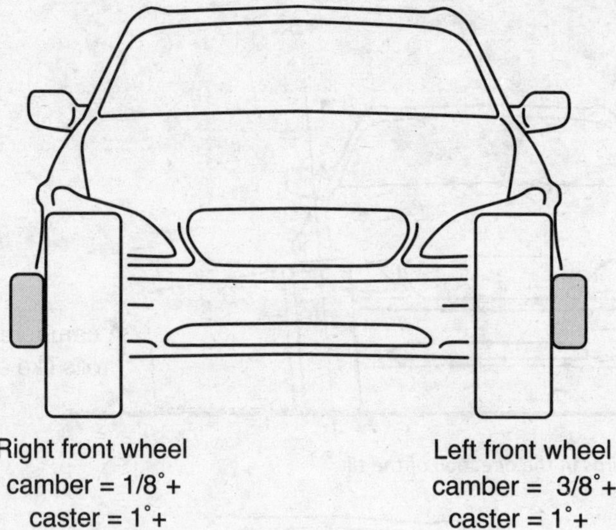

FIGURE 15-38 *Camber setting to offset road crown.*

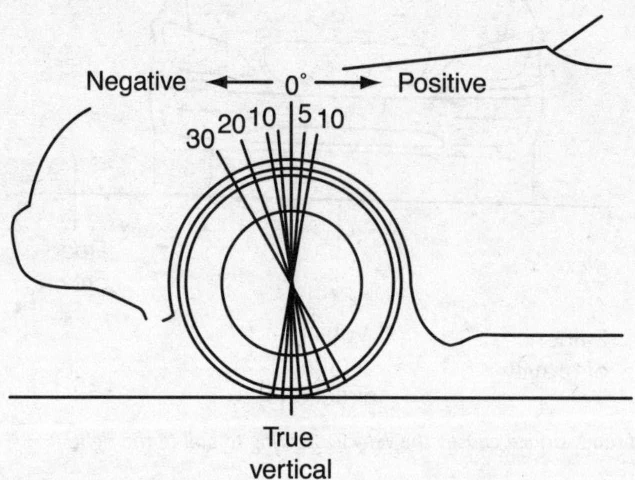

FIGURE 15-39 *Positive and negative caster.*

Negative caster occurs when the centerline of the upper strut mount and ball joint is tilted toward the front of the vehicle in relation to the spindle and wheel vertical centerline.

Effects of Positive Caster

If a piece of furniture mounted on casters is pushed, the casters turn on their pivots to bring the wheels into line with the pushing force applied to the furniture. Therefore, the furniture moves easily in a straight line (Figure 15-40).

Any force exerted on the pivot causes the wheel to turn until it is lined up with the force on the pivot, because the weight on the wheel results in resistance to wheel movement (Figure 15-41).

Most bicycles are designed with positive caster. The weight of the bicycle and rider is projected through the bicycle front forks to the road surface. The tire pivots on the vertical centerline of the

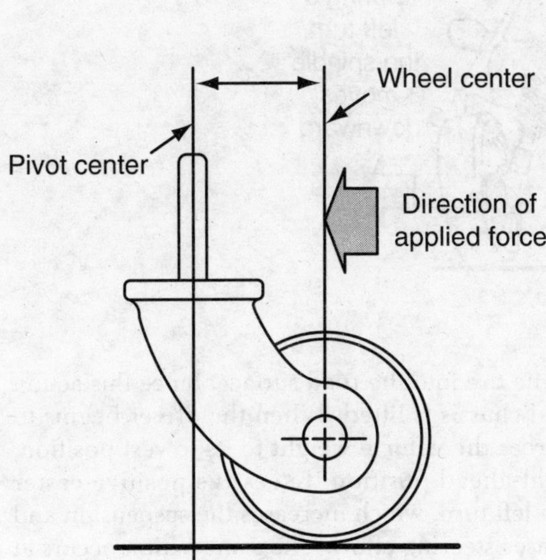

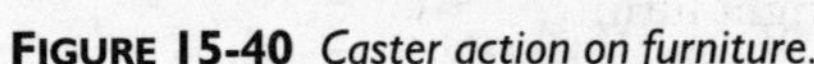

FIGURE 15-40 *Caster action on furniture.*

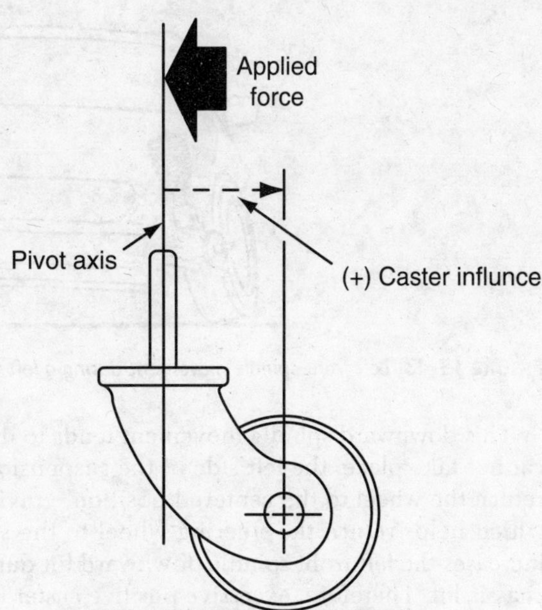

FIGURE 15-41 *Furniture caster wheel aligned with the force on the pivot.*

spindle and wheel when the handle bars and front wheel are turned. Notice that the caster line through the center of the front forks is tilted rearward in relation to the vertical centerline of the spindle and wheel as viewed from the side (Figure 15-42).

Since the pivot point is behind the caster line where the bicycle weight is projected against the road surface, the front wheel tends to return to the straight-ahead position after a turn. The wheel also tends to remain in the straight-ahead position as the bicycle is driven. Therefore, the caster angle on a bicycle front wheel provides the same action as the caster angle on a piece of furniture.

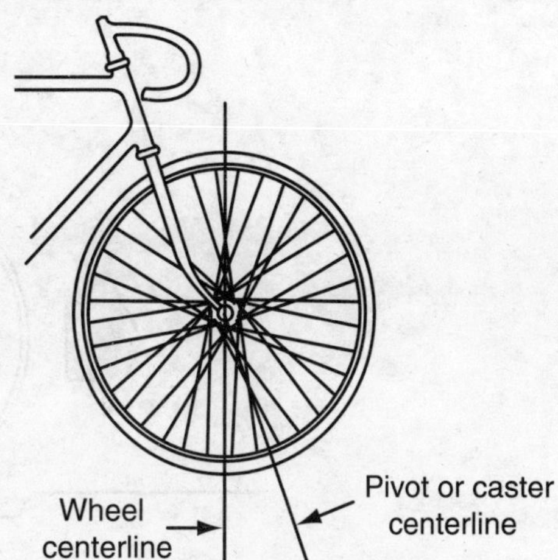

FIGURE 15-42 *Caster line on a bicycle.*

Positive caster projects the vehicle weight ahead of the wheel centerline, whereas negative caster projects the vehicle weight behind the wheel centerline. Since positive caster causes a larger tire contact area behind the caster pivot point, this large contact area tends to follow the pivot point. This action tends to return the wheels to a straight-ahead position after a turn. It also helps maintain the straight-ahead position. Positive caster increases steering effort because the tendency of the tires to remain in the straight-ahead position must be overcome during a turn. The returning force to the straight-ahead position is proportional to the amount of positive caster. Positive caster helps maintain vehicle directional stability.

Excessive positive caster is undesirable because it increases steering effort and creates a very rapid steering wheel return. If the caster angle were 0°, the front spindles would rotate horizontally in relation to the road surface. However, a positive caster angle causes the left front spindle to tilt toward the road surface during a left turn (Figure 15-43).

FIGURE 15-43 *Left front spindle movement during a left turn.*

This downward spindle movement tends to drive the tire into the road surface. Since this action cannot take place, the left side of the suspension and chassis is lifted. When the driver begins to return the wheel to the centered position, gravity forces the vehicle weight to its lowest position, which helps return the steering wheel to the straight-ahead position. Excessive positive caster increases the left front spindle downward tilt during a left turn, which increases the suspension and chassis lift. Therefore, excessive positive caster increases steering effort. The same action occurs at the right front spindle, but this spindle tilts downward during a right turn.

Harsh riding may be caused by excessive positive caster because the caster line is actually aimed at some road irregularities (Figure 15-44). Excessive positive caster may cause the front wheels to shimmy from side to side at low speeds.

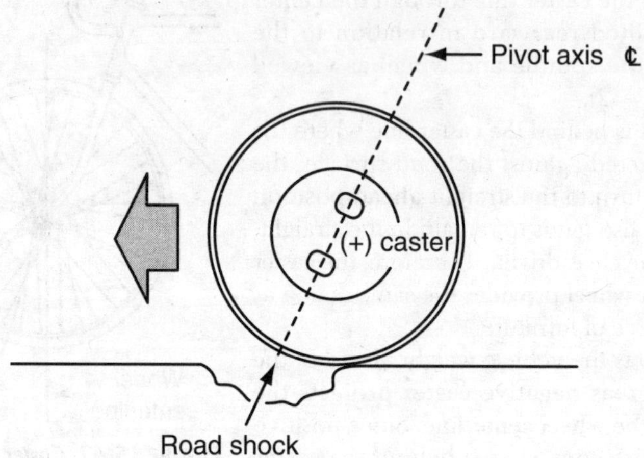

FIGURE 15-44 *Harsh riding quality caused by excessive positive caster.*

When the caster line is aimed directly at the road irregularity, road shock is transmitted through the ball joint and upper strut mount to the suspension and chassis. A small degree of positive caster or a negative caster setting allows the front wheel to roll into a road depression without the caster line being aimed at the hole in the road. Therefore, this type of caster line improves ride quality.

Positive caster is used on most front-wheel-drive vehicles. If one front wheel has more positive caster than the other front wheel, the steering pulls toward the side with the least amount of positive caster.

Improper front wheel caster may be caused by an improperly positioned front cradle on a front-wheel-drive car. For example, if one or both sides of the cradle are driven rearward in a front-end collision, the front wheel caster is moved from a negative position toward a positive position. This condition may cause steering wander, reduced directional control, and slower steering wheel return.

Some car manufacturers recommend less positive caster on the left front wheel than on the right front wheel to offset the steering pull to the right caused by the road crown. If the caster adjustment is used to compensate for road crown, the camber on both front wheels should be the same. The most important facts about positive caster are the following:

1. Positive caster helps the front wheels return to the straight-ahead position after a turn.
2. Correct positive caster provides improved directional stability of a vehicle.
3. Excessive positive caster produces harsh riding quality.
4. Excessive positive caster promotes sideways front **wheel shimmy**.
5. The left front wheel may be adjusted with less positive caster than the right front wheel to compensate for road crown.

Effects of Negative Caster

Negative caster moves the centerline of the upper strut mount and lower ball joint behind the vertical centerline of the spindle and wheel at the road surface. If this condition is present, the friction of the tire causes the tire to pivot around the point where the centerline of the upper strut mount and ball joint meets the road surface. When this occurs, the wheel is pulled away from the straight-ahead position, which decreases directional stability.

Negative caster reduces steering effort. Since excessive positive caster increases road shock transmitted to the suspension and chassis, negative caster reduces this shock and improves ride quality. This improvement occurs because the front wheel rolls into a road depression without the caster line being aimed at the hole in the road.

Effects of Suspension Height on Caster

When the rear springs become sagged or overloaded, the caster on the front wheels becomes more positive. This action explains why front wheel shimmy may occur when a trunk is severely overloaded.

If the rear suspension height is above the vehicle manufacturer's specification, the caster on the front wheels becomes less positive. Under this condition, the front wheel caster may change from positive to negative. This explains why a vehicle may have reduced directional stability and control when the rear suspension height is raised.

On many short-and-long arm front suspension systems, the inner front end of the upper control arm is higher than the inner rear side of this arm where it is attached to the frame. This design causes the front wheel caster to become more positive if the front suspension height is lowered. When the front suspension height is above the vehicle manufacturer's specification, the front wheel caster becomes less positive.

Most front-wheel-drive cars have a MacPherson strut front suspension system with a slightly positive caster setting. Therefore, the top strut mount is tilted rearward. If the front suspension height is lowered on this type of front suspension system, the front wheel caster becomes less positive. Conversely, if the suspension height is raised, positive caster increases. The most important facts about negative caster include the following:

1. Negative caster does not help return the front wheels to the straight-ahead position after a turn.
2. Negative caster contributes to directional instability and reduced directional control.

3. Negative caster does not contribute to front wheel shimmy.
4. Negative caster reduces road shock transmitted to the suspension and chassis.

SAFETY FACTORS AND CASTER

Directional Control

As explained earlier in this chapter, positive caster provides increased directional stability and control, whereas negative caster reduces directional stability. Therefore, front wheel caster must be adjusted to the manufacturer's specifications to maintain vehicle directional control and safe handling characteristics.

Suspension Height

We have already explained how incorrect front or rear suspension height results in changes in front wheel caster. Therefore, abnormal suspension heights may contribute to reduced directional control and unsafe steering characteristics.

WARNING: Improper caster adjustment may result in decreased directional stability of the vehicle and reduced driving safety.

STEERING TERMINOLOGY

In the automotive service industry, certain terms are used for specific steering problems. Some of these problems are related to camber and caster, others are caused by various suspension or steering defects. Technicians must be familiar with both the steering terminology and the causes of the problems.

A front-wheel-drive vehicle with unequal-length drive axles produces some **torque steer** on hard acceleration. Some front-wheel-drive vehicles, especially those with higher horsepower, have equal-length front drive axles to reduce torque steer. On a front-wheel-drive vehicle, torque steer is aggravated by different tire tread designs on the front tires or uneven wear on the front tires.

Bump steer occurs if the tie-rods are not the same height, meaning one of the tie-rods is not parallel to the lower control arm. This condition may be caused by a bent or worn idler arm or pitman arm on a parallelogram steering linkage. On a rack and pinion steering system, worn steering gear mounting bushings may cause this unparallel condition between one of the tie-rods and the lower control arm.

Memory steer may be caused by a binding condition in the steering column or in the steering shaft universal joints. A binding upper strut mount may result in memory steer. Negative caster or reduced positive caster also causes memory steer.

Steering pull is the tendency of the steering to gradually pull to the right or left when the vehicle is driven straight ahead on a level road. Steering pull or drift may be caused by improper caster or camber adjustments. **Steering drift** is the tendency of the steering to slowly drift to the right or left when driving straight ahead on a level road.

When **steering wander** occurs, the vehicle tends to steer in either direction rather than straight ahead on a level road surface. Steering wander may be caused by improper caster adjustment.

STEERING AXIS INCLINATION (SAI) DEFINITION

On front-wheel-drive vehicles with MacPherson strut front suspension systems, **steering axis inclination** (**SAI**) refers to the inward tilt of a line through the center of the top strut mount and the center of the lower ball joint in relation to the true vertical line through the center of the tire. These two lines are viewed from the front of the vehicle, and the SAI line always tilts inward in relation to the true vertical line (Figure 15-45).

Many rear-wheel-drive cars have a short-and-long arm front suspension system with unequal-length upper and lower control arms and a ball joint mounted in each control arm. The steering knuckle and spindle pivot on the ball joints as the wheels are turned. On this type of front suspension, the SAI line runs through the upper and lower ball joint centers. The **included angle** is the sum of the SAI angle and the camber angle (Figure 15-46).

If the camber angle is positive, this angle is added to the SAI angle to obtain the included angle. A negative camber angle must be subtracted from the SAI angle to calculate the included angle. On some truck front suspension

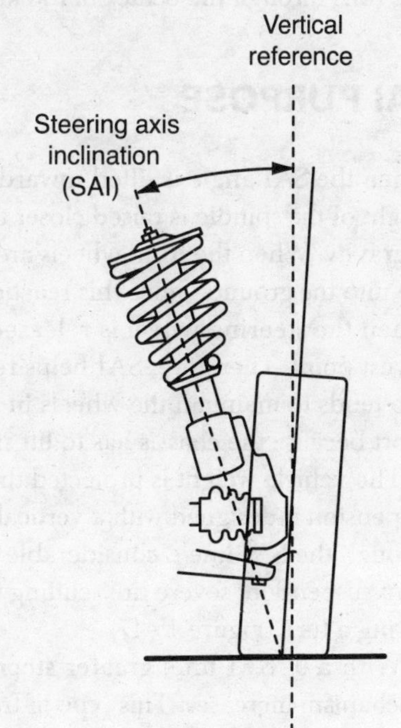

FIGURE 15-45 *Steering axis inclination angle.*

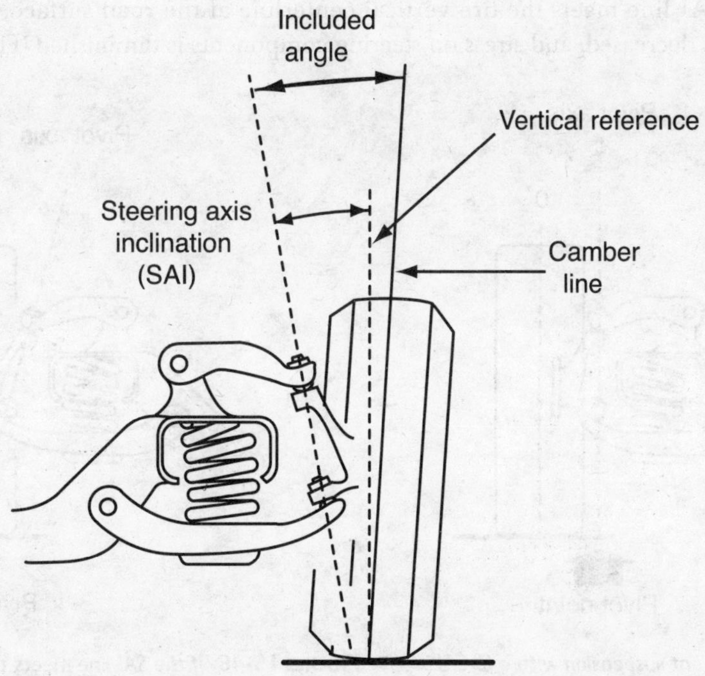

FIGURE 15-46 *Steering axis inclination and included angle.*

systems, the steering knuckle pivots on a king pin that is mounted in an I beam-type front axle. The SAI line on this type of suspension is referred to as a **king pin inclination (KPI)** line. This invisible line runs through the center of the king pin.

SAI PURPOSE

When the SAI angle is tilted toward the center of the vehicle and the wheels are straight ahead, the height of the spindle is raised closer to the chassis. This action lowers the height of the vehicle because of gravity. When the front wheels are turned, each spindle moves through an arc that tries to force the tire into the ground. Since this reaction cannot take place, the chassis lifts when the wheels are turned. When the steering wheel is released after a turn, the vehicle weight has a tendency to settle to its lowest point. Therefore, SAI helps return the wheels to the straight-ahead position after a turn, and it also tends to maintain the wheels in the straight-ahead position. However, SAI does increase steering effort because the chassis has to lift slightly on turns.

The vehicle weight is projected through the SAI line to the road surface. Let us assume that a front suspension is designed with a vertical 0° SAI line. Under this condition, the vehicle weight is projected through the SAI line a considerable distance inside the true vertical tire centerline. With this type of front suspension, severe tire scuffing would occur because the tire and wheel pivot around the SAI line during a turn (Figure 15-47).

With a 0° SAI line, greater steering effort is required during a turn and stress on the steering mechanism increases. This type of front suspension design causes excessive road shock and kick-back on the steering wheel during a turn, because the distance between the SAI line and the tire vertical line returns the wheels to the straight-ahead position.

When the SAI line meets the tire vertical centerline at the road surface, tire wear is reduced, steering effort is decreased, and stress on steering components is diminished (Figure 15-48).

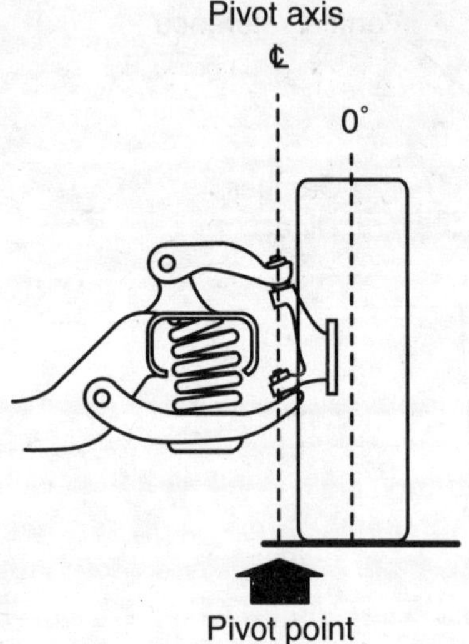

FIGURE 15-47 *Front suspension with a 0° SAI line.*

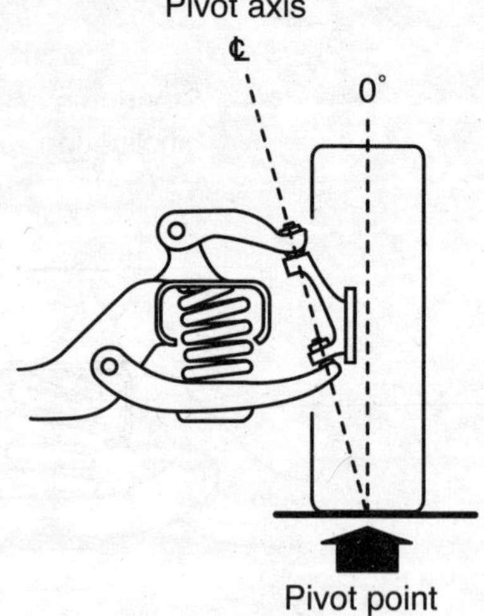

FIGURE 15-48 *If the SAI line meets the tire vertical centerline at the road surface, tire wear is reduced, steering effort is decreased, and stress on the steering components is diminished.*

The point at which the SAI line and the tire vertical centerline intersect could be positioned closer together by designing the front suspension with excessive positive camber. However, this design would result in rapid wear on the outside edge of the tire tread. A correct SAI line reduces the need for excessive positive camber.

MacPherson strut front suspension systems have a much greater SAI angle (12° to 18°) compared with short-and-long arm front suspensions in rear-wheel-drive cars (6° to 8°). Front-wheel-drive cars require the higher SAI angle for directional stability. Positive caster also provides directional stability. Since SAI helps maintain the front wheels in the straight-ahead position, SAI reduces the need for excessive positive caster.

SAI AND SAFETY FACTORS

On MacPherson strut suspension systems, an incorrect SAI angle may indicate that the upper strut mount is out of position, the lower control arm is bent, or the center cross member is shifted. Any of these defects may be caused by collision damage.

When the SAI angles are unequal on the left and right front suspension, serious handling problems may occur. These problems include torque steering during hard acceleration, steering pull during sudden stops, and bump steer. Torque steer is the tendency to pull to one side on hard acceleration because of unequal-length drive axles on a front-wheel-drive vehicle. Unequal SAI angles aggravate torque steer. Bump steer refers to unequal toe and/or camber changes that jerk the car to one side during front suspension jounce and rebound. Therefore, incorrect SAI angles may cause hazardous driving situations and contribute to serious accidents. Technicians must inspect the SAI angle during a wheel alignment.

If the SAI angle is correct and the included angle and camber are less than specified, bent components such as the strut or spindle are indicated. On the type of suspension that requires inward or outward upper strut movement to adjust camber, the SAI angle changes with this movement. When an eccentric bolt between the strut and steering knuckle is used for camber adjustment, the SAI angle will not change if the camber is adjusted.

It is very important to remember that a camber adjustment on many front suspension systems also changes the SAI angle. For example, if the upper control arm on a front suspension system with upper and lower ball joints is shimmed outward to increase positive camber, the SAI angle will change with the camber angle. Therefore, the included angle remains the same. The camber may be adjusted to specification, but the SAI angle and included angle could be out of specification. This is especially true on MacPherson strut suspension systems where collision damage may bend front struts or shift the upper strut towers. A service technician who inspects and adjusts the camber angle while ignoring the SAI and included angles may be overlooking serious and dangerous front suspension defects.

SCRUB RADIUS

Scrub radius affects steering quality related to stability and returnability. However, scrub radius is not an alignment angle and it cannot be measured on conventional alignment equipment. Scrub radius is the distance from the point where the tire vertical line contacts the road to the location where the line through the upper strut center and the ball joint center meets the road surface. **Positive scrub radius** occurs when the line through the strut and ball joint meets the road surface inside the tire vertical centerline. A **negative scrub radius** is when the line through the strut and ball joint centers meets the road surface outside the tire and hub centerline (Figure 15-49).

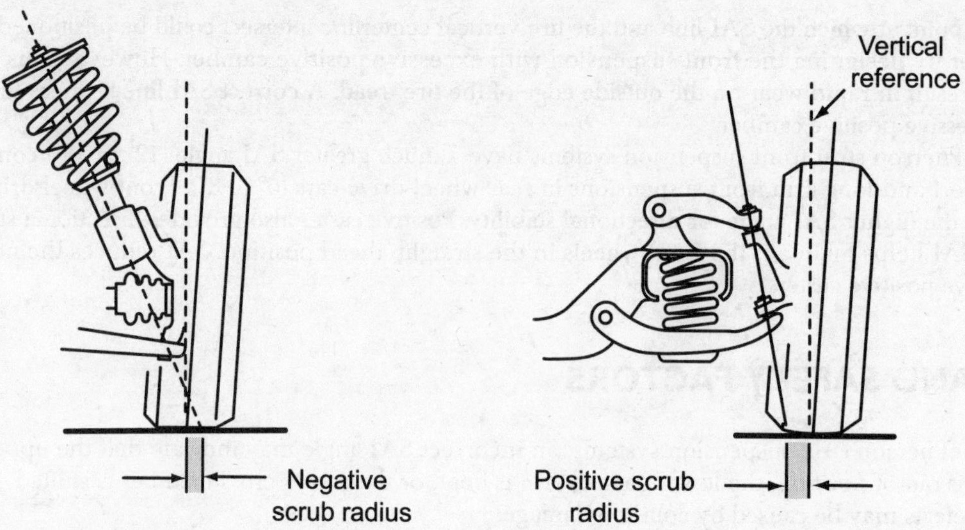

FIGURE 15-49 *Scrub radius.*

Conventional short-and-long arm front suspension systems usually have positive scrub radius. Many front-wheel-drive vehicles have negative scrub radius.

When negative scrub radius is used in front-wheel-drive vehicles, straight-line braking is ensured and directional stability is maintained. As the vehicle moves forward, negative scrub radius tends to turn the front wheels inward. This action causes unequal forces applied to the steering to act inboard of the steering axis and pull the vehicle from any induced swerve. In a front-wheel-drive vehicle, a swerve to one side may be caused by one front wheel being on an ice patch while the other front wheel is on dry pavement. A failure of one-half the diagonal brake system, a sudden blowout of one front tire, or a grabbing brake on one front wheel will also cause a vehicle to swerve.

If a vehicle has positive scrub radius and the right front brake grabs, both the positive scrub radius and the grabbing brake tend to turn the right front wheel outward, and the vehicle pivots around the right front wheel. This action induces a swerve to the right.

When a right front brake grab occurs with negative scrub radius, the brake grab causes the right front wheel to turn outward, and the vehicle tends to pivot around the right front wheel. However, the negative scrub radius tends to turn the right front wheel inward. The two forces on the right front wheel cancel each other to maintain directional stability.

Scrub Radius and Safety

If front tires that are larger in diameter than specified by the car manufacturer are installed, directional control may be affected. Large tires raise the chassis farther from the road surface, which changes the scrub radius. The installation of larger front tires could change a positive scrub radius to a negative scrub radius.

Reversing the front rims so they are inside out creates a significant scrub radius change and adversely affects directional control. This practice is not recommended by car manufacturers.

WARNING: Installing larger tires, or different rims than the ones specified by the vehicle manufacturer, changes the scrub radius, which may result in reduced directional control, collision damage, and personal injury.

WHEEL SETBACK

Wheel setback is a condition in which one wheel is moved rearward in relation to the other wheel (Figure 15-50). Setback will not affect handling unless it is extreme. Collision damage may drive one front strut rearward and cause extreme setback. Setback can also occur on rear wheels, but it is more likely to occur on front wheels because of collision damage. Some computer four wheel aligners have setback measuring capabilities.

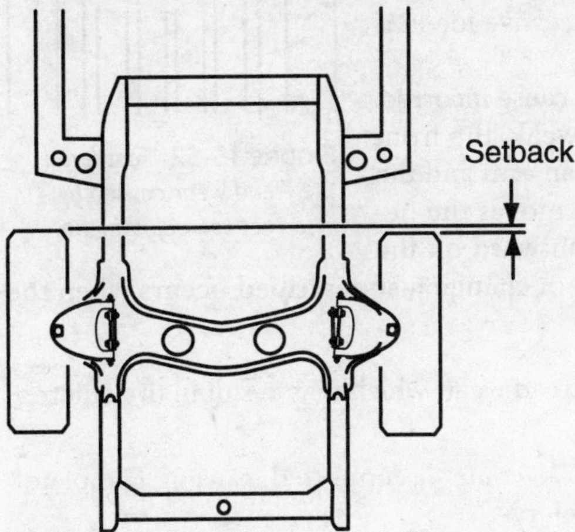

FIGURE 15-50 *Setback.*

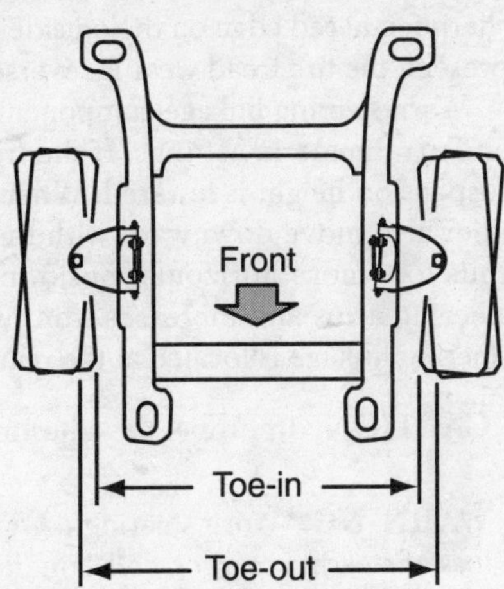

FIGURE 15-51 *Toe-in and toe-out.*

TOE DEFINITION

When the distance between the rear inside tire edges is greater than the distance between the front inside tire edges, the front wheels have a **toe-in** setting. **Toe-out** occurs when the distance between the inside front tire edges exceeds the distance between the inside rear tire edges (Figure 15-51).

TOE SETTING FOR FRONT-WHEEL-DRIVE AND REAR-WHEEL-DRIVE VEHICLES

On a front-wheel-drive vehicle, the front drive axle torque forces the front wheels toward an increased toe-in position. Therefore, car manufacturers usually specify a slight toe-out position for the front wheels on these vehicles.

On rear-wheel-drive vehicles, front tire friction on the road surface moves the wheels toward the toe-out position when the car is driven. On this type of vehicle, manufacturers usually specify a slight toe-in on the front wheels. The front wheels are adjusted to a slight toe-in or toe-out with the vehicle at rest so the wheels will be parallel to each other when the vehicle is driven on the road. A slight amount of lateral movement always exists in steering linkages. Forces acting on the front wheels try to compress or stretch the steering linkages when the vehicle is driven. Whether a compressing or stretching action occurs on the steering linkage depends on whether the steering linkages are located at the rear edge or front edge of the front wheels.

TOE ADJUSTMENT AND TIRE WEAR

Ford Motor Company has calculated that a toe-in error of 1/8 in. (3.17 mm) is equivalent to dragging the tires crosswise for 11 ft. (3.3 m) for each mile the vehicle is driven. This crosswise movement causes severe feathered tire tread wear (Figure 15-52). Improper toe adjustment is the most common cause of rapid tire tread wear.

Excessive toe-out causes wear on the inside of the tire tread ribs and a sharp feathered edge on the outside of the tread ribs. If excessive toe-in is present, the tire tread wear is reversed.

Worn steering linkage components such as tie-rod ends cause incorrect and erratic toe-in settings. If the front springs become weak, the front suspension height is lowered. When this occurs, the pitman arm and the idler arm move downward with the chassis. This action moves the tie-rods to a more horizontal position that tends to push outward on the steering arms and increases front wheel toe-in. The toe-in change just described occurs when the steering linkage is located at the rear of the front wheels.

Feathered edge

FIGURE 15-52 *Feathered tire tread wear caused by incorrect toe adjustment.*

CAUTION: Improper toe adjustment causes rapid tire tread wear, which may result in tire failure.

WARNING: Worn steering components may suddenly become disconnected, causing complete loss of steering control, collision damage, and personal injury.

TURNING RADIUS

Front and Rear Wheel Turning Action

When a vehicle turns a corner, the front and rear wheels must turn around a common center with respect to the **turning radius** (Figure 15-53). On most front suspension systems, the front wheels pivot independently at different distances from the center of the turn, and therefore the front wheels must turn at different angles. The inside front wheel must turn at a sharper angle than the outside wheel. This is because the inside wheel is actually ahead of the outside wheel. When this turning action occurs, both front wheels remain perpendicular to their turning radius, which prevents tire scuffing.

Steering Arm Design

An understanding of a lever moving in a circle is necessary before an explanation of steering arm design and operation. If a lever moves from point A to B, it pivots around point O and moves through a horizontal distance A to B (Figure 15-54).

Lever movement through arc B to C is much greater than the movement through arc A to B. However, during arc B to C, the lever moves through horizontal distance B to C and this distance is the same as horizontal distance A to B.

The steering arms are connected from the tie-rod ends to the steering knuckles. Steering arms and linkages maintain the front wheels parallel to each other when the vehicle is driven straight ahead. However, the steering arms are not parallel to each other. If the steering linkage is at the rear edge of the front wheels, the steering arms are closer together at the point where the tie-rods connect than at

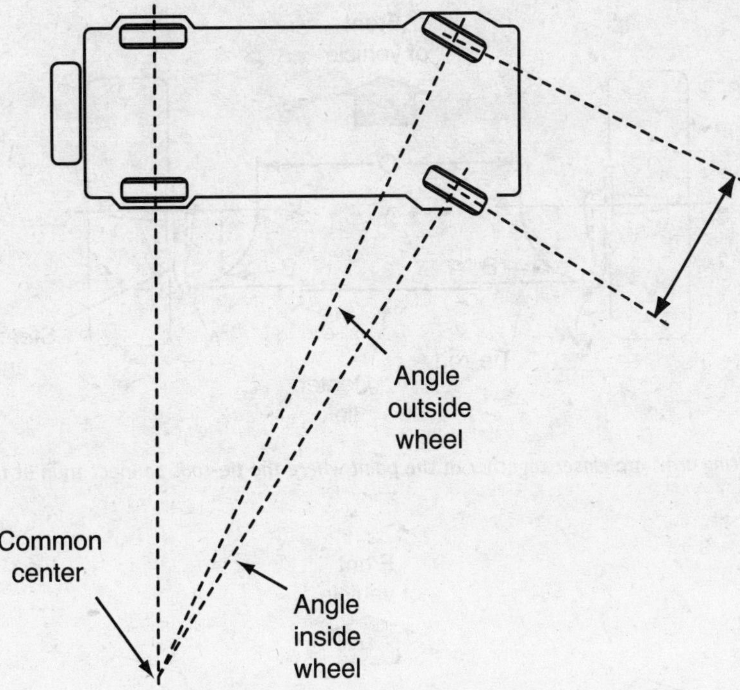

FIGURE 15-53 *Front and rear wheels turning around a common center.*

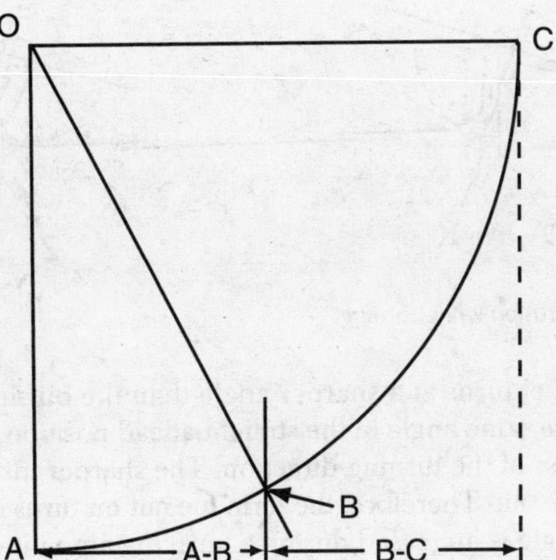

FIGURE 15-54 *Lever movement in a circle.*

their spindle pivot point (Figure 15-55). When the steering linkage is positioned at the front edge of the front wheels, the steering arms are closer together at their spindle pivot point than at the tie-rod connecting point.

When the front wheels are turned on a vehicle with the steering linkage at the rear edge of the front wheels, the angle formed by the inside steering arm and linkage increases, whereas the angle of the outside steering arm and linkage decreases. The inside steering arm moves through the longer arc X, and the outside steering arm moves through shorter arc Z (Figure 15-56).

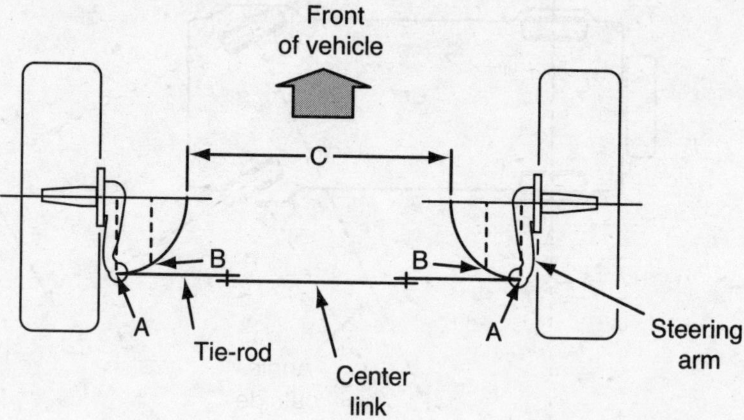

FIGURE 15-55 *Steering arms are closer together at the point where the tie-rods connect than at their spindle pivot points.*

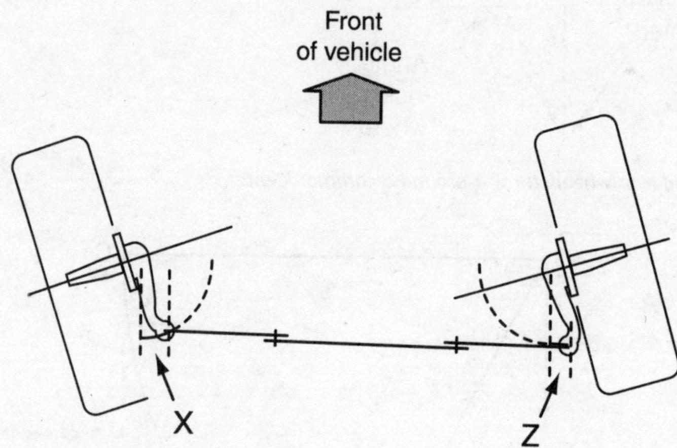

FIGURE 15-56 *Steering arm operation while turning.*

Therefore, the inside wheel turns at a sharper angle than the outside wheel. Since both steering arms are designed to have the same angle in the straight-ahead position, the inside front wheel always has a sharper angle regardless of the turning direction. The sharper inside wheel angle during a turn causes the inside wheel to toe out. Therefore, the term **toe-out on turns** is used for this steering action. If the front wheel turning angle is increased during a turn, the amount of toe-out on the inside wheel increases proportionally.

Slip Angle

During a turn, centrifugal force causes all the tires to slip a certain amount. The amount of tire slip increases with speed and the sharpness of the turn. This tire slip action causes the actual center of the turn to be considerably ahead of the theoretical turn center (Figure 15-57).

The **slip angle** on different vehicles varies depending on such factors as vehicle weight and type of suspension.

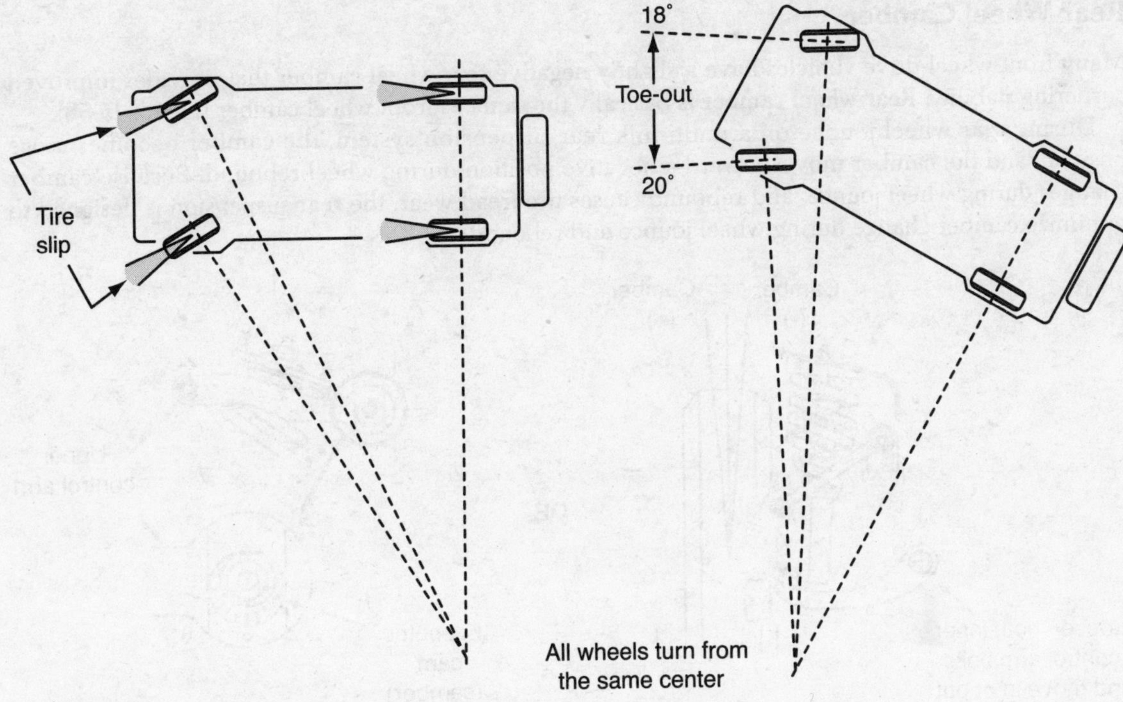

FIGURE 15-57 *Slip angle during a turn.*

REAR WHEEL ALIGNMENT

Rear Wheel Alignment Diagnosis

Customer complaints that indicate rear wheel alignment problems are the following:

1. The front wheel toe is set correctly and the steering wheel is centered on the alignment rack, but the steering wheel is not centered when the vehicle is driven straight ahead.
2. The steering pulls to one side, but there are no worn suspension parts, defective tires, or improper front suspension alignment angles.
3. The vehicle is not overloaded and there are no worn suspension parts or improper front suspension alignment angles, but tire wear occurs.

Defects That Cause Incorrect Rear Wheel Alignment

These suspension or chassis defects cause incorrect rear wheel alignment:

1. Collision damage that results in a bent frame or distorted unitized body
2. A leaf-spring eye that is unwrapped or spread open
3. Leaf-spring shackles that are broken, bent, or worn
4. Broken leaf springs or leaf spring center bolts
5. Worn rear upper or lower control arm bushings
6. Worn trailing arm bushings or dislocated trailing arm brackets
7. Bent components such as radius rods, control arms, struts, and rear axles

Rear Wheel Camber

Many front-wheel-drive vehicles have a slightly negative rear wheel camber that provides improved cornering stability. **Rear wheel camber** is basically the same as front wheel camber (Figure 15-58).

During rear wheel jounce on a multi-link rear suspension system, the camber becomes more positive, and the camber moves toward a negative position during wheel rebound. Because camber changes during wheel jounce, and rebound causes tire tread wear, the rear suspension is designed to minimize camber change during wheel jounce and rebound.

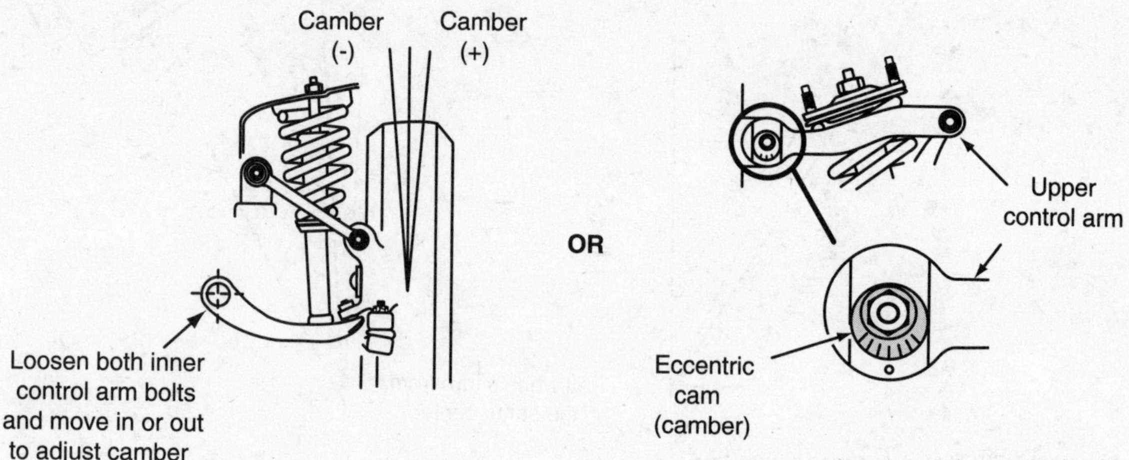

FIGURE 15-58 *Rear wheel camber.*

Rear Wheel Toe

On a front-wheel-drive vehicle, driving forces tend to push back the rear wheel spindles. Therefore these rear wheels are designed with zero toe-in or a slight toe-in depending on the vehicle (Figure 15-59). Correct **rear wheel toe** is important to obtain normal tire life.

On a multi-link rear suspension system with the toe adjustment link mounted in a level position, the toe moves toward a toe-in position during wheel jounce or rebound. These toe changes cause rear tire tread wear.

REVIEW QUESTIONS

Short Answer Essays

1. Explain why four-wheel alignment is essential on unitized body cars with semi-independent or independent rear suspension.
2. Explain why the front wheels are not placed in the exact vertical position for proper wheel alignment.
3. Describe the camber change during front wheel jounce.
4. Explain the camber change during front wheel rebound.
5. Explain why excessive positive camber wears the outside edge of the tire tread.

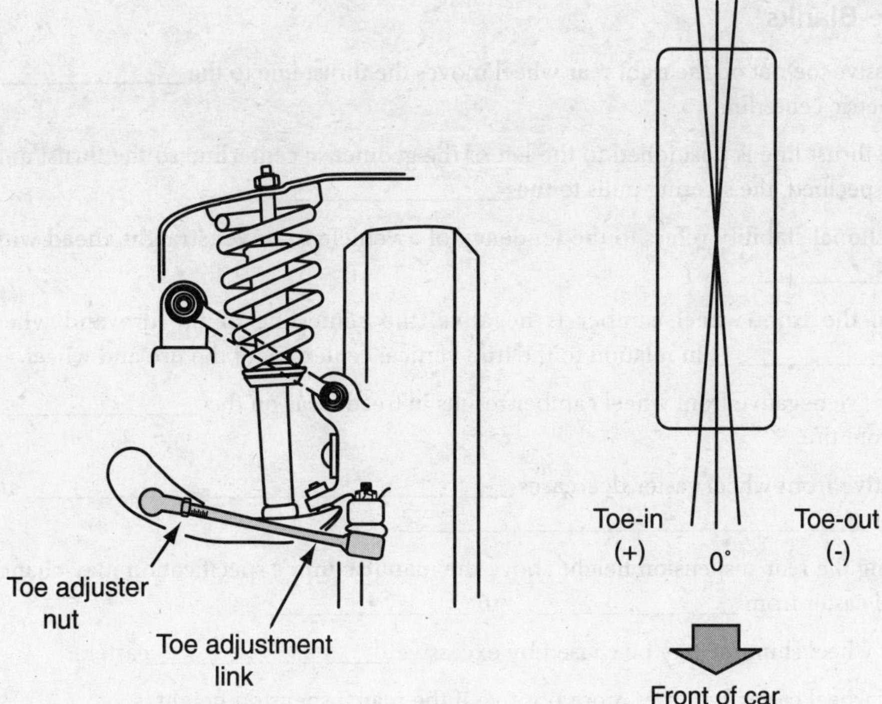

FIGURE 15-59 *Rear wheel toe.*

6. Explain how the front wheel camber may be adjusted to compensate for road crown.
7. Explain why positive caster provides increased directional stability.
8. Describe how positive caster provides increased steering wheel returning force.
9. Explain why positive caster causes harsh riding quality.
10. Describe how the caster adjustment may be used to compensate for road crown.
11. Define steering axis inclination (SAI).
12. Explain the included angle.
13. Explain how SAI helps to return the steering wheel to the center position after a turn.
14. Define negative scrub radius and positive scrub radius, including the type of suspension system on which each condition is used.
15. Describe front wheel setback.
16. Define toe-in and toe-out.
17. Describe the type of tire tread wear caused by an improper toe setting.
18. Explain the turning angle of each front wheel during a turn.
19. Describe three customer complaints that may indicate rear wheel alignment problems.
20. Describe six defects that may cause incorrect rear wheel alignment.

Fill-in-the-Blanks

1. Excessive toe-out on the right rear wheel moves the thrust line to the ________________ of the geometric centerline.
2. If the thrust line is positioned to the left of the geometric centerline so the thrust angle is more than specified, the steering pulls to the ________________.
3. Directional stability refers to the tendency of a vehicle to travel straight ahead without being ________________.
4. When the front wheel camber is negative, the centerline of the tire and wheel is tilted ________________ in relation to the true vertical centerline of the tire and wheel.
5. Excessive negative front wheel camber results in tread wear on the ________________ edge of the front tire.
6. Negative front wheel caster decreases ________________ and steering wheel ________________.
7. Raising the rear suspension height above the manufacturer's specification may change the front wheel caster from ________________ to ________________.
8. Front wheel shimmy may be caused by excessive ________________ caster.
9. Front wheel caster becomes more positive if the rear suspension height is ________________.
10. If the front suspension height is lowered on a MacPherson strut suspension, the front wheel caster becomes ________________.
11. A 3° difference in the SAI angle on each side of the front suspension may cause ____________ during hard braking.
12. A 3° difference in the SAI angle on each side of the front suspension may cause increased ____________ during hard acceleration.
13. When a front suspension has a positive scrub radius, the SAI line meets the road surface ____________ the true vertical centerline of the tire.
14. A negative scrub radius tends to turn the front wheels ____________ when the car is driven.
15. Most rear-wheel-drive cars have a ____________ scrub radius.
16. The front wheel toe on many rear-wheel-drive cars is adjusted to a slight ____________ setting.
17. When the steering linkage is located at the rear edge of the front tires, sagged front springs ____________ the toe-in.
18. During a turn, the ____________ front wheel turns at a sharper angle.
19. When the steering linkage is positioned at the front edge of the front wheels, driving forces tend to ____________ the steering linkages.
20. During a turn, centrifugal force causes all the tires to slip a certain amount, and the actual center of the turn is shifted ____________ of the theoretical center of the turn.

Multiple Choice

1. While diagnosing the vehicle geometric centerline and thrust line:
   A. The front and rear wheels should be parallel to the geometric centerline.
   B. The thrust angle is the difference between the front wheel camber and SAI angles.
   C. If the thrust angle is more than specified, front wheel shimmy may occur.
   D. A bent front cradle may cause the thrust angle to be more than specified.

2. While diagnosing rear axle offset and sideset:
   A. If the rear axle is offset so the thrust line is moved to the left of the geometric centerline, the steering pulls to the left.
   B. When rear axle sideset occurs, one rear wheel is moved rearward in relation to the opposite rear wheel.
   C. On a semi-independent rear suspension system, worn trailing arm bushings may cause rear axle offset.
   D. On an independent rear suspension system, a worn lower ball joint may cause rear axle offset.

3. A front-wheel-drive vehicle with an independent rear suspension pulls to the right when driving straight ahead. All the front suspension alignment angles are within specifications. The most likely cause of this problem is:
   A. Excessive toe-out on the right rear wheel.
   B. Excessive negative camber on the right rear wheel.
   C. Excessive toe-out on the left rear wheel.
   D. Excessive positive camber on the left rear wheel.

4. All of these statements about the vehicle thrust line and steering pull are true EXCEPT:
   A. Excessive toe-out on the left rear wheel moves the thrust line to the left of the vehicle centerline.
   B. Excessive toe-in on the right-rear wheel moves the thrust line to the right of the vehicle centerline.
   C. If the thrust line is moved to the left of the vehicle centerline, the steering tends to pull to the right.
   D. Excessive toe-out on the right-rear wheel causes the steering to pull to the left.

5. While diagnosing suspension and wheel alignment problems:
   A. Road crown has no effect on vehicle steering or wheel alignment.
   B. Vehicle loads have no effect on wheel alignment.
   C. Steering angles are designed to reduce tire wear and provide directional control.
   D. Wheel alignment angles do not affect riding quality.

6. All of these statements about computer wheel aligners are true EXCEPT:
   A. Some front wheel sensors contain optical sensors for toe measurement and strings connected to the rear wheel sensors.
   B. Vehicle specifications and the alignment program may be stored on CDs.
   C. Digital photos of suspension adjustments and inspection points are available.

D. Signals from high-frequency transmitters in wheel sensors may be blocked by a steel toolbox.

7. While driving straight ahead, a front-wheel-drive car pulls to the right. The most likely cause of this problem is:
   A. More positive camber on the left front wheel compared to the right front wheel.
   B. Sagged front springs and improper front wheel toe setting.
   C. Less positive caster on the right front wheel compared to the left front wheel.
   D. The SAI on the right front wheel is 1 1/2° more than the SAI on the left front wheel.

8. While adjusting front wheel camber and diagnosing camber-related problems:
   A. During front wheel jounce travel, the positive camber increases.
   B. Excessive positive camber on a front wheel causes premature wear on the inside edge of the tire tread.
   C. If the right front wheel camber is +1 1/2° and the left front camber is +1/2°, the steering pulls to the left.
   D. Excessive positive camber on both front wheels may cause front wheel shimmy.

9. A driver complains of harsh riding and the suspension height is normal. The most likely cause of this problem is:
   A. Excessive negative camber on both front wheels.
   B. Excessive positive caster on both front wheels.
   C. The left front wheel has more positive caster than the right front wheel.
   D. Both front wheels have negative camber and negative caster.

10. Excessive positive caster may cause all of these problems EXCEPT:
    A. Front wheel shimmy.
    B. Harsh ride quality.
    C. Excessive steering effort.
    D. Slow steering wheel return.

11. When measuring front wheel alignment angles, to calculate the included angle on the left front wheel when the camber on this wheel is positive:
    A. Add the camber to the toe setting.
    B. Add the camber to the SAI angle.
    C. Add the SAI to the caster angle.
    D. Subtract the SAI from the toe setting.

12. While diagnosing problems related to scrub radius:
    A. If the SAI line contacts the road surface inside the vertical tire and wheel centerline, the scrub radius is negative.
    B. Front-wheel-drive cars usually have a negative scrub radius and driving forces move the front wheels outward.
    C. If the SAI line contacts the road surface outside the tire and wheel vertical centerline, driving forces turn the front wheels outward.
    D. Larger than specified front tires may change the scrub radius from positive to negative.

13. While diagnosing front wheel toe problems:
    A. The front wheels are set to a straight-ahead position on most front-wheel-drive cars.

B. Driving forces tend to move the front wheels toward a toe-in position on a rear-wheel-drive car.
C. Improper toe adjustment may cause feathered wear on the front tire treads.
D. Sagged front springs may increase the front wheel toe-out on a short-and-long arm suspension system.

14. While diagnosing and adjusting turning radius:
A. When a vehicle is making a left turn, the left front wheel turns at a sharper angle than the right front wheel.
B. Improper turning radius may be caused by a bent tie-rod on a short-and-long arm suspension system.
C. Improper turning radius may be caused by an improperly positioned rack and pinion steering gear on a front-wheel-drive car.
D. Improper turning radius is adjusted by turning an eccentric strut-to-steering-knuckle bolt.

15. When performing a rear wheel alignment, a typical front-wheel-drive car has:
A. A zero toe or a slight toe-in.
B. A $^{11}/4_{2}^{\circ}$ positive camber setting.
C. A $^{11}/4_{2}^{\circ}$ setback setting on the left rear wheel.
D. A 3° positive caster setting on both rear wheels.

16. A front-wheel-drive car has an improper toe-out on turns setting, and a visual check indicates all the steering linkage and suspension components are satisfactory. The most likely cause of this problem is:
A. A bent lower control arm.
B. A bent front strut.
C. A front strut tower that is out-of-position.
D. A bent steering arm.

17. All of these statements about SAI and front spindle movement are true EXCEPT:
A. When the steering wheel is turned, the front spindle movement is parallel to the road surface.
B. When the SAI angle is increased, the steering wheel returning force is increased.
C. The SAI angle tends to maintain the wheels in a straight-ahead position.
D. Greater SAI angle is necessary on front-wheel-drive cars to provide directional stability.

18. All the front alignment angles on a front-wheel-drive car are set to specifications and the steering wheel is centered on the alignment rack, but when the car is driven straight ahead the steering pulls to the right.
Technician A says the most likely cause of this problem is incorrect rear wheel toe.
Technician B says the most likely cause of this problem is incorrect rear wheel camber.
Who is correct?
A. A only
C. Both A and B
B. B only
D. Neither A nor B

19. A light-duty truck with a one-piece rear axle housing and a leaf spring rear suspension has excessive toe-out on the left rear wheel and too much toe-in on the right rear wheel. The most likely cause of this problem is:

A. A broken center bolt in the left rear spring.
B. Both rear springs are sagged.
C. A bent rear axle housing.
D. Worn-out rubber bushings in the shock absorbers.

20. While discussing scrub radius:

A. Most front-wheel-drive cars have a positive scrub radius.
B. If the SAI line meets the road surface outside the tire vertical centerline, the scrub radius is positive.
C. Scrub radius is adjusted by shifting the upper strut tower on a MacPherson strut front suspension.
D. Incorrect scrub radius may be caused by larger than specified front tires.

INDEX